glossary
of
communications

ROBERT J. MURRAY

glossary of communications

by emerson c. smith

published by telephony

TELEPHONY PUBLISHING CORP.
53 West Jackson Blvd.
Chicago, Illinois 60604

Glossary of Telephone Words and Terms
First Edition: January, 1954
Second Edition: November, 1954

Glossary of Communications
First Edition: July, 1971

Copyright © 1971 by Emerson C. Smith
Library of Congress Catalog Card Number: 70-169786

Printed in the United States of America

*To Norma, for her patience while
I researched and wrote it.*

introduction

I am glad to recommend this new, much enlarged edition of Glossary of Communications by Emerson C. Smith. He is exceptionally qualified by his broad experience to define the multitude of terms used in modern telecommunications.

Following graduation as an Electrical Engineer from Ohio Northern University he went with the Ohio Bell Telephone Company, and for fifteen years was a Transmission Engineer in their Akron Division. During World War II he was loaned to Harvard University where he taught, and engaged in product engineering on radar countermeasures equipment at Harvard's Radio Research Laboratory. After the war he returned to Ohio Bell as an Outside Plant Engineer. In 1947 he resigned to become Transmission and Protection Engineer of Hawaiian Telephone Company (then Mutual Telephone), and in 1950 became their Chief Engineer. In 1954 he left Hawaiian Telephone to form Emerson C. Smith & Associates, Consulting Communication Engineers.

His consulting work, mostly for the U. S. Army and U. S. Navy, has brought additional varied experiences. It has included the engineering of aerial and buried cables on Oahu, submarine cable at the Midway Islands, dial central offices on Oahu and Midway, traffic studies, numbering and switching plans on Okinawa and Taiwan, a microwave radio relay toll system for Cambodia, and a tropospheric scatter backbone toll system for Indonesia.

His intimate knowledge of all types of telecommunications is reflected in the clear, concise, information-packed definitions you will find in this Glossary.

A. W. Baerresen
Telephone Traffic Consultant

San Clemente, Calif. June, 1971

About the author

Emerson C. Smith is eminently qualified by years and diversity of engineering experience with Bell and Independent operating companies to prepare a glossary of this magnitude on communications. Since compiling the original Glossary of Telephone Words and Terms in 1954, he has meticulously gathered, analyzed and sorted every known word and term related to communications. However, the industry is constantly changing and expanding in its technology, developments and applications. The author, therefore, already has processed hundreds of new terms and will be pleased to receive comments and suggestions regarding terms which should be included in the next edition of the Glossary of Communications. He may be addressed in care of Telephony.

Additional copies of this book
may be obtained from
TELEPHONY PUBLISHING CORP.
53 West Jackson Blvd.
Chicago, Illinois 60604

preface

The first edition of the Glossary of Telephone Words and Terms was published January 1954 to give engineering employees of the Hawaiian Telephone Company a better understanding of standard telephone terms and to encourage expression of their thoughts in mutually understood language.

A somewhat enlarged second edition was published by TELEPHONY as a serial between 3 July 1954 and 31 July 1954, followed by its publication November 1954 as a booklet. By January, 1971 65,000 persons had bought the Glossary, and hopefully it has contributed to their better understanding of telecommunication terms.

Since 1954 there have been important and sweeping changes in the art and science of telecommunications, and the words and terms relating to it have proliferated at an ever increasing rate. To meet present day needs, this new edition of the Glossary has been expanded over seven-fold to 7,389 terms. Its new title, Glossary of Communications, acknowledges that telecommunication today implies much more than voice communication by telephone. Today it includes also digital communication of data, secure voice, and teletypewriter signals, and visual communication by facsimile, Picturephone, and television. Transmission systems now include coaxial cable, microwave radio relay, tropospheric scatter radio, and communication satellites in addition to the older cable, wire, and simple carrier facilities. Vacuum tubes have been replaced by transistors in printed circuits, and these are being replaced by integrated circuits. Switching systems now make extensive use of common-control, and electronic switching systems are in everyday use. These new techniques have generated a multitude of new terms which you will find in this expanded new edition.

Although the primary purpose of this Glossary is to define terms as they are used today, care has been taken to identify certain usage as "slang" or "colloquial." Words which are frequently misused, such as "communications," "exchange," and "receiver," are fully explained.

Three appendices are provided to supplement the definitions of words and terms. Appendix A provides meanings for the abbreviations, alphabetical designations, and acronyms in common use today. These meanings will enable understanding of writing made unintelligible by undefined abbreviations. Appendix B presents the fundamental laws, rules, and theorems of electricity, magnetism, and physics which apply to telecommunications. Some, such as Ohm's Law, are more familiar than others but all contribute to our understanding of modern telecommunications. Appendix C provides formulae and other data which will be found useful in your daily work.

The author hopes you will use this new Glossary frequently, and that you will be rewarded for your diligence by better understanding and greater facility in the use of telecommunication terms.

Emerson C. Smith
Honolulu, Hawaii

June, 1971

contents

how to use this glossary

Use it as you would a dictionary, remembering that:

a. Words and multi-word terms are listed in alphabetical sequence, except that all listings of a particular noun are grouped together, so that the listings for "cable, aerial" through "cable, wire-armored" precede the listing for "cable count."

b. When a term consists of a noun plus an adjective or attributive noun the term will be found listed under the noun, except in those cases where the attributive noun is the more distinctive word, such as "satellite."

c. Terms which contain numerals are listed as if spelled out. Thus "L4 carrier" will be listed as if spelled "L four carrier."

d. There are generous cross-references to help you find terms which you might look for in more than one place.

e. When a word or term has several senses, the different meanings are numbered (1), (2), etc.

f. When a single word may be used either as an adjective or noun or as a noun or verb, all meanings are under a single listing and are designated "adj," "n," or "v," as appropriate.

abbreviations used in this glossary

AC	Alternating current	EHF	Extremely-high frequency
adj	Adjective	EHS	Extra high strength
AM	Amplitude modulated	EIA	Electronic Industries
AMA	Automatic message		Association
	accounting	EKG	Electrocardiogram
ARQ	Automatic repeat request	ELF	Extremely-low frequency
ASCII	American Standard Code	EMF	Electromotive force
	for Information	E-W	East-to-West
	Interchange		
ATB	All trunks busy	F	Fahrenheit
AWG	American Wire Gauge	FM	Frequency modulated
BTU	British thermal unit	GHz	Gigahertz
BWG	British Wire Gauge		
		HF	High frequency
CAMA	Centralized automatic	HU	High usage
	message accounting	Hz	Hertz (Cycles per second)
CATV	Community antenna		
	television	I	Current in amperes
CCIR	Comité Consultatif	IBM	International Business
	International des Radio-		Machines
	communications	ID	Inside diameter
CCITT	Comité Consultatif Inter-	IF	Intermediate frequency
	national Télégraph et	ILF	Infra-low frequency
	Téléphone	IPM	Interruptions per minute
CCS	Hundred call-seconds	ISB	Independent sideband
CFM	Cubic feet per minute	ITA #2	International Telegraph
CO	Central office		Alphabet #2
COMSAT	Communication Satellite	ITT	International Telephone
	Corporation		and Telegraph
cpm	Cards per minute		
		kHz	Kilohertz
D	Diameter		
dB	Decibel	LF	Low frequency
dBm	Decibels above one	LTB	Last trunk busy
	milliwatt	LUF	Lowest useable frequency
DC	Direct current		
DCS	Defense Communication	mc	Megacycles
	System	MDF	Main distributing frame
DECCO	Defense Commercial	MF	Medium frequency.
	Communications Office		Multi-frequency.
DDD	Direct Distance Dialing	MHz	Megahertz
DP	Dial pulse	MUF	Maximum useable
DSA	Dial service auxiliary		frequency
	(switchboard)		
DTMF	Dual tone multifrequency	N	Any digit, from 2 to 9
		n	Noun
E	Electrical pressure	NASA	National Aeronautics and
	in volts		Space Agency
E&M	A method of signaling	n pl	Noun, plural
EC	Electrical communica-	NPA	Numbering Plan Area
	tions. Extra control.		

OD	Outside diameter
OF	Overflow
OK	All correct
P	Power in watts
PABX	Private automatic branch exchange
PAX	Private automatic exchange
PBX	Private branch exchange
PCM	Pulse code modulation
pps	Pulses per second
psi	Pounds per square inch
psig	Pounds per square inch, gauge
PVC	Polyvinyl chloride
Q	Quality
R	Resistance in ohms
R-C	Resistance-capacitance
RF	Radio frequency
RFI	Radio frequency induction
RMS	Root-mean-square. (Also rms)
SF	Single frequency
SHF	Super-high frequency
SPDT	Single pole, double throw
SPST	Single pole, single throw
SSB	Single sideband

TASI	Time assignment of speech intelligence
TDM	Time division multiplex
TLP	Transmission level point
TSP	Toll Service Position
TSS	Toll Switching System
TTC	Terminating Toll Center
TTMF	Touch-tone multi-frequency
TV	Television
TWX	Teletypewriter exchange
TX	Terminating toll operator
UHF	Ultra-high frequency
v	Verb
VHF	Very-high frequency
vi	Verb, intransitive
VLF	Very-low frequency
VNL	Via net loss
vt	verb, transitive
W-E	West-to-East
WECo	Western Electric Company
X	Any digit, from 0 to 9
X-Bar	Crossbar
Y	A digit, either 0 or 1

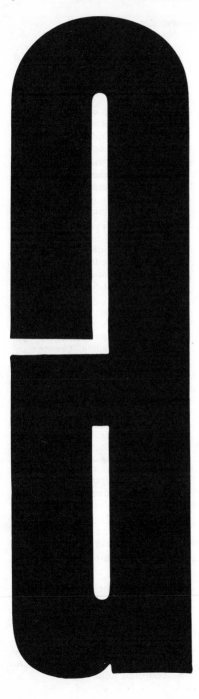

A and B leads, *n.* Designation of leads derived from the midpoints of the two 2-wire pairs comprising a 4-wire circuit. Derivation may be by retard coils or repeating coils. Used for duplex signaling or for E&M signals.

abandoned call, *n.* Call on which the calling party disconnects without cancelling the call, before a report of "busy" or "don't answer" has been received.

"A" battery. See "battery, filament."

abbreviated dialing, *n.* Capability of dialing a 2 or 3 digit code in lieu of a 7 or 10 digit telephone address. Available in common-controlled offices with translation capability. The user's telephone must be equipped with a DTMF keyset having an "A" button to denote the "end of address" and thereby inform the office that it is not an incompletely dialed number.

abbreviated dialing, pool, *n.* Abbreviated dialing where a number of subscribers use the same abbreviated dialing codes.

abbreviated dialing, unique, *n.* Abbreviated dialing using a short code which is not used by any other subscriber.

"A" Board toll call, *n.* A station-to-station call to a toll point, generally short-haul, which is completed at an "A" board instead of at a toll board.

abrasion resistance, *n.* Ability of a cable or wire to resist surface wear, particularly during installation.

abscissa, *n.* A distance along the horizontal or x-axis of a graph.

absence of ground, *n.* An ungrounded condition of the bank contact of an idle trunk. "Ungrounded" may indicate either that the contact is open, or connected to negative battery.

absorber, digit, *n.* A unit of telephone switching equipment into which an excess digit can be dialed without causing any response except to make the equipment ready to receive the next digit dialed. Usually included as an added function of a selector. See also "selector, digit-absorbing."

absorption, *n.* (1) Reduction in the level of a super-high frequency radio signal by passing through foliage, rain, or the oxygen of the air. Rain absorbs strongly at 22,000 mc, and oxygen at 60,000 mc. (2) The loss of acoustic energy when sound waves pass through a body.

absorption, auroral, *n.* Absorption of radio waves by the particles radiated from the sun during auroral activity.

absorption loss, *n.* The loss of power in a transmission circuit which results from coupling to a neighboring circuit.

absorption peak, *n.* Abnormally high attenuation at a particular frequency as a result of absorption loss.

accentuation, *n.* Emphasis, which see.

acceptance test, *n.* A test made to demonstrate the degree of compliance with specified requirements.

acceptor. See "semiconductor, p-type."

access, *n.* (1) A point of entry or a means of entry into a circuit. (2) The action of entering or connecting to a circuit.—*v.* To connect to a circuit.

access, random memory, *n.* A method of information retrieval in which any desired word in the memory is accessed according to its address, and only that word is read out.

access, sequential memory, *n.* A method of information retrieval in which the complete memory is scanned and each word is, in its turn, read out, worked upon, then rewritten.

access circuit, *n.* Relay equipment connected to a trunk (as line equipment is connected to a line) which receives the call and extends it to an idle equipment unit which will process the call.

access code. See "code, access."

access line, *n.* A circuit between a subscriber's telephone or PBX and the switching center which serves them. Modern designation for "subscriber's loop" and "PBX trunk."

access point, dedicated plant. See "point, access."

account, clearing, *n.* Temporary account into which costs are collected, to be later divided and charged against direct work accounts.

account code, *n.* Numerical code for classifying revenues or expenses, or transfers of property. Follows a system set up by the Federal Communications Commission.

accounting, *v.t.* Measuring results and status, usually in financial terms, for organization units and functional areas.—*n.* Procedure of recording revenues, expenses, and capital expenditures. Also the work of compiling statistics.

Accounts, Uniform System of, *n.* A grouping of units of plant, identified by standard numerical codes, specified by the Federal Communications Commission for the accounts of telephone companies engaged in interstate commerce.

accumulator, *n.* (1) The British term for a storage battery. (2) A computer storage device which maintains a running subtotal of all numbers it receives.

accuracy, *n.* Of a measuring instrument, the difference between the instrument reading and the true value. See also "resolution."

acid, battery, *n.* The dilute sulphuric acid that serves as the electrolyte in a lead-acid storage battery.

acid copper chromate. See "chromate, acid copper."

acoustics, *n.* (1) The science of sound. (2) The acoustical properties of an enclosed space.

acoustic shock, *n.* The physical pain, dizziness, and sometimes nausea caused by hearing a sudden very loud sound. The threshold of pain is about 120 dBm.

acoustic shock reducer. See "reducer, acoustic shock."

acquisition, satellite, *n.* The entire process of searching for, locating, and aligning the tracking equipment to follow a communication satellite.

acrylic resin, *n.* A synthetic resin made from acrylic acid, or from an acrylic acid derivative. Is transparent and has a high index of refraction. Examples: Lucite, Plexiglas.

active, *adj.* Containing, or connected to and using, a source of energy.

active material, *n.* (1) The thorium oxide used to coat the hot cathode of an electron tube to increase emission of electrons. (2) The lead oxide or nickel oxide used in the plates of storage batteries.

activity factor, *n.* A decimal fraction less than one, representing the fraction of the busiest traffic hour that a single voice channel would probably be actively in use with speech being transmitted. Silent periods in the speech are not counted. A typical activity factor is in the range 0.25-0.35.

adapter, *n.* A device for connecting two parts of an apparatus, which would not be directly connectable because of incompatible dimensions, terminations, voltages, currents, frequencies, etc.

adapter, dial, *n.* Circular plate used to mount a rotary dial in a dial mounting.

adapter, four-wire extension line, *n.* An equipment which acts as a four-wire line adapter for 2-6 four-wire telephones on one line. Corrects for bridging loss, and provides a talkback path.

adapter, four-wire line, *n.* An equipment which provides an interface between a four-wire telephone and a four-wire line. The adapter furnishes talking battery to the telephone and converts telephone loop signaling to E & M signaling on the line.

adapter, line, *n.* A unit to provide the interface between a 4-wire telephone

and a 4-wire station line. It provides talking battery to the 4-wire phone, and converts loop signals from the phone to E&M signals toward the 4-wire switching center.

adapter, long line, *n.* A unit of central office relay equipment which can be connected in series with a subscriber's line which exceeds the central office resistance limit, and which will enable the line to signal and supervise properly.

adapter, touch-tone, *n.* A unit which serves as an interface between touch-tone (DTMF) telephone sets and key telephone equipment using DC signaling. The adapter converts the multifrequency tone generated by touch-tone telephone sets into relay operations which initiate DC signals.

addendum, *n.* (1) An appendix or supplement to written material. (2) A subsection added to a practice or other instruction.

adder, Boolean, *n.* A digital logic device whose output depends upon the condition of two inputs, as follows:

Input A	Input B	Output
—	—	+
+	+	—
+	—	—
—	+	—

adder, full, *n.* A solid-state logic device which adds binary digits and can accept a "carry" from the previous stage. It consists of two half-adders and an inverter. It has two binary inputs and a "carry" input, and provides a "sum" output and a "carry" output. Used as an adder in all stages except the units digit.

adder, half, *n.* A solid-state logic device which adds binary digits. It consists of two AND gates, an OR gate, and an inverter. It has two binary inputs, a "sum" output, and a "carry" output. Since it has no carry input, it can be used only to add the units digit. To add the tens, hundreds, etc., digits, a full adder having a carry input is required.

adder, modulo-2, *n.* A digital logic device whose output depends upon the condition of two inputs, as follows:

Input A	Input B	Output
—	—	+
+	+	+
+	—	—
—	+	—

additional period, *n.* The unit of time used for measuring and charging for time in excess of the initial period.

additional time. See "overtime."

add-on, *n.* A service available at some PABX's and centrex offices in which the station receiving an incoming call can add on another station for a three-way conference, without the assistance of an operator.

address, *n.* (1) The destination of a message in a communication system. (2) The group of digits comprising a complete telephone number: area code + central office code + line number. (3) The location in storage of information in a data processing system.

address, call, *n.* The last four digits of the telephone number.

address, international telephone, *n.* A code not exceeding twelve digits which will specify a unique address for any telephone in the world. It will consist of (a) a country or regional identity code of one, two, or three digits, (b) a three digit numbering plan area code, (c) a two or three digit central office code, plus (d) a four digit station number.

address, memory, *n.* The location of a word in a memory unit.

address, message, *n.* That portion of the message that specifies the destination and the handling. A telephone address includes the precedence digit, two routing digits, a 3-digit area code, a 3-digit central office code, and a 4-digit line number.

address, telephone, *n.* The complete 10-digit number which specifies the location of a particular telephone. Consists of a 3-digit area code, plus a 3-digit central office code, plus a 4-digit station number.

addresser, push button, *n.* A device which, upon selecting and pushing one of a group of push buttons, will transmit one of a group of pre-set teletypewriter addresses. Used with teletypewriter exchange service.

address name, *n.* The name or address, or both, under which a telephone may be listed.

adjuster, cord, *n.* A device for temporarily altering the length of a hanging electrical cord.

adjuster, spring. See "bender, spring."

adjuster, zero. See "zero adjuster."

adjustment table. See "table, trunk adjustment."

admittance, *n.* A measure of the ease with which alternating current flows in a circuit. It is the reciprocal of impedance, and is expressed in mhos. Admittance is the vector sum of a resistive component called "conductance" and a reactive component called "susceptance."

admittance, surge, *n.* The reciprocal of "surge impedance," which see.

admittance, transfer, *n.* The reciprocal of transfer impedance. See also "impedance, transfer."

adsorption, *n.* The adhesion of gas or liquid molecules to the surfaces of solids or liquids with which they are in contact.

aerial, *adj.* In the air, as aerial cable. —*n.* A radio antenna (British).

aging, *n.* The change in properties of a material with time.

air, off the, *adv.* Existing in a radio broadcast transmission, and available to be picked up and demodulated by the public.—*adj.* Not broadcasting.

air, on the, *adj.* (1) Connected to a radio transmitter which is broadcasting. (2) Existing in a radio broadcast transmission.

air-core, *adj.* Describing a coil which does not have magnetic material in its magnetic circuit.

air gap, *n.* A small gap left in the magnetic circuit of a closed-core transformer which increases the magnetic reluctance and prevents saturation of the core.

alarm, *n.* A visual signal (lighted lamp) or an audible signal (bell or buzzer) which alerts personnel to the existence of an abnormal condition.

alarm, battery, *n.* Signal calling attention to the fact that the battery is not being charged, or that the battery voltage is too high or too low.

alarm, carrier, *n.* An alarm which is actuated when the carrier supply of a carrier system is interrupted or drops in level by 15 dB. See also "disconnect-make busy."

alarm, contactor, *n.* Signal calling attention to low pressure in a pressurized cable system.

alarm, emergency, *n.* A lamp and loud-ringing bell alarm which alerts central office personnel to serious trouble, such as (a) low or high office voltage, (b) major fuse operation, or (c) ringing machine failure.

alarm, equipment, *n.* An alarm, audio and/or visual, which denotes some malfunction of equipment.

alarm, high voltage, *n.* A bell alarm in a dial central office which sounds when the DC voltage being supplied to the equipment rises above 53 volts.

alarm, low-high voltage, *n.* A bell alarm in a central office, actuated by a voltmeter relay, which occurs when the central office battery voltage is too low, or too high.

alarm, low-voltage, *n.* A bell alarm in a dial central office which sounds when the DC voltage being supplied to the equipment falls to 45 volts.

alarm, major carrier, *n.* A visual and aural indication of carrier trouble that disables more than twelve channels.

alarm, MDF, *n.* Two pilot or telltale lamps, mounted at the top of each protector vertical of a main distributing frame. A lighted lamp gives indication of the operation of a heat coil on that side of the vertical.

alarm, minor carrier, *n.* A visual and/ or aural indication of carrier trouble that does not disable more than twelve channels.

alarm, non-emergency, *n.* A lamp and buzzer alarm which alerts central office personnel to troubles which require correction but are not of an emergency nature, such as permanent, release, and supervisory alarms.

alarm, office, *n.* Warning signal calling attention to some abnormal condition in a central office.

alarm, pilot, *n.* An alarm which is actuated when the pilot tone which is transmitted with each group of carrier channels is interrupted, for any reason.

alarm, release. See "release alarm."

alarm, remote, *n.* An alarm indication at a central test point of an abnormal condition at some remote point. See also "alarm sender."

alarm, transfer, *n.* An alarm caused by the transfer of a load from the normal unit to a standby unit. The transfer might be between (a) power sources, (b) ringing machines, (c) tone sources, or (d) translators.

alarm, undervoltage. See "undervoltage alarm."

alarm panel, gas pressure, *n.* A relay rack mounting panel which will accommodate up to ten alarm modules, each of which can be connected to a gas alarm pair to provide audible and visual alarms when a contactor or pressure guard has operated due to low gas pressure in the cable to which it is connected. After receiving an alarm, the resistance of the alarm pair can be measured to determine which of the several contactors bridged on the alarm pair has operated.

alarm sender, *n.* A central office device which transfers alarm signals from an unattended office to a testboard or switchboard at a nearby attended office. From there, the attendant can dial back to the alarm sender and receive a coded signal which indicates the type of trouble.

alerting lamp, *n.* Same as a "line lamp," which lights to alert an operator when there is an incoming call on the associated line or trunk. Some trunks have two alerting lamps—one for routine and one for precedence calls.

alerting signal, *n.* A signal that is sent toward users and subscribers to indicate an incoming call. Traditionally, a ringing signal.

ALGOL, *n.* Algorithmic language. An arithmetic language used to provide computation instructions to a computer.

algorithm, *n.* An ordered sequence of mathematical steps that always produce the correct answer to a problem, though the solution may be more lengthy than necessary.

align, *v.* To adjust the tuning of a multi-stage device so that all stages are adjusted to the same frequency, or so that they work together properly.

alignment, *n.* The process of adjusting a long circuit or a multi-stage device so that all stages are working at the proper level or frequency.

alignment chart, *n.* A chart having three or more scales across which a straightedge can be placed to provide a graphical solution for a particular problem. Also called a "nomograph."

alive, *adj.* (1) Energized. (2) Connected to a source of electrical voltage. (3) Charged so as to have an electrical potential different than that of the earth. (4) Reverberant, as a room in which sound reflects and echoes.

all-channel amplifier. See "amplifier, all channel CATV."

Allen screw, *n.* A screw having a hexagonal socket set in its head, by which it can be turned.

Allen wrench, *n.* A bent hexagonal rod of the dimensions to fit the socket in the head of an Allen screw. Used as a wrench to turn the screw.

alley arm. See "arm, side."

alligator clip, *n.* A test clip having long, narrow jaws.

all-number calling (ANC), *n.* Calling, using telephone numbers consisting of seven numerals (NNX-XXXX) rather than two letters plus five numerals.

allocated circuit, *n.* A communication circuit designated for the especial use of one or more users.

allocation, frequency, *n.* A bank of radio frequencies designated for a particular service. International allocations were made by the International Telecommunication and Radio Conferences at Geneva in 1959 and 1963. Sub-allocations in the United States are made by the Federal Communications Commission in accordance with their Rules and Regulations dated 1 Dec. 1965.

allotter, *n.* A switch which determines which one of a group of identical units of equipment will be used next. Some types are also called a "distributor."

allotting, PBX, *n.* A feature of a dial office which permits spreading calls to the directory number of a large PBX over several number groups. It prevents number group congestion, and permits a single directory number. (#5 XBar)

allowance, timing. See "timing allowance."

alloy, *n.* A mixture or solid solution of two or more chemical elements, which has metallic properties.

all-relay automatic system, *n.* Switching system which uses only relays to accomplish the switching.

all trunks busy, *n.* A condition when all trunks in a particular group are busy. Abbrev: ATB.

alnico, *n.* An alloy of aluminum, nickel, and cobalt with iron which retains magnetism well. Used to make permanent magnets.

alpeth, *adj n.* A type of telephone

cable sheath featuring an 8-mil corrugated aluminum tape applied longitudinally with an overlap, and a polyethelene jacket overall. It is light-weight, flexible, and has a low electrical resistance.

alphabet, phonetic, *n.* A method of passing alphabetic information over a poor communication circuit, with a word substituting for a letter. The following phonetic alphabet has been standardized by the International Civil Aviation Organization.

ALFA	JULIETT	SIERRA
BRAVO	KILO	TANGO
CHARLIE	LIMA	UNIFORM
DELTA	MIKE	VICTOR
ECHO	NOVEMBER	WHISKEY
FOXTROT	OSCAR	X-RAY
GOLF	PAPA	YANKEE
HOTEL	QUEBEC	ZULU
INDIA	ROMEO	

alphanumeric, *adj.* Describing a designation which consists of both letters and numerals.

alternate route, *n.* A route available for completing a call when all direct or first-choice route trunks are busy.

alternate route pattern. See "search pattern."

alternate routing, *n.* The procedure at a switching center by which a call which encounters an all trunks busy (ATB) condition in the first choice route is offered another route to or toward the terminating switching center.

alternate triples, *n.* In automatic alternate routing of toll calls, three groups of three alternate trunk routes which are available, but which employ "lateral routing."

alternating current (AC), *n.* An electric current which continually varies in amount, and reverses its direction periodically. The plot of current *vs.* time is usually a sine wave.

alternation, *n.* One-half of an alternating current cycle. The complete rise and fall of a current traveling in one direction.

alternator, *n.* An alternating current generator.

alternator, tone, *n.* An alternating current generator, usually an inductor alternator, which generates the several tones: busy tone, dial tone, etc., used in a central office. See also "tone, - - -."

alt-route, *v.* To route a circuit over an alternate path.

alt-route, automatic, *v.* The action of a common-controlled central office in testing sequentially trunks over several alternate routes in attempting to complete a call.

aluminum, *n.* A light-weight, silvery-gray metal which is ductile and malleable. It is only 30% as heavy as copper, but has 60% more resistance than copper.

aluminum, EC grade, *n.* Aluminum which is 99.45% pure, and thus is suitable for use in making electrical conductors.

Alumoweld, *adj.* A trade-marked name applied to steel wire products having a heavy welded coating of aluminum.

ambient, *adj.* Surrounding; on all sides.

ambient temperature, *n.* The temperature of the surrounding medium, such as air, gas, or liquid, which comes into contact with an object and thereby cools or warms it.

American Morse code. See "code, Morse."

American Standard Code for Information Interchange. See "code, ASCII."

American Wire Gauge (AWG), *n.* A scale of measurement for non-ferrous (copper, bronze, etc.) wires. Also called the Brown & Sharpe (B&S) gauge. See also "gauges, wire."

ammeter, *n.* An instrument for measuring the strength of an electric current in amperes.

ammeter, clamp-on, *n.* An alternating current ammeter which has a built-in current transformer whose core can be clamped around the conductor in which current is to be measured.

ammonium dihydrogen phosphate, *n.* A stable artificial crystal whose piezoelectric effect is seven times as great as quartz. Has no water of crystallization, has a low curie point, and is insensitive to temperature.

amp, *n.* Abbreviated form of "ampere."

amperage, *n.* The rate of current flow in a circuit, expressed in amperes.

ampere, *n.* Unit of electric current, or rate of flow of electricity. One coulomb per second. One volt impressed across a resistance of one ohm causes a current of one ampere to flow.

ampere-hour, *n.* The quantity of electricity represented by a current of one ampere that flows for one hour.

ampere-turns, *n. pl.* A measure of the magnetomotive force generated by a coil, equal to the current through the coil (in amperes) times the number of turns in the coil.

amplidyne, *n.* A DC servo generator used as a power amplifier. A small amount of field excitation can control a large power output and provide very rapid response.

amplification, *n.* The act of increasing the amplitude or strength of a signal.

amplification, current, *n.* Of a transducer, the ratio of the current in a specified load impedance to the current in the transducer input circuit.

amplification, power, *n.* The process of amplifying a signal to produce a gain in power, as distinguished from voltage amplification.

amplification, voltage, *n.* Of a transducer, the ratio of the voltage across a specified load impedance to the voltage across the transducer input.

amplification factor. See "factor, amplification."

amplifier, *n.* Device, usually electrical, which receives a signal at a low level and sends it out at a higher level, without appreciable distortion of the waveform.

amplifier, all-channel CATV, *n.* A very broadband amplifier which will pass and amplify equally all VHF television channels and the FM broadcast channels.

amplifier, audio, *n.* An amplifier designed to amplify frequencies within the useful audio range, 70 to 15,000 hertz, but not to amplify noise frequencies outside of that range.

amplifier, balanced, *n.* An amplifier circuit in which there are two identical signal branches connected so as to operate in phase opposition having input and output connections each balanced to ground.

amplifier, bridging, *n.* An amplifier whose high-impedance input bridges on to the circuit from which the input signals come. The high-impedance bridge has only a very small loss to the through circuit. Used for monitoring.

amplifier, broadband, *n.* An amplifier capable of amplifying a wide band of frequencies without objectionable distortion.

amplifier, buffer, *n.* An amplifier stage used to isolate a frequency-sensitive circuit from variations in the load presented by following stages.

amplifier, CATV main line, *n.* A pole-mounted or messenger-suspended weatherproof amplifier designed for insertion at intervals in a coaxial CATV feeder cable. Provides about 25 db gain over the band 50-220 MHz, and is powered by low-voltage 60 Hz AC fed over the coaxial cable.

amplifier, Class A, *n.* An electron tube amplifier in which the grid bias and alternating signal voltages are such that plate current flows at all times.

amplifier, Class B, *n.* An electron tube amplifier in which the grid bias is at the cutoff value so that the plate current is zero when no signal voltage is applied to the grid, and so that plate current flows for one-half of each cycle when an alternating signal is applied to the grid.

amplifier, Class C, *n.* An electron tube amplifier in which the grid bias is greater than the cutoff value so that the plate current is zero when no alternating signal voltage is applied to the grid, and so that plate current flows for appreciably less than one-half of each cycle when an alternating signal voltage is applied to the grid.

amplifier, compensated, *n.* An amplifier which is made wideband by the addition of low-frequency compensation and high-frequency compensation, which see.

amplifier, compression, *n.* An amplifier used to feed a sound system where the input signal varies over a very wide range. A typical compression amplifier having an input signal which varies by 50 dB will produce an output which varies by 20 dB.

amplifier, differential, *n.* An amplifier having two similar input circuits connected so as to respond to the difference between two voltages or currents and effectively suppress voltages or currents which are alike in the two input circuits.

amplifier, direct current, *n.* An amplifier capable of amplifying direct voltages. It generally employs resistive coupling between stages.

amplifier, hard-of-hearing, *n.* Transistor amplifier, made an integral part of a telephone set or operator's telephone set plug, to amplify the received signal. Permits hard-of-hearing persons to use the telephone, or act as telephone operators.

amplifier, heterodyne CATV, *n.* A single-channel TV amplifier which does not demodulate the television signal but instead down-converts it to an intermediate frequency (IF), amplifies it at IF, then up-converts it to the original channel.

amplifier, intermediate frequency, *n.* The central stages of a superheterodyne radio receiver which amplify the signals after they have been converted to a fixed intermediate frequency by a frequency converter. See also "frequency, intermediate."

amplifier, isolation, *n.* A buffer amplifier.

amplifier, line, *n.* An amplifier, common to all channels in one direction, which is used to compensate for line loss. Normally associated directly with the line.

amplifier, magnetic, *n.* An electrical device in which the flow of a heavy alternating current through a reactor can be controlled by a relatively weak direct current which is used to saturate the core of the reactor and thus reduce its reactance. Used on battery chargers as a means of closely regulating their output voltage.

amplifier, microphone, *n.* An amplifier which can take the output of a low-level microphone and amplify the signal to a level required to drive a power amplifier.

amplifier, monitoring, *n.* Device which, when bridged on a circuit, absorbs a negligible amount of energy, but amplifies that energy so that it can be heard in an earphone or measured.

amplifier, operational, *n.* A DC amplifier having high gain, wide bandwidth, low noise, and low output impedance which can be combined with a passive network to provide an analog device.

amplifier, operator's headset, *n.* A small transistorized amplifier with volume control which plugs into the operator's jacks on a switchboard, and can be used to amplify the received volume on an operator's head telephone set. For the use of hard-of-hearing operators.

amplifier, parametric, *n.* An amplifier which uses a varying parameter, such as reactance, to take power from a local source of energy and use it to amplify an input signal. The local source of energy is usually a pump oscillator, operating at twice the frequency of the signal to be amplified.

amplifier, power, *n.* An amplifier designed to produce a gain in signal power, as distinguished from a voltage amplifier.

amplifier, program, *n.* A high-quality audio amplifier whose gain is practically constant over the audio range. Used on radio broadcast (program) circuits.

amplifier, pulse, *n.* A wideband amplifier capable of amplifying pulses without distortion.

amplifier, push-pull, *n.* A balanced power amplifier using a pair of triode electron tubes in phase opposition, fed from and feeding to a center-tapped transformer. It has a desirable low output impedance, and distortion is low because of cancellation of second harmonics.

amplifier, sense, *n.* In a memory system, an amplifier which takes a weak pulse derived from sensing (reading) a memory element and increases its power to a level where it can operate logic devices or drive other memory elements.

amplifier, single-channel CATV, *n.* An amplifier which has the bandwidth for a single television channel, and is tuned to a particular channel.

amplifier, tuned radio frequency, *n.* A radio frequency amplifier in which each stage is tuned to the frequency of the radio signal.

amplifier, 227-type, *n.* A miniature, transistorized amplifier with 600 or 1200 ohm impedance used as the amplifying element in voice repeaters. Available with (227B) or without (227A) built-in lightning protection for use on aerial or underground cable pairs, respectively.

amplifier, voltage. See "voltage amplifier."

amplify, *v.* To increase the amplitude or magnitude, particularly of an electrical signal.

amplitude, *n.* (1) The extreme range of a fluctuating quantity, such as an alternating current. (2) The instantaneous value of a fluctuating quantity. See "RMS" and "Peak."

amplitude, pulse, *n.* The maximum instantaneous value of a pulse.

amplitude modulation, *n.* Process by which a continuous "carrier" wave is caused to vary in amplitude corresponding to the amplitude of the modulating signal.

ampoule, carbon monoxide detector, *n.* Thin glass vial which, when crushed, releases a chemical into the covering absorbent sack which changes color if in the presence of carbon monoxide. Used to check the atmosphere in a manhole before a cable splicer enters.

analog circuit switch, *n.* A switch used to interconnect circuits for real-time transmission of analog signals.

analog signal, *n.* A nominally continuous electrical signal that varies in amplitude or frequency in response to changes of sound, light, heat, position, or pressure.

analog-to-digital converter. See "converter, analog-to-digital."

analog value, *n.* A value which is continuously variable, such as a current or voltage.

analyzer, circuit, *n.* Several meters or meter circuits in a single case, enabling the measurement of several ranges of voltage and current. Also called a "multimeter."

analyzer, harmonic. See "harmonic analyzer."

analyzer, line fault, *n.* A measuring instrument which uses the radar principle to detect and locate any line fault which causes an impedance irregularity. Pulses are transmitted to the fault and their travel time, out and back, is analyzed to give the distance to the fault.

analyzer, network, *n.* An aggregation of electric circuit elements which can be interconnected to stimulate real electric networks. The performance of the real network can then be inferred from measurements on the model network.

analyzer, spectrum, *n.* A measuring device consisting of a calibrated cathode ray tube display device combined with a tuneable narrowband (50 Hz) filter. Harmonic components of the signal to be analyzed can be isolated by the filter and measured separately. Intended for use with a spectrum generator at the sending end of the transmission facility.

analyzer, traffic, *n.* Device for obtaining traffic usage data which periodically (every 100 seconds) scans groups of trunks to determine how many are busy, then periodically (usually once an hour) prints a record of the usage in CCS.

analyzer, wave, *n.* An instrument consisting of an adjustable tuned circuit and a microammeter which can be used to measure the frequency and amplitude of the several sine wave components of a complex current or voltage wave.

analyzer, waveform. See "waveform analyzer."

anchor, *v.t.* To fasten to an anchor.—*n.* (1) Any device which holds something secure. (2) A device buried in the ground, to which anchor rods and guys are fastened.

anchor, cone, *n.* Anchor of sheet steel formed into a truncated cone with anchor rod attachment at the apex. Made only in an 8-inch (6,000 lb.) size.

anchor, cross-plate, *n.* A pair of structural steel plates, about 8x16 inches, deeply ribbed and with an anchor rod hole at the center. After they are placed in the bottom of the hole, the plates are positioned at right angles, thus forming an anchor 16 inches square.

anchor, expanding, *n.* Earth fastening device consisting of a metal disc with expanding blades which increase the effective diameter. It is buried in a dug slot and the blades are then expanded by driving.

anchor, guy, *n.* An anchor buried in the ground, having an anchor rod which extends above the earth's surface to which a guy may be attached.

anchor, hammer drive, *n.* A hollow aluminum tube to be placed in a hole drilled in a masonry wall. A nail driven into the tube expands it and securely holds the nail.

anchor, hollow wall, *n.* A slotted metal tube having a long machine screw into a nut at the inner end of the tube. When placed in a hole in a hollow wall, turning the screw deforms the tube until it bears on the inside of the wall, and forms a secure anchor for the machine screw.

anchor, log, *n.* Earth anchor made of a log, a split log, or two split logs crossed, to which an anchor rod is fastened.

anchor, plate, *n.* A heavy steel plate, about 8x27 inches, bent into a section of a cylinder for strength, with an anchor rod hole in the center.

anchor, pole key, *n.* A pair of heavy steel plates, about 7x27 inches, bolted together at their centers. They can be opened to a crossed position and placed against the butt of a pole to brace it against unbalanced loads.

anchor, rock, *n.* A long thimble eye bolt, ¾" D x 30" long, whose shank may be expanded by turning after being placed in a hole drilled in rock.

anchor, screw, *n.* An earth anchor made of a spiral or screw shaped plate welded to a heavy guy rod. The combination is turned to screw it into the ground. Only a small "starter hole" is required.

anchor, swamp, *n.* A large screw anchor, particularly effective in swampy ground.

anchor, wood screw, *n.* A small fiber, lead, or plastic tube to be placed in a hole drilled in a masonry wall. A wood screw driven into the tube expands it and securely anchors the screw.

AND gate, *n.* A circuit having several inputs, and in which no current flows from the output unless every input is energized simultaneously with the same polarity.

anechoic chamber, *n.* A room lined with material which traps sound waves in channels where the sound is perfectly absorbed, so that the room is acoustically dead. Used for testing microphones and loudspeakers.

angle, radio take-off, *n.* The angle between a horizontal line extending from the radiation center of an antenna and a line extending from the same point to the radio horizon. If the horizon is below the horizontal, the take-off angle is negative. High positive take-off angles cause high radio path attenuation.

angle of arrival, *n.* The vertical angle between the surface of the earth and the line of propagation of a radio wave which arrives at a receiving antenna.

angle of departure, *n.* The vertical angle between the surface of the earth and the line of propagation of a radio wave which departs from a transmitting antenna.

angle of deviation. See "pull."

angle of incidence. See "incidence angle."

angle of reflection, *n.* The angle measured between a wave or beam being reflected from a surface and a perpendicular to the surface.

Angstrom unit, *n.* A unit of length used to describe very short wave lengths. One Angstrom unit is one ten-billionth of a millimeter.

anhydrous, *adj.* (1) Dry. (2) Containing no water.

anion, *n.* An atom with a surplus of electrons, and thereby having a negative charge. So called because it is attracted to the anode, or positive electrode.

anisotropic, *adj.* Exhibiting electrical or optical properties having different values when measured along axes in different directions.

anneal, *v.* To soften a metal, such as copper, by subjecting it to high heat with subsequent cooling.

annealing, *n.* The removal of hardness from a metal by heating it to approximately 1000 degrees Fahrenheit, and then allowing it to cool very slowly.

announcement, vacant number, *n.* (1) "I'm sorry, the number you have reached is not in service at this time. If you need assistance, please hang up and dial your operator. This is a recording." (2) "I'm sorry, the number you have reached is not in service at this time. If you need assistance, please stay on the line and an operator will answer. This is a recording." (Used when the announcement machine is equipped with automatic cut-through to operator.)

announcement L, *n.* "I'm sorry, we are unable to complete your call as dialed. Please check the number and dial again or ask your operator for assistance. This is a recording."

announcement N, *n.* "I'm sorry, all circuits are busy now. Will you try your call again later, please? This is a recording."

announcement P, *n.* "I'm sorry, your call did not go through. Will you please hang up and try again? This is a recording."

announcement X, *n.* (Change wording as required by the situation.) "I'm sorry, unexpected damage to telephone equipment in (or near)_____ _____has delayed your call. Emergency calls may be placed with your operator. This is a recording."

announcement machine, *n.* A recording machine which is used to provide a recorded message to a subscriber when he reaches a vacant or disconnected number, or when his call is blocked or unduly delayed.

announcement trunk, *n.* A trunk connected to a device which plays a recorded announcement when a call is connected.

announcer, automatic time, *n.* A machine which provides accurate verbal announcements of clock time from magnetic recordings on tape or drum. The subscriber dials a number or code to access a connector terminal or selector level trunk connected to the announcer. Time announcements are provided every 10-15 seconds, and sometimes are preceded by a 5 second commercial announcement.

announcer, automatic weather, *n.* A machine which provides automatic verbal announcements of a current weather report up to four minutes in length from a spiral recording on a magnetic drum.

announcer, automatic time-temperature, *n.* An automatic time announcer which also announces the air temperature. See also "announcer, automatic time."

announcer, intercept, *n.* An automatic announcer which can be connected to vacant selector levels or to vacant connector terminals and used to give a "vacant number announcement."

annoyance call trap. See "trap, annoyance call."

annual transmission variations, *n.* The total transmission variation which may be expected over a typical year for a particular transmission facility, which is due solely to the annual variation of temperature and weather.

annular, *adj.* Ring-shaped.

annunciator, *n.* An electrical indicator which shows the source of calls. See "drop, magneto."

anode, *n.* (1) Positive pole or element. (2) The outermost positive element in a vacuum tube, also called the plate. (3) The positive element of battery or cell. (4) A galvanic anode.

anode, galvanic, *n.* Bar of base metal, usually magnesium but sometimes aluminum or zinc, buried in the earth and connected to an underground cable. Forms a battery and keeps the cable sheath slightly nega-

tive, thus preventing electrolytic corrosion.

anode, magnesium, *n.* A bar of magnesium buried in moist earth and connected by a wire to the sheaths of buried or underground lead-sheathed cables. Acts as a battery to keep the cable sheaths at a negative potential to earth, and thus to inhibit electrolytic corrosion.

anodize, *v.* To form a thin film of oxide on a metal in an electrolytic bath. These films may provide mechanical protection, chemical stability, or insulation.

anolyte, *n.* The portion of electrolyte in an electrolytic cell adjacent to the anode, or the electrolyte on the anode side of a permeable membrane in the cell.

anomalous propagation. See "propagation, anomalous."

answer, night trunk, *n.* Service provided on some PABX's in which a call to the PABX listed number during unattended periods can be answered from any station by dialing a special code.

answer, preferential. See "preferential answering."

answer, universal night, *n.* A feature of some PABX's which permits any station to answer an incoming trunk call at night, when no attendant is present, by dialing a single digit.

answer-back, *n.* A signal sent by a data receiver to a data transmitter indicating that it is ready to receive data, or is acknowledging the receipt of data.

answer-back unit. See "unit, answer-back."

answering, sequential. See "sequential answering."

answering jack, *n.* The jack associated with a subscriber's line, circuit, or trunk signal into which the operator plugs to answer a call.

answering service, telephone, *n.* Service provided at a centralized bureau which answers telephone calls for clients when they are not in their offices to receive the calls. Messages are recorded, information provided, and appointments made.

answering set, telephone. See "set, telephone answering."

answer signal, *n.* A supervisory signal transmitted when the called telephone answers. It is commonly a loop closure on the loop from the called telephone to the central office, and a current reversal from the central office to the calling telephone.

answer supervision, *n.* (1) An off-hook signal transmitted toward the calling end of a switched connection when the called party answers. (2) The extinguishing of the cord supervisory lamp when the called telephone answers.

answer time. See "time, answer."

antenna, *n.* An elevated device for radiating or receiving radio waves. It changes electrical currents into electro-magnetic radio waves, and vice versa.

antenna, all-channel, *n.* A broadband television or FM radio antenna.

antenna, aperiodic, *n.* A non-resonant antenna designed to have a constant impedance over a wide range of frequencies due to the suppression of reflections within the antenna system.

antenna, artificial, *n.* A device which simulates a real antenna in its essential impedance characteristics and has the necessary power handling capabilities, but which does not radiate or receive radio waves.

antenna, beam. See "antenna array."

antenna, billboard, *n.* A broadside antenna array having a flat screen reflector.

antenna, boresight, *n.* A small receiving antenna whose azimuth from a large satellite earth station antenna is very accurately known. By its use the pointing mechanism of the large antenna can be accurately calibrated.

antenna, broadband, *n.* An antenna which is not sharply resonant, and

which will provide adequate gain across a relatively wide band of frequencies. Examples: Television receiving and log-periodic antennas.

antenna, Cassegrain. See "Cassegrain antenna."

antenna, coaxial, *n.* An antenna that is fed at the junction between a quarter-wave extension of the center coaxial conductor and a quarter-wave radiating sleeve.

antenna, corner reflector, *n.* A microwave antenna consisting of an active dipole in the corner of two flat rectangular metal mesh reflectors which intersect at a 90-degree angle.

antenna, dielectric lens. See "antenna, lens."

antenna, dipole, *n.* A bi-directional antenna consisting of a straight wire one-half wavelength long, cut at the center for connection to a feed line. Its impedance is 72 ohms.

antenna, directional, *n.* An antenna that radiates or receives better in one direction than other directions.

antenna, discone, *n.* An omni-directional radio-frequency radiator whose impedance can be directly matched to a 50-ohm coaxial feeder over a four-to-one frequency band. Consists of two configurations of radiating wires, one a disc parallel to the earth, and the other a cone whose apex is at the center of the disc.

antenna, double-doublet, *n.* A pair of half-wave doublets crossed at a 90-degree angle at their centers. It is very broadband (8:1) and gives a bi-directional pattern with horizontal polarization.

antenna, doublet, *n.* A dipole antenna.

antenna, dummy. See "dummy antenna."

antenna, folded-dipole, *n.* A dipole whose ends are connected together by a conductor. Its impedance is 300 ohms.

antenna, Hertz, *n.* An antenna in which the ground is not an essential part, such as a dipole. Its resonant frequency depends only upon its physical size. See also "antenna, Marconi."

antenna, horn, *n.* A microwave antenna formed by flaring the end of a waveguide into the shape of a horn.

antenna, horn-reflector, *n.* An RF feed horn which extends to a section of a parabolic reflector set at a 45-degree angle. Radiation is reflected out a window in the horn. Used for the earth terminal of satellite links.

antenna, image. See "image antenna."

antenna, isotropic, *n.* A hypothetical antenna radiating or receiving equally well in all directions.

antenna, lens, *n.* An arrangement of dielectric or metal elements arranged in a lattice of varying thickness which is placed in front of a microwave antenna to concentrate the radio beam.

antenna, log-periodic, *n.* An array of active dipole elements in which the dipole lengths and the element spacings increase logarithmically as they get farther from the feeder. Propagation is in the direction from the elements toward the feeder.

antenna, long-wire, *n.* A directional antenna consisting of a single straight wire whose length is several times greater than its operating wavelength.

antenna, loop, *n.* An antenna consisting of several turns of wire in the same plane arranged to enclose an area in the electromagnetic field.

antenna, Luneberg lens, *n.* A microwave antenna consisting of a circular array of radio-refractive elements. A radio wave from any point in azimuth will be focused at the surface of the lens diametrically opposite from the direction of incidence.

antenna, Marconi, *n.* An antenna with which a ground connection is essential. See also "antenna, Hertz."

antenna, MUSA, *n.* Multiple unit steerable antenna. An antenna consisting of a large number of stationary antenna elements, the signals

from which can be combined in varying phase relationships so as to steer the major lobe of the composite antenna.

antenna, non-resonant. See "antenna, aperiodic."

antenna, omni-directional, *n.* An antenna which radiates or receives equally well in all directions in a horizontal plane.

antenna, parabolic, *n.* A microwave antenna made highly directional by the use of a parabolic reflector.

antenna, periodic. See "antenna, resonant."

antenna, periscope, *n.* A parabolic antenna mounted near ground level and directed vertically to illuminate a passive reflector set at 45 degrees at the top of a tower. This reflector redirects the radio beam horizontally toward the distant radio station.

antenna, quarter-wave, *n.* A dipole antenna having an electric length equal to one-quarter of its working wavelength. Its physical length will be somewhat shorter than one-quarter wavelength.

antenna, resonant, *n.* An antenna in which the impedance varies as the frequency is altered, due to reflections or standing waves within the antenna system.

antenna, rhombic, *n.* A high-gain, medium bandwidth antenna much used for very long high-frequency radio circuits. Consists of one, or several, horizontal wires in a diamond shape, fed at one apex and terminated with a resistor at the opposite apex. The length of each side of the diamond is 3 to 5 wavelengths. Its direction of transmission is from the feeder toward the termination, and is elevated 5-10 degrees above the horizon, dependent upon the height of the antenna above ground.

antenna, series-fed, *n.* A vertical antenna which is insulated from ground and fed at its lower end.

antenna, shunt-fed, *n.* A vertical antenna whose base is grounded, with the feeder attached at a level above the ground.

antenna, single channel, *n.* An antenna whose dipole frequency-determining element is cut to a precise length so as to be resonant at the frequency of one particular TV or FM channel.

antenna, steerable, *n.* An antenna consisting of a multitude of dipoles in front of a reflector. The signals from the individual dipoles can be combined in any desired phase relationship to steer the major lobe in any direction.

antenna, top-loaded, *n.* A vertical antenna which is enlarged at the top, thereby changing the current distribution on the antenna and improving its radiation pattern.

antenna, turnstile, *n.* An antenna which has one or more pairs of dipoles crossed at 90 degrees and placed one above the other on a vertical mast. Is omni-directional and, in a more elaborate form, is much used for television broadcasting.

antenna, uni-directional, *n.* An antenna which radiates or receives most of its energy in only one direction.

antenna, wave, *n.* A low-frequency antenna consisting of a single horizontal wire at least one wavelength long, pointed toward the distant station and with the distant end terminated to ground in its characteristic impedance.

antenna, whip, *n.* An antenna consisting of a thin flexible metal tube fed at one end, similar to most auto radio antennas.

antenna, Yagi, *n.* A very directional microwave antenna consisting of a half-wave dipole, having several parasitic dipoles in front (directors) plus several parasitic dipoles in back (reflectors) of the active dipole to increase the directivity. The common television receiving antenna is a Yagi.

antenna array, *n.* A multiplicity of antenna elements coupled together for the purpose of making the antenna directional.

antenna feed. See "feed, antenna."

antenna gain. See "gain, antenna."

antenna pattern, *n.* A graphical representation of the strength of radiation from an antenna to all points 360 degrees in azimuth. Usually a two-dimensional graph although the radiation field is three-dimensional.

antennas, nested rhombic, *n. pl.* A pair of rhombic antennas, with the small contained inside the larger.

anti-jamming, *n.* Action taken to avoid, cancel, or nullify the effects of enemy jamming of a communication system.

antilogarithm, *n.* The decimal number corresponding to a given logarithm.

antimony, *n.* A gray crystalline metal. Used in alloys, particularly with lead to give strength to storage battery plates.

antimony battery. See "cell, lead-antimony storage."

anti-node, *n.* A point on a transmission line where there is a standing wave at which the wave, current or voltage, has its maximum amplitude.

anti-resonance, *n.* Parallel resonance, which see.

anti-seize compound, *n.* A lubricant especially formulated to inhibit cohesion between sliding or rotating parts made of the same metal.

antisidetone circuit, *n.* A telephone circuit designed to reduce sidetone, which is the hearing of one's own voice in the receiver when talking into the transmitter of a telephone.

anti-sidetone telephone set, *n.* Telephone set having a balancing network connected so that only a small part of the transmitter power reaches the receiver.

anti-stuffing device. See "kit, anti-stuffing coin return."

"A" operator, *n.* An operator at a local manual or dial service "A" board who answers subscriber line or trunk signals and completes local and "A" board toll calls.

aperiodic, *adj.* Not periodic. Without periodic vibrations. Describing circuits or antennas which are not resonant.

aperiodic antenna. See "antenna, aperiodic."

aperture, *n.* The clear diameter of the parabolic reflector of a microwave antenna.

apogee, *n.* The point in its orbit when a satellite is at the greatest distance above the earth. See also "perigee."

"A" position, *n.* A switchboard position in a local central office where subscriber's lines and operator trunks terminate, and where calls originated by subscribers are completed.

apparatus, *n.* (1) any complex device, (2) the equipment or instruments used for a specific purpose.

apparatus, station, *n.* The equipment installed at a subscriber's premises, and required to give him telephone or other communication service.

appearance, *n.* A connection of a circuit to terminals, or to contacts of switch banks, from which point it is available for use or connection to equipment or other circuits.

Appleton layers, *n. pl.* The F_1 and F_2 layers of the ionosphere.

applique, *adj.* Applied or fastened on. —*n.* Circuit element applied to a basic circuit to perform an added function.

applique circuit, *n.* A circuit that can be added to a complete basic circuit to increase, or change, the possible applications of the basic circuit. For example, some carrier telephone equipment designed for dial signaling can be converted to ringdown signaling through the use of an applique circuit.

arc, *n.* Flow of electric current in a flame-like stream of incandescent gas particles.—*v.i.* To form an arc.

arc-back, *n.* In an electron tube, a failure of rectifying action which results in electron flow from anode to cathode.—*v.i.* To fail in rectifying, resulting in a reverse flow of current.

arc chute, *n.* A narrow box-like structure between circuit breaker contacts which confines the arc when the contacts break, and uses convection to elongate and extinguish the arc.

Architects & Builders Service, *n.* A service of the telephone company which encourages builders to make adequate provision for telephone conduits and outlets in new buildings, and provides advice to architects regarding the design of adequate facilities.

arcing, *n.* A luminous passage of current through ionized gas or air.

area, *n.* A territory with definite, limiting boundaries.

area, accounting, *n.* Geographic location with defined boundaries for which separate bookkeeping records are maintained.

area, base rate, *n.* The innermost portion of an exchange area, in which all types of telephone service are given without mileage charges.

area, central office, *n.* Territory which receives telephone service from one central office.

area, cross-sectional, *n.* The area of the end of a wire which has been cut at right angles to its length. The cross-sectional area of a stranded wire is the sum of the cross-sectional areas of the individual wires.

area, exchange, *n.* A geographic unit established for the administration of telephone service in a specified area, usually a city, town, or village and its environs. One schedule of charges applies to the entire exchange area. It is served by one or more central offices and their associated outside plant.

area, foreign, *n.* A numbering plan area other than the numbering plan area in which the calling customer is located.

area, fringe. See "fringe area."

area, heavy loading, *n.* Territory in which the weather history is such that overhead wires may be subjected to the following conditions: Horizontal wind pressure of 4 pounds per square foot, temperature of 0 degree F, ice of ½ inch radial thickness.

area, home, *n.* The numbering plan area in which a calling customer is located.

area, light loading, *n.* Territory in which the weather history is such that overhead wires may be subjected to the following conditions: Horizontal wind pressure of 9 pounds per square foot, temperature of +30 degrees F, no sleet or ice.

area, local telephone service, *n.* The geographical area within which are located the telephone stations which a customer may call at local rates in accordance with provisions of a local tariff.

area, maintenance, *n.* Area assigned to one group which does all repair, replacement, and maintenance work within the area.

area, medium loading, *n.* Territory in which the weather history is such that overhead wires may be subjected to the following conditions: Horizontal wind pressure of 4 pounds per square foot, temperature of +15 degrees F, ice of ¼ inch radial thickness.

area, multi-office exchange, *n.* An exchange area served by several, or many, central office units.

area, numbering plan, *n.* A geographical area in which central office codes are not duplicated. See "numbering plan area" for a full discussion.

area, operating, *n.* Area in which all construction, maintenance and repair, and operating is assigned to one group. A complete telephone company may consist of several operating areas plus an executive headquarters.

area, primary service, *n.* An area surrounding a radio transmitting station in which the service is characterized by steady ground-wave propagation and negligible fading and interference from other stations.

area, secondary service, *n.* An area surrounding a radio transmitting station in which the service is characterized by both ground-wave and sky-wave reception, and by some fading and interference from other stations.

area, service, *n.* A geographical area within which all telephones are served from a single central office, or from a single switching center which contains several central office units.

area, testing, *n.* Area assigned to one group who performs all trouble testing. Usually combines both testboard and repair service functions.

area code, *n.* A three-digit code which precedes the central office code in the complete 10-digit telephone number. Used when the called telephone is in a numbering plan area different from that of the calling telephone. The first digit is never a "1" or "0"; the second digit is always a "1" or "0."

arm. See also "crossarm." "buckarm."

arm, buck. See "buckarm."

arm, cable, *n.* A horizontal member of angle steel with one or two braces, attached to a pole and used to support from one to four aerial cables on messenger.

arm, cable extension, *n.* Short arm of heavy angle steel used to hold an aerial cable away from the pole, thus bringing it in line with adjacent poles.

arm, cable form, *n.* A branch or leg off the main section of a cable form.

arm, cross. See "crossarm."

arm, extension, *n.* (1) A crossarm attached to the pole near one end, thus supporting the wires to one side of the pole to clear an obstruction. (2) A crossarm fastened vertically to the top of a pole for greater height.

arm, guard, *n.* (1) Short crossarm placed over the messenger and in line with an aerial cable to prevent damage to the cable from the climbing of linemen. (2) Regular crossarm placed over telephone open wires to prevent power wires from falling onto them.

arm, side, *n.* A crossarm which is placed to one side of a pole so that the wires will clear an obstruction. Usually placed so the pole is between pins 2 and 3 of the crossarm.

arm, transmitter, *n.* A supporting device, usually adjustable, which holds a telephone transmitter in the proper position for use.

armature, *n.* (1) The movable part of a magnetic circuit. (2) The portion of a relay or buzzer which is attracted by the electromagnet. (3) The rotating portion of a direct current generator or motor, or of an alternating current motor. (In an alternating current generator it is the field which rotates, and the assembly of windings which are fixed is known as the "stator.")

armature winding, *n.* The windlng of a rotating electrical machine in which current is induced when it cuts a magnetic field. The armature may either be fixed or rotating.

armor, *n.* A protective covering consisting of steel tapes or wires placed over the sheath of a telephone cable designed for direct burial or submarine use. See also: "cable, submarine," "cable, tape-armored," or "cable, wire armored."

armor, caged, *n.* Cable armor in which the armor wires are inside a polyethelene jacket. Used on some submarine cables.

armored cable. See "cable, armored."

ARQ—Automatic repeat request, *n.* A process of error control which detects errors in digital transmission by parity checks, and which requests retransmission when an error is detected within a block of characters.

array, antenna, *n.* An arrangement of two or more directional antennas, spaced and connected so that they are in phase and their effects are additive.

array, broadside, *n.* A uni-directional or bi-directional antenna array whose individual radiating elements are all in the same plane. The direction of propagation is perpendicular to this plane.

array, collinear, *n.* An antenna array in which half-wave elements are arranged end-to-end in the same horizontal or vertical line.

arrary, end-fire, *n.* A uni-directional or bi-directional antenna array whose radiating elements are parallel, one behind the other, and whose direction of propagation is perpendicular to the length of the individual radiating elements.

array, linear, *n.* A multi-element antenna in which the individual dipole elements are arranged end-to-end.

array, stacked. See "stacked array."

arrester, *n.* (1) Device which diverts high voltages to ground and away from the equipment thus protected. (2) The voltage limiting portion of a protector. (3) A lightning arrester. See also "protector, - - -."

arrester, gas-filled, *n.* Protector consisting of opposing spaced metal electrodes sealed into a tube filled with neon or argon gas. The gas ionizes, and therefore conducts, at a lower voltage and more reliably than a gap in air. It is therefore an accurate, self-clearing, low-voltage protector.

arrester, gas tube surge, *n.* A protector unit which will drain static or overvoltages by means of a discharge through a rare gas: Neon, argon, Xenon, etc. Provides very fast discharge times, and is self-clearing.

articulation, *n.* The act or manner of forming speech sounds clearly and distinctly. It is not necessary that the sounds convey intelligence.

artificial line, *n.* A network that simulates a real transmission line.

ASCII. See "code, ASCII."

asphalt, *n.* A dark-colored, viscous-to-solid, complex hydrocarbon. Found natural or obtained by evaporation of petroleum. A variety of bitumen.

assembly, *n.* A grouping of components to accomplish a particular function.

assembly, cable, *n.* A cable with plugs or connectors on each end.

assigned frequency, *n.* A radio frequency which has been designated for use by a particular radio station.

assigner, *n.* (1) A person who receives requests for service (service orders) and assigns the outside and inside plant facilities which will be used. (2) A part of the common-logic of switching centers which assigns units of common control equipment (registers, senders, DTMF receivers, MF 2/6 transceivers) to calls as required.

assigning, *n.* The work done by an assigner.

assignment, frequency, *n.* The assignment of a particular radio frequency to a particular radio station for a specific purpose, to provide maximum utilization of the available radio frequencies with minimum interference. Radio frequency assignments in the United States are made by the Federal Communications Commission.

assistance, directory, *n.* The modern term which has superseded "information service." The providing of telephone numbers to users who are not able to find the listing in their directory.

astatic, *adj.* Describing a mechanical system without bias or tendency toward a particular position.

asynchronous, *adj.* Not synchronous.

atmosphere, *n.* The gaseous envelope surrounding the Earth, composed of 78% nitrogen, 21% oxygen, 0.9% argon, plus some carbon dioxide and water vapor. The atmosphere is divided into several layers, as follows:

Troposphere	0-10 miles
Stratosphere	10-50 miles
Ionosphere	50-370 miles
Exosphere	370 + miles

atmosphere, explosive, *n.* Air holding in suspension dust, metal particles, or flammable gas in such proportions that they may ignite explosively.

atmospheric duct. See "duct, atmospheric."

atmospherics, *n.* (1) Extraneous, disturbing noise currents induced in wire line circuits as the result of lightning, northern lights, dust storms, and snow storms. (2) Interference to radio reception caused in the same manner.

attachment, authorized, *n.* Equipment, apparatus, circuit or device not furnished or maintained by the Telephone Company but which is authorized for attachment or connection to facilities of the Telephone Company. Examples are: electrocardiograph machines, electroencephalograph machines, data terminals, etc.

attachments, *n.* All of the plant elements (cables, crossarms, brackets, hooks, etc.) which are fastened to a supporting structure such as a pole.

attachments, foreign, *n.* (1) Attachments to the poles of one company by any other company or agency. (2) Unauthorized devices connected by subscribers to their telephones, for the purpose of monitoring, recording, or connecting to a radio transceiver.

attachments, tree, *n.* Elements of telephone plant fastened to a tree for support.

attack time, *n.* The time required to enable a voice-operated device, such as a VOGAD or echo suppressor, after speech starts. Usually set between 5 and 20 milliseconds; short enough not to clip the first speech syllable, and long enough not to operate on impulse noise.

attempt, *n.* The offering of a telephone call by a calling subscriber. If "completed," the "attempt" becomes a "message." A subsequent attempt is a "retrial."

attempt, subsequent, *n.* Any attempt to complete a toll call after the initial attempt.

attendant, *n.* (1) The operator of a local switchboard. (2) Any employee who observes equipment to see that it operates properly.

attendant, PBX, *n.* A person who operates a PBX switchboard, sometimes with other non-conflicting duties.

attendant exclusion, *n.* Feature of some PABX trunk equipments which prevents the PABX attendant from entering a busy trunk call unless recalled.

attendant recall, *n.* A feature of some PABX's which enables a station engaged in a trunk call to recall the attendant by flashing the hookswitch and dialing "O." When the attendant answers, a three-way conference connection exists.

attendant's cabinet, *n.* An attendant's switchboard at a PABX.

attendant's switchboard, *n.* A manually-operated switchboard associated with a dial central office, used to provide "assistance" service.

attended, *adj.* Said of a facility, such as a telephone central office, which normally has maintenance personnel in attendance during the normal working hours.

attended PAX, *n.* A private automatic switching system which includes a switchboard with an attendant who answers calls on incoming trunks and completes them to the station. Abbreviated: PABX.

attended public telephone, *n.* A public telephone with an attendant who accepts calls, assists customers using the service, and makes collections.

attenuate, *v.t.* To reduce or make smaller.

attenuation, *n.* The reduction in energy which accompanies the passage of an electric wave through lines, equipment, or space. Can be defined in terms of its effect on voltage and current, or upon power. The amount of attenuation is usually expressed in decibels or decibels per unit length.

attenuation, free space. See "loss, free space."

attenuation, rain, *n.* The attenuation of radio waves when passing through rain or clouds which are heavily moisture laden. It is important at microwave frequencies.

attenuation constant, *n.* Of a traveling plane wave, the decrease of a field component (or voltage, or current) in the direction of propagation, given in nepers per unit length. It is the real part of the "propagation constant."

attenuation equalizer. See "equalizer, attenuation."

attenuator, *n.* A device for reducing the energy of a wave without introducing distortion. Attenuators are commonly combinations of fixed or adjustable resistances. By properly proportioning the series and shunt elements, the impedance of an attenuator, as viewed from either or both ends, may be made to have almost any desired value independent of the value of attenuation. In its many different forms and applications, the attenuator becomes known as a pad, gain control, level adjustor, volume control, etc.

attraction, *n.* The force that exists between two unlike magnetic poles (N and S) or between two unlike static charges ($+$ and $-$).

Attraction, Law of Electrostatic. See "Coulomb's Law" in "Appendix B."

AT-type repeater. See "repeater, negative impedance."

audibility, *n.* A measure of the ease with which a sound can be heard, expressed as the number of decibels above the level of a similar sound which can just be heard.

audible, *adj.* Describing a sound which can be heard by a normal human ear.

audible ringing tone, *n.* The tone which is sent back to the calling telephone to indicate that the called telephone is being rung. It consists of a 400 Hz tone modulated with 40 Hz, and timed to coincide with the ringing signal. See also "ring-back tone."

audible signals. See "tones."

Audichron, *adj. n.* Registered name of a company which makes and leases equipment for automatically announcing time, temperature, and weather information over telephone connections. The information is recorded on spiral tracks on a magnetic drum, rather than on magnetic tape.

audio, *adj.* Describing signals or equipment involving frequencies which can be heard by the human ear. (20 to 20,000 Hertz).

audio frequency, *n.* Any of the frequencies which, as sound, can be heard by the human ear, *ie:* 20 to 20,000 Hertz.

audiogram, *n.* A graph showing the hearing loss in each ear separately, plotted against frequency.

audiometer, *n.* An instrument used to measure one's hearing ability.

auditing, *v.t.* Reviewing the accuracy of information provided by accounting, and judging the adequacy of and compliance with established policies and procedures.

auger, earth, *n.* A motor-driven auger of about 16-inch diameter mounted on a construction truck and used to bore holes for anchors and poles.

aural, *adj.* Received through the sense of hearing.

aurora borealis, *n.* A night phenomenon in the high latitudes consisting of luminous bands in the sky from highly ionized gases in the ionosphere, caused by sun-spot activity. Usually accompanied by some disruption of communications from the heavy earth currents which the aurora induces.

authentication, *n.* A security measure intended to protect a communication system against fraudulent transmissions.

authenticator, *n.* A group of letters or numerals, or both, inserted at a predetermined point in a message or transmission for the purpose of at-

testing to the authenticity of the message.

AutoDialer, *n.* An auxiliary device for a telephone which will automatically dial any of a group of pre-programmed telephone numbers when the corresponding button is pushed.

AUTODIN, *n.* A high-speed data communications network of the Defense Communications System, designed to provide world-wide data communications for the U.S. Department of Defense and other U.S. Government agencies. Acronym for AUTOmatic DIgital Network.

automanual telephone system. See "system, automanual telephone."

automatic, *adj.* Describing the actions of a device or machine which are taken without human supervision in response to certain predetermined conditions.

automatic alternate routing, *n.* A method of toll switching in which a call which encounters an "all trunks busy" (ATB) condition on the first route tested is automatically and rapidly offered in sequence to one or more alternate routes for completion.

automatic answer, *n.* The answering of a call to an unattended telephone by a machine which plays a recording stating that the called party is away temporarily, and (sometimes) inviting the caller to leave a message.

automatic frequency control (AFC). See "control, automatic frequency."

automatic gain control (AGC), *n.* A feature of some amplifiers and radio receivers which provides a substantially constant output even though the signal input varies over wide limits.

automatic message accounting (AMA), *n.* System which automatically records all of the data of subscriber-dialed long distance calls needed for billing purposes.

automatic number identification (ANI), *n.* Automatic equipment at a local dial central office used on customer-dialed toll calls to identify the calling station and transmit its identity to the CAMA equipment by sending multifrequency pulses over the same trunk after the dial pulsing is completed.

automatic sensitivity control (ASC). See "control, automatic sensitivity."

automatic signal trunk, *n.* A trunk arranged so that plugging into it automatically operates the line signal at the far end. Also called a "straightforward trunk." The military call it a "plug-supervision trunk."

automatic switching. See "system, automatic switching."

automatic tape relay. See "relay, automatic tape."

automatic telephone system. See "system, automatic telephone."

automatic toll ticketing (ATT, SATT), *n.* A system which permits subscriber dialing of toll calls and automatically makes a record of (1) calling number, (2) called number, (3) time of day, and (4) duration of call. This record may be used to automatically print a toll ticket, and to produce punched cards for accounting and billing.

automatic volume control (AVC), *n.* A self acting gain control which maintains the output of a radio receiver constant despite variations in received signal strength.

AUTOSEVOCOM, *n.* A world-wide secure voice transmission system of the Defense Communications Agency, having crypto-secure telephones homed on wide-band switchboards interconnected by narrowband trunks. Acronym for Automatic Secure Voice Communications.

auto start, *adj.* Said of a system where loss of primary power initiates action to automatically start a standby generator and transfer the load from the primary input bus to the standby generator output bus.

autotransformer, *n.* Voltage, current, or impedance transforming device in which a part of the winding is common to both the primary and secondary circuits.

AUTOVON, *n.* Acronym for AUTOmatic VOice Network. A worldwide common-user voice communication network of the U.S. Defense Communications System. Important 4-wire stations and 2-wire PBX's are homed on 4-wire common-controlled automatic switching centers which are interconnected by high-quality 4-wire trunks. The system is capable of 4-level preemption, conferencing, off-hook service, alternate secure voice or data. There will be 67 switching centers in the continental United States, nine in Canada, eleven in Europe, one in the Caribbean, and six in the Pacific.

auxiliary, *adj.* (1) aiding or assisting, (2) subsidiary, (3) additional, supplementary.

auxiliary power, *n.* An alternate source of power serving as a backup for the primary power source.

availability, *n.* (1) A measure of the time a system is operational compared to the total time it is in service. (2) The percentage of total trunks in a group which can be accessed by a particular switch.

availability, full, *adj. n.* The condition of a switching system where each input to a switching stage has access to every output from the stage. See also "graded multiple," a method of multipling trunks which does not give full availability.

availability, satellite, *n.* The determination by probability theory that a satellite will be within sight of both earth terminals at a predetermined date.

avalanche effect, *n.* The cumulative multiplication of carriers in a semiconductor caused by an electric field across the barrier region strong enough so that electrons collide with valence electrons, releasing new electrons which have more collisions, which release more electrons, etc.

average, *n.* An arithmetical term indicating the quotient obtained by adding a plurality of figures, then dividing by the number of figures.

average value, *n.* Of a complex or sinusoidal alternating wave, an average of many instantaneous amplitudes taken periodically during one-half cycle of the wave. If the wave is sinusoidal, the average value is 0.637 times the peak value.

award, incentive, *n.* Public recognition, sometimes with a token money payment, as a reward for having made a suggestion which improved operations or reduced costs.

axial lead, *n.* A connecting lead from a resistor or capacitor which comes out from an end, along the axis.

azimuth, *n.* The horizontal angle that a line (or the direction of the major lobe of an antenna) makes with the north-south line, measured eastward from the north. The azimuth of an antenna which points southwest is 225 degrees.

babble, *n.* The sum of the crosstalk from a number of channels, the result being unintelligible.

back-acting switch, *n.* A finder switch.

backboard, *n.* A board which can be fastened to a masonry, metal, or plastered surface and used to mount small pieces of equipment. Serves also to insulate from ground, cold, heat, or dampness.

back brace. See "brace, back."

back contacts, *n. pl.* Break contacts.

back cord, *n.* That cord of a pair which is farther from an operator.

back electromotive force. See "force, back electromotive."

backfill, *n.* The material used in refilling a trench or the space around a newly set pole.—*v.t.* (1) To replace earth in a trench or in the space around a pole. (2) To refill an excavation with any material.

back-haul, *n.* The negative advance in a toll switching network when a permissable routing takes the call farther from its ultimate destination.

backhoe, *n.* An automotive tool for the digging and filling of trenches. A pneumatically-operated hinged boom having a toothed bucket on its outer end, the inner end of the boom being supported on a tractor.

back lobe. See "lobe, back."

backoff, multiple access satellite, *n.* Reducing the radiated power of a satellite earth station to avoid the generation of excessively high intermodulation products in a communication satellite used for multiple access.

back porch, *n.* In a television picture signal, the portion of the signal which lies between the trailing edge of the horizontal synchronizing pulse and the trailing edge of the corresponding blanking pulse.

backstop, *n.* The portion of a relay which limits the movement of the armature away from the pole-piece.

back-to-back connection, *n.* The connection together of (1) two radio systems, baseband to baseband, or (2) two carrier systems, group to group or channel to channel, or (3) two selecting switches, such as line finder and connector, from jacks to jacks.

back-to-back coupling, antenna, *n.* The fraction, expressed in db, of the power transmitted from an antenna which would be received by a similar antenna on the same tower but pointing in the opposite direction.

back-to-front ratio. See "ratio, front-to-back."

backup facility, *n.* Any facility, such as a radio transmitter or an engine generator, which stands by for use when the facility normally used fails.

baffle, *n.* An acoustic shielding structure or partitions used to increase the effective length of the audio transmission path between two points in an acoustic system as, for example, between the front and back of a loudspeaker.

balance, active, *n.* In two-wire telephone repeater operation, a test made with the circuit in working condition at the hybrid transformer which shows the degree of balance between the network and the impedance of the line.

balance, hybrid, *n.* The degree of impedance balance achieved between opposite legs of a hybrid junction. The better the balance, the greater is the "transhybrid loss."

balance, line. See "line balance."

balance, longitudinal, *n.* A measure of the difference in impedance of the two sides of a circuit. There are two basic methods of measurement: a. (Bell System) measure the value of the series impedance inserted in one side of the circuit which restores it to perfect balance, or, b. (CCITT) measure the loss in decibels between the longitudinal circuit and the metallic circuit.

balance, precision. See "precision balance."

balance, terminal, *n.* The adjustment of all 2-wire toll connecting trunks terminating at a toll center, and the adjustment of the balancing network associated with their 4-wire terminating set, so that their impedance will satisfactorily match (18 db ERL) that of the toll trunks to which they may be connected.

balance, through, *n.* The adjustment of the impedance of all intertoll trunks terminating at a toll office to have the same impedance, so that there will be no impedance irregularity when the trunks are connected together.

balanced circuit, *n.* A circuit whose two sides are equal from the standpoint of series resistance, reactance, shunt leakage, and capacitance.

balanced line, *n.* A transmission line which is electrically symmetrical; that is: the two sides of the line have equal series resistance, series inductance, shunt capacitance, and leakage to ground.

balanced load. See "load, balanced polyphase."

balanced modulator. See "modulator, balanced."

balanced system. See "system, balanced polyphase."

balanced termination. See "termination, balanced."

balanced three-wire system. See "system, balanced three-wire."

balancing, terminal, *n.* In a toll office, the adjusting of the impedance of toll connecting or toll terminating trunks so as to obtain an adequate return loss at the junction with intertoll trunks.

balancing network. See "network, balancing."

balancing unit. See "unit, balancing."

balcony, *n.* A platform with a hand rail fastened to the pole below a cable terminal, used to support persons working in the terminal.

balcony, distributing frame, *n.* Elevated platform with a guard rail to facilitate working on the upper part of the distributing frame.

ballast lamp. See "lamp, ballast."

balun, *n.* An acronym meaning "balanced-unbalanced." A device used to connect an unbalanced (coaxial) transmission line to a balanced antenna, or vice versa. Sometimes called a "bazooka" (slang).

banana jack, *n.* A single-conductor jack which accepts a banana plug. Simply a cylindrical metal sleeve insulated from its mounting.

banana plug, *n.* A single-conductor plug having a banana-shaped spring metal tip.

band, *n.* A range of frequencies between upper and lower limits. By agreement of the ITU, these bands are designated:

# 2	ELF	(extremely low)	below 300 Hz
# 3	ILF	(infra-low)	300-3000 Hz
# 4	VLF	(very low)	3-30 kHz
# 5	LF	(low freq)	30-300 kHz
# 6	MF	(medium freq)	300-3000 kHz
# 7	HF	(high freq)	3-30 MHz
# 8	VHF	(very high)	30-300 MHz
# 9	UHF	(ultra high)	300-3000 MHz
#10	SHF	(super high)	3-30 GHz
#11	EHF	(extremely high)	30-300 GHz

band, amateur radio, *n.* Any of the frequency bands reserved for use by licensed amateur radio stations, such as:

1800 —	2000	kHz
3500 —	4000	kHz
7000 —	7300	kHz
14000 —	14350	kHz
21000 —	21450	kHz
28.00 —	29.70	MHz
50.00 —	54.00	MHz
144. —	148.	MHz
220 —	225.	MHz
420 —	450.	MHz
1215 —	1300	MHz
2300 —	2450	MHz
3300 —	3500	MHz
5650 —	5925	MHz

band, broadcast, *n.* Any of the several bands of radio frequencies allocated for broadcasting to the public. The most important are:

Service	Band
AM Broadcast	540-1600 kHz
Television (Ch 2-4)	54-72 MHz
Television (Ch 5-6)	76-88 MHz

Educational FM	88.1-91.9 MHz
FM Broadcast	92.1-107.9 MHz
Television (Ch 7-13)	174-216 MHz
Television (Ch 14-83)	470-890 MHz

band, citizen's, *n.* One of two radio-frequency bands which may be used for low power radio transmissions by U.S. citizens without requirement for a license. Either 26.965-27.225 or 462.55-469.95 megahertz.

band, communication satellite, *n.* Any of the bands of radio frequencies allocated for use by communication satellites.

Space frequencies:
3700-4200 and 7250-7750 MHz.
Earth frequencies:
5925-6425 and 7900-8400 MHz.

band, guard, *n.* A frequency band left vacant between two channels to give a margin of safety against mutual interference.

band, frequency, *n.* A range of frequencies between a lower and an upper limit.

band, microwave frequency, *n.* Any of the bands designated by letters in accordance with the following table. These designations originated during World War II to describe radar bands, and they have no official status.

Band	Frequency Range	
P	0.225 to	0.390 GHz
L	0.390 to	1.550 GHz
S	1.55 to	5.20 GHz
X	5.20 to	10.90 GHz
K	10.90 to	36.00 GHz
Q	36.00 to	46.00 GHz
V	46.00 to	56.00 GHz
W	56.00 to	100.00 GHz

band, radio frequency, *n.* Any of the following bands, which were published in the Radio Regulations of the International Telecommunication Union in 1959.

Band	Frequency Range	
2 (ELF)	30 to	300 Hz
3 (VF)	300 to	3000 Hz
4 (VLF)	3 to	30 kHz
5 (LF)	30 to	300 kHz
6 (MF)	300 to	3000 kHz
7 (HF)	3 to	30 MHz
8 (VHF)	30 to	300 MHz
9 (UHF)	300 to	3000 MHz
10 (SHF)	3 to	30 GHz
11 (EHF)	30 to	300 GHz
12 —	300 to	3000 GHz

(The upper limit is included in each band; the lower limit is excluded.)

band, television broadcast. See "band, broadcast."

band, transmission, *n.* The band of frequencies which is passed by a filter, or by a loaded or repeatered line.

bandage, cable splicer's, *n.* Rubber ribbon about 4 inches wide, used for wrapping around a cable splice to temporarily protect it from moisture.

bandage, triangular, *n.* A 40-inch right triangle of sterile unbleached muslin used as an arm sling, for holding compresses in place, or for securing splints. A component of all first aid kits.

band elimination filter, *n.* A filter which attenuates frequencies within its "rejection band," but passes frequencies above and below this band.

bandpass filter, *n.* A filter which allows free passage to frequencies within its "pass band" but attenuates frequencies above and below that range.

band rejection filter. See "filter, band elimination."

bands, cable splice, *n. pl.* Oversize hose clamps, to be placed circumferentially around large cable splice sleeves to prevent them from bulging when the cable is pressurized with gas.

band splitter. See "splitter, band."

band spreading, *n.* The spreading of tuning indications over a wide scale range to facilitate tuning in a crowded band of frequencies.

bandstop filter. See "filter, band elimination."

bandwidth, *n.* A range of frequencies between upper and lower limits. Two methods of specifying are in common use: (a) Between the high and low frequencies where the power level is 3 db below that at mid-band, and (b) 10 db below.

bandwidth, necessary, *n.* Of a radio transmitter for a given class of emission, the minimum value of occupied bandwidth to ensure transmission at the rate and with the quality required, under specified conditions.

bandwidth, nominal, *n.* The total frequency band allocated for a channel, including a guard band. A voice channel has a nominal bandwidth of 4 kilohertz, though filters may degrade all but the band 300 to 3500 hertz.

bandwidth, occupied, *n.* The bandwidth of a modulated signal, excluding all components weaker than 5% of the carrier, or 5% of the strongest side frequency if its level exceeds that of the carrier.

bandwidth, useful. See "useful bandwidth."

bandwidth ratio (BWR), *n.* Of a radio communication system, the ratio which in decibels is equal to ten times the common logarithm of a quantity consisting of the "occupied bandwidth" of the entire baseband, divided by the assigned "channel bandwidth."

bank, *n.* (1) In automatic switching, an assembly of fixed contacts formed into a rigid unit. Wires are connected to one side and moving contacts ("wipers") move over the other. (2) A group of pieces of similar equipment placed near to each other and operating in conjunction.

bank, line, *n.* The lower bank, or banks, of contacts which give access to the line or talking circuit on a Strowger-type step-by-step switch.

bank, sleeve, *n.* The upper bank of a step-by-step switch which contains only the sleeve contacts, usually 100 contacts in a selector or connector bank and 200 contacts in a linefinder bank.

bank, vertical, *n.* On a two-motion

step-by-step switch, a vertical bank of eleven contacts at the side of the switch which a wiper attached to the switch shaft contacts during its vertical stepping motion. The bank permits class-marking each bank level.

bank assembly, *n.* Two or more banks mounted one above the other on a switch frame.

bank points, *n.* Total number of bank contacts appearing at each switch position, including both the line bank(s) and private (control) bank.

bar, *n.* (1) Any piece of metal which is much longer than it is wide or thick. (2) A rigid steel rod used for digging, lifting, or prying. (3) An acoustic unit of sound pressure equal to one million dynes per square centimeter. (4) A black horizontal or vertical line used in a television test pattern.

bar, crow, *n.* A heavy steel pry and digging bar of rectangular cross-section having a single-bevel chisel point.

bar, digging, *n.* Steel bar about 8 feet long; one end pointed, the other chisel-ended for loosening dirt and paving.

bar, expanding and tamping, *n.* A 10-foot long wooden handle having a 20-pound slotted steel head which fits over the rod of an expansion anchor and is used to expand the anchor and to tamp earth firmly around the rod.

bar, pinch, *n.* Heavy bar, about 4 feet long, with a curved chisel end for prying.

bar, tamping, *n.* Steel bar, about 8 feet long, having a square end for packing loose dirt about a pole.

bare, *adj.* Describing a conductor which is not covered with insulating material.

barium titanate, *n.* A piezoelectric material, now largely superseded by lead zirconate titanate.

barretter, *n.* The temperature sensitive element of a bolometer, used for radio-frequency power measurements. Usually a fine platinum wire sealed in a vacuum. See also "bolometer."

barrier, *n.* A partition for the insulation or isolation of electric circuits.

barrier code, *n.* A digit inserted for the purpose of preventing a misdialed local call from resulting in an extra charge call. In common-control offices, the prefix "1" is a barrier code.

base, *n.* (1) The part of a junction transistor which separates the emitter and collector regions. (2) The portion of an electron tube which carries the terminal pins.

base, flag, *n.* A 7-pound round cast iron base having a hole for a warning flag staff. Has a rounded bottom so that it maintains an upright position.

baseband, *n.* The total frequency band occupied by the aggregate of all the information signals used to modulate a carrier.

baseband, multiplex, *n.* The total frequency band occupied by all transmitted or all received signals on the transmission facility side of the multiplexing equipment. In the case of multiplex equipment using two-wire transmission facilities, it is the frequency band occupied by both transmitted and received signals.

baseband, radio, *n.* The frequency band available for the transmission of all of the combined signals with which the radio can be modulated.

baseband regulation. See "regulation, baseband."

base rate area. See "area, base rate."

base region, *n.* In a transistor, the region between the emitter and collector, into which the holes or electrons are injected.

base station, mobile. See "station, mobile base."

basilar membrane, *n.* The primary transducer in the human inner ear which converts sound waves to nerve impulses which are interpreted by the brain as sound.

bass, *adj. n.* Musical sounds having a pitch which would be written on the bass clef in musical notation. Below "middle C," or 256 hertz.

Bat-Tap, *n.* A device used to obtain a lower voltage from a battery, such as 24 volts from a 48 volt battery, without tapping the battery. A voltage-divider consisting of selenium coated iron plates, stacked in quantity such that the voltage drop will be 0.5 volt per plate. "Bat-Tap" is a name registered by the Lorain Products Corporation.

battery, *n.* A group of several cells connected together to furnish current by conversion of chemical, thermal, solar, or nuclear energy into electrical energy. A single cell is sometimes improperly called a battery. See also "cell, - - -."

battery, "A." See "battery, filament."

battery, alkaline, *n.* Any of several types of primary or storage batteries which use an alkaline electrolyte, as opposed to an acid electrolyte. The alkaline electrolyte is usually a solution of potassium hydroxide.

battery, "B." See "battery, plate."

battery, "C." See "battery, grid."

battery, central office, *n.* A group of storage cells connected in series to provide a 48 volt direct current supply to a central office. A lead-acid storage cell has a nominal voltage of 2 volts, which increases to 2.15 volts when being charged and drops to 1.85 volts when being discharged. The normal central office battery therefore consists of 23 cells, increased to 26 cells when the chargers are inoperative.

battery, common, *n.* A battery (usually 48 volts) which serves as a central source of energy for many similar circuits.

battery, filament, *n.* Source of energy which heats the filaments of vacuum tubes. ("A" battery)

battery, flashlight, *n.* A group of several "D" size dry cells, 1-5/32" OD X 2-1/4" long.

battery, floating, *n.* A storage battery

which operates in parallel with the central office load and battery chargers. It (a) serves as a stand-by source of power, (b) absorbs peak loads, (c) stabilizes the voltage, (d) short-circuits noise voltages.

battery, grid, *n.* Source of energy which supplies the steady negative voltage required for biasing the grids of vacuum tubes. ("C" battery)

battery, lead-acid storage. See "cell, lead-acid storage."

battery, local, *n.* Source of talking power located at the subscriber's station, usually consisting of three dry cells in series.

battery, negative. See "negative battery."

battery, nickel-iron storage. See "cell, nickel-iron storage."

battery, nuclear, *n.* A source of direct current derived from the radiations of a radioactive material. Potentially useful in communications satellites.

battery, PBX, *n.* Source of direct current power for the operation of a private branch exchange. Usually a 24 volt or 48 volt storage battery.

battery, plate, *n.* Source of direct current power which causes current to flow in the plate circuit of a vacuum tube. ("B" battery)

battery, quiet, *n.* Talking battery, which see.

battery, signaling, *n.* Source of direct current power used to operate lamps and alarms for signaling and supervision, and to operate relays and stepping magnets. Usually a 48 volt storage battery with filters in the load circuits to prevent their noise from getting back to the battery.

battery, stationary, *n.* A storage battery designed for service in a fixed position.

battery, storage, *n.* A group of storage cells connected in series. See also "cell, (type) storage" and "battery, central office."

battery, talking, *n.* Source of low-impedance direct current power fitted with a filter which makes it noise free and suitable for supplying power to telephone lines. Usually a 48 volt storage battery.

battery, testing, *n.* Source of high-voltage, (150 volts) low-current power used at testboards and test desks to operate voltmeters and wheatstone bridges.

battery, transmission, *n.* Talking battery.

battery and ground pulsing, *n.* A method of sending DC pulse address information over a trunk which is of too high resistance to permit loop pulsing, by connecting battery and ground at the originating office to the trunk only during the pulsing period with such a polarity that the batteries at the originating and terminating ends of the trunk are in a series-aiding connection, thus doubling the current flow and the pulsing range. After pulsing is completed, the originating office battery is disconnected and the trunk is held by current through the loop circuit.

battery eliminator, *n.* A device consisting of a rectifier plus filter, capable of supplying DC power at the required voltage without the use of a battery. To substitute for a battery it must have an output of (a) low impedance and (b) low noise level.

battery tap, *n.* A device for obtaining a lower voltage from a central office battery without the use of dropping resistors or counter-EMF cells. Consists of a tapped stack of copper-oxide rectifier units.

baud, *n.* A unit of transmission speed of digital signals. It is the reciprocal of the length in seconds of the shortest element of the digital code. For example, if a teletypewriter is operating at 60 wpm, the length of the shortest element of the 7.42-unit code is 22 milliseconds. The baud rate is therefore $1/0.022 = 45.45$ bauds.

Baudot code, *n.* The five-unit code used for teletypewriter signals. Originated by Baudot in 1874. See also "code, ITA #2."

baud rate, *n.* Standard digital transmission rates are determined by the formula $75x2^n$

$$75x2 = 150 \text{ bauds}$$
$$75x4 = 300 \text{ bauds}$$
$$75x8 = 600 \text{ bauds}$$
$$75x16 = 1200 \text{ bauds}$$
$$75x32 = 2400 \text{ bauds}$$

bay, *n.* (1) Row of racks or frames on which equipment, in the form of panels or shelves, is mounted. (2) One unit of an antenna array.

bay, equal level patching, *n.* A patching facility, either voice frequency or base-band frequency, at which all circuits appear at a uniform level both input and output, E-W and W-E (usually –2 dbm) to facilitate patching without transmission adjustments.

bayonet, *n.* A metal or wooden member used as a pole top extension.

bayonet base, *n.* A cylindrical lamp base having two locking pins spaced 180 degrees. Used on automotive lamps, ballast lamps, etc.

bazooka, *n.* A balun (slang).

"B" battery. See "battery, plate."

BCH code, *n.* Any of the many Bose-Chauduri-Hocquenghem error control codes, which are cyclic error detecting and correcting codes used for data transmission.

bead, *n.* Glass, ceramic, or plastic insulator through which the inner conductor of a coaxial transmission line passes, and by means of which the inner conductor is supported in a position coaxial with the outer conductor.

beam, radio, *n.* A radiation of radio waves which is very sharply directional.

beam antenna, *n.* An antenna array, which see.

beamwidth, antenna, *n.* The angle between the points in space where the power radiated from the antenna is 3 dB lower than the maximum power radiated along the axis of the antenna.

bearing, *n.* A direction, measured in degrees from true north or true south. A bearing never exceeds 90 degrees. It is written "N 37 degrees 5'E," or "S 15 degrees 29'W" meaning "from the South, 15 degrees 29 minutes toward the West."

bearing, magnetic, *n.* A direction in azimuth given in relation to the north direction shown by a magnetic compass, without correction for magnetic declination.

bearing, true, *n.* A direction in azimuth given in relation to true north.

beat, *n.* A beat note.—*v.t.* (1) In splicing, to hammer in the end of the lead sleeve so that it fits the cable sheath. (2) In measuring, to connect two oscillators together, adjusting one until no throbbing is heard in a connected receiver. The oscillators are then at the same frequency.

beat, zero. See "zero beat."

beat frequency, *n.* A new wave which is created when two different frequencies are combined in a non-linear circuit. Its frequency is the difference between the two combined frequencies.

beat-frequency oscillator. See "oscillator, beat-frequency."

beat in, *v.t.* (1) In cable splicing, to reduce the diameter of the end of a lead sleeve by beating with a hardwood cable dresser. (2) To adjust one of a pair of oscillators until they produce the same frequency, as denoted by the lack of a beat note in a connected receiver.

beating, *n.* A phenomenon in which two periodic waves having different frequencies produce a resultant having periodic variations of amplitude.

beat note, *n.* The audible tone created when two different frequencies are combined in a non-linear circuit, or combined as sound waves in air.

beats, *n. pl.* The periodic variations of amplitude which result when two periodic waves having different frequencies are superimposed.

beep tone, *n.* An intermittent audio tone (commonly a 1/5 second spurt of 1400 Hz) superimposed on a voice circuit as a warning.

beeswax, *n*. Purified beeswax is used for impregnating or boiling out cable forms and cores of acetate and cotton cables to render them moisture resistant and to prevent the insulation from fraying. Used at a temperature of 375 degrees F. Available in one pound cakes.

Bel, *n*. The fundamental division of a logarithmic scale for expressing the ratio of two powers, which are in the ratio of one to ten. The Bel is an impractically large unit, so the "decibel" (one-tenth of a Bel) is used instead.

bell, *n*. An electro-mechanical device in which an electrically vibrated clapper repeatedly strikes a gong which gives out a musical tone.

bell, loud-ringing, *n*. A telephone bell equipped with 6-inch gongs, and usually in a weatherproof case. For installation out of doors or in very noisy locations.

bell, single-stroke, *n*. A bell which gives out one single note each time it is energized.

bell, telephone. See "ringer, polarized."

bell, weatherproof, *n*. A telephone bell having all parts except the two gongs inside a weatherproof case, and usually with oversize 6-inch gongs. For installation out of doors.

bell box. See "box, bell."

Bellboy, *n*. A Bell System service which provides a paging signal originating at any dial telephone and carried over a radio channel to a miniature pocket radio receiver carried by a customer. When the customer's Bellboy number is dialed, the pocket receiver buzzes three times at 30-second intervals, indicating that he should call his home office.

bell-tapping, *n*. The intermittent jingling produced by a telephone ringer when a dial is operated on the same line.

belt, body, *n*. Heavy belt passed around the waist, equipped at the sides with two "D" rings for fastening the "safety belt." Also has loops for holding tools.

belt, cable, *n*. Any layer of insulation over a cable core and under the outer jacket.

belt, integral, *n*. In cable construction, a layer of insulating material applied by extrusion over two or more twisted or parallel insulated conductors so as to form a round smooth diameter.

belt, safety, *n*. Heavy, adjustable belt passed around a pole and snapped to the "D" rings of the body belt, allowing a man to work at the top of a pole without danger of falling.

belt, tool, *n*. A wide, padded, extra-strong nylon and/or leather belt for buckling about the body of linemen just above the hips. Has two "D" rings for attaching the safety strap, and loops, thong, and hooks to hold pliers, wrench, tape, knife, gloves, etc.

belts, Van Allen. See "Van Allen belts."

bend, cast iron pipe, *n*. Cast iron pipe of 3-inch ID formed into a 90-degree bend of 30-inch or 24-inch radius. Used to bring subsidiary conduit from the ground at a pole or building.

bend, E-plane, *n*. A waveguide bend in which the longitudinal axis of the waveguide remains in a plane parallel to the plane of the electric field vector.

bend, H-plane, *n*. A waveguide bend in which the longitudinal axis of the waveguide remains in a plane parallel to the plane of the magnetic field vector.

bend, waveguide. See "waveguide bend."

bender, cable, *n*. Tool used to put bends in stiff cables when placing them in manholes or vaults, or on cable racks.

bender, piezoelectric, *n*. Piezoelectric element consisting of two thin rectangular piezoelectric slabs bonded to each side of a thin metal strip, oriented such that application of voltage causes one slab to expand and the other to contract, thus resulting in flexing like a bimetallic strip.

bender, spring, *n.* A small hand tool used to bend and adjust the springs of relays and keys.

benefits, employee, *n.* Payments by a telephone company to its employees covering payments for illness, disability, pensions, and death.

Beverage antenna. See "antenna, wave."

bias, *n.* (1) A uniform displacement of like signal transitions resulting in a uniform lengthening or shortening of all marking signals. (2) Holding a relay in the spacing condition with a constant spacing current. The marking condition is achieved with an opposing marking current of twice the value. (3) The effect of the line or equipment adjustment on teletypewriter signals.—*v.t.* To influence or to dispose to one direction, as a DC voltage, with a spring, or with a magnet.

bias, cathode, *n.* Electron tube bias obtained by placing a resistor in the cathode return circuit, thereby making the cathode positive to ground.

bias, forward, *n.* Connecting a voltage to a semiconductor diode with a polarity such that the voltage aids the movement of carriers across the potential barrier. With forward bias the p-type material is positive and the n-type material is negative.

bias, grid, *n.* A negative voltage applied to the control grid of an electron tube with respect to the cathode potential. It establishes operation at the desired point on the characteristic curve of the tube.

bias, internal, *n.* The bias, either marking or spacing, which may exist within a machine such as a teletypewriter as a result of mechanical adjustments.

bias, magnetic, *n.* A steady magnetic field applied to keep a relay from operating. Used instead of a mechanical bias applied with a spring.

bias, marking, *n.* Distortion of telegraph or digital signals in which all marking signals are lengthened.

bias, mechanical, *n.* The application of mechanical restraint by means of a spring, to hold a relay armature in its spacing position or to hold a telephone ringer armature to prevent bell tapping.

bias, negative, *n.* A voltage applied to the control grid of an electron tube to make it negative with respect to the cathode. Places the tube on the proper part of its operating characteristic curve.

bias, positive, *n.* Of a digital or telegraph signal, the lengthening of marking pulses and a corresponding shortening of the spaces.

bias, reverse, *n.* Connecting a voltage to a semiconductor diode, with the p-type material negative and the n-type positive, so that the voltage pulls the carriers away from the junction and thereby stops current flow.

bias, self, *n.* Bias provided to the control grid of an electron tube by the voltage drop across a resistor in the cathode circuit.

bias, spacing, *n.* Distortion of telegraph or digital signals in which all spacing signals are lengthened.

biased ringer. See "ringer, biased."

biax memory element, *n.* A memory element consisting of a ferrite block having two non-intersecting holes at right angles to each other. One hole carries the "write" and "sense" winding; the other hole, the "read" winding.

bidirectional, *adj.* Having equal effectiveness in two directions which are separated by 180 degrees in azimuth.

bifilar winding, *n.* A winding consisting of two insulated conductors side by side. Used to (a) produce two balanced windings, (b) to get maximum coupling between two windings, or (c) to produce a resistor with minimum inductance.

bifurcated, *adj.* Describing a flat spring which is split into two halves at the end. Used to form "twin contacts," which see.

billboard reflector. See "repeater, passive."

billing, *n.* Process of accumulating costs, adding expenses, and preparing a statement for the amount to be paid.

bill-to-third-number call, *n.* A toll telephone call which is charged to a third number, not the number of the calling or called party, which requires the operator to write a memo ticket.

binary, *adj.* Having two possible states or values.

binary cell, *n.* An elementary storage element which can be placed in either of two stable states, such as zero or one, open or closed, non-operated or operated.

binary coded decimal, *n.* A number in decimal form with each digit expressed in binary (base 2) form. Widely used in electronic data processing.

binary digit, *n.* One unit of information in binary (two-level) notation.

binary state, *n.* Either of the two conditions of a bistable device, the "one" state or the "zero" state.

binaural, *adj.* (1) Involving the use of both ears. (2) describing sound which affects two ears differently to produce a stereophonic effect.

binaural effect, *n.* The capability of the brain to determine the direction from which a sound is coming by analyzing the difference in arrival time and intensity at the two ears.

binder, *n.* A spirally served thread or tape used to hold cable pair groups together pending completion of the cable manufacturing operations.

binder, directory, *n.* A hard-cover book binder which is used to hold and protect a telephone directory in a paystation booth.

binder, load, *n.* A chain winch having grab hooks on both ends. Used to tighten the chains which fasten heavy loads to trucks or trailers.

binding post, *n.* A hand-operated screw terminal used to make electrical connections to wires.

bipolar, *adj.* Having two magnetic poles.

bird, *n.* An artificial satellite. (slang).

Birmingham Wire Gauge, *n.* A scale of measurement for ferrous (iron or steel) wires, previously called the Stubs Iron Wire Gauge. See also "gauges, wire."

BIS-COBOL, *n.* A computer programming language using common Business Oriented Language amended for the specific requirements of a Business Information System.

bisector, angle, *n.* A metal pantograph measuring device which can be used to bisect a corner angle in a telephone line and thus determine where to locate an anchor guy.

bistable, *adj.* Having two stable conditions or states.

bit, *n.* Acronym for "binary digit," which see.

bit, car, *n.* A wood bit, 18 inches long, much used by linemen for boring bolt holes in poles. Available in sizes from 1/4 inch to 1 1/4 inches, in 1/16 inch increments.

bit, check, *n.* A bit associated with a character or block in order to check for an error within the character or block. Also called a "parity bit."

bit, electrician's, *n.* A wood bit, 18 inches long, used by electricians for boring holes in interior wooden partitions. Available in sizes from 4/16 to 13/16 inch.

bit, overhead, *n.* Any bit other than an information bit.

bit, parity, *n.* A check bit that indicates that the total number of binary "one" bits in a character or word (excluding the parity bit) is odd or even. In an odd parity system the total number of "one" bits (including the parity bit) is always odd.

bit, service, *n.* An overhead bit which is not a check bit. It may serve as a request for a repeat, as a sequence number, etc.

bit-parallel, *adj.* Describes a method of information transfer in which all of the "bits" (binary digits) constituting one alpha-numeric character are transmitted simultaneously on parallel transmission paths.

bit rate, *n.* The speed at which digital information is transmitted, usually expressed in bits per second.

bit-serial, *adj.* Describes a method of information transfer in which each "bit" (binary digit) is transmitted sequentially, one after another. The teletypewriter uses bit-serial transmission.

black, *adj.* Refers to the type of transmission facility, type of signal, or area which contains either (a) encrypted classified information, or (b) unclassified information.

black area, *n.* An area in which classified communications exist only in an encrypted form.

black box, *n.* A unit of interface equipment, specified only in terms of its performance.

black circuit, *n.* A circuit which may be routed over unprotected communication facilities either because (a) it carries no sensitive (classified) information, or (b) the information it carries is encrypted.

blackout, *n.* (1) The interruption of radio communications above about 1500 kHz by ionospheric absorption caused by solar flares. (2) The intentional interruption of radio communications in order to deny the enemy access to intelligence.

blade, switch, *n.* The flat metal moving contact of a switch which enters a fixed contact.

blank, apparatus, *n.* A piece of plastic, metal, or wood intended to cover or fill the space reserved for future installation of a unit of apparatus.

blanket, rubber, *n.* Square of rubber sheeting used for temporarily protecting open cable splices.

blanketing, *n.* The action of a power-

ful radio signal or interference in rendering a receiving set incapable of receiving the desired signals.

blanking, *n.* (1) The act of cutting off a channel or device for a short interval. (2) In television, the cutting off of the electron beam in the picture tube during the time the beam is retracing to its starting position.

blasting, *n.* Severe distortion due to overloading sound reproducing equipment.

bleeder, *n.* A high resistance connected across the DC output of a high voltage power supply which serves to discharge the filter capacitors after the power supply has been turned off, and to provide a stabilizing load.

bleeding, *n.* The appearance of drops of wood preservative, such as creosote, on the surface of a pole.

block, *n.* (1) A group of bits (binary digits) transmitted as a unit, over which a parity check procedure is applied for error control purposes. (2) Any of the various special blocks which are listed below.

block, carbon. See "block, protector."

block, connecting, *n.* An insulating block or base equipped with screw, clip, or spring terminals and used to terminate wires, cables, cords, or as a socket to hold plug-based relays.

block, discharge, *n.* A protector block.

block, fuse, *n.* A block of insulating material arranged to mount fuses, a battery bus-bar, and an alarm bus-bar.

block, matrix, *n.* Moulded plastic block equipped with horizontally and vertically aligned rows of clip terminals. Used to hold diodes for ringer control.

block, ocean. See "ocean block."

block, protector, *n.* Rectangular block of carbon, or porcelain block with carbon insert, providing two opposing carbon surfaces separated by a small air gap. One carbon is connected to ground; the other to a line wire. The gap breaks down and provides a path to ground for voltages over 350 volts. One element of a protector.

block, snatch, *n.* A single pulley or "sheave" in a framework or "shell" having one side of the shell hinged so that the block can be inserted in a length of rope when the rope ends are not available for threading through the block. Used to tighten a rope, or to deflect its path.

block, tackle, *n.* A pulley or system of several pulleys in a frame called a "shell." Used with rope to gain a mechanical advantage, so that a small pull on the rope end will be multiplied to a much larger force at the block. Available for most rope sizes 3/8-inch and larger, and having one, two, or three pulleys called "sheaves."

block, terminal, *n.* (1) An insulating mounting for a set of terminal lugs, equipped with a fanning strip, and arranged for mounting on a distributing frame or other equipment. Available with 2, 3, 4, 5, 6, or 8 terminals per row, and 20, 25, or 26 rows per block. (2) An insulating block holding pairs of binding posts which are internally connected to a stub cable. Commonly in 10, 16, 25 and 50 pairs sizes.

block, wire terminal, *n.* Moulded plastic blocks with one, three, or six pairs of binding posts, used in ready-access terminals to provide a bridging point for drop wires.

block, wooden, *n.* A piece of wood simulating a carbon block, and used in main distributing frame protectors to keep the springs from grounding when protection is not required.

block and tackle, *n.* An arrangement of one or more pulley blocks with rope, for hoisting heavy objects or for pulling wire or strand.

block cable. See "cable, block."

blocked impedance. See "impedance, blocked."

blocking, *n.* The inability of the calling subscriber to be connected to the called subscriber because either (a) all paths are busy, or (b) because idle paths in the calling group cannot access idle paths in the called group.

blocking, Erlang B, *n.* Assumes that a call which is blocked is abandoned immediately.

blocking, Erlang C, *n.* Assumes that a blocked call is willing to wait indefinitely for an idle trunk.

blocking, Poisson, *n.* Assumes that a blocked call is held, up to the total intended holding time. If a trunk becomes idle the call seizes it and uses it for the remaining portion of the holding time.

blow, *v.i.* When a fuse operates to open a circuit, it is said to "blow."

blower, *n.* (1) A motor driven air pump for ventilating manholes. (2) A fan for cooling equipment.

blower, manhole, *n.* A centrifugal fan driven by an electric, gasoline, or propane motor, used to ventilate manholes. Provides about 800 CFM of fresh air through an 8-inch hose.

blowout, magnetic, *n.* The use of a permanent magnetic field across the contacts of a circuit breaker to lengthen, and thereby extinguish, any arc which forms when the contacts open.

board. See "switchboard," "testboard," "patchboard," "information board," "service observing board."

board, DSB. See "switchboard, dial system B."

board, inward toll, *n.* That portion of the toll switchboard which handles traffic incoming over toll circuits from other cities.

board, linen test. See "strip, test."

board, outward toll, *n.* That portion of the toll switchboard which handles traffic which originates from a local subscriber, and is passed over toll circuits to, or toward, its destination in another city.

board, patch. See "patchboard" and "bay, equal-level patching."

board, power, *n.* A unit of central

office equipment at which the production and distribution of central office direct current power is monitored and controlled, from chargers to battery to load. Typically a two-section vertical panelboard about 5 feet wide by 7 feet high containing the following panels:

(a) Motor-generator or rectifier control
(b) Charger paralleling panel
(c) Discharge panel
(d) End cell control panel
(e) Ringing machine control panel
(f) Distribution fuses
(g) Voltmeter and ammeter, with switch
(h) Supervisory relays and fuses
(i) Alarm lamps

board, printed wiring, *n.* An insulating board which holds a printed circuit with associated components. Often arranged with terminals along one edge so that it can be plugged into a shelf connector.

board, service observing, *n.* A special switchboard or turret whose monitoring circuits can be connected by shoes to selected subscriber's lines and trunks. A trained service observer monitors calls, from line signal to disconnect, and records the speed of answer and the accuracy and quality of the operator's work.

board, tag. See "strip, test."

board, terminal, *n.* A flat insulating board which mounts a group of terminals.

board, test. See "testboard," "testboard, toll," and "test desk, local."

board, test and control, *n.* A toll testboard with face equipment which is an exact duplicate of that on the outward toll switchboard. Used for making operating and talking tests and 1000 Hz transmission measurements on working toll circuits. The test and control board operator can busy-out circuits, and refer them to the primary toll testboard for the clearing of trouble.

board, toll. See "switchboard, toll."

board, transposition running, *n.* Tool used for the installation of transposed open wire circuits. Consists of a triangular frame pulled by the winch line and equipped with three swivels to which six open wires can be attached. As the new wires are pulled past a transposition pole the swivels are rotated as required to form the transpositions.

board, trunk, *n.* A frame for mounting selector or repeater switches. See "frame, switch."

body-capacitance, *n.* Capacitance to ground introduced into an electric circuit by the proximity of the human body.

boiling out, *n.* The act of ridding paper-insulated cable cores of moisture by immersing them in paraffin heated to 380 degrees F.

boil out, *v.t.* To immerse a paper-insulated cable core into melted paraffin at 380 degrees F to boil off any moisture that may be in the insulation.

bolometer, *n.* A device used for measuring radio-frequency power. The RF power is passed through a temperature sensitive resistor (barretter, or thermistor) which heats and changes resistance. The bolometer resistor element is made one arm of a bridge circuit, thus enabling measurement of the power by balancing the bridge circuit.

bolt, angled thimbleye, *n.* A thimbleye bolt having the eye bent down at a 45-degree angle. Facilitates the attachment of an anchor guy.

bolt, carriage, *n.* A bolt having a large oval head with a short square shank under the head which prevents the bolt from turning while the nut is being tightened. Used to fasten fittings to wooden crossarms.

bolt, double-arming, *n.* A headless galvanized bolt threaded its entire length and fitted with four nuts and square washers. Used to tie two crossarms together for double-arm construction.

bolt, expansion, *n.* A bolt designed for anchoring in masonry. Inserted in a drilled hole in masonry and tightened to draw a wedge into an expanding anchor.

bolt, machine, *n.* A heavy bolt with a square head, threaded only at one end with coarse series threads.

bolt, stove, *n.* A fractional-inch bolt, ranging in size from ⅛-inch to ⅜-inch, and having either a round button or a flat head. Used with a square nut.

bolt, thimbleye, *n.* A galvanized through bolt having a thimble-shaped eye in place of the square head. Allows connection of a guy to the bolt without additional hardware.

bolt, through, *n.* A galvanized, square-head machine bolt long enough to go entirely through the pole and used to fasten cable suspension clamps and crossarms to the pole. Available in ⅜, ½, ⅝, ¾, and 1-inch diameters in lengths up to 24 inches.

bolt, twin-eye, *n.* A bolt with a thimble eye having two grooves to accommodate two guy strands.

bond, *n.* A low-resistance electrical connection between two lead cable sheaths, between two ground connections, or between similar parts of two circuits.—*v.t.* To place an electrical bond.

bond, temporary cable, *n.* A five-foot length of flexible insulated wire having battery clips on both ends. Used to provide a sheath bond across a cable splice.

bonding, *n.* The act of connecting together the sheaths of all lead covered cables in a manhole, or in a cable vault. Bonding is usually done with a tinned copper ribbon, 1/16"x3/8", soldered to the cable sheaths.

Boolean algebra, *n.* A branch of mathematics which solves problems in logic by the use of a special algebra which uses the operators AND, OR, NOT, NOR, NAND, etc. Useful in solving switching problems. Also called "symbolic logic."

booster, negative impedance, *n.* A transistor-diode-capacitor network inserted in the line at 12000 ft. intervals, powered by the line current, which can provide low-loss distortionless transmission over non-loaded cable circuits. Reducing the booster spacing increases the bandwidth: 12000 ft. spacing for 7 kHz; 6000 ft. spacing for 18 kHz. That bandwidth is adequate for data carrier use. The booster is not a negative impedance repeater, and does not use a matching transformer or balancing network.

booth, telephone, *n.* An enclosure, about 30 inches square by 87 inches high, having a split door on one side, which houses a pay telephone and protects its user from ambient noise and weather.

booth, wall telephone, *n.* A wall or shelf mounted booth for a pay telephone, having a back and sides only. When acoustically treated it attenuates all but low-frequency ambient noise.

"B" operator, *n.* An operator who connects calls incoming over trunks from an "A" board to the subscriber's station lines which terminate on her "B" board.

borer, earth. See "auger, earth."

borer, increment, *n.* Tool for taking wood samples from a pole to determine depth of creosote treatment or extent of rot.

boresight antenna. See "antenna, boresight."

bounce, contact, *n.* An undesired momentary reopening of a relay contact due to rebound after closing.

bowing, *n.* Deflection sideways of an aerial cable in rings due to excess length in a section or span.

box, apparatus, *n.* Wall mounted box with easily removable cover used to mount apparatus, while concealing cabling and protecting against mechanical injury, dust, and weather.

box, battery, *n.* Case holding dry cells for a subscriber's local battery telephone set.

box, bell, *n.* A wall mounted metal or plastic box having a hinged or removable cover which contains those elements of a complete telephone station which are not contained in the associated hand telephone set, such as a ringer.

box, black, *n.* Slang term for "interface equipment." Usually implies that such equipment either does not presently exist, or cannot be precisely described.

box, cable, *n.* Box of steel or wood in which cable pairs are terminated. See also "terminal, cable."

box, cable terminal, *n.* Sheet metal box with hinged cover. Provided with knockouts at each end for cable or wires, and used to house terminal blocks.

box, jack, *n.* Box mounted on a distributing frame and holding jacks which are wired to the testboard. Used to connect test cords which are equipped with shoes for making test connections to the protectors and terminal blocks.

box, junction. See "junction box."

box, pull. See "pull-box."

box, ringer, *n.* A metal or plastic box having a hinged or removable cover, used to mount a ringer.

box, stuffing, *n.* A pipe nipple with threaded gland which compresses a rubber sealing washer around a cable sheath. Used to provide a watertight entrance to underground terminals or buried closures.

box, switch, *n.* Portable case equipped with switches and relays, used for maintaining continuity in open wires while cutting in transpositions.

box, terminal, *n.* Box containing a cable terminal.

bounce, contact, *n.* Rebound of a closing contact, causing momentary opening of the circuit.

"B" position, *n.* A switchboard position in a local office where trunks from other offices terminate, and where incoming calls on these trunks are completed to subscriber's lines in the multiple or by dialing.

brace, *n.* (1) A device which supports or adds firmness. (2) A cross-arm brace. (3) A pole brace.—*v.t.* To strengthen or make firm by supporting the weight of.

brace, alley arm. See "brace, diagonal."

brace, back, *n.* A 5½ ft. long brace, of 1½"x1½"x3/16" steel angle, used to brace the horizontal pull on a side arm.

brace, crossarm, *n.* A flat steel strap mounted diagonally from pole to crossarm to hold the crossarm in a horizontal position.

brace, diagonal, *n.* A 7 ft. long brace, of 1¾"x1¾"x3/16" steel angle, used as a brace for a side arm. See also "back brace" and "vertical brace."

brace, guard arm, *n.* A steel strap mounted diagonally from pole to guard arm to hold the guard arm in a horizontal position. Similar to a crossarm brace, except that it has a 90-degree twist and bolts to the bottom of the guard arm.

brace, pole, *n.* Brace used on a corner pole which cannot be guyed. Consists of a second pole set into the ground a short distance from the line pole, and with its upper end fastened to the line pole.

brace, push, *n.* A pole brace in which the brace member is in compression.

brace, vertical, *n.* A 30-inch long brace, of 1½"x1½"x3/16" steel angle, used as a brace vertically from the end of the diagonal brace to the next higher crossarm.

braces, extension crossarm. See "brace, diagonal," "brace, back," and "brace, vertical."

bracket, break iron, *n.* A flat steel bracket which mounts on the top of an open wire crossarm by a bolt through the pin hole and has, on each outer end, a steel insulator pin with cob. Permits deadending an open wire in each direction.

bracket, dead-end, *n.* A clevis and single-groove insulator which bolts on the side of a crossarm and is used for dead-ending an open wire conductor.

bracket, phantom transposition, *n.* A bracket for transposing a phantom circuit of four wires. Holds three pins and insulators.

bracket, point transposition, *n.* An aluminum casting that mounts on top of a crossarm and holds four single-groove glass insulators which allow the two wires of a pair to interchange pin positions within the bracket.

bracket, span transposition, *n.* A point transposition bracket supported by the wires which permits making a point transposition in mid-span.

bracket, transposition, *n.* Metal fixture with a pin and insulator, used on a cross-arm to permit the turnover of open wires where they are transposed to different pin positions.

bracket, wooden pole, *n.* Wedge shaped piece of locust wood tapering to a threaded pin at the top. Bracket is nailed to the pole and an insulator, for supporting line wires, is screwed onto the pin.

braid, *n.* A group of fibrous or metallic filaments interwoven into cylindrical shape to form a covering over one or more wires.

braid, glass, *n.* A braid covering made from spun glass fibers, used to provide mechanical or thermal protection to the conductor or cable which it covers.

brake, ladder, *n.* An automatic brake that locks the wheels of a rolling ladder whenever anyone stands on the ladder.

branch point. See "node."

brand, pole, *n.* A designation burned into the surface of a pole with a branding iron, about 10-12 feet from the butt. Gives, as a minimum, the length and class of the pole, the species of wood, type of treatment, and the last two digits of the year when processed.

break, *n.* In wires or cables, an interruption in the physical or electrical continuity of the conductors, sheath, or messenger. —*v.* To interrupt a telegraph, teletypewriter, or data transmission by sending a "space" for longer than one second.

break, percent, *n.* In a series of pulses generated by make-break contacts, the percentage time that the contacts are open compared to the total make plus break time.

break contacts, *n. pl.* Pairs of contacts which part and open a circuit when a key or relay is operated.

breakdown, *n.* (1) A disruptive current discharge through insulation. (2) Failure of insulation for any reason. (3) Initiation of a spark discharge between two electrodes. (4) A puncture in insulation.

break-down, *v.t.* To apply a high voltage to a high-resistance fault, thereby causing it to break down to a low-resistance fault which can be located more easily.

breaker, circuit, *n.* (1) A device which interrupts the flow of current in a circuit when the current exceeds a predetermined value. (2) A device which interrupts the flow of current when the current reverses direction, or when there is a pre-determined deviation of current, voltage, or impedance from a standard value.

breaker, trip-free, *n.* A circuit breaker which will function to open the circuit it protects in the event of a fault, even though the operating handle is being held in the "closed" position.

break-in, *n.* (1) On a telegraph or teletypewriter circuit, the interruption of oncoming transmission by opening the circuit momentarily. (2) The changing of directional transmission at an echo suppressor when Talker #2 interrupts Talker #1.

break-in, attendant, *n.* Override capability provided on some PABX's enabling the operator to break-in on a busy connection.

break iron. See "bracket, break iron."

breakout, *n.* (1) A pair or group of pairs in a cable which terminates somewhere other than at the ends of the cable. (2) A channel, channel group, or supergroup in a carrier system which terminates somewhere other than at the ends of the carrier system. See also "drop-and-insert."

bridge, *n.* (1) The connection of one circuit in parallel with another without interrupting the continuity of the first. (2) A wheatstone bridge, or a capacitance bridge. (3) A strap which connects two adjacent terminals.—*v.t.* To connect one circuit in parallel with another. To make a bridged connection.

bridge, capacitance, *n.* Instrument using a balanced electrical network for measuring the capacity for holding electrical charge, in units of farads, microfarads, or micromicrofarads.

bridge, conference, *n.* A network used for interconnecting three or more lines or trunks to provide a conference connection. Frequently includes amplifiers to compensate for losses in the network.

bridge, extension. *n.* A bridging network used to connect an extension telephone to a line.

bridge, holding. See "holding bridge."

bridge, impedance, *n.* Instrument using a balanced electrical network for measuring impedance. Gives results in terms of resistance and equivalent reactance, both in ohms.

bridge, transmission. See "transmission bridge."

bridge, Wheatstone, *n.* Instrument using a balanced electrical network for measuring electrical resistance in ohms. Sometimes also capable of making Varley loop and Murray loop resistance measurements.

bridge, Wien. See "Wien bridge."

bridge circuit, *n.* A measuring network of four elements connected in a diamond configuration. A potential is connected across a pair of opposite nodes and an indicator across the other pair of nodes. If the bridge circuit is balanced, no potential appears across the indicator.

bridged connection, *n.* A connection of a circuit across, or in parallel with, another circuit.

bridged multiple, *n.* The usual arrangement of a multiple switchboard where the several jack appearances are bridged together. The jacks do not need cutoff springs, for that function is performed by the cutoff relay. See also "series multiple."

bridged tap, *n.* Any portion of a cable pair which is not a useful part of the circuit. An extension of the cable pair beyond the point where it is used, or a branch cable which has bridged pairs. A bridged tap impairs transmission, for it acts as a capacitor bridged across the circuit.

bridge-duplex telegraph. See "telegraph, bridge-duplex."

bridge lifter. See "inductor, saturable."

bridge rectifier. See "rectifier, bridge."

bridge transformer, *u.* A hybrid coil, which see.

bridging, *n.* The shunting of one electrical circuit by another.

bridging wiper, *n.* A wiper or wiper assembly which connects with the next contact in a level of bank contacts before breaking contact with the previous contact.

bridle wire, *n.* Paired insulated wires used to connect open wire pairs to a cable terminal, or to pole-mounted equipment, or to interconnect open wire pairs on different pin positions.

bridling, *n.* Bridle wires.—*v.t.* (1) To place insulated paired wire from a cable terminal to open wires on the same pole. (2) To interconnect open wires at buck arms with bridle wire.

Briggs logarithm, *n.* A common logarithm whose base is 10.

brilliant, *adj.* Describing reproduced sound which contains a full range of high frequencies.

British Thermal Unit (BTU), *n.* The quantity of heat required to raise the temperature of one pound of water one degree Fahrenheit.

broadband, *adj.* Describes a transmission facility having a bandwidth greater than 20 kHz.

broadcast, *n.* A radio or television transmission intended for reception by the public.—*v.t.* To initiate a broadcast transmission.

broadcast band. See "band, broadcast."

broadcast conference. *n.* A special type of conference connection where the originator can talk to all the conferrees simultaneously, but allow them to talk back only to him.

broadside array. See "array, broadside."

bronze, electrical, *n.* A bronze combining good conductivity, high tensile strength, and corrosion resistance. Of many varieties, of which a typical one contains:

Copper —98.5%
Tin — 1.4%
Silicon — 0.1%

Brown & Sharpe gauge, *n.* A scale of measurement for non-ferrous (copper, bronze, etc.) wires. Now usually called the American Wire Gauge. See also "gauges, wire."

brush, *n.* A carbon block or metal leaf spring used to make sliding contact with a rotating contact, such as the commutator of a generator or the slip rings of a ringing machine.

brush, carding, *n.* Flat brush having bristles of short steel wires, used to clean cable sheaths before wiping or soldering.

brush, terminal, *n.* A brush with long bristles used for cleaning binding posts in a cable terminal.

buckarm, *n.* Crossarm set parallel to the direction of the pole line, and at right angles to other crossarms on the same pole. Used for branch pole lines ("side leads"), or for changing direction of an open wire pole line by 90 degrees.

bucket, canvas, *n.* Heavy canvas bucket with leather bottom and rope handle. Used by linemen to safely raise tools and materials to the pole top.

bucket, coin pull, *n.* On a coin telephone, the metal receptacle at the bottom of the coin return chute which must be pulled forward to gain access to the returned coins. In both its closed and open positions it acts to prevent access to the return chute.

bucket, lineman's. See "bucket, canvas."

buckling, plate, *n.* The deformation or warping of storage battery plates due to an excessively high rate of charge or discharge.

budget, *n.* A program of services and work expressed in terms of the money required.—*v.t.* To formulate detailed projections of resource requirements for programs, allocating available funds, and balancing priorities which compete for limited resources.

buffer, *n.* (1) A device used as an interface between two circuits or equipments to reconcile their incompatibilities or to prevent variations in one from affecting the other. (2) A circuit used for transferring data from one unit to another when temporary storage is required because of different operating speeds, or times of occurrence of events.

buffer, data, *n.* A data storage device used to compensate for a difference in data rate, or time of occurrence of signals.

buffer, motor-generator, *n.* A directly coupled motor-generator set, in which primary power drives the motor which drives the generator which supplies power to the load.

buffer amplifier. See "amplifier, buffer."

bug, *n.* (1) Hidden trouble in a circuit or piece of equipment. (2) A semi-automatic ·key for sending radio telegraph code signals.—*v.* (1) To tap, or bridge onto, a line. (2) To connect or place a device which will permit eavesdropping on a telephone call.

building-out, *n.* The process of adding capacitance or resistance (or both) to a cable pair so that its electrical length is correct, thus eliminating an impedance irregularity.

building-out unit, line. See "unit, line building-out."

built-up circuit, *n.* A toll circuit composed of two or more toll circuits temporarily connected.

built-up circuit call, *n.* Call involving the use of a built-up circuit between the originating toll center and the terminating toll center.

built-up connection, *n.* Connection composed of a built-up circuit.

bulb, *n.* The glass envelope which encloses an electron tube or incandescent lamp.

bulb, light, *n.* An electric lamp, which is the correct term.

bulge, *n.* Of a transmission facility, the non-linearity of the increase in attenuation with frequency.

bulging, earth, *n.* The abnormal condition in which microwave radio waves are bent away from the earth, due to high earth surface temperatures or increasing water vapor in the air with altitude.

bulk-encrypted, *adj.* Describing information on several channels which are encrypted simultaneously by a single encryption device. The usual arrangement would employ time division multiplex to combine several pulse code modulated (PCM) channels into a single PCM signal for encryption.

bunching, *n.* (1) The act of grouping pairs together and tying them for identification and testing. (2) The grouping of electrons in a velocity-modulated vacuum tube. (3) The connecting together of wires on a bunching block.

bunch strand, *n.* A number of conductor strands in a cable which are twisted together in the same direction and with the same length of lay.

bureau, centralized intercept, *n.* A centralized location where operators handle intercept calls which were too specialized for handling at an "automatic intercept center."

buried cable, *n.* A cable installed directly in the earth without the use of underground conduits.

burnisher, contact, *n.* Spring steel blade in an insulating holder. The blade is sand-blasted, giving the effect of a very fine file, used to clean contacts.

burn ointment, *n.* Tannic acid jelly, packed in ⅛-oz tubes, placed in first aid kits for the treatment of burns.

burst, *n.* Interference to, or interruption of, a digital signal. An error burst should not affect more than 350 bits.

burst noise, *n.* An unwanted signal characterized by an excessively large interfering effect extended over a relatively short but finite time interval.

bus, *n.* A heavy conductor, or group of conductors, to which several units of the same type of equipment may be connected.

Conductors	Use
1	Ground
2	DC
3	AC, 3 phase delta
4	AC, 3 phase wye

busbar, *n.* A heavy rectangular bar of copper or aluminum, used for bus connections on power boards and storage batteries. Busbars have two advantages over heavy stranded wire: (1) they radiate heat better, and therefore run cooler, and (2) they are stronger and better able to resist the bending stresses caused by heavy short-circuit currents.

bushing, pin, *n.* A wooden plug, 1¼″ diameter x 3⅞″ long, having a 9/16″ D concentric hole. Used to fit steel insulator pins to a crossarm bored for wooden pins.

busy, *adj.* (1) In use. (2) Not idle. (3) Not available for use. (4) In an "off-hook" condition.

busy-back, *n.* Busy tone. Dial tone interrupted 60 times per minute. Its frequency is 600/120 Hz. See also "tone, busy" and "tones, supervisory."

busy clip. See "clip, busy."

busy count, *n.* A count of the number of times that a trunk group busy condition occurs. See also "all trunks busy" and "last trunk busy."

busy hour, *n.* (1) The hour when a communication switching system carries the most traffic. (2) The busiest hour of the busiest day of a normal week, excluding holidays, week-ends, and special event days.

busy key, *n.* A lever switch on a unit of dial central office equipment which can be used to make the unit "busy" in preparation for testing or working on it.

busy lamp, *n.* Lamp provided on a switchboard to indicate to the operator that the circuit is busy.

busy out, *v.* To ground the "C" lead of a line or trunk, or to take any other action which causes the line or trunk to test "busy" to an incoming call.

busy signal, *n.* An audible, flashing, or audible and flashing signal at the rate of 60 impulses per minute, indicating that the called line is busy.

busy switch, *n.* A small cam-operated switch placed on step-by-step automatic switches to permit busying of the switch while it is being worked on.

busy test, *n.* Test made by an operator to determine if a line is busy. If she hears a click when she touches the tip of her plug to the sleeve of a jack, that line or trunk is busy.

busy time, *n.* The total time in seconds that a circuit is held busy.

busy tone, *n.* An audible signal returned to the calling party to indicate that the called line is busy. See also "tone, line busy" and "tone, trunk busy."

busy visual, *n.* A very small annunciator drop, mounted ten-per-strip like a lamp strip, and used above toll line jacks to provide a busy indication. Preferred to busy lamps because of a lower heat output.

butt, *n.* (1) The large end of a pole. (2) That end of a pole which is set in the ground. (3) The point at which the sheath or jacket of a cable terminates.

buttinski, *n.* A hand test telephone used by telephone installers, repairmen, and central office switchmen. Consists of a metal handle with a transmitter on one end and receiver and rotary dial on the other end. Equipped with a slide switch having three positions: (a) talk/listen, (b) monitor, and (c) 1500-ohm loop test. (slang)

button, push. See "pushbutton."

button, transmitter, *n.* The cup-like container that holds the carbon granules in some types of telephone transmitters.

butt step. See "step, wooden butt."

butt wrap, *n.* A spiral wrapping of tape over a cable core in which the trailing edge of one wrap just meets the leading edge of the next wrap with neither overlap nor spacing.

butyl rubber, *n.* A synthetic rubber which is a copolymer of butylene with isoprene. Used as an insulation in high-voltage cables.

buzz, *n.* A low-pitched continuous humming sound which contains many higher harmonics.—*v.* To check the continuity of electrical circuits using a battery and buzzer.

buzzer, *n.* An audible signaling device which gives a buzzing sound through vibration of a vibrating reed actuated by self-interrupted direct current or by alternating current.

BX cable. See "cable, BX."

bylink, *n.* A fast link. A link designed and liberally provided so that connection can be made to common register-senders and be ready to receive pulsing within one-tenth second after seizure. Used to avoid second dial tone.

bypass, *n.* (1) An electrical device which shunts out or away from the main circuit a selected current or frequency, such as separating direct from alternating current. (2) In gas pressurizing of cables, a pipe which permits gas to flow around a plug or stricture in the cable.—*v.t.* To cause to be shunted or passed around.

bypass, data. See "disabler, tone."

bypass capacitor, *n.* A capacitor that provides an alternating current path, of relatively low impedance, around some other circuit element such as a resistor.

bypass valve, *n.* Valve in a gas bypass, permitting it to be closed at will.

byte, *n.* A group of binary digits which is the smallest addressable unit of information in a memory. Frequently consists of eight information bits plus a parity bit.

cabinet, apparatus, *n.* Cabinet of metal, wood or plastic for wall or floor mounting. Used to house apparatus. Frequently equipped with a frame or gate for mounting plates.

cabinet, attendant's, *n.* The attendant's switchboard at a PABX.

cabinet, equipment, *n.* A cabinet with removable door made to house relays or other equipment when installed on a customer's premises.

cabinet, key, *n.* A small turret mounting keys, line lamps, and busy lamps used to permit a telephone station to pick-up, hold several lines. Replaced by key telephone sets.

cabinet, test. See "test turret."

cable, *n.* Assembly of insulated conductors into a compact form which is covered by a flexible, waterproof protective covering.

cable, aerial, *n.* Cable suspended in the air on poles or other overhead structures. Usually implies the use of a "messenger strand" to which the cable is lashed for support.

cable, air-spaced coaxial, *n.* A coaxial cable in which the space between the inner and outer conductors is not filled with a solid dielectric. One type has a polyethylene string wound helically on the center conductor; another type uses spaced discs or beads on the center conductor to provide the proper conductor spacing. These cables have a lower transmission loss than solid dielectric cables.

cable, armored, *n.* A cable having one or two layers of steel tapes or steel wires spirally applied to the sheath to provide mechanical protection. See also "cable, tape-armored" and "cable, wire-armored."

cable, banded, *n.* Two or more cables which are held together by stainless steel bands.

cable, beaded coaxial, *n.* A coaxial cable whose dielectric is largely air or gas, with the center conductor positioned with spaced ceramic or polyethylene beads.

cable, block, *n.* Distribution cable within a city block, installed on poles or building walls, or within buildings from the point of entrance to a cross-connecting terminal, a distributing frame, or to the junction with the house cable.

cable, branch, *n.* Cable which leaves a main cable to reach some secondary point. May be a "distribution cable."

cable, building-out, *n.* Cable, constructed to have high capacitance per unit length, bridged across a loaded cable to increase its apparent length, and thus to "build-out" a loading section to its correct length. Commonly, a building-out cable has more pairs of finer gauge than the cable it builds out, and one pair is connected in series to simulate the higher resistance while other pairs are bridged to give the correspondingly higher capacitance.

cable, buried, *n.* A cable installed directly in the earth without the use of underground conduits.

cable, BX, *n.* Insulated power conductors enclosed in a flexible spiral metal armor.

cable, coaxial, *n.* (1) A cable having several coaxial lines under a single protective sheath. (2) A coaxial line.

cable, color coded, *n.* A cable, such as switchboard cable, in which each conductor is separately identifiable by means of its color coding.

cable, combination, *n.* A cable which contains both pairs and quads.

cable, composite, *n.* A cable in which conductors of different gauges or types are combined under one sheath. Differences in length of twist are not considered here as constituting different types.

cable, connector, *n.* Vinyl-jacketed, color-coded 24 AWG cables with ends terminated in standard cable connectors. In 12, 25, 40, 50, 75, and 100 pair sizes and lengths of 4, 8, 30, 50, 80, 100, and 200 feet. Used as an extension cable for connecting between plug-ended telephone sets and connector-ended terminals or apparatus cabinets.

cable, corrosion proof, *n.* Cable having an insulating, protective covering over the metallic sheath as a protection from electrolysis.

cable, deep-sea submarine, *n.* An armorless coaxial cable designed for laying in the depths of the ocean to be used for intercontinental carrier telephone transmission. Consists of a high tensile strength, non-twisting steel wire strand used within the center copper conductor tube. This is surrounded by polyethylene insulation, then aluminum or copper outer conductor tapes, and the whole covered with a polyethylene jacket.

cable, distribution, *n.* (1) A cable having terminals from which subscribers may be fed. (2) A branch from a feeder cable used for distribution to subscribers.

cable, entrance, *n.* Cable which connects to an open wire line and brings its circuits into the central office. Avoids multi-crossarm open wire leads in the center of town.

cable, ETV, *n.* Cable used to carry multi-channel educational television signal. A single ⅜″ coaxial tube surrounded by 0, 16, 37, or 63 19 AWG pairs, and a plastic sheath.

cable, even-count, *n.* Normal, modern cable for exchange use, so designated because it does not have an extra pair for each 100 pairs or fraction thereof.

cable, exchange, *n.* (1) A paired cable used principally for subscriber's lines. (2) Cable having a high capacitance per unit length: 0.085 mf. per mile.

cable, feeder, *n.* One of several large cables which leave a central office, each to serve a specific area.

cable, figure-8, *n.* Cable for aerial use having the pairs and the supporting messenger strand both covered by a plastic sheath. The cross-section is a figure "8."

cable, flat station wiring. See "wire, flat station."

cable, fuse, *n.* Cable with 24 AWG or 26 AWG conductors used to bring exposed circuits to a fuseless station protector, or used between exposed outside plant cable and the central office protection.

cable, gopher-protected, *n.* A cable for buried use having extra steel tape protection to discourage damage by gophers.

cable, house, *n.* A distribution cable within the confines of a single building or a series of related buildings but excluding cable run from the point of entrance to a cross connecting box, terminal frame, or point of connection to a block cable.

cable, inside wiring, *n.* Thermoplastic insulated and jacketed cable with fully color-coded 24 AWG copper conductors. Available in 6, 12, 16, 21, 25, 50, 75, and 100 pair sizes.

cable, integral messenger, *n.* Figure-8 cable.

cable, intermediate, *n.* A section of cable inserted in an open wire line.

cable, jute-protected, *n.* A cable for buried use having the sheath covered by a multi-layer wrapping of tarred hemp for protection from moisture and bruising.

cable, lashed, *n.* An aerial cable fastened to its supporting messenger by a continuous spirally wrapped steel wire.

cable, lateral, *n.* (1) A branch from a feeder cable. (2) A branch from an underground cable which goes up a pole and connects to an aerial cable.

cable, layer type, *n.* Multipair cable in which the pairs are formed into concentric layers, with adjacent layers having opposite direction of lay.

cable, lead covered, *n.* Cable which has an extruded sheath of copper-bearing lead. Now largely superseded by plastic sheathed cable.

cable, loaded, *n.* Cable having "loading coils" inserted in its pairs at regular intervals for the reduction of transmission loss.

cable, local, *n.* A cable composed wholly or in part of bulk wire held in a cable formation by sewing with twine.

cable, L1 coaxial, *n.* The original Bell System coaxial cable (1940-1952) using 0.270 inch, then ⅜ inch, coaxial tubes with repeaters spaced 8 miles to transmit a bandwidth of 3 MHz giving 480-600 voice circuits per pair of tubes.

cable, L3 coaxial, *n.* A Bell System transmission system between 1953-1964 which used ⅜-inch coaxial tubes with repeaters spaced 4 miles to transmit a bandwidth of 8 MHz, giving 1860 voice circuits per pair of tubes.

cable, L4 coaxial, *n.* A Bell System transmission system from 1965 which uses ⅜-inch coaxial tubes with repeaters spaced 2 miles to transmit a bandwidth of 18 MHz and give 3600 voice circuits per pair of tubes.

cable, lossy. See "lossy cable."

cable, multiple sheath, *n.* Cables equipped with several coaxial sheaths for extra protection. Examples are: Buried Tape-Armored (BT), Gopher Protected (GT), High-Dielectric Strength.

cable, nonmetallic sheathed, *n.* An assembly of two or more insulated power conductors with an outer sheath of moisture-resistant, flame-retardant fibrous material. Used for low-voltage surface power wiring.

cable, paired, *n.* Cable in which the conductors are combined in pairs, *i.e.:* two wires which are twisted about each other. Each wire of the pair has its distinctive color of insulation.

cable, paper insulated, *n.* Cable in which the conductors are individually insulated with dry, mineral-free, spirally-wrapped paper tape.

cable, plastic insulated, *n.* Cable in which the conductors are individually insulated with a plastic covering, usually polyethylene, extruded directly onto the conductors.

cable, pressurized, *n.* Telephone cable which is protected against the entrance of moisture at sheath breaks by filling the interior of the cable with dry air, or nitrogen, at a pressure of about 7 psig for aerial cables and 10 psig for underground cables, permitting this pressure to drop to 2 psig at the far end of the cables. Either a sharp reduction in gas pressure or a sharp increase in the rate of gas flow actuates alarms to call attention to the presence of a leak.

cable, pre-wiring, *n.* Loosely cabled groups of 24 AWG copper insulated pairs, without an overall jacket. Used to cable telephone outlets prior to the placement of walls in new buildings. Available in 2, 3, 4, 5, and 6 pair sizes.

cable, protective, *n.* Small gauge (24 ga.) cable used when heavy gauge cables are brought into central offices. Forms a fusible link to localize trouble, yet avoids the use of fuses.

cable, pulp insulated, *n.* Cable in which the conductors are individually insulated with a mineral-free paper tube, formed from paper pulp directly on the conductor.

cable, quadded, *n.* Cable in which the conductors are combined in four-wire units called "quads." Each quad consists of two pairs twisted together and held with a spirally-applied "binder string."

cable, radio-frequency, *n.* Cable suitable for the transmission of radio-frequency energy, such as coaxial cable.

cable, ribbon, *n.* A cable whose conductors lie side by side in a single plane. Usually has a moulded polyethylene insulation.

cable, riser, *n.* (1) The portion of house cable which runs vertically. (2) Cable which runs vertically on a pole.

cable, self-supporting. See "cable, figure-8."

cable, service, *n.* Small 1, 2, or 6-pair cable used to feed a single subscriber. Usually lead sheathed and installed buried or in pipe conduit.

cable, shielded, *n.* A cable having an electrostatic shield around the pairs and inside the sheath. The shield is usually a wrapping of metal tapes.

cable, silk & cotton. See "cable, terminating."

cable, spiral-four. See "spiral-four."

cable, stalpeth sheathed. See "stalpeth."

cable, strip, *n.* A flat, ribbon-like cable consisting of 2 to 100 PVC insulated wires of 16 to 28 AWG laid parallel and permanently bonded together. Used for equipment harnesses, and for under-rug multi-conductor cable.

cable, stub, *n.* Short branch from a main cable, giving access to a relatively large number of pairs from the main cable without the necessity of opening the main cable splice. The end of the stub is often sealed for use at a later date. Pairs in the stub are referred to as "stubbed-out pairs."

cable, submarine, *n.* (1) Cable having insulation and a spirally-wrapped wire armor making it suitable for use in shallow water where it may be abraded. (2) Cable, frequently of coaxial construction and without armor, which is suitable for transocean cables in deep water. See also "Submarine cable system, - - -."

cable, submarine, France-Canada A, *n.* A double coaxial cable installed in 1959 between Clarenville, Canada and Penmarch, France. It has 48 3kHz channels on a baseband of 20-164 kHz. It has 114 repeaters in a length of 2205 nautical miles. Also called the TAT-2A cable.

cable, submarine, Guam-Japan, *n.* A single coaxial cable placed in 1964 between Agana, Guam and Ninomiya, Japan. It has 128 3kHz channels, and contains 74 repeaters in a length of 1434 nautical miles. Owned by AT&T and KDD.

cable, submarine, Guam-Philippines, *n.* A single coaxial cable placed in 1964 between Agana, Guam and Baler Bay, P.I. It has 128 3kHz channels, and has 76 repeaters in a length of 1468 nautical miles. Owned by AT&T and Philippines Tel. Co., Ltd.

cable, submarine, Hawaii-Guam, *n.* A single coaxial placed in 1964 between Makaha, Oahu, Hawaii and Agana, Guam. It has 128 3kHz channels, with 200 repeaters in a length of 3843 nautical miles. Owned by AT&T and Hawaiian Telephone Company.

cable, submarine, Hawaii tie, *n.* A single coaxial cable placed in 1964 just offshore of Oahu Island, Hawaii, between the submarine cable terminals at Hanauma Bay and Makaha. It has 96 4kHz channels on basebands 108-516 and 648-1052 kHz. It has one repeater in its 10 nautical mile length. Owned by AT&T and Hawaiian Telephone Company.

cable, submarine, Japan-Hawaii, *n.* A single coaxial cable from Makaha, Hawaii to Ninomiya, Japan, placed in 1964 which goes via Midway, Wake, and Guam. Its length is 5635 nautical miles with 290 repeaters. It has 128 3kHz channels on basebands 108-516 and 648-1052 kHz. Owned by AT&T, KDD, and Hawaiian Telephone Company.

cable, submarine, Scotland-Canada, *n.* Twin coaxial cables installed in 1956 between Clarenville, Canada and Oban, Scotland. It has 102 repeaters in a length of 1942 nautical miles. It has 39 3kHz and 6 4kHz channels on a baseband of 20-164 kHz. Owned by GPO, AT&T, and COTC. Also called the TAT-1A cable.

cable, submarine, shore-end, *n.* An armored coaxial cable designed to give protection to the shallow-water portion of intercontinental submarine cables. Consists of a solid copper inner conductor, polyethylene insulation, a longitudinal copper tape outer conductor, covered with a black polyethylene sheath plus one or two layers of neoprene-coated steel armor wires.

cable, submarine, single tube, *n.* The type of submarine cable facility being placed today, carrying the W-E and E-W carrier transmission on a single coaxial tube with bi-directional repeaters. Typical directional bands are 108-516 and 648-1052 kHz.

cable, submarine, TAT-1A. See "cable, submarine, Scotland-Canada.

cable, submarine, TAT-2A. See "cable, submarine, France-Canada A."

cable, submarine, TAT-3, *n.* A single coaxial placed in 1963 between Widemouth, Gr. Britain and Tuckerton, New Jersey. It has 183 repeaters in a length of 3518 nautical miles. It has 128 3kHz channels on basebands 108-516 and 648-1052 kHz. Owned by AT&T and the British GPO.

cable, submarine, TAT-4, *n.* A single coaxial cable placed in 1965 from Tuckerton, N.J., USA to St. Hilaire de Riez, France. It has 128 channels of 3kHz width on basebands 108-516 and 648-1052 kHz. It does not use TASI. It has 186 repeaters in a length of 3599 nautical miles. Owned by ITT, RCA, and Western Union.

cable, submarine, TAT-5, *n.* A transatlantic cable, scheduled for activation in 1970, which will carry 720 two-way voice channels between the United States and Southern Europe.

cable, submarine, Transpacific A, *n.* The Sydney-Auckland section of a single coaxial cable placed in 1962 from Canada to Australia. It has 50 repeaters in a length of 1273 nautical miles, and has 12 4kHz and 64 3kHz channels on basebands 60-300 and 360-608 kHz. Also called the Commonwealth Pacific Cable. Owned by C&W, COTC, NZPO, and OTC.

cable, submarine, Transpacific B, *n.* A Commonwealth Pacific cable. The Auckland-Suva, Fiji section of a single coaxial cable placed in 1962 between Canada and Australia. It has 50 repeaters in a length of 1260 nautical miles, and has 12 4kHz and 64 3kHz channels on sidebands 60-300 and 360-608 kHz. Owned by

C&W, COTC, NZPO, and OTC.

cable, submarine, Transpacific C, *n.* A Commonwealth Pacific cable. The Suva, Fiji to Keawaula, Hawaii section of a single coaxial cable placed in 1963 between Canada and Australia. It has 118 repeaters in a length of 3073 nautical miles, and has 12 4kHz and 64 3kHz channels on basebands 60-300 and 360-608 kHz.

cable, submarine, Transpacific D, *n.* A Commonwealth Pacific cable. The Keawaula, Hawaii to Port Alberni, British Columbia section of a single coaxial cable placed in 1963 between Canada and Australia. It has 100 repeaters in a length of 2545 nautical miles, and has 36 4kHz and 32 3kHz channels on a 60-300 kHz baseband.

cable, submarine, Transpacific E, *n.* A Commonwealth Pacific cable. The Port Alberni, B.C. to Vancouver, B.C. section of a single coaxial cable placed in 1963 between Canada and Australia. It has 4 repeaters in a length of 81 nautical miles, and has 36 4kHz and 32 3kHz channels on a 60-300 kHz baseband.

cable, submarine, Type SA, *n.* A coaxial deep-sea cable having a 0.460-inch core diameter, 1.12-inch outside diameter, and 43 ohms impedance.

cable, submarine, Type SB, *n.* A coaxial deep-sea cable having a 0.620-inch core diameter, a 1.25-inch outside diameter, and 54 ohms impedance.

cable, submarine, Type SD, *n.* A coaxial deep-sea cable having a one-inch core diameter, a 1¼-inch outside diameter, and 44 ohms impedance.

cable, submarine, Type SF, *n.* A coaxial deep-sea cable having a 1½-inch core diameter, a 1¾-inch outside diameter, and 60 ohms impedance.

cable, submarine, USA-Alaska A, *n.* Twin coaxial cables installed in 1956 between Port Angeles, California and Ketchikan, Alaska. It has 118 repeaters in a length of 750 nautical miles, and has 48 4kHz channels on a 20-164 kHz baseband. Owned by AT&T.

cable, submarine, USA-Bermuda, *n.* A single coaxial cable installed in 1961 between Manahawkin, N.J. and Flatts, Bermuda. It has 38 repeaters in a length of 750 nautical miles, and has 80 3kHz channels on basebands 60-300 and 360-608 kHz. Owned by AT&T and C&W.

cable, submarine, USA-Hawaii A, *n.* Twin coaxial cables installed in 1957 between Point Arenas, California and Hanauma Bay, Oahu, Hawaii. It has 114 repeaters in a length of 2204 nautical miles, and has 48 3kHz channels with TASI on a baseband of 20-164 kHz. Owned by AT&T and Hawaiian Telephone Company.

cable, submarine, USA-Hawaii B, *n.* A single coaxial cable placed in 1965 between San Francisco, California and Makaha, Oahu, Hawaii. It has 110 repeaters in a length of 2200 nautical miles, and has 128 3kHz channels with TASI on basebands 108-516 and 648-1052 kHz. Owned by AT&T and Hawaiian Telephone Company.

cable, submarine, USA-Jamaica, *n.* A single coaxial cable placed in 1963 between Florida City, and Kingston, Jamaica, West Indies. It has 43 repeaters in a length of 834 nautical miles, and has 128 3kHz channels on basebands 108-516 and 648-1052 kHz. Owned by C&W, West Indies Ltd., and AT&T.

cable, submarine, USA-Puerto Rico, *n.* A pair of coaxial cables installed in 1959 between West Palm Beach, Florida and San Juan, Puerto Rico. It has 59 repeaters in a length of 1127 nautical miles, and has 48 3kHz channels on baseband 20-164 kHz. Owned by RCA and ITT.

cable, submarine, USA-Virgin Islands, *n.* A single coaxial cable placed in 1964 between Florida and Magens Bay, V.I. It has 61 repeaters in a length of 1179 nautical miles, and

128 3kHz channels. Owned by AT&T and ITT.

cable, swept coaxial, *n.* A coaxial cable which has been checked by a swept-frequency test, and has been certified to be free of impedance irregularities by the manufacturer.

cable, switchboard, *n.* Cables for interconnecting central office equipment, or for terminating equipment on distributing frames. Conductor insulation is usually fully color-coded, conductors are usually tinned, and combined in various combinations of singles, pairs and triples.

cable, tape-armored, *n.* Cable having spirally-wrapped steel tapes applied over the sheath to prevent mechanical damage when used as buried cable.

cable, terminating, *n.* A lead-sheathed telephone-type cable having conductor insulation which will not fray. Used to extend paper insulated cables which enter a central office cable vault on to the distributing frame where they will be terminated. Terminating cables are of two types: (a) Textile insulated, having the conductors wrapped with two layers of cellulose acetate yarn then one layer of cotton, color-coded, and lacquered to prevent fraying, (b) Plastic insulated, having the conductors insulated with polyethylene covered with a layer of polyvinyl chloride which is color-coded. Both types have 22 AWG copper conductors, and are available in 51, 101, 202, 303, 404, and 606 pair sizes.

cable, tie, *n.* (1) Cable between two distributing frames, (2) cable between two PBX's, (3) a cable connecting two other cables.

cable, tip, *n.* Cable insulated with silk-and-cotton which is spliced to paper insulated outside plant cables when it is necessary to bring them into a central office for termination on a distributing frame. Also called "terminating cable."

cable, toll, *n.* (1) Cable in which most

or all of the pairs or quads are used for toll circuits. (2) Cable having low capacitance per unit length: 0.064 mf. per mile.

cable, trunk, *n.* Cable used for interoffice trunk circuits. Usually a loaded, paired cable.

cable, underground, *n.* Cable installed in subsurface conduits terminating at intervals in manholes, thus permitting the placing, replacing, or removal of cables at will.

cable, unit type, *n.* Multipair cable in which groups of pairs are stranded together into units, and the units are stranded together to form the core of the cable.

cable, video, *n.* Cable containing video pairs, usually surrounding a core of ordinary pairs. Available with 1, 2, 3, 4, 5, or 6 video pairs. See also "pair, video."

cable, waterblocked, *n.* A cable specially constructed without internal voids so that it will not allow the longitudinal passage of water under normal ground water pressure. The voids in the Bell System waterblocked cables are filled with a compound of 85% petroleum jelly and 15% polyethylene.

cable, wire-armored, *n.* A cable which has a single layer, or two opposed layers, of spirally wrapped steel wires for mechanical protection. Used on the shore end of undersea cables, or on buried cables which are subject to being washed out by floods.

cable assembly. See "assembly, cable."

cablecast, *v.t.* To broadcast a locally originated program, of movies or slides, over a CATV cable distribution system.

cable fill. See "fill."

cable hook. See "hook, underground cable."

cable lasher. See "lasher, cable."

cable layer. See "layer, cable."

cable rack. See "rack, cable."

cable rack, underground. See "rack, underground cable."

cable shears. See "shears, cable."

cables, twin submarine, *n. pl.* A type of submarine cable facility used before 1960, which consisted of two parallel coaxial cables, one carrying the west-to-east and the other the east-to-west transmission on a bandwidth of 20-164 kilohertz.

cable system, L-1 coaxial, *n.* The original transcontinental coaxial toll cable used between 1939-1951 which originally carried 480 channels on a pair of ⅜-inch coaxial tubes. This capacity was later increased to 600 channels per pair of tubes. The transmission band used was 68-2788 kilohertz.

cable system, L-3 coaxial, *n.* The longhaul toll cable system used between 1952-1966 to provide 1860 channels per pair of ⅜-inch disc-insulated coaxial tubes using the transmission band 312-8284 kilohertz. Both 8-tube and 12-tube cables were used.

cable system, L-4 coaxial, *n.* The cable system initiated in 1967 which provides 3600 two-way voice channels on a pair of ⅜-inch disc-insulated coaxial tubes. Six mastergroups use the transmission band 0.564-17.548 megahertz. Cables with nine coaxial tubes are standard for underground use, but 20-tube cables are available for buried use, thus giving a single cable capacity of 32,400 channels.

cable system, submarine. See "submarine cable system, Types SB, SD, and SF."

cabling, *n.* (1) The act of twisting together two or more wires, pairs, or pair groups by machine to form a cable. (2) The act of installing distribution cable, particularly in a new area.

calcium battery. See "cell, lead-calcium storage."

Calculagraph, *n.* A time-clock device for use at switchboards to stamp the "time of day" and total "elapsed time" on the backs of tickets which record subscribers' toll calls.

calculating circuit, *n.* Any of the circuits which perform basic arithmetical operations, such as adding, subtracting, multiplying, or dividing.

calibrate, *v.t.* (1) To adjust a meter or other measuring device so that it reads correctly. (2) To determine meter error by comparison with a standard.

calibration, *n.* The process of comparing an instrument or device with a standard to determine its accuracy or to devise a corrected scale.

call, *n.* An effort by a subscriber to obtain a telephone connection.

call, assistance, *n.* A call which the customer may or may not have been able to dial directly, but on which he dials zero to reach the operator for assistance.

call, collect. See "collect call."

call, credit card. See "credit card call."

call, free-code, *n.* A telephone call, such as to "information," which the terminating equipment recognizes from the code dialed as one to be handled on a free-service basis.

call, interzone. See "interzone call."

call, local, *n.* Any telephone call for a destination within the local service area of the calling station.

call, long distance. See "long distance call."

call, lost, *n.* A call offered to automatic switching equipment when all trunks from the equipment are busy.

call, no-hunt, *n.* In a crossbar office, a call made from the trunk test frame or message register rack. This call will not hunt in a terminal hunting group. If the terminal dialed is busy, busy tone is returned to the tester.

call, person-to-person, *n.* A telephone call in which the calling party specifies that he wishes to reach a particular person or private-branch-exchange extension. These calls are chargeable from the time the desired person or private-branch-exchange extension answers.

call, reverting, *n.* A customer-dialed call between two customers served by the same telephone line.

call, service code, *n.* A customer call to a service desk, such as information, repair, test desk, long distance, which is identified by the code dialed, often a "11X" or "X11" code.

call, special instruction, *n.* A call which involves charges to a third party, charges to a credit card, or a request for time and charges.

call, station-to-station, *n.* A telephone call in which the calling party does not specify that he wishes to reach a particular person or private-branch-exchange extension at the called point. A station-to-station call is chargeable from the time anyone at the called number answers.

call, toll, *n.* Any telephone call, subject to charge, for a destination outside of the local service area of the calling station.

call, TX, *n.* A call which terminates at a position where the operator handles through traffic.

call address, *n.* The last four digits of the telephone number.

call-a-matic telephone, *n.* A repertory dialing phone which stores a repertory of 500 numbers on a polyester film tape, and automatically dials any selected one at the push of a button. Signaling is dual tone multifrequency.

call circuit, *n.* A talking circuit directly from one operator to another. The operator ("A" operator) who originates the call has a choice of ten call circuit buttons. When she depresses a button, it connects her directly to a particular operator at the distant ("B") switchboard.

call circuit operation, *n.* The use of a "call circuit" (which see) to pass traffic from an "A" switchboard to a "B" switchboard (which see). The "A" operator receives from the subscriber a call for a number in the "B" office. She presses a call circuit button and passes the number to the "B" operator. The "B" operator passes to the "A" operator the number of an idle trunk from "A" office to "B" office, which appears "plug-ended" (which see) at the "B" operator's position. Both operators then put up the call simultaneously: the "A" operator to the trunk, and the "B" operator to the called number.

Call Commander, *n.* The Automatic Electric Company's registered name for a multiple key telephone set, which see.

call delay, *n.* The delay suffered by a call which arrives at automatic switching equipment such as a line-finder and finds the equipment busy processing another call. This delay is considered to be acceptable if not over 1½ % of the calls are delayed by 3 seconds during the busy hour.

Call Director, *n.* The Bell System's registered name for a multiple key telephone set, which see.

call distribution, automatic. See "distribution, automatic call."

called line, *n.* The line to which a call is directed.

called number, *n.* The number of the telephone to which a call is directed, including the area code, central office code, and line number.

called office, *n.* The central office in which the called telephone is reached.

called party, *n.* The person specified on a person-to-person call, or the person who talks on a station-to-station call.

called-party holding. See "holding."

called place, *n.* The city, town, or locality to which a call is made.

called station, *n.* The telephone to which a call is directed.

call-forwarding, *n.* A service available in some central offices whereby calls dialed to the telephone of an authorized subscriber may, when he so instructs, be routed to any other desired number.

call indicator, *n.* A lamp display on a switchboard position which shows the operator the number which was dialed from an automatic office.

call indicator equipment, *n.* Equipment used at a manual switchboard on trunks incoming from a dial office. The last four digits of the telephone number dialed by the distant caller are displayed visually on a lamp panel in front of an idle B operator who reads the number and then completes the connection to the called line.

calling, abbreviated, *n.* A service available in some common-controlled dial offices whereby a customer can dial one or two digits to reach up to eight or thirty telephone numbers, respectively. The desired numbers, each consisting of up to 14 digits, are placed in the customer's assigned central office repertory storage, which is accessed by the translator which receives his one or two dialed digits.

calling, off-net. See "off-net calling."

calling, selective radio. See "selective calling."

calling, speed. See "calling, abbreviated."

calling, three-way, *n.* A feature of some dial offices whereby a third party can be added to a two-way conversation, without the assistance of an operator.

calling, touch. See "touch calling."

calling area, *n.* The area within which a subscriber is able to call without the assistance of an operator.

calling device, *n.* A device which generates the pulses required to actuate an automatic switching system. A dial, or card dialer.

calling line, *n.* The line from which a call originates.

calling number, *n.* The number of the telephone at which a call originates.

calling party, *n.* The person who originates or who is specified on a person-to-person call, or on a station-to-station call the person who talks.

calling party holding. See "holding."

calling place, *n.* The city, town, or locality at which a call originates.

calling station, *n.* The telephone from which a call originates.

call-through test set. See "test set, call-through."

call waiting, *n.* Feature of some dial offices and PABXs, as follows: If a second call is made to a busy line, caller #2 gets ringback tone while the called party gets a call waiting tone that alerts him to the waiting call. He can then hold either caller #1 or caller #2 while he talks to the other.

call-waiting tone, *n.* A service available to some subscribers in common-control offices, such that when a call is made to a subscriber having the service, if his line is busy a tone will be placed on the line at intervals as a signal that a call is waiting for him. The calling party will also hear the tone.

calorie, *n.* The quantity of heat required to raise the temperature of one gram of water one degree Centigrade. One BTU is equal to 252 calories.

CAMA operator, *n.* The operator at a centralized automatic message accounting switchboard, who obtains the calling number on a subscriber dialed toll call and records it by key pulsing it into the automatic message accounting (AMA) equipment for billing purposes.

CAMA switchboard, *n.* The manual portion of a centralized automatic message accounting (CAMA) system in which an operator is brought into the call dialed by the subscriber in order to obtain the calling number and key pulse it into the associated automatic message accounting (AMA) equipment where it is automatically recorded before the call is advanced to the called telephone.

camera tube, *n.* The electron tube used in a television camera to convert an optical image into an electrical signal.

camp, camp-on, *v.* In an automatic switching system, to cause a call to stand and wait on a busy line terminal until the line becomes idle.

camp-on busy, *n.* Feature of some automatic switching systems—when the called line is found to be busy the calling party waits, and when the called party's line becomes free the waiting call goes through automatically.

can, safety, *n.* A red enameled metal can with spring-loaded cap used for gasoline for a cable splicer's furnace. The spring-loaded cap relieves pressure in the can.

cancelled call, *n.* An uncompleted call on which no further action is to be taken. It may have been cancelled by the calling party or because of rules of the operating practice.

cancelling, loss, *n.* The use of a negative impedance converter to nullify the loss of circuit components, such as the resistance loss of an inductor.

candle, stearin, *n.* A stubby candle 4 inches long, composed of stearic acid. Used by cable splicers as a flux in soldering and wiping lead joints. See also "stearin."

cannibalize, *v.t.* To remove components from one piece of equipment for use in repairing another like equipment.

cap, binding post, *n.* Neoprene insulating cover which can be slipped over binding posts in terminals to protect them from inadvertent shorts or grounds from the tools of workmen. Have a slot and hole in the side to accommodate a wire which may be terminated on the binding post. Available in black and red.

cap, cable, *n.* A short neoprene tube with closed end used to place over a cut end of communication cable during shipment or placing operations. Equipped with a stainless steel hose clamp for sealing. It may be equipped with a tire valve for introducing gas.

cap, cast iron pipe, *n.* A cast iron fitting which forms the transition fitting between an iron pipe bend and a U-cable guard.

cap, drop wire end, *n*. A ½-inch D clear plastic tube 3 inches long with one closed end. Used to cover the tagged end of an idle drop wire to protect the wire and tag.

cap, grid, *n*. A cylindrical metal cap, typically about ¼-inch diameter, placed on the top of an electron tube glass envelope and used as a terminal for the control grid.

cap, lamp, *n*. A translucent or transparent glass lens held in a brass rim about ⅜″ OD. Fits into a switchboard lamp strip to cover the lamp. Available in colors and in coded markings having special meanings for the operator.

cap, plug. See "plug, attachment."

cap, reducing, *n*. Case iron fitting used at the base of a pole or at a building wall to permit interconnecting a subsidiary conduit to a pipe riser or cable "U-guard" on the pole or wall.

capacitance, *n*. The property of an electric system comprised of conductors and associated dielectrics which determines, for a given rate of change of potential difference between the conductors, the displacement currents in the system. Also the property which determines how much electrical charge will be stored in the dielectric for a given potential difference between the conductors.

capacitance, battery, *n*. The electrical capacitance of a central office battery, which acts as a shunt filter to absorb impulse noise. This capacitance approximates 25,000 microfarads per ampere-hour of battery capacity.

capacitance, distributed, *n*. The capacitance that exists between the turns in a coil or choke, or between adjacent conductors or circuits, as distinguished from the capacitance which is concentrated in a capacitor.

capacitance, interelectrode, *n*. The capacitance existing between the electrodes in an electron tube.

capacitance, office cabling, *n*. The sum of the capacitances of the switchboard and testboard multiple, and the cabling from terminal equipment to the switching equipment.

capacitance, stray. See "stray capacitance."

capacitance unbalance. See "test, capacitance unbalance."

capacitive coupling. See "coupling, capacitive."

capacitive reactance. See "reactance, capacitive."

capacitor, *n*. A device for storing electric energy, blocking the flow of direct current, and permitting the flow of alternating current to a degree permitted by the frequency and its capacitance. Consists of one or several pairs of conducting plates separated by a dielectric, which may be air, waxed or oiled paper, mica, glass, Mylar, etc.

capacitor, air, *n*. A capacitor which uses air as the dielectric material between its plates.

capacitor, blocking, *n*. A capacitor used to block a flow of direct current, while allowing an alternating current to pass.

capacitor, building-out, *n*. A capacitor used to increase the capacitance of an electrical circuit to a standard value.

capacitor, bypass, *n*. A capacitor connected to provide a low-impedance path for high frequency alternating currents around a resistor or other circuit element.

capacitor, ceramic, *n*. An accurate, stable capacitor whose dielectric is a ceramic, such as barium titanate. Can be constructed so as to have a zero, negative, or positive temperature coefficient.

capacitor, coupling, *n*. A capacitor which joins two circuits or amplifier stages by allowing alternating currents to pass but blocking direct currents.

capacitor, electrolytic, *n*. A fixed capacitor, having a relatively high capacitance due to a very thin, electrically-formed non-conducting chemical dielectric film. To maintain this dielectric film, the electrolytic capacitor must always be connected with correct polarity.

capacitor, mylar, *n.* A fixed capacitor constructed like a paper capacitor, but using a very thin sheet of mylar plastic. Smaller than a paper capacitor of the same rating.

capacitor, padder, *n.* A trimmer capacitor in the oscillator circuit of a superheterodyne radio receiver which permits calibration of the low-frequency range so that it tracks with the tuning dial markings.

capacitor, paper, *n.* A fixed capacitor composed of two strips of metal foil separated by a thin sheet of waxed paper, after which the assembly is rolled into a cylindrical form. In telephone practice it is usually flattened and potted in a rectangular metal can.

capacitor, trimmer, *n.* A small capacitor, usually adjustable by screwdriver, which is placed in parallel with a larger capacitor and used to tune the circuit more precisely.

capacitor, variable, *n.* A capacitor whose capacitance can be varied by varying the separation between a pair of plates, or by varying the depth of insertion of interleaved plates. Most widely used for tuning radio frequency circuits.

capacitor, voltage-variable. See "varactor."

capacity, *n.* (1) Capacitance. (2) The rated load-carrying capability of a device or machine. (3) The ability to carry current. (4) The ability to perform work.

capacity, ampere-hour, *n.* The ability of a storage battery to furnish a certain constant current over a specified period of time (usually 8 hours). Thus a 200 ampere-hour battery can supply 25 amperes for 8 hours. See also "drain, busy-hour battery."

capacity, current-carrying, *n.* The maximum current which can be carried continuously without damage to a conductor, device, or machine. It is determined by the temperature which the insulation can withstand, and by the ambient temperature.

car, cable, *n.* A wooden seat, $6''x21''$, chain supported from a pair of wheels which roll on the cable suspension strand. Used to support a cableman or lineman while he is working on the cable in mid-span.

carbon brush. See "brush."

carbons, *n. pl.* The voltage limiting elements of an arrester. Small rectangular blocks of carbon used in pairs separated by a small air-gap across which the high-voltage jumps. See also "block, protector."

carbon transmitter. See "transmitter, telephone."

card, circuit layout record, *n.* Printed card, usually $5''x8''$, on which is entered the circuit name and number, together with a tabulation of the circuit facilities and associated equipment with its transmission loss. Special cards for repeatered and carrier-derived circuits have also the repeater and carrier gains, levels, etc.

card, data, *n.* A card which can be punched with holes to represent letters or digits. The standard card is $7\frac{3}{8}$-inches wide by $3\frac{1}{4}$-inches high and has 80 vertical columns which can be punched in Hollerith code to represent 80 characters. Each column is divided into two sections, the lower having ten punch positions, zero through nine, and the upper having punch positions 11 and 12 also called the X and Y zone punches, respectively.

card, dial number, *n.* The $1\frac{1}{2}$-inch diameter white card used in the center of a telephone dial to display the area code and telephone number. Furnished in punch-out strips of four.

card, Porta-a-Punch, *n.* A type of data card made by IBM which is pre-perforated and printed so that the punchings desired can be manually pushed out with a stylus after inserting the card in a frame called a Porta-a-Punch board.

card, printed wiring. See "board, printed wiring."

card, repair, *n.* Record card for each telephone line which lists the telephone number, subscriber's name and address, type of service and equipment, the cable and pair assignment, and the central office line equipment assignment. This card is held at the repair desk. Each report of trouble is posted on the card before it is handed to the test-deskman, who tests the outside and inside plants to locate the trouble before directing the repairman in clearing it.

card, station number, *n.* The card associated with each telephone dial which shows the area code and telephone number. With rotary dials it is 1½ " diameter; with pushbutton dials it is ½ "x1⅞ ".

card, subscriber's line. See "record, line card."

card, trouble history, *n.* Record card for a particular circuit or service on which all troubles (date, indication, and findings) are listed as they occur.

card dialer telephone set, *n.* A complete telephone set arranged for card dialing. Enlarged desk telephone has slot back of dial in which perforation-coded dialing cards are inserted and pushed down. A "start" button energizes a 15 volt 60 Hz motor in the set which drives the dialer mechanism.

carrier, *n.* (1) High-frequency sinusoidal current which can be modulated with voice or digital signals for bulk transmission via cable or radio circuits. (2) In a semiconductor, the mobile electron or mobile hole which carries the current.

carrier, equivalent 4-wire, *n.* Carrier having separate transmit and receive paths via "high-group" and "low-group" frequencies on a single pair of wires.

carrier, exchange, *n.* A carrier system for application on paired exchange trunk cables to derive additional trunks. A typical system provides 24 voice channels plus associated signaling on two cable pairs. Power for intermediate carrier repeaters, when used, is supplied from an office terminal.

carrier, exchange trunk, *n.* A type of carrier telephone system applied to exchange cables to derive central office trunks. A typical system derives 24 voice channels from two cable pairs by frequency division of the band 21-403 kHz. Signaling is accomplished by time division of a single signaling channel.

carrier, frequency-shift. See "frequency-shift carrier."

carrier, handline, *n.* A spring steel loop having a rawhide strap for fastening to a lineman's body belt. Used when necessary to carry a handline up a pole or ladder safely. It will hold the weight of the handline, but will release it if placed under tension.

carrier, high-density. See "high-density carrier."

carrier, majority, *n.* In a semiconductor, the type of carrier (electron or hole) which constitutes more than half of the total carriers.

carrier, minority, *n.* In semiconductors, the type of charge carrier that constitutes less than half of the total carriers. In n-type material the minority carriers are holes; in p-type material they are electrons.

carrier, short-haul, *n.* A carrier system designed for use over distances of 10-200 miles.

carrier, subscriber's, *n.* A carrier system designed to derive up to twenty subscribers' station lines from two cable pairs.

carrier, suppressed, *n.* A method of transmission in which one or more sidebands are transmitted but the carrier is not transmitted.

carrier, television sound, *n.* The frequency modulated subcarrier which carries the audio portion of a television signal. See also "signal, television."

carrier, twin-channel. See "twin-channel carrier."

carrier, voice frequency telegraph, *n.* A wire carrier system which divides a 300-3300 hertz voice channel into twenty-six frequency-shift telegraph channels spaced at 120 hertz.

carrier frequency, *n.* (1) The frequency of an unmodulated carrier wave. (2) Any of the frequencies which are suitable for use as carriers.

carrier leak, *n.* In balanced modulators, as used in suppressed-carrier transmission systems, the balance may not be perfect. The resultant small amount of carrier power which remains in the modulated signal is called "carrier leak."

carrier line, *n.* Any transmission line used to carry a carrier circuit.

carrier loading. See "loading, carrier."

carrier repeater. See "repeater, carrier."

carrier signaling, *n.* Voice circuits on carrier very often use a telegraph carrier on one of the voice channels to carry all of the associated supervision and signaling circuits. Others may use a signaling frequency within the voice band, still others a frequency in the guard band between the voice channels.

carrier system, *n.* A method of transmitting electrical intelligence by modulating it onto a higher frequency carrier wave, then at the receiving end recovering the original intelligence by the reverse process of demodulation. Useful because many channels of intelligence can be modulated on one carrier wave, and carried on a single transmission channel.

carrier system, 43A1 telegraph, *n.* A versatile, frequency-shift telegraph carrier system. The individual channels operate at any of 25 mid-band frequencies from 425 Hz to 5050 Hz. The drop side may be arranged for neutral, loop or electronic hub operation.

carrier system, four-wire, *n.* A wire carrier system which uses two separate pairs, one for West to East transmission and the other for East to West transmission.

carrier system, K-type, *n.* An early basic Bell System carrier having twelve voice channels in the band 12-60 kilohertz.

carrier system, L-type multiplex, *n.* A heavy-duty multiplex facility providing up to 1860 4kHz channels over radio or toll cable facilities.

carrier system, N2, *n.* A 12-channel, short-haul, voice carrier for use on toll and exchange cables. Uses two cable pairs for the directional bands: 172-268 kHz, and 36-132 kHz. Is compandored.

carrier system, N3, *n.* A packaged 24-channel, short-haul voice carrier for use on toll or exchange cables. Uses two cable pairs for the two directional bands: 36-132 kHz and 172-268 kHz. Is compandored and delay equalized.

carrier system, 0, *n.* An open-wire line carrier providing 16 compandored voice channels on one pair of wires.

carrier system, two-wire, *n.* A wire carrier system which uses only a single pair of wires. Different frequency allocations are used for the West to East and East to West directions.

carrier system, T-1, *n.* A 24-channel, transistorized, time-division, pulse-code modulation, voice carrier used on exchange cable to provide short-haul trunks. Uses two pairs, in one or two cables, for two directions of transmission. Requires regenerative pulse repeaters at 6000 feet intervals.

carrier system, T2, *n.* A short-haul toll carrier system using time division and pulse code modulation, and capable of transmitting 6.3 megabits per second (96 voice channels) on paired cables.

carrier system, T4, *n.* A long-haul toll carrier system using time division and pulse code modulation, and capable of transmitting 281 megabits per second (4032 voice channels, or 168 T1 systems) on coaxial cable.

carrier telephony, *n.* Telephony in which the signal is transmitted at carrier frequencies, the transmitted wave being a carrier wave which has been modulated by a voice-frequency wave.

carrier-to-noise ratio. See "ratio, carrier-to-noise."

carrier transmission, *n.* A means of transmitting information electrically in which the transmitted wave is a wave resulting from the modulation of a single-frequency sinusoidal wave by a complex modulating wave.

carrier wave. See "wave, carrier."

cart, cable splicer's, *n.* Two-wheeled enclosed trailer used for carrying a cable splicer's tools and materials.

Carterfone, *n.* A trade-marked acoustically-coupled device intended to couple a two-way radio circuit with local or long distance telephone facilities.

cascade connection, *n.* A connection of sections of amplifiers, networks, etc., where the output of one section feeds the input of the next section.

case, coil, *n.* Case, usually of welded steel, to house and protect loading coils. Cases are available for aerial, underground (manhole) or buried installation; and are equipped with a stub cable connected to the load coils.

case, loading coil. See "case, coil."

case, splice, *n.* Cast metal housing with a semi-cylindrical cavity, used in identical pairs to clamp around a cable splice to provide a closure. Requires also sealing cord, sealing tape, and sealing washers to make the closure gas and moisture tight.

case, strand-mounted loading coil, *n.* A loading coil case, usually made from a 4⅜-inch OD lead pipe, which is light enough to be lashed to the cable messenger in mid-span. Available in sizes up to 50 coils.

Cassegrain antenna, *n.* A high gain parabolic antenna with a straight horn feed through the center of the parabola. Energy from the horn impinges on a convex reflector at the focus of the parabola, and from there is reflected back to the main parabolic reflector.

cathode, *n.* (1) A source of electrons. (2) The negatively charged pole or element from which the current (a flow of electrons) leaves.

cathode, cold, *n.* A cathode in an electron tube which releases electrons at room temperature, aided by the presence of gases within the tube envelope.

cathode, hot, *n.* An electron tube cathode in which electron emission is produced by heat.

cathode, indirectly heated, *n.* In an electron tube, a cathode which is a coated tube which encloses a heating element. Avoids noise and bias potential from the heater supply voltage.

cathode follower, *n.* An electron tube circuit having a very low output impedance, a high input impedance, and a negative gain. The input signal is applied between control grid and ground, and the output signal is taken from cathode to ground. See also "emitter follower."

cathode ray tube. See "tube, cathode ray."

cathode sputtering. See "sputtering, cathode."

cation, *n.* An atom with a deficiency of electrons, and therefore having a positive charge.

catwhisker, *n.* A small, sharp-pointed wire used to make contact with a sensitive point on the surface of a semiconductor. The early semiconductor diodes and the earlier crystal detectors used catwhiskers.

cavity, resonant, *n.* A metal box, cylindrical or rectangular, of such dimensions that it will support electromagnetic oscillations if excited at a microwave frequency.

"C" battery. See "battery, grid."

CCS, *n.* Hundred call-seconds. The unit in which amounts of telephone traffic are measured. One call which lasts for one hundred seconds constitutes one CCS.

CCSA. See "switching arrangement, common control."

CCSD, Command Communication Service Designator (DCS), *n.* An alphanumeric combination of eight characters used to identify individual circuits established for the Defense Communications System (DCS).

cell, *n.* (1) One unit of a battery which converts chemical energy into electrical energy. (2) A photocell. (3) A solar cell. (4) A unit for the storage of binary data.

cell, alkaline, *n.* A primary dry cell giving 1.5 volts, and having a very low internal resistance and high service capacity. Consists of a zinc anode, a high-density manganese dioxide cathode, and a potassium hydroxide electrolyte.

cell, counter EMF, *n.* A nickel and sodium hydroxide electrolytic cell used in series with the central office battery so that the net (difference) voltage is correct for the equipment. Does not have an EMF of its own, but opposes a drop of 1.5 volts to the battery current.

cell, dry, *n.* A small source of energy derived from the reaction of an acid or alkaline paste on dis-similar metals or on a metal and a carbon electrode. The normal open-circuit voltage is 1.5 volts, the paste is sealed in normal use, and it cannot be recharged.

cell, dry counter EMF, *n.* A series stack of three selenium coated iron plates which gives a voltage drop of 1.5 volts. These stacks are paralleled as required for the necessary current capacity. Used in series with a small central office battery: one DCEMF cell with a 24-cell battery, or three DCEMF cells with a 26-cell battery. Remain in the circuit when the battery is floated, but are shorted out if the charger output should fail.

cell, fuel. See "fuel cell."

cell, lead-acid storage, *n.* A storage cell in which both plates are lead-antimony or lead-calcium grids filled with sponge lead for the negative plate and lead peroxide for the positive plate. On discharge, the material in both plates is converted to lead sulfide. The electrolyte is a solution of sulfuric acid having a specific gravity of 1.200. The cell voltage is nominally 2 volts, rising to 2.15 volts on float and dropping to 1.85 volts on discharge.

cell, lead-antimony storage, *n.* The usual type of lead-acid storage cell in which the plates are made of a lead-antimony alloy. It can be used with either "float" or "charge-discharge" operation.

cell, lead-calcium storage, *n.* A newer type of lead-acid storage cell, in which the plates are made of a lead-calcium alloy. Improves the useful life of the cell, but necessitates "float" charging the cell. The "charge-discharge" method of operating the cell cannot be used.

cell, Leclanche, *n.* A dry cell.

cell, magnesium, *n.* A primary cell having a negative electrode made of magnesium or its alloy.

cell, memory, *n.* A device, such as a magnetic core, in which one binary digit of information can be stored for reading at a later time.

cell, mercury, *n.* A small dry cell giving a constant voltage of 1.35 volts, much used in hearing aids. Consists of a pure zinc anode, a mercuric oxide cathode, and an electrolyte of potassium hydroxide saturated with zinc oxide.

cell, nickel-cadmium storage, *n.* A storage cell identical with the nickel-iron storage cell except that the negative plate is filled with sponge cadmium and finely divided metallic iron.

cell, nickel-iron storage, *n.* A storage cell in which the positive plate consists of perforated nickeled-steel tubes filled with nickel oxide and the negative plate consists of perforated nickeled-steel rectangular pockets filled with equal parts of ferrous oxide and finely divided metallic iron, both immersed in a potassium hydroxide electrolyte of 1.200 specific gravity, and enclosed in a welded nickeled steel case. The cell voltage is about 1.25 volts.

cell, photoconductive, *n.* A semiconductor device whose resistance varies with the amount of light falling on it.

cell, photovoltaic, *n.* A semiconductor device which generates a voltage dependent upon the amount of light falling on it.

cell, pilot. See "pilot cell."

cell, primary, *n.* A cell that converts chemical energy into electrical energy by irreversible chemical reactions, and that cannot be recharged by passing an electric current through it. See also "cell, secondary."

cell, secondary, *n.* A storage cell.

cell, silver-cadmium, *n.* A small, lightweight sealed storage cell having a long shelf life. It has been used in communication satellites.

cell, silver oxide, *n.* A small dry cell giving a constant voltage of 1.5 volts, and much used in hearing aids and electric watches. It consists of a pure zinc anode, a depolarizing silver oxide cathode, and a potassium hydroxide or sodium hydroxide electrolyte. Maximum current output is about 10 milliamperes.

cell, solar, *n.* A silicon junction diode consisting of a thin (0.4 micron) n-type layer diffused onto p-type silicon. The cell is about 1x2x0.04 centimeters, and produces 22 milliwatts at about 0.4 volts per cell in full sunlight. They are wired in series-parallel to produce a useful output. Used to power communication satellites.

cell, standard, *n.* A primary cell which is accurately reproducible, and can therefore serve as a standard of electromotive force. The usual standard cell has electrodes of cadmium and mercury with a saturated electrolyte of cadmium sulphate and mercurous sulphate, giving an open-circuit potential of 1.0183 volts.

cell, storage, *n.* (1) A cell that converts chemical energy into electrical energy by a reversible chemical reaction and that may be recharged by passing a current through it in the direction opposite to that of its discharge. (2) One unit of a storage battery, consisting of one or more positive plates, two or more negative plates, plate separators, an electrolyte, and a container with cover. (3) A magnetic core or similar device for the storage of binary data.

cells, end. See "end cells."

cellulose acetate, *n.* An acetic acid ester of cellulose which is a tough thermoplastic material. Used to impregnate cotton insulation on wires.

cent, *n.* The interval between two musical sounds whose basic frequency ratio is the twelve-hundredth root of two. Some common intervals in cents are:

Interval	Cents
Unison	0
Major second	200
Major third	300
Perfect fourth	500
Perfect fifth	700
Major sixth	900
Major seventh	1100
Octave	1200

center, automatic digital message switching (ADMSC), *n.* A part of the AUTODIN network consisting of the following subsystems: 1. Automatic digital message switch (ADMS). 2. Modems performing signal conversion between the ADMS and the transmission facilities. 3. Communications security equipment. 4. A technical control facility.

center, automatic intercept, *n.* A center where intercepted calls are received and processed automatically by (a) connection to a vacant number announcement, (b) connection to an announcement machine which gives the correct number, or (c) transfer of the call to an operator at a centralized intercept bureau.

center, automatic teletypewriter switching, *n.* A tape relay center in which the incoming message preamble is automatically decoded to determine (a) its destination, (b) its security classification, and (c) its precedence. Following that, it is automatically transmitted on the proper outgoing circuit.

center, communication. See "communication center."

center, load, *n.* A power panelboard serving one particular area of a building.

center, non-automatic relay, *n.* A digital message switching center which relays messages by manual means, *i.e.*: by receiving incoming messages on paper tape or punched cards and manually transferring these tapes or cards to a tape or card transmitter on the proper outgoing line.

center, switching, *n.* An installation at which switching equipment interconnects lines and trunks on a circuit switching basis.

center, tape relay, *n.* A switching center in a message switching network, where teletypewriter messages are received on paper tape, then relayed by tearing off the tape message and inserting it into a tape transmitter on the proper outgoing circuit. See also "major relay center" and "minor relay center."

center, telephone switching, *n.* A location or a building where telephone calls are switched. It may contain one or several "central offices."

center, test, *n.* Central location which combines repair clerk and test desk functions for its area of responsibility. Receives subscriber's reports of trouble, tests the lines and equipment involved, locates the trouble, dispatches a repairman, and re-tests after the trouble is cleared.

center, toll. See "toll center."

centers, toll switching, *n. pl.* The hierarchy of centers which constitute the "control switching points" of the distance dialing network. In order of their importance they are:
Class 1 — Regional Centers (RC)
Class 2 — Sectional Centers (SC)
Class 3 — Primary Centers (PC)
They receive calls from, and switch calls to, the lower class offices in the hierarchy. These are:
Class 4C — Toll Center (TC)
Class 4P — Toll Point (TP)
Class 5   — End Office (EO)

center tap, *n.* A connection to the electrical midpoint of a coil, resistor, or transformer winding.

centi-. A prefix meaning "the one-hundredth part of."

centigrade (C°), *n.* The metric scale of temperature, on which water freezes at 0 degrees C and boils at 100 degrees C. Absolute zero is —273 degrees C. To convert a Centigrade temperature to Fahrenheit, multiply by 9/5 and add 32.

Centralized Automatic Message Accounting (CAMA), *n.* A system similar to automatic message accounting (AMA), but located at a central office which serves several adjacent central offices. If automatic number identification (ANI) is not included, the call is routed to an operator who obtains the calling number and dials it into the equipment.

central office, *n.* (1) A place where the switching of telephone calls is done, whether automatic or manual. (2) A 10,000-line unit in an automatic switching center.

central office, Unigauge, *n.* A #5 crossbar central office that has been equipped with a 72 volt battery supply, 2500 ohm line relays and range extenders to take advantage of the economies of the "Unigauge System," which see.

central office area. See "area, central office."

central office equipment (COE), *n.* Apparatus used in a telephone central office for the furnishing of communication services.

central office name, *n.* The designation by which a central office unit is known. It may be a name, or letters, two letters and a numeral, or three numerals.

central office numeral, *n.* A number added to a central office name to distinguish between several central office units bearing the same name. For instance: WAbash-1, WA-2, etc.

CENTREX, *n.* Service providing direct inward and outward dialing for PABX extensions. The PABX is assigned a distinct central office code, and made a part of the numbering plan. A main listed number will give access to the PABX operator.

centrex-CO, *n.* Centrex service with the switching equipment located in the central office.

centrex-CU, *n.* Centrex service with the switching equipment located on the customer's premises.

ceramic, polycrystalline, *n.* A ceramic material, such as barium titanate, having a crystalline structure in which all molecules are similarly oriented and regularly arranged. It may be made piezoelectric by pretreatment with a polarizing electric field.

cgs system, *n.* The metric system of measurements, based on use of the units centimeter-gram-second.

chad, *n.* The small circle or rectangle of paper which is removed when a paper tape or data card is punched.

chadless tape, *n.* A type of punched paper tape in which the hole is not punched out completely, but left hanging by a small attachment on the leading edge. Cannot be read electrically or photoelectrically.

chain circuit, *n.* A circuit consisting of a number of make contacts in series, each contact made by operation of one relay. The circuit is therefore not closed until all relays are operated simultaneously. Used for all-trunks-busy registration, etc.

chain relay, *n.* A relay which forms one link in a chain circuit.

chair, lineman's safety, *n.* A cable car, which see.

chair, operator's, *n.* A special swivel chair for use at telephone switchboards. Has a ventilated padded seat, a padded backrest, and a full ring footrest.

challenge, *n.* The action of an operator who enters a circuit and asks:
(1) May I help you?
(2) What number are you calling?
(3) Are you waiting?
    etc.
—*v.t.* To enter a circuit and make a challenge.

chamber, binding post, *n.* A sealed metal chamber having an insulating panel equipped with binding posts, and a stub cable connected to the binding posts. Used as a cable terminal.

chamber, fuse, *n.* A cable terminal in which all of the cable pairs are terminated in 7-ampere tubular fuses. Used at the junction of underground cable with toll open wire, or other junctions where a fuse is needed. Rarely used today.

chamber, splicing. See "splicing chamber."

change, *n.* A serially numbered modification, applicable to all copies of a publication. A change is promulgated in the same manner as, and to the same holders of, the basic publication.

change out, *v.* To replace.

changer, frequency. See "frequency changer."

channel, *n.* The smallest subdivision of a circuit (or of a trunk route), by means of which a single type of communication service is provided, *i.e.,* a voice channel, teletypewriter channel, or a data channel.

channel, adjacent, *n.* The band of frequencies immediately above or below the reference channel.

channel, AM broadcast, *n.* Any of the 10 kilohertz wide bands of radio frequencies which extend from 535 to

1605 kilohertz, and are used for standard amplitude-modulated radio broadcasts.

channel, crossbar, *n.* A combination of line link, a junctor, and a trunk link which, when crosspoints close, forms a path to connect a line with a trunk, or a trunk with a trunk.

channel, crossbar originating, *n.* In a crossbar central office, the combination consisting of the district link, the office junctor, and the office link.

channel, crossbar terminating, *n.* In a crossbar central office, the combination consisting of an incoming link, line junctor, and line link.

channel, dropped, *n.* Any of the channels of a multichannel carrier system which are terminated at some repeater point intermediate between the terminals of the system. See also "drop-and-insert."

channel, FM broadcast, *n.* Any of the 200 kilohertz wide bands of radio frequencies which extend from 88.1 to 107.9 megahertz. The portion of the band from 88.1 to 91.9 megahertz is reserved for educational broadcasts.

channel, outboard. See "outboard channel."

channel, pilot, *n.* A single frequency carrier channel which carries a tone used to actuate automatic level regulators, or alarms, or both.

channel, public music, *n.* A channel on CATV which provides music to CATV subscribers without an additional charge. Music is picked up from a broadcasting station or from magnetic tapes and transmitted on the CATV cable using a spare TV channel or FM broadcast channel.

channel, radio, *n.* A band of radio frequencies sufficiently wide to permit radio communication. The bandwidth required depends both on the frequency and the type of modulation.

channel, SCA, *n.* Subsidiary carrier authorized channel. A channel which carries program material modulated onto a radio frequency subcarrier on a CATV system or an FM broadcast signal.

channel, service, *n.* An order wire channel on a radio system, usually in the band 300 Hz-12 kHz, below the multiplex spectrum.

channel, subscription music, *n.* A channel FM-modulated with continuous music which is applied to a CATV cable, but which cannot be demodulated by a standard FM receiver. The customer pays a monthly fee for the necessary demodulator and amplifier.

channel, telegraph, *n.* A communication path between two points which is suitable for transmitting telegraph signals. The bandwidth required depends upon the signaling speed.

channel, telephone, *n.* A communication path between two points suitable for carrying voice message traffic.

channel, television, *n.* A band of radio frequencies 6 megahertz wide used for the broadcasting of television signals. The principal channels are as follows:

Channel	Megahertz
2	54-60
3	60-66
4	66-72
5	76-82
6	82-88
7	174-180
8	180-186
9	186-192
10	192-198
11	198-204
12	204-210
13	210-216
14-83	470-890

channel, voice, *n.* A transmission path suitable for carrying analog voice signals, covering a frequency band of 250-3400 Hz.

channel bank, *n.* That portion of a carrier multiplex terminal consisting of a group of 12 channels which is modulated as a group.

channel bank equipment, *n.* Equipment for frequency multiplexing of a 12-channel carrier group.

channelization, *n*. The assignment of circuits to channels, and the arrangement of those channels into groups and supergroups.

channel modulation, *n*. Translation of a 4 kHz voice channel to a higher frequency to form part of a 12-channel carrier group.

character, *n*. (1) Any conventional mark, sign, or symbol used in writing or printing. (2) Any group of binary digits which represents a mark, letter, numeral, sign, or symbol.

character, magnetic, *n*. An alphanumeric character printed with magnetic ink so that it can be read by a machine.

characteristic, *n*. (1) The identifying properties of an electrical circuit. (2) A graphical representation of the electrical properties of a circuit or equipment. (3) The whole number, or integral, part of a logarithm.

characteristic, impedance, *n*. A graph of the impedance of a circuit plotted against frequency.

characteristic, transfer, *n*. The relation, as shown by a graph, of the voltage at one electrode to the current at another electrode with all other electrode voltages being kept constant.

characteristic distortion. See "distortion, characteristic."

characteristic impedance, *n*. (1) The impedance that a transmission line would have if it were infinitely long. (2) Iterative impedance, which see.

character-serial, *adj*. Describes a method of information transfer in which each alphanumeric character is transmitted separately and sequentially, one after another. Almost all record and data communications use character-serial transfer.

charge, *v*. (1) To replenish the electrical charge in a battery. (2) To store electrical energy in a capacitor. (3) To put down as a debt against a name or account.

charge, constant-voltage, *n*. A charge for a storage battery in which the voltage at the battery terminals is held at a constant value throughout the charge.

charge, electric, *n*. Electric energy stored as stress on the surface of a dielectric.

charge, equalizing. See "equalizing charge."

charge, initial period, *n*. On a toll call, the minimum charge which is made, permitting conversation for the initial period, usually 3 minutes.

charge, other line. See "other line charge."

charge, overtime, *n*. On a toll call, the charge made for conversation exceeding the initial period.

charge, powder, *n*. A blank cartridge, .22 caliber or .25 caliber, used to actuate a powder-powered tool. The cartridges are color-coded to indicate the weight of the gunpowder charge, as follows:
Brown-Sub-light, Green-Light, Yellow-Medium, Red-Heavy, Purple-Extra-Heavy.

charge, residual, *n*. A small charge remaining in the dielectric of a capacitor after a single quick discharge.

charge, space, *n*. The negative charge produced by the cloud of electrons existing in the space between the cathode and plate in an electron tube, formed by the electrons emitted from the cathode in excess of those immediately attracted to the plate.

charge, trickle, *n*. A continuous charge of a storage battery at a very low rate. The end cells of a central office battery are almost never used, so they are given a trickle charge to keep them fully charged at all times.

chargeable time, *n*. The time interval used in determining message charges, expressed in whole minutes. It is derived from the answer time (station-to-station) or start of conversation (person-to-person), the disconnect time, and timing allowance for interruptions.

charge computer, *n.* An automatic computer which determines the charges on a toll call by consulting its memory for rates (defined by a "rate treatment number") and multiplying these rates by the duration of the call in minutes. Initial period charges and overtime period charges are computed separately, then added.

charge key supervision, *n.* The use of a charge key for extending the called party answer condition, as observed by an operator, to the originating end of the connection for message charging purposes.

charge lamp, *n.* A lamp associated with a charge key, which remains lighted until the charge key is pressed.

charger, *n.* A device, rectifier or DC generator, which supplies direct current at a voltage suitable for charging a storage battery.

charger, constant voltage, *n.* A battery charger which maintains a constant output voltage, thus allowing the charging current to taper off as the battery becomes charged, and finally allowing the battery to "float," supplying any minor variations in the load current. See also "floating battery."

charger-eliminator, *n.* A battery charger with a low-noise, low-impedance output which can either charge a storage battery or supply the DC load directly, without a storage battery in parallel.

Charges, Law of Electric. See "Appendix B."

charging current. See "current, charging."

chart, earth's radius, *n.* A radio profile chart whose horizontal lines are curved exactly as is the earth's surface. A "worst case" chart which will show the profile when there is no atmospheric refraction of the radio waves.

chart, 4/3 earth's radius, *n.* A radio profile chart whose horizontal lines are curved to correspond to an earth having a radius 4/3 times larger than the actual earth. This provides an automatic correction for normal atmospheric refraction of the radio waves.

chart, profile, *n.* A chart showing the clearance of a microwave radio path over the terrain between two adjacent antennas. It plots to scale the elevation of the antennas, and intervening hills, ridges, buildings. Several types are used. See "chart, earth's radius, and "chart, 4/3 earth's radius."

chassis, *n.* The metal box or frame on and in which components of an electronic equipment are mounted.

chatter, *n.* The vibration or multiple rebound of relay contacts, or of a relay armature.

check, parity, *n.* A method of checking the accuracy of transmission of digital data by adding a "parity bit" so that the total number of "ones" in each character is always odd. Thus if the character contains an even number of "ones," a "one" bit is transmitted after the character, while if the character contains an odd number of "ones," a "zero" bit is transmitted. At the receiver, a count is made of the number of "ones" in each character and if the parity is even the character is known to be in error. This can then trigger a request to re-transmit.

check bit, *n.* An extra binary digit inserted in the code for a character or word as a check that it has been transmitted correctly. See also "parity."

checking, pulse. See "pulse checking."

checking multiple, *n.* A special multiple of subscriber lines provided at some DSA boards which enables the "A" operator to check the correctness of the calling number by means of a cord tip test which produces a tone.

checking operator service, *n.* Service in which telephone calls are processed automatically except for the calling in of an (checking) operator to (a) obtain the number of the calling telephone, (b) to handle a collect or person-to-person call, or to quote time and charges, etc.

checking service, *n.* The service provided by a checking operator who is called in on a subscriber-dialed automatic-ticketed toll call only to obtain the number of the calling telephone and key it into the ticketer.

check out, *n.* The tests or observations made to determine the condition or status of an item.—*v.t.* To make such tests or observations.

chimney, manhole, *n.* The vertical passage, usually 36-42 inches in diameter, between the roof of the manhole and the manhole frame and cover. Made of brick which can be removed if the street level should be lowered later.

chip, semiconductor, *n.* A thin, square slice of semiconductor material, about 0.04 inch on a side, used to construct a transistor or integrated circuit.

chisel, cold, *n.* A heavy, double-bevel, hardened steel chisel capable of cutting metal.

chock, wheel, *n.* A triangular, laminated wooden block placed against a truck tire to assist the truck brakes in holding the vehicle while parked on slopes, or while pulling cable or strand.

choke, *n.* An inductor which presents a high impedance to alternating currents without appreciably impending the flow of direct currents. See also "coil, retardation."

choke, audio-frequency, *n.* An inductor which presents a considerable impedance to audio-frequency currents but little to direct currents. Generally wound on a ferromagnetic core.

choke, radio-frequency, *n.* An inductor which presents a considerable impedance to radio-frequency currents, but very little to direct currents. Generally uses an air core or a powdered-iron core.

choke, smoothing, *n.* An audio-frequency choke used at the output of a power-supply filter to reduce ripple.

choke, swinging, *n.* An audio-frequency choke used at the input of a power-supply filter for better voltage regulation. Its core is operated saturated with flux. Its inductance is at a maximum for small currents, and changes (swings) to a minimum for large currents.

choke coil. See "coil, retardation."

chopper, *n.* A device which interrupts a direct current signal at an audio rate so that it can be passed through a transformer.

chromate, acid copper, *n.* A chemical, $CuCr_2O_7$ x $2H_2O$, used to impregnate wood to prevent damage by marine borers, such as teredos.

chrominance, *n.* The difference, specified colorimetrically, between a particular color and a reference color (usually white) having equal luminance.

chronopher, *n.* A device which can provide electrical information giving the time-of-day and date.

chute, coin, *n.* The portion of a coin telephone which accepts coins (5, 10, and 25 cents) and conducts them to the coin relay hopper. Consists of a devious metal chute which conducts the coins past permanent magnets which divert slugs into the coin return receptacle, and causes the good coins to strike a bell and gong which indicate coin denominations to the operator. See also "tones, coin" and "relay, coin."

cipher, *n.* A random-type signal produced by combining an intelligence signal with a key signal.

cipher key. See "key, cryptographic."

ciphony equipment. *n.* Equipment which can be used to encrypt telephone signals. Usually accomplished by converting the analog voice signals to digital signals, then combining with a digital key signal.

circuit, *n.* (1) The complete electrical path between terminals over which telecommunications are provided. (2) A network of circuit elements: resistances, reactances, semiconductors, etc. to perform a specific function. (3) A schematic diagram of a circuit. See also: "calculating circuit," "connecting circuit," counting circuit," locating circuit," lockout circuit," and "register circuit."

circuit, allocated, *n*. A circuit designated for the specific use of one user.

circuit, antisidetone. See "antisidetone circuit."

circuit, approved, *n*. A circuit which has been approved to carry classified (confidential, secret, etc.) information in plain language (without encryption). Usually requires a circuit in heavy metallic conduit, run in the open so that it can be visually inspected.

circuit, black. See "black circuit."

circuit, carrier, *n*. A transmission path, on open wire, cable, or radio, over which signals are transmitted by means of a carrier wave.

circuit, closed, *adj*. Describing a program circuit, audio or video, between two points, not for broadcast use.—*n*. A completed electrical circuit.

circuit, common-battery, *n*. A circuit using a centralized source of battery power which is common to many such circuits.

circuit, common-user, *n*. A circuit which provides a communication service to a number of users, only one of whom can use the service at a particular time.

circuit, composite. See "composite circuit."

circuit, cord, *n*. (1) Part of a manual switchboard. The assemblage of answer cord, calling cord, and associated equipment. (2) The circuit which interconnects two switchboard cords through keys, relays, coils, and lamps to provide talking battery, ringing power, and supervision.

circuit, duplex, *n*. A circuit which permits independent communica-

tions in both directions simultaneously. If a telegraph circuit, it implies the use of "duplex signaling."

circuit, electric, *n*. A path consisting of conductors and/or interconnected circuit elements through which an electric current can flow.

circuit, engineered, *n*. A standby or on-call circuit engineered and configured to meet a specific customer requirement.

circuit, four-wire, *n*. A circuit using two one-way transmission paths, which may be two carrier paths or two pairs (four wires) of metallic conductors.

circuit, free service, *n*. A telephone message circuit giving toll service for which no direct toll charge is collected.

circuit, grounded, *n*. A circuit which is connected to earth at one or more points.

circuit, ground return, *n*. A single-wire circuit which uses the earth for its return path. At one time used for DC telegraph circuits. Not suitable for telephone use.

circuit, grouping, *n*. A circuit used to connect two or more switchboard positions together so that one operator may handle the several switchboard positions from one position. Also called a "position transfer circuit."

circuit, guard. See "guard circuit."

circuit, hold and trace, *n*. A supervisory circuit for a toll office with jack apearances on the toll switchboard. When the operator encounters a faulty toll circuit she connects it to the hold and trace circuit which holds the toll circuit busy, and applies a 2100 Hz tracing tone interrupted 120 IPM.

circuit, holding. See "holding circuit."

circuit, longitudinal, *n*. A circuit formed by one or more wires in parallel, having its return through the earth or through another group of conductors.

circuit, magnetic, *n*. A closed path of "magnetic flux," which is forced through the "reluctance" of a magnetic circuit by a "magnetomotive force."

circuit, message, *n.* A circuit used for completing toll telephone calls.

circuit, metallic, *n.* A circuit which is entirely in wire, not via the earth or via carrier or radio.

circuit, multiple, *n.* A circuit in which two or more similar elements are connected in parallel.

circuit, night alarm. See "night alarm circuit."

circuit, on-call, *n.* A circuit which is permanently designated, but which is activated only upon the request of the user. Furnished when the customer's need is unpredictable.

circuit, open-wire, *n.* A circuit made up of a pair of bare conductors separately supported on spaced insulators, which are usually supported on crossarms or brackets.

circuit, oscillatory, *n.* A circuit which will support electrical oscillations.

circuit, parallel, *n.* A circuit whose elements are all connected across the circuit or to the same pair of terminals, so that the same voltage is across all the elements and the current divides between the elements in inverse proportion to their impedance.

circuit, phantom, *n.* A telephone circuit obtained by superimposing an additional circuit on two existing physical circuits by means of center-tapped repeating coils. Each of the physical circuits used in deriving a phantom circuit is called a "side circuit."

circuit, physical. See "physical circuit."

circuit, plugging-up, *n.* The supervisory circuit associated with a plugging-up cord.

circuit, polar, *n.* A circuit used for polar telegraphy. See "telegraph, polar."

circuit, pony. See "pony circuit."

circuit, printed. See "printed circuit."

circuit, private line, *n.* A leased communication path, local or toll, assigned for the private use of one customer and having no connection to the public telephone system.

circuit, program supply. See "program circuit."

circuit, radio. See "radio circuit."

circuit, red. See "red circuit."

circuit, resonant, *n.* A circuit having capacitance and inductance in such proportions as to make it resonant. See also "resonance, parallel" and "resonance, series."

circuit, ring-down, *n.* Circuit on which signaling is accomplished by manually applied ringing current. At the switchboard the ringing signal will be DC or 20 Hz, becoming 20 Hz, 135 Hz, 1000/20 Hz, or SF on the circuit.

circuit, series, *n.* A circuit whose elements are all connected end-to-end so that the same current flows through all of the elements in sequence. The voltage across the circuit is the sum of the voltages across the individual elements.

circuit, short. See "short circuit."

circuit, short-period, *n.* A circuit which is used for only a specified period each day. See also "on-call circuit."

circuit, side. See "side circuit."

circuit, sidetone, *n.* An outmoded but efficient circuit previously used in common-battery telephone sets. The talker heard room noise and his own voice loudly reproduced by the receiver. Now replaced by the "anti-sidetone circuit."

circuit, simplex. See "simplex circuit."

circuit, solid-state. See "solid-state circuit."

circuit, straight-forward, *n.* Circuit on which the signaling is automatic and in one direction.

circuit, sweep. See "sweep circuit."

circuit, talk-back. See "talk-back circuit."

circuit, tank. See "tank circuit."

circuit, telecommunication, *n.* A complete electrical path between end terminal instruments over which telecommunications are provided.

circuit, telegraph, *n.* A circuit used for telegraph or teletypewriter communication. See also "telegraph,—," "carrier system, telegraph," and "frequency shift."

circuit, terminal grade. See "terminal circuit."

circuit, tertiary. See "tertiary circuit."

circuit, thin film, *n.* A circuit whose elements are films only several molecules thick formed on an insulating substrate.

circuit, three-phase, *n.* An electric power circuit having three alternating voltages which differ in phase by one-third of a cycle, or 120 electrical degrees.

circuit, through. See "through circuit."

circuit, toll, *n.* An intertoll trunk. A circuit between two toll offices, regardless of their class.

circuit, transfer, *n.* A circuit which connects communication centers of two separate networks to accomplish the transfer of traffic between these networks.

circuit, trigger. See "trigger circuit."

circuit, trunk. See "trunk,—."

circuit, tuned, *n.* A circuit which is adjusted to be resonant at a particular frequency.

circuit, two-wire, *n.* The normal metallic circuit using two ungrounded wires.

circuit, unbalanced. See "unbalanced circuit."

circuit, via grade. See "via circuit."

circuit, vibrating, *n.* A low audio-frequency circuit connected to a winding of a telegraph receiving relay which tends to vibrate the relay armature, thus aiding weak received signals in breaking the relay's inertia of rest.

circuit, wetted. See "wetted circuit."

circuit breaker. See "breaker, circuit."

circuit equivalent. See "equivalent, circuit."

circuit layout. See "engineering, circuit layout."

circuit layout record. See "record, circuit layout."

circuit switching, *n.* A method of handling traffic through a switching center by interconnecting incoming and outgoing circuits. See also "message switching."

circuit unit. See "unit, circuit."

circularly-polarized, *adj.* Describing an electromagnetic wave, such as radio or light, whose plane of polarization rotates through 360 degrees as the wave propagates in a forward direction. Rotation may be either right-hand or left-hand. See also "polarization, circular."

circular mil, *n.* The unit used to specify the cross-sectional area of round conductors. The area of a circle whose diameter is one mil, or 0.001 inch.

circulating power, *n.* Reactive power, which see.

circulator, radio frequency, *n.* A form of duplexer used to couple several microwave equipments to the same antenna. It has a negligible loss in a forward direction between consecutive ports, but a 20 db loss in the reverse direction. Circulators are usually made of a ferrite material.

citizen's band. See "band, citizen's."

cladding, *n.* The application of one metal over another metal so that the junction between the two metals is continuously welded.

clamp, *n.* A device designed to grip or press two or more parts together. Usually operated by screws or bolts. —*v.t.* To fasten with a clamp.

clamp, armor, *n.* A fitting which grips the armor of a buried or submarine cable where it leaves a manhole or anchorage, and prevents longitudinal movement of the cable.

clamp, beam, *n.* A U-shaped casting having a set screw which can be used to fasten it to the flange of a steel I beam. A tapped hole in the casting permits attachment of insulators, cable suspension clamps, etc.

clamp, bonding ribbon, *n.* A tinned copper strap, of the same material as the bonding ribbon, used to fasten bonding ribbon to a manhole wall. Mounts with a hammer drive or screw anchor.

clamp, cable, *n.* A U-shaped metal strap which can be placed over a cable to fasten it to a flat surface. Has one or two ears with holes for screw fastening.

clamp, cable lashing, *n.* A two-piece, one-bolt galvanized steel clamp used to secure cable lashing wire at the end of a span.

clamp, cable strain relief, *n.* A device used to fasten an aerial cable (paired or coaxial) to the suspension strand at points where the cable terminates. Prevents cable tension being transmitted to the terminal, and also prevents migration of the cable.

clamp, cable suspension. See "clamp, suspension."

clamp, corner suspension, *n.* A suspension clamp having bent ends for use on poles where the suspension strand forms a corner.

clamp, crossover, *n.* Grooved steel plates with bolts, permitting the clamping together of two aerial suspension strands at the point where they cross. Prevents abrasion and relative movement, and provides an electrical bond.

clamp, drop wire, *n.* An assembly of a copper shell to a brass wedge having a wire bail. Used to fasten parallel drop wire to a drive hook or span clamp.

clamp, drop wire span, *n.* A two-piece grooved metal device fitted with a hook which can be bolted onto a cable supporting strand in mid-span and used to attach clamps of drop wires which distribute from mid-span.

clamp, grade, *n.* A clamp which fastens an aerial cable to its suspension strand. Used on hills or at dead-ends to prevent slipping of the cable.

clamp, ground, *n.* Device for fastening a ground wire to an earth connection such as a water pipe.

clamp, ground rod, *n.* A one-piece, one-bolt clamp used to fasten a wire to a ground rod.

clamp, guy, *n.* A two-piece three-bolt galvanized steel clamp having two parallel grooves on its jaws which will grip guy strands.

clamp, lashing wire, *n.* A two-piece one-bolt clamp used for securing cable lashing wire at the end of each span.

clamp, one-hole cable, *n.* A cable clamp which has only one ear by which it is fastened.

clamp, pressure testing, *n.* A pressure testing valve with a rubber gasket which can be clamped over a temporary hole in a cable sheath. Used to make one-time gas pressure readings.

clamp, span, *n.* A two-piece, one-bolt galvanized steel clamp which can be applied to a cable messenger in mid-span. Has a steel hook for the attachment of drop wire clamps, enabling the attachment of drops in mid-span.

clamp, strand, *n.* A two-piece, three-bolt clamp used to fasten two parallel strands together, or to form a loop in a guy strand.

clamp, strand crossover, *n.* A two-piece, two-bolt galvanized steel clamp used to clamp together two messenger strands where they cross at right angles in midspan.

clamp, strand ground, *n.* A U-shaped one-piece, one-bolt, galvanized steel clamp for clamping a cable bonding ribbon against a cable messenger strand.

clamp, suspension, *n.* A two-piece, three-bolt clamp used for supporting a suspension strand at a pole.

clamp, three-bolt. See "clamp, strand."

clamping, *n.* Preventing a pulsed signal from drifting with respect to a reference voltage by tying some repetitive portion of the waveform to that reference voltage. Also called "DC restoration."

clamps, splicer's platform, *n., pl.* A pair of heavy, hinged bronze clamps from which a splicer's platform can be suspended from a cable messenger. The weight of the platform tightens the clamps to the messenger.

clasp, cable, *n.* Device for surface mounting of ınside wiring cables. A soft steel strip 1½ inch to 4 inches long having a central screw hole. Clasp is screwed to surface, then ends are bent out and around the cable.

classified information, *n.* Information which is designated "CONFIDENTIAL," "SECRET," "N O F O R N" (No Foreigners), "TOP SECRET," etc, and to which access is restricted.

class mark. See "mark, class-of-service."

class of pole, *n.* A numerical classification from 1 to 10, which defines both the minimum breaking strength and minimum top circumference of a pole. The definition is as follows:

Pole Class	Breaking Strength	Top Circ.
1	4500 lbs.	27 inches
2	3700 lbs.	25 inches
3	3000 lbs.	23 inches
4	2400 lbs.	21 inches
5	1900 lbs.	19 inches
6	1500 lbs.	17 inches
7	1200 lbs.	15 inches
8	—	18 inches
9	—	15 inches
10	—	12 inches

The circumference of pole classes 1-7 tapers 0.63 inches per linear foot. Breaking strength is the horizontal load that can be applied two feet from the top of the pole with the pole set at the normal depth in solid earth.

class of service, *n.* A subgrouping of telephone customers for the sake of rate distinctions. This may distinguish between individual and party, between business, residence, and coin, between flat-rate and message-rate, and between restricted and extended area service.

class of service tones, *n. pl.* (1) On trunks from community dial offices, any one of several tones that designate by pitch or number of spurts the class of service being answered; *i.e.,* coin line, message rate, restricted service. etc. (2) Tones used at switchboards to indicate the class of service of the calling subscriber when more than one class is served by the same trunk group. Class of service may be indicated by either a high tone, low tone, or absence of tone.

Class 1 office. See "regional center."

Class 1 Toll Center, *n.* Any of the about 300 toll centers for which the Long Lines Department prepares an individual route sheet showing the routes to all other Class 1 offices. They form the basic pattern for routing Long Lines traffic.

Class 2 office. See "sectional center."

Class 2 Toll Center, *n.* All toll centers not designated as Class 1 toll centers. Each Class 2 toll center has trunks to one or more Class 1 toll centers through which originating and terminating Long Lines traffic is routed.

Class 3 office. See "primary outlet."

Class 4C office. See "toll center."

Class 4P office. See "toll point."

Class 5 office. See "end office."

c lead, *n.* The third wire of three (+, —, and c) which constitute a trunk between switches of a dial central office. This is the wire which controls the guarding, holding, and releasing of switches. When grounded it indicates a busy trunk, when open or ungrounded it indicates an idle trunk.

cleaning, ultrasonic, *n.* The cleaning of durable articles by immersing them in a solvent which is violently agitated by a sound wave having a frequency of 20-30 kilohertz.

elear, *adj.* Intelligible. Without encryption. *v.* (1) To rid of trouble. (2) To release, disconnect, or disengage equipment or a circuit from use and restore it to an idle condition. (3) To restore a memory device to its original or zero state. (4) To open the end of a cable and make certain that its pairs are not shorted, crossed, or grounded.

clearance, *n.* (1) Separation or spacing. (2) The separation of telephone plant from power plant or other hazardous structures. (3) Height of telephone plant above ground, or roadway, or rails.

clear text, *adj.* or *n.* Communications, digital or analog signals, which are not encrypted and from which the information can be extracted relatively easily.

cleat, *n.* An assembly of two pieces of porcelain or other insulating material provided with grooves for holding one or two wires at a fixed spacing from the mounting surface and from each other, and with screw holes for fastening to the mounting surface. Seldom used today, since open wiring is seldom used.

clevis, insulator, *n.* A U-shaped galvanized steel strap having a mounting bolt hole at the bottom of the U and a steel pin through both arms of the U. Mounts on a crossarm and supports a knob insulator on the pin.

click, key, *n.* A sharp noise induced in neighboring circuits when a key is opened or closed.

click reducer. See "reducer, acoustic shock" and "varistor."

climbers, lineman's, *n.* Step-shaped irons with straps for fastening to the legs, equipped with sharp spurs and used for climbing poles.

climbers, tree, *n.* Lineman's climbers having extra long gaffs which will penetrate tree bark and go into solid wood, thus allowing trees to be climbed safely.

climbing space. See "space, climbing."

clip, adhesive cable, *n.* A plastic cable clip backed with rubberized adhesive which will adhere to smooth, dry walls without screws.

clip, alligator, *n.* A test clip having long, narrow serrated jaws.

clip, battery, *n.* A metal clip having spring toothed jaws which can be snapped on a battery post, and also having a screw terminal to which a wire can be connected.

clip, busy, *n.* A spring clip for insertion in the busy jack of equipment which is not equipped with a busy key. The end of the busy clip is bent down at a right angle and used to hold a trouble ticket.

clip, drop wire, *n.* A sheet metal clip that folds around a drop wire and supports it at points intermediate between the dead-ends.

clip, fuse, *n.* Spring contacts which contact and hold the ferrules of a cartridge fuse.

clip, strand, *n.* An S-shaped flat metal strap used instead of wire, serving to hold ends of wire strand.

clip, test. See "test clip."

clipper, *n.* A circuit which limits its output waveform to a specific maximum level, even though the input voltage exceeds the corresponding amount.

clipping, *n.* The deforming of speech signals due to limiting the maximum amplitude of the signals.

clock, *n.* (1) A primary source of synchronizing signals. (2) A device for measuring and indicating time. (3) An ultra-stable square wave oscillator capable of maintaining a precise output frequency for long periods of time. Used to synchronize digital transmission systems.

clock, switchboard, *n.* A digital clock made like a message register, used on a switchboard position to provide clock time to the operator.

clock circuit, *n.* A circuit which provides accurately timed pulses of uniform length which can be used to control and synchronize other circuits.

close coupling. See "coupling, close."

closed core. See "core, closed."

closure, buried ready-access, *n.* A device which provides ready access to buried cable conductors which are brought up a riser pipe to a stainless-steel capped splicing chamber in a concrete tile handhole.

closure, cable, *n.* Any of the several types of housings that can be fastened around a cable splice to make it watertight without making a wiped joint with a lead sleeve.

closure, ready access, *n.* A cover for enclosing splices in non-pressurized plastic insulated cables. It consists of a pair of polyethylene end plates with cable nozzles, a steel frame to which 6-pair wire terminal blocks or loading coils can be bolted, and a polyethylene cover of "U" cross-section which is lowered over the whole to make it weathertight, but not gas-tight.

closure, splice, *n.* A housing of moulded insulating material used for closing splices in polyethylene insulated aerial cables. Housing is held closed by clamps or clips, and suspended from the strand on brackets.

closure, terminal, *n.* A splice case having an 11-pair or 16-pair terminal on one of the splice case halves.

closure, vault cable, *n.* A large hard plastic cylindrical sleeve fitted with two moulded end caps, one with a single nozzle for the main entrance cable, the other with multiple nozzles for the several stub cables. Used in cable vaults to cover the splice between the entrance cable and the main distributing frame stub cables.

cloth, catch, *n.* A cloth, about 8x10 inches, of several layers of cotton ticking, in which a cable splicer catches the molten solder as he pours it on the joint he is wiping. The hot solder held to the bottom of the joint helps to bring it up to wiping temperature.

cloth, wiping, *n.* A heavy curved cloth pad of cotton ticking. Used to mould and form the wiping solder when making wiped joints in lead-sheathed cables.

CLR card. See "card, circuit layout record."

CLR trunk. See "recording-completing trunk."

coat, splice, *n.* (1) A ready-access closure. (2) A split plastic case which can be clamped over splices or terminal blocks in plastic-sheathed aerial cable to provide a weathertight cover.

coaxial, *adj.* Having a common axis. —*n.* A coaxial cable.

coaxial cable, *n.* A cable having several coaxial lines under a single protective sheath.

coaxial line, *n.* A transmission line consisting of a central wire or tube completely surrounded by an outer tubular conductor. The two conductors have a common axis, and are separated by a solid dielectric or by dielectric spacers, sometimes augmented by an insulating gas. A coaxial line has no external field, and is not disturbed by external fields.

cob, insulator, *n.* The wooden or plastic bushing which covers the end of a steel insulator pin, and is threaded to take a glass or porcelain pin insulator.

CODAN, *n.* Carrier operated device, anti-noise. A device which silences a radio receiver except when a modulated carrier signal is received.

code, *n.* A system of signals for communication.

code, access, *n.* The preliminary digit or digits that a user must dial to be connected to a particular outgoing trunk group. For instance, PAX users dial "9" to be connected to a "city" trunk.

code, accounting, *n.* Any of the numerical codes which the Federal Communications Commission uses to identify plant accounts. For instance:

Code	Type of Plant
211	Land
212	Buildings
221	Central Office

Code	Type of Plant
231	Station equipment
232	Station connections
241	Pole line
242	Cable
243	Aerial wire
244	Underground conduit
261	Office equipment
264	Vehicles & work equipment

code, American Morse. See "code, Morse."

code, area, *n.* A unique 3-digit code which presently (1971) has either a "1" or a "0" as the middle digit. When the area code is prefixed to a 7-digit telephone number it forms a unique telephone address which is not duplicated anywhere within the United States and Canada. These 152 area codes are almost all used, and it will soon be necessary to use the 63 NNO codes. When those are used, the area code will become an NXX code, with almost 800 possible codes.

code, ARQ, *n.* A seven-unit code for synchronous teletypewriter use which provides a parity check and "automatic repeat request" (ARQ) for each character.

code, ASCII, *n.* American Standard Code for Information Interchange. An 8-bit code (one bit is for parity check) which gives 128 combinations. Used for both synchronous and non-synchronous teletypewriter and data transmission. Developed by the American Standards Association.

code, barrier. See "barrier code."

code, Baudot, *n.* The 7.42 unit, five information bit code used for asynchronous (start-stop) teletypewriter transmission. Named for Emile Baudot (1845-1903), the French electrician who invented the printing telegraph. See also "code, ITA #2."

code, BCD, *n.* An 8-bit code (of which one bit is used for odd parity check) used by IBM. Provides 88 characters, plus 16 functions.

code, BCH. See "BCH code."

code, binary coded decimal (BCD), *n.* A compression of the Hollerith code in which two binary bits replace the three zone bits and four binary bits replace the nine data bits. Used as an internal code within data processing equipment.

code, cable color, *n.* Cables having ten or more conductors or pairs sometimes use a color code consisting of the following colors: black, brown, red, orange, yellow, green, blue, violet, gray, and white, repeated as required.

code, central office, *n.* Any of the 792 NNX codes which can be used as an address for a 10,000-line unit of central office. Eight N11 codes of the 800 NNX codes are reserved for service codes.

code, Codel, *n.* A coding system for storing digital information on four or five relays, from which it is available on a parallel basis within the same central office. The five-relay system uses the "two-out-of-five" code. The four-relay system uses relays designated "W," "X," "Y," and "Z," operated as follows:

$$
\begin{array}{ll}
1 - W+X & 6 - Y+Z \\
2 - W+Y & 7 - W \\
3 - W+Z & 8 - X \\
4 - X+Y & 9 - Y \\
5 - X+Z & 0 - Z
\end{array}
$$

code, color, *n.* (1) A system of colors applied to the insulation of cable conductors to permit their easy identification. The traditional color code is based on repetitive use of the five colors blue, orange, green, brown, slate. (2) A code specified by the EIA to identify the electrical value and accuracy of a resistor or capacitor.

code, constant ratio data, *n.* A data transmission code in which the number of zeros (spaces) and ones (marks) in a binary code word is fixed. A "code word" being a group of bits that represents a single alphanumeric character. The 3-out-of-7 ARQ code and the IBM 4-out-of-8 Data Transceiver Code are both constant ratio codes. Constant ratio codes can be used only for error detection, and therefore depend upon repeated transmission to obtain correction.

code, data interchange, *n.* A variant of the ASCII code in which some printing characters are replaced by non-printing control characters, and the parity is specified to be odd.

code, destination, *n.* The complete 10-digit number which constitutes a telephone address, comprised of a 3-digit area code plus a 3-digit office code plus a 4-digit station number.

code, directing, *n.* Extra digits, such as "11," "0X," or "X1X," ahead of the directory number of the called station to enable a customer or operator to dial outside of the normal numbering area.

code, extended binary coded decimal interchange (EBCDIC), *n.* An extension of the BCD code to eight binary bits, giving it the capability to handle control character codes.

code, field accounting, *n.* Any of the several numerical codes which linemen, cable splicers, and installers use in reporting the units of plant which they install. These codes vary from company to company. Here is one sample:

Code	Type of Plant
1	Pole lines
2	Aerial cable
3	Underground cable
4	Buried cable
6	Aerial wire
7	Underground conduit
8	Stations
9	Drop wire

code, Fieldata, *n.* A data code developed for use with military field data sets. It uses 8 bits per character, of which the eighth is a parity bit and the seventh is a control bit. There are two varieties of the Fieldata code. The standard form uses odd parity, while the paper-tape form uses even parity.

code, five-unit start-stop teletypewriter, *n.* Any of the several applications

of the International Telegraph Alphabet #2 to printing telegraph operation.

Pulses per character	WPM	Baud	Millisec/ Character	Where Used
7.42 unit	61.3	45.5	163	Bell System
7.00 unit	65.0	45.5	154	Western Union
7.50 unit	66.7	50	150	CCITT-Europe
7.42 unit	76.7	56.9	130.4	All U.S.
7.42 unit	100.	74.2	100.	All U.S.

code, four-out-of-eight, *n.* A fixed ratio data code in which four bits are always "ones" and the other four bits are always "zeros." Provides good accuracy and easy error detection.

code, geometric parity check, *n.* Any of the error control codes for data transmission which depend upon both horizontal and vertical parity checks on the code word arranged into a rectangular matrix called a block.

code, Golay, *n.* An error-correcting code for data transmission which consists of 12 information bits plus 11 redundant bits. It is the most economical code capable of correcting all patterns of three or fewer errors.

code, Gray, *n.* A code particularly suited to transmit digital information concerning angular position obtained from a coded commutator.

code, Hollerith, *n.* The system which assigns a meaning to the various arrangements of punched holes on an 80-column data card. See also "Hollerith code."

code, instruction, *n.* An artificial language for expressing instructions to be carried out by a switching system.

code, International Morse, *n.* A system of coded signals consisting of dots and dashes, each representing a particular letter, numeral, or mark. Used for manual radio telegraph communication.

code, ITA #2, *n.* International Telegraph Alphabet No. 2. The standard code for start-stop teletypewriter operation, commonly known as the

Baudot code. It consists of a one-unit open start pulse, five one-unit information bits, and a 1.42-unit closed stop pulse. It has both a letters shift and a figures shift, and provides 28 characters with each. There are several versions, among them "communications" and "weather."

code, Moore. See "code, ARQ."

code, Morse, *n.* A system of coded signals consisting of dots, dashes, and intra-symbol spaces. Each symbol represents a particular letter, numeral, or mark. Used for manual transmission of messages over circuits terminated in keys and Morse sounders.

code, multiple address, *n.* A code which specifies the addressees of a multiple-address message.

Code, National Electrical (NEC). See "National Electrical Code."

Code, National Electrical Safety (NESC). See "National Electrical Safety Code."

code, NNO, *n.* A three-digit switching code, of which the first two digits may be any number from 2 to 9 and the last digit is zero. Ultimately to be used as central office codes, but temporarily used as numbering plan area (NPA) codes.

code, NNX, *n.* A central office code, the code which identifies one particular 10,000-line unit of subscribers' lines. "N" is any number from 2 to 9, and "X" is any number from 0 to 9.

code, NXX, *n.* Any of the 800 theoretically possible numbering plan area codes. Assigned after all NO/1X and NNO codes are exhausted.

code, NO/1X, *n.* Any of the 160 earliest numbering plan area codes, in which the second digit is either zero or one.

code, plant accounting, *n.* A one or two digit number suffixed by the letters C, X, R or M, used in reporting labor, material, or other components of costs incurred in the construction, maintenance, opera-

tion, and removal of telephone outside plant. The letter C indicates construction, X indicates removals, R repairs and maintenance, and M rearrangements and changes. When work is done on toll plant, the letter suffix is preceded by the letter T.

code, redundant, *n.* A code which uses more signal elements than are necessary to represent the intrinsic information.

code, regional identity, *n.* A one, two, or three digit code which will be used to specify the country or region for international dialing of calls. The CCITT assignments are as follows:

1 —North America, including Hawaii and the Caribbean Islands
2 —Africa
3&4—Europe
5 —South America, Cuba
6 —South Pacific (Australasia)
7 —USSR
8 —North Pacific (Eastern Asia)
9 —Far East and Middle East
0 —Spare

code, ringing, *n.* A sequence of long and short rings used to signal a particular party on a party telephone line.

code, route, *n.* A two-digit code which precedes the ten-digit telephone number when it is necessary to specify a special grade of circuit, as for data calls.

code, simple parity check, *n.* A code of any length, composed of "n" information bits plus one parity bit. The parity bit is selected so as to make the total number of "ones" in the code word either always odd or always even. It will detect all odd-numbered error occurrences.

code, switching center. See "code, central office."

code, telegraph, *n.* A system of coded signals corresponding to the letters, numerals, and marks used in telecommunication. See also: "code, Morse," and "code, International."

code, teletypewriter, *n.* A system of five marks and/or spaces sent serially, each combination representing a particular letter, numeral, or mark. See also "code, Baudot" and "code, ITA #2."

code, terminating toll center, *n.* A distinctive 3-digit code used by outward operators or testmen in distant cities to reach inward, information, delayed call operators or test lines at a terminating toll center. The first digit of a TTC code is always a zero or one.

code, ternary, *n.* A code in which any code element may have any of three values.

code, toll authorization, *n.* By dialing a special unlisted code, a subscriber may prevent toll calls being placed from his telephone, until he removes the restriction by dialing an "unlatch" code.

code, toll center. See "code, terminating toll center."

code, two-out-of-five, *n.* Code used for parallel transmission of digital information, or for the storing of digits on five memory units such as magnetic cores or codelreeds. Each of the five bits of information is assigned a numerical value, such as 0-1-2-4-7. Each pair of bits can then represent a particular digit, as follows:

Code	Digit
0-1	1
0-2	2
1-2	3
0-4	4
1-4	5
2-4	6
0-7	7
1-7	8
2-7	9
4-7	0

code, UNIVAC, *n.* An 8-bit code used by Sperry-Rand for high-speed printers. Provides 63 permutations.

code call, *n.* A system whereby dialing 3 digits (from 1 to 5) will register the code dialed on a rotary switch which then repeats it to a group of chimes or horns. The person called may go to any phone and dial an answer code to talk to the calling party.

code conversion, *n.* The capability of a sender in a switching system to both delete digits and prefix digits as required. Also called "code substitution."

code converter. See "converter, code."

code number, *n.* A number or combination of numbers used to reach certain positions or desks, or for some other special purpose. See also "directing code."

coded ringing, *n.* A system of selectively calling subscribers on a multiparty line by distinctive combinations of long and short rings.

coded speech, *n.* Speech that has been converted into a multi-level digital signal.

code element, *n.* One of the discrete conditions or events in a code, such as the presence or absence of a pulse.

code group, *n.* A combination of several letters used to represent one or several words of plain text in a commercial telegram.

codelreed, *n.* A relay-type digital storage unit used in translators. It consists of a reedcapsule biased with a permanent magnet, inserted into a bobbin having a "set" and a "reset" winding. A momentary pulse on the set winding operates the relay contacts, which are then held operated by the permanent magnet. To restore the codelreed, a momentary pulse is sent through the reset winding.

code 911, *n.* An industry universal emergency code which can be dialed from any phone (even a paystation) without charge to report any kind of emergency.

codes, error control, *n. pl.* Any of the many types of codes which can be used for the detection and correction of errors in data transmission. Several important types are:
a. Constant ratio codes.
b. Simple parity check codes.
c. Geometric parity check codes.
d. BCH codes.

codes, hotel service, *n.* The initial digit dialed on a hotel PABX extension which directs the call to the proper service:

"0" — Hotel operator
"9" — City trunk
"8" — Long-distance operator
"7-2" — Room-to-room calling
"1" — Message Waiting Desk

codes, operator, *n. pl.* Codes used for reaching auxiliary service operators, as follows:

11NX — Leave word
118 — Toll station
141 — Route
131 — Information
121 — Inward

codes, toll center operator, *n. pl.* When a toll center operator is to be accessed over an intertoll trunk, one of the following codes may be suffixed to the toll center code.

Inward, or toll DSA   + 121
Information operator   + 131
Route operator   + 141
Toll station operator   + 181
Leave word operator   + 11X

codes, toll center operator (dial), *n. pl.* When a toll center operator must be reached over an intertoll trunk, one of the following codes is dialed.

Universal operator   — 1150
Conference operator   — 1151
Mobile operator   — 1152
Marine operator   — 1153
Toll terminal operator — 1154

coding, duobinary, *n.* A signal design technique that codes and shapes binary data signals into a special waveform, characterized by three voltage levels. This process results in a two-to-one bandwidth compression, thus providing twice the data capacity for a given bandwidth. Duobinary coding also permits the detection of errors without the addition of error-checking bits to characters.

coefficient, coupling, *n.* A decimal number between zero and one which represents the degree of coupling between two circuits.

coefficient, greatest overall, *n.* The sum of the transmission coefficients of all links and equipments of an end-to-end telegraph circuit.

coefficient, reflection, *n.* A number, less than one, which is the ratio between the amplitude of the reflected wave and the amplitude of the incident wave. In terms of the two mismatched impedances, it is equal to the difference of the two impedances divided by their sum.

coefficient, telegraph transmission, *n.* A figure which represents the transmission degradation contributed by a particular link in a telegraph system. The sum of the coefficients, which is not permitted to exceed 10, indicates the overall performance. Coefficients are derived on the basis of the distortion contributed, as follows:

Coefficient	% Distortion	One Character in Error Per
1	4.9	100 Billion +
2	7.5	100 Billion +
3	9.6	100 Billion +
3.5	10.5	100 Billion +
4	11.2	100 Billion
5	12.8	800 Million
6	14.0	25 Million
6.5	14.8	8 Million
7	15.2	2,500,000.
8	16.2	500,000.
9	17.2	150,000.
10	18.0	44,000.

coefficient, temperature, *n.* A decimal fraction which expresses how much some property of a material, such as expansion or resistance, will change for each one degree Centigrade change in temperature.

coefficient, traffic, *n.* The amount of operator work time required to process an average call of a particular class, specified in "units" of 15.65 seconds each. A call which takes 63 seconds of operator time has a coefficient of $(63/15.65 =)$ 4.0.

coefficient, transmission, *n.* A number indicating the probable performance of a transmission circuit. The numerical value of the transmission equivalent is inversely related to the transmission quality of the circuit.

coefficient of expansion, *n*. The change in length of a body, per unit of length, for a change of one degree in temperature.

coefficient of resistance. See "resistivity, temperature coefficient of."

coercive force, *n*. The value of magnetomotive force required to reduce residual magnetic flux to zero.

coherent light. See "light, coherent."

coherent pulse, *adj*. Describing pulse transmission in which a fixed phase relationship is maintained from one pulse to the next.

coil, *n*. One or more turns of wire, in a cylindrical or doughnut shape, used to create a magnetic flux or to add inductance to a circuit.

coil, antisidetone induction, *n*. An induction coil having balanced windings and a compromise balancing network for use in an antisidetone telephone set.

coil, choke. See "choke" and "coil, retardation."

coil, drainage, *n*. A high-impedance retardation coil connected across a circuit, with its center-tap connected to ground. Used to drain static electric charges to ground.

coil, dummy heat, *n*. Small brass rod used to replace a heat coil when over-current protection is not required.

coil, exploring, *n*. Large diameter (2-3 ft.) coil of wire, usually without a magnetic core, used with a head receiver or other indicator for locating underground cables, etc., by the current which they induce in the exploring coil.

coil, heat, *n*. A protective device used in series with the line at a main distributing frame, which operates to open and ground the line if excess current flows. Consists of a small coil of resistance wire around a grounding pin held unoperated by easily-fusible solder. Normal type has a resistance of 3.45 ohms, will carry 350 milliamps for 3 hours, or

operate in 210 seconds on 540 milliamps. See also "heat coil, indicating" and "heat coil fuse."

coil, hybrid, *n*. A four-winding transformer used at the junction between a 2-wire and a 4-wire circuit. Effectively separates the transmit and receive paths.

coil, induction, *n*. Small transformer used in telephones or operator's telephone circuits to perform three functions: (1) Transforms the varying direct current in the transmitter circuit to voice frequency AC on the line. (2) Matches the impedance of the transmitter and receiver to that of the line, and (3) reduces the sidetone.

coil, lattice-wound. See "honeycomb coil."

coil, loading, *n*. Balanced coils of wire around a highly permeable magnetic core, constituting an inductance which can be inserted in series with a cable circuit at regular intervals to improve transmission. See also: "spacing, load coil."

coil, phantom, *n*. (1) A repeating coil used to match the terminal (drop) impedance to the lower phantom circuit impedance. (2) One of the pair of coils used to derive a phantom circuit.

coil, repeating, *n*. The telephone industry's term for a voice-frequency transformer. A small voice-frequency transformer characterized by (a) a closed core, (b) a pair of identical balanced primary (line) windings, (c) a pair of identical but not necessarily balanced secondary (drop) windings, and (d) low transmission loss at voice frequencies. Permits (a) transfer of voice currents from one winding to another by magnetic induction, (b) the matching of line and drop impedances, and (c) the longitudinal isolation of the line from the drop.

coil, retard, *n*. A retardation coil.

coil, retardation, *n*. A coil having a large inductance which retards sudden changes of the current flowing through its winding. Also called a "retard coil."

coil, shading, *n.* A heavy copper one-turn coil placed around a portion of the pole pieces of an induction motor that produces a rotating field to start the motor.

coil, side circuit, *n.* One of a pair of repeating coils used on each of two pairs of wires to derive a phantom circuit.

coil, simplex, *n.* A repeating coil used on a pair of wires to derive a simplex circuit.

coil, toroidal. See "toroidal coil."

coil, voice. See "voice coil."

coil-loaded, *adj.* Describing a cable or transmission line which has inductance in the form of coils inserted at intervals along the pair or line to reduce attenuation losses.

coil loading, *n.* The use of series inductance (loading coils) at regular intervals in a cable communication circuit to improve its transmission characteristics. See "loading."

coin box, *n.* A sealed metal box within a locked compartment in a coin telephone, into which coins drop when they are collected.

coinbox telephone. See "coin telephone."

coin chute. See "chute, coin."

coincidence circuit, *n.* A circuit consisting of several gates in parallel, from which an output signal is produced only when all inputs are present simultaneously.

coincident transmission. See "transmission, parallel."

coin collector, *n.* (1) A coin telephone. (2) A person who makes the rounds of coin telephones and replaces the full coin box with an empty one.

coin control, *adj.* Describing the keys and equipment by which an operator controls the collecting and refunding of coins at coin telephones.

coin-free services, *n.pl.* Any of the service codes or operators which, when accessed from a coin tele-

phone, will automatically return any coins which were deposited.

Emergency number	911
Assistance	0
Fire	117
Repair Service	114
Information	113
NPA Information	1+555-1212
Zone call	1+7 digits
Toll call	1+10 digits
INWATS	1+10 digits

coin pilot lamp, *n.* A lamp signal mounted in the piling rail at each position equipped with coin control keys which should light when a collect or return key is operated on the position.

coin relay. See "relay, coin."

coin service, *n.* A public, semipublic, or customer class of telephone service which uses a coin-collecting device as a part of the station equipment.

coin signals. See "tones, coin denomination."

coin supervisory circuit, *n.* Relay group connected to a trunk that is serving a coin call. Provides coin collect battery at the end of a completed charged call, or coin refund battery if the call is not completed or if it is one for which no charge is made. (#5 X-Bar)

coin telephone, *n.* A public telephone with a coin-collector which accepts coins (5-10-25¢) for the payment of call charges.

coin test. See "test, coin."

coin timing circuit, *n.* Equipment provided on some coin box trunks which automatically times customer dialed calls from coin telephones, and signals the operator when the initial period has expired.

cold cathode. See "cathode, cold."

cold flow, *n.* The permanent deformation or elongation of a material by a mechanical force, without the aid of softening by heat.

cold joint, *n.* A soldered connection which was inadequately heated, with the result that the wire is held in place by rosin flux, not solder.

cold work, *n.* The repeated flexing or rolling of a metal without annealing it after the work. Cold working makes a metal brittle and hard.

collar, manhole, *n.* A short manhole chimney, only 2-3 bricks high, used to allow a small change in street grade without disturbing the manhole.

collar, relay. See "slug."

collator, *n.* A punched card processing machine which will take two decks of punched cards and combine them into a single deck, all in sequence with respect to one item of data on the cards.

collect, *v.t.* At a prepay telephone, the transferring by an operator of the coin deposit from the holding tray to the coin cash box.

collect call, *n.* A type of toll telephone call in which the calling party asks that the charges be billed to the called party, whose permission must then be secured in advance of completing the call.

collect key, *n.* The key which an operator depresses to collect the deposit at a coin telephone.

collector, *n.* The terminal of a transistor device which corresponds to the plate, or anode, in an electron tube.

collector, coin. See "telephone, coin" and "paystation."

collector ring, *n.* A slip ring, which see.

collocated, *adj.* (1) In the same building, or (2) separated by not more than 25 ohms of cable.

color, *n.* A characteristic of light which can be specified by describing its hue (dominant wavelength), luminance (its amplitude), and chroma (its purity or saturation).

color burst, *n.* In a color television signal, a short burst of unmodulated color subcarrier which is transmitted during the blanking pulse for each scan line. Intended to synchronize the color receiver subcarrier oscillator with that of the television broadcast station.

color code, *n.* In all types of switchboard cable, the outer insulation on the conductors is colored in accordance with a pattern so that each conductor can be identified. This pattern makes use of the "blue, orange, green, brown, slate" sequence for wire colors paired with white, red, black, red-white, black-white and red-black mates.

color code, protector. See "protector color code."

color signal. See "signal, color picture."

column, card, *n.* Any of the 80 columns of a data card into which data is entered by means of punched holes.

column, crossbar, *n.* An equipment group of 100 lines, 10 each on the 10 primary switches located in a vertical row on a line link frame.

combination switch, *n.* An automatic switch which can perform two functions using two different circuits, depending on which of two circuits it is accessed. For instance, a combined toll and local connector.

combined distributing frame (CDF), *n.* A frame consisting of both main distributing frame and intermediate distributing frame elements installed as a continuous unit.

combined switch train, *n.* A group of automatic switches arranged to handle both toll and local traffic with the same switches.

combined toll DSA board, *n.* A switchboard at which the functions of both an outward toll switchboard and a DSA switchboard are performed.

combiner, *n.* Device which combines the outputs of two or more diversity receivers to produce one reliable output, free from fading. See also "combiner, linear," "combiner, switching," and "combiner, ratio-squared."

combiner, channel, *n.* A device which will accept several or many radio frequency signals and combine them for delivery to a CATV network, while providing isolation between inputs. Several signals could be combined with a passive hybrid device; many signals would require an active device similar to a "multi-coupler," which see.

combiner, diversity, *n.* A device which will combine two identical signals received over diverse routes so as to yield a maximum of 3 db improvement in signal-to-noise ratio than from either signal alone. Used to obtain a usable signal even in the presence of selective fading on a radio transmission path.

combiner, linear, *n.* A diversity combiner which simply adds the two receiver outputs together.

combining, post-detection, *n.* The combining of two diversity signals at either baseband or channel frequency.

combiner, ratio-squared, *n.* A diversity combiner which adds the two receiver signals together in proportion to their freedom from noise.

combiner, switching, *n.* A diversity combiner which monitors the signal from both receivers, senses the noise or pilot tone or both, and selects the better signal of the two. The switching can introduce errors and transients.

combining, pre-detection, *n.* The combining of two diversity signals at an intermediate (IF) frequency.

combining, optimal switching, *n.* A technique of diversity combining in which an automatic switching device continually monitors the pilots and noise levels from both diversity receivers, determines which signal is best, then connects that receiver to the baseband circuit.

come along, *Colloquial.* See "puller, strand."

Command Communications Service Designator (CCSD). See "CCSD."

command conference system. See "system, command conference."

common-base, *adj.* Describing a transistor connection which gives the following circuit properties:

Voltage gain	— 100 to 200
Current gain	— Less than 1
Power gain	— Medium
Input impedance	— Extremely low
Output impedance	— Extremely high
Phase change, input to output	— Zero

common battery, *n.* A battery (commonly 48 volts) which serves as a central source of electrical energy for many similar circuits.—*adj.* Describing equipment which is designated to be powered from a central "common" battery.

common-battery signaling. See "signaling, common-battery."

common battery system, *n.* System in which all talking battery for telephone stations is supplied from the serving central office.

common-channel interoffice signaling (CCIS), *n.* A method of transmitting all signaling information for a group of trunks by encoding it and transmitting it over a separate voice channel using time-division digital techniques.

common-collector, *adj.* Describing a transistor connection which gives the following circuit properties:

Voltage gain	— Less than 1
Current gain	— 20 to 100
Power gain	— Low
Input impedance	— Extremely high
Output impedance	— Extremely low
Phase change, input to output	— Zero

common-control, *adj.* Describes an automatic telephone system in which the dial pulses from the calling telephone (which constitute the address of the called phone) are registered, analyzed, and re-sent in the form of a routing code to operate switches as required to establish the desired connection.

common-control equipment, *n,* Equipment which controls the setting up of connections through the talking path equipment. It consists of:

    a. Registers.
    b. Markers or translators.
    c. Senders.
    d. Coin control, message register, or AMA equipment.
    e. Equipment to provide temporary connections via connectors or links.

common control office, *n.* A central office which receives dial pulses or DTMF signals from calling stations, or dial pulses, MF signals, or revertive pulses from other offices. It stores the digits (except in calls terminating in step-by-step or panel offices, determines the routing, and routes it accordingly. Common control offices are of the following types:

    a. Common control step-by-step
    b. Panel (obsolescent)
    c. Crossbar
    d. Electronic

common-emitter, *adj.* Describing a transistor connection which gives the following circuit properties:

Voltage gain	— 300 to 600
Current gain	— 20 to 100
Power gain	— High
Input impedance	— Low
Output impedance	— Medium
Phase change, input to output	— 180 degrees

common equipment, *n.* Any equipment which is used in some manner by a number of channels or equipments. Common equipments are usually provided in duplicate for greater reliability.

common-mode, *adj.* Describes a method of operating central office equipment so that long line adapters and voice-frequency repeaters are shared by a number of long subscriber loops, thus reducing the cost per loop.

common-mode operation, *n.* The sharing of certain equipment, such as long line adapters and voice-frequency repeaters, among a number of subscribers' lines by placing the common equipment within the switching system instead of associating one unit of equipment with each line.

common return, *n.* A return conductor that serves two or more circuits in returning a current to its source or to ground.

common strap, *n.* A continuous piece of wire which connects a terminal of one circuit to like terminals on adjacent circuits, for the purpose of supplying battery or ground or to serve as a common wire for listening, ringing, etc.

common-user service, *n.* A communication service in which circuits are allocated to switching centers for use in completing all offered traffic. The opposite of dedicated service.

commons, *n.pl.* A group of leads that have appearances or access points at a number of similar equipments.

common-user circuit, *n.* A circuit allocated to furnish communication to a number of users, who access it through a switching facility.

common wire, *n.* Any wire supplying battery, ground, ringing, or tone to several components in the same circuit or to a number of adjacent circuits.

communication, *adj.* Pertaining to communication.—*n.* (1) A transmitting and/or receiving of information, signals, or messages. (2) The information thus received.

communication, wire. See "wire communication."

communication center, *n.* Also "comm center." A unit where teletypewriter messages are placed on circuits for transmission to other centers, or are removed from circuits after reception from other centers.

communications, *n.pl.* (1) The aggregate of several modes of communication used to convey information, signals, or messages. (2) The art and science of communicating, as a study. (Note: COMMUNICATIONS is a plural noun, never an adjective. The adjective form does NOT have the terminal "s.")

communications, record. See "record communications."

Communications Satellite Corporation (COMSAT), *n.* A common carrier company, created in 1962 and jointly owned by a group of large communication companies, which provides communication service via satellite. It owns 53% of the International Telecommunications Satellite Consortium, and is its manager.

Communications Service Authorization (CSA). See "CSA."

community antenna relay service (CARS), *n.* A service authorized by the Federal Communications Commission to relay TV programs to CATV systems. The band from 12700 to 12950 megahertz is allocated.

community antenna television (CATV), *n.* A service, sometimes by telephone common-carriers, which for a fee distributes television programs via cable into poor reception areas. Signals are picked up at a suitable location, all usable channels are amplified, and the signals are fed by coaxial distribution cables to the homes of those who subscribe to the service.

community automatic exchange (CAX), *n.* A small automatic telephone office designed to serve a small community. Usually unattended.

community dial office (CDO), *n.* A small automatic central office, located and sized to serve a small community. Usually unattended, and often having trunks to only one other office. Operator services are provided from a nearby attended office, called an "operator office."

community-of-interest, *n.* A grouping of telephone users who generate most of their traffic in calls to each other.

commutation, *n.* (1) The act of transferring an output circuit from one input to another at a time when the current is zero. (2) The act of the generator output brushes in transferring from one armature coil when the current has dropped to zero to the next coil before its current starts to build up. (3) The transfer of current from one anode to another in a gas tube.

commutator, *n.* A cylindrical or circular assembly of electrical contacts, insulated from each other, which make contacts with fixed current-collecting brushes as the commutator rotates.

companding, instantaneous, *n.* A process which reduces quantizing noise on pulse code modulated signals by passing the analog signals through a compressor before quantizing. At the receiver the reverse process must be applied, with expansion following the decoding operation.

companding, syllabic, *n.* The action of a compandor which is just fast enough to correct the level of individual syllables of speech.

compandor, *n.* Acronym for "compressor-expandor." A device used at the two ends of a 4-wire circuit. The transmitting terminal compresses the volume range offered from the talkers. At the receiving terminal, an expandor restores the original volume range. Permits the transmission of signals at a higher average level, thus improving the signal-to-noise ratio.

comparator, *n.* A device which compares two different signals and provides an output when they differ in frequency, phase, or power level.

compensation, *n.* Correction of a sloping loss-frequency characteristic of the transmission facility by an inverse characteristic of an amplifier or other connected equipment. See also "equalizer."

compensation, earth potential, *n.* Polar duplex signaling sets use a path via earth or "ground." When the earth has a widely different potential at the two terminals of the circuit this requires compensation by: (1) adjusting the balancing winding of the polar relay to provide exact balance for a particular ground potential (requires frequent readjustment), or (2) connecting the balancing windings of the polar relays at the two ends of the circuit in series over an interoffice earth potential compensation lead. (This arrangement is self-adjusting.)

compensation, high-frequency, *n.* In a wideband amplifier, the addition of a small inductance in series with the load resistor, in order to extend the high frequency response of the amplifier.

compensation, low-frequency, *n.* On a wideband amplifier, a parallel R-C network in series with the load resistor which serves to extend amplifier response to lower frequencies.

compensation, temperature. See "temperature compensation."

Compensation Theorem. See "Appendix B."

compensator, impedance, *n.* A resistance-inductance network bridged on a loaded trunk at the central office to improve the return loss at the higher frequencies. It makes the impedance of the cable pair more uniform and predominantly resistive from 1000 cycles up to 85% of its cutoff frequency.

complement, cable, *n.* A group of pairs in a cable which have some characteristic in common. They may all terminate at the same location, or all have the same type of loading, etc.

completed call, *n.* Call on which the service desired has been furnished. Loosely, any call on which conversation has satisfactorily started.

complex wave, *n.* A waveform which varies from instant to instant, but can be resolved into a number of sine wave components each of a different frequency and probably of a different amplitude.

compliance, *n.* The reciprocal of stiffness. In a mechanical vibrating system compliance acts in the same way capacitance does in an electrical oscillating system. An important property of telephone receiver diaphragms. Measured in centimeters of displacement per dyne of force.

component, circuit, *n.* An element of a circuit, such as a resistor, capacitor, coil, transformer, or transistor.

component, reactive, *n.* That part of impedance which is due solely to reactance, either capacitive or inductive.

component, resistive, *n.* That part of impedance which is due solely to resistance.

composite, *adj.* Designating components of a composite circuit.—*n.* Method of deriving two grounded direct-current telegraph circuits from a single telephone circuit, all three circuits being mutually independent.

composite cable. See "cable, composite."

composite circuit, *n.* A DC signaling path on one side of a talking circuit, derived by connecting the composite circuit through a low-pass filter and the talking circuit through a high-pass filter. Each pair can provide two composite circuits.

composite set, Type C, *n.* Set of filters used for composite signaling on cable or open wire. Can be used either at intermediate or terminal points.

composite set, Type D, *n.* A set of filters used for composite signaling on cable or open wire, but only at terminal points. Not for distance dialing. Similar to Type C, but less versatile and less expensive.

composite set, Type E, *n.* A set of filters used for composite signaling on cable circuits only. May be used either at intermediate or terminal points. Not as versatile or expensive as Type C.

composite signaling. See "signaling, composite."

composite signaling equipment—long haul, *n.* Equipment which may be used to derive composite channels from circuits up to 12,000 ohms resistance.

composite signaling equipment—short haul, *n.* Equipment which may be used to derive composite channels on cable circuits of 4,800 ohms resistance, or 90-100 miles of copper open wire.

compound, *n.* An insulating or jacketing material made by mixing two or more ingredients.—*v.* To mix together two or more ingredients to make one material.

compression, *n.* The act of reducing the volume range of an electrical signal, usually of an audio frequency signal.

compressor, *n.* (1) Electrical device which reduces the volume range of a signal. (2) The compression portion of a "compandor."

compromise network. See "network, compromise."

computer, *n.* An electrical device which can accept information, process it mathematically in accordance with previous instructions, and provide the results of this processing.

computer, analog, *n.* A computer which uses an electrical analog value for each continuous variable input, and produces an analog output.

computer, charge. See "charge computer."

computer, digital, *n.* A computer that processes information represented by discrete or discontinuous data.

COMSAT. See "Communications Satellite Corporation."

comsec. See "security, communication."

concentrating switch. See "out-trunk switch."

concentration jack circuit, telegraph, *n.* Jack circuit on a telegraph service position which is used to interconnect (concentrate) the group of lines and loops which work together. Each concentration jack circuit includes a test jack per line or loop leg and a common hub jack.

concentrator, *n.* A switching system arranged to connect a large number of inputs to a smaller number of outputs.

concentrator, line, *n.* Two similar units of equipment, one in the central office the other usually pole-mounted near a remote group of subscribers to be served. A group of subscriber lines (usually 49) is connected and supervised over a small number of trunks and control lines (typically 13) from the field unit back to the central office.

concentrator, station line, *n.* An all-relay concentrator used to reduce the number of cable pairs required between multi-key telephone sets and the key telephone system line circuit units.

concentrator, telegraph, *n.* A switching arrangement by means of which a number of subscriber lines or station sets may be connected to a lesser number of trunk lines or operating positions through the medium of automatic switching devices in order to obtain more efficient use of facilities.

concentrator, WECo 1A line, *n.* A crossbar switching device used to reduce the number of cable pairs required to serve remote locations. Can serve 98 remote lines and 2 test lines over 20 trunks plus 2 control pairs. Requires two units: one in the central office and the other at the remote location.

concentrator-identifier, *n.* Equipment which concentrates calls from many lines onto a few trunks and furnishes line number identification over the trunk or a separate data link. Used to concentrate central office lines for answering at a "telephone answering service" switchboard.

concentricity, *n.* In a wire or cable, the degree to which the conductor is in the exact center of the insulation which surrounds it.

concentric-lay, *adj.* Describing a cable

in which the pairs (or quads) are arranged in concentric layers. The layers alternate between a left-hand spiral and a right-hand spiral.

concentric line. See "coaxial line."

condenser, *n.* Outmoded term for capacitor.

condition, *v.t.* To add or adjust circuit equipment so as to bring circuit losses, levels, distortion, or impedances within established standards.

conditioning, *n.* Equipment modifications or adjustments necessary to match transmission levels and impedances and to equalize transmission and delay.

conditioning, circuit, *n.* Actions taken and/or equipments provided to correct circuit non-linearities, levels, or impedances to established standards.

conditioning, schedule D1 (DCS), *n.* Conditioning which will provide a circuit suitable for 2400 baud data transmission.

conditioning, schedule D2 (DCS), *n.* Conditioning which will provide a circuit suitable for data transmission at 300-1200 baud.

conditioning, schedule N2 (DCS), *n.* Conditioning which will provide a circuit suitable for 75-100 wpm teletypewriter, or 47-75 baud data transmission.

conditioning, schedule N3 (DCS), *n.* Conditioning which provides a circuit suitable for 150 wpm teletypewriter, or 76-150 baud data transmission.

conditioning, schedule S1 (DCS), *n.* Conditioning which provides a circuit having a regenerative repeater on both ends, and suitable for narrow-band secure voice or 2400 baud data.

conditioning, schedule S2 (DCS), *n.* Conditioning which will provide a circuit with a regenerative repeater on one end, suitable for narrow-band secure voice or 2400 baud data.

conditioning, schedule S3 (DCS), *n.* Conditioning which will provide a circuit without regenerative repeaters, suitable for narrow-band secure voice or 2400 baud data.

conditioning, schedule V1 (DCS), *n.* A non-equalized circuit suitable only for non-secure voice, facsimile, or 10-40 cpm data transmission.

conditioning, schedule V2 (DCS), *n.* A conditioning which will produce a circuit suitable for AUTOVON access circuits or AUTOVON trunks.

conditioning, schedule Z1 (DCS), *n.* Conditioning which will provide a metallic circuit without regeneration, transmitting a band 10 Hz-50,000 Hz, and suitable for a loop from a wideband secure voice set to a secure voice automatic switch.

conditioning, schedule Z2 (DCS), *n.* Conditioning which will provide a metallic circuit without regeneration, transmitting a band 10 Hz-50,000 Hz, and suitable for the loop from a wideband secure voice set to a manual PBX.

conditioning, schedule Z3 (DCS), *n.* Conditioning providing a metallic circuit without regeneration, transmitting a band of 10 Hz-50,000 Hz, suitable for wideband secure voice trunks.

conditioning, schedule Z4 (DCS), *n.* Conditioning which will provide a circuit via carrier facilities, transmitting a band 10 Hz-50,000 Hz, and suitable for a wideband secure voice loop.

conductance, *n.* (1) A measure of the ability of a substance to conduct electricity. It is the reciprocal of resistance, and is expressed in "mhos." (2) The resistive component of "admittance," which see.

conductance, mutual, *n.* Transconductance, which see.

conduction, *n.* The flow of electricity, heat, or sound along or through a substance called a "conductor." Electricity flows in metals through the movement of electrons, and in semiconductors through the movement of electrons or holes.

conductivity, *n.* Conductance. The ability of a substance to conduct an electric current.

conductivity, n-type, *n.* The conduction in a semiconductor due to the movement of electrons.

conductivity, percent, *n.* An expression of the ability of a material to conduct electricity, expressed as a percentage of the conductivity of copper.

conductivity, p-type, *n.* The conduction in a semiconductor due to the movement of "holes."

conductor, *n.* (1) Anything, such as a wire or cable which is suitable for the carrying of an electric current. (2) One wire of a pair of wires. (3) That part of an electrical circuit which carries the current, as opposed to the dielectric.

conductor, adjacent, *n.* Any conductor next to another conductor, particularly those in the same layer of a multilayer cable.

conductor, aluminum, *n.* A conductor, solid or stranded, made wholly of aluminum. In the communications (EC) grade, it is 99.45% pure aluminum.

conductor, annular, *n.* A conductor consisting of a number of wires stranded in three reversed concentric layers around a saturated hemp core.

conductor, flat, *n.* A wire manufactured in a flattened or tape form, rather than round or square.

conductor, solid, *n.* An electrical conductor which consists of a single wire.

conductor, steel-reinforced aluminum (ACSR), *n.* A high-strength stranded conductor for long-span use having aluminum wires surrounding a high-strength steel wire core.

conductor, stranded, *n.* An electrical conductor which consists of a number of small conductors twisted together. For instance, a #4/0 conductor may be composed of seven #6 AWG wires, twelve #8 AWG wires, or nineteen #10 AWG wires.

conduit, *n.* A pipe or tube, of tile, asbestos-cement, plastic or steel, which is placed underground to form ducts through which cables can be passed.

conduit, asbestos-cement, *n.* Asbestos-cement pipe having a ⅜-inch wall thickness and suitable for electrical conduits, either for exposed work or for direct burial in the earth. Joined by tapered couplings. Available in 2, 3, 3½, 4, 4½, 5, and 6-inch inside diameters and 10 foot lengths (2″ in 5 ft. lengths).

conduit, clay tile, *n.* A multiple duct sectional conduit, 24 inches long, made of vitrified clay tile. See also "conduit, multiple duct."

conduit, concrete. See "conduit, monolithic."

conduit, corrugated, *n.* A plastic conduit, in sizes from 1¼″ to 4″ ID, with a corrugated wall giving extreme flexibility, used where complicated compound curves are needed. Requires encasement in concrete.

conduit, creosoted wood, *n.* A single-duct conduit consisting of a 6-8 foot length of creosoted wood of octagonal cross-section having a hole bored lengthwise. Joined with a bell-and-spigot joint. Not used today.

conduit, fibre, *n.* Treated fibre pipe used as electrical conduit, and suitable for underground use. Joined by drive-on tapered couplings.

conduit, lateral, *n.* A conduit run, usually multi-duct, which branches from the main conduit run. It frequently leads to an aerial cable or to a building cable.

conduit, main, *n.* (1) A multi-duct conduit run which carries feeder, or feeder and distribution cables. (2) A principal conduit run.

conduit, monolithic, *n.* A one-piece underground conduit structure constructed by pouring concrete around flexible tubular rubber forms which are pulled ahead as the casting proceeds.

conduit, multiple duct, *n.* (1) One-piece sectional conduit, usually of clay tile, having two (1x2), three (1x3), four (2x2), six (2x3), nine (3x3), or twelve (3x4) integral ducts. (2) A conduit run made up of several single-unit pipes or conduits.

conduit, plastic, *n.* Polyvinyl chloride rigid pipe suitable for electrical conduits, either exposed or underground. Made in two weights, one for direct burial and the other for encasement in concrete. Joined by drive-on tapered couplings. Available with inside diameters from ½ inch to 6 inches.

conduit, protected, *n.* An underground conduit, single or multi-unit which is protected from inadvertent digging by concrete, applied as (a) top protection, (b) top and bottom protection, or, (c) complete encasement.

conduit, rigid metal, *n.* Metal pipe of standard weight and thickness used to contain interior wiring. Available in ten foot lengths with threaded pipe couplings.

conduit, riser, *n.* Conduit which runs in a vertical direction, on a pole or in a building.

conduit, steel, *n.* Standard galvanized or black enameled steel pipe used as electrical conduit. Is satisfactory only in dry, above ground installations.

conduit, subsidiary, *n.* A single or two-duct conduit leading to a terminal or building.

conduit, thin wall asbestos-cement, *n.* Asbestos-cement pipe having a ¼-inch wall thickness. Used for underground electrical conduit where concrete encasement is required. Available in the same sizes and lengths as regular weight conduit.

conduit, thin-wall metallic, *n.* Metal conduit for inside wiring having the same inside diameter as rigid metal conduit, but with a thin wall (3/64 inch for ¾ inch conduit). Available in ten foot lengths, unthreaded, which must be joined with threadless compression fittings. Known also as "electrical metallic tubing" or "EMT."

conduit, wrought iron, *n.* Standard wrought iron pipe used for conduit. Resists corrosion well.

conduit run, *n.* (1) The path taken by a conduit or group of conduits. (2) A group of conduits, whether building conduits or underground conduits.

conference, broadcast, *n.* Conference call initiated from one station to many other stations to make an announcement. Of several types: (a) for one-way talking, or (b) permitting called conferees to talk back to the initiator.

conference, meet-me, *n.* Conference call established by requesting each participant to dial a special "meet-me" conference number which automatically connects him with the conference initiator and the other connected conferees.

conference, preset, *n.* Conference call initiated by one party dialing an assigned conference number. The central office equipment then connects and rings the other parties to the conference.

conference, progressive, *n.* Conference in which an operator calls each participant in sequence as instructed by the initiator, notifies him of the conference, and connects him to the group.

conference, teletypewriter, *n.* Conference between conferees at the two ends of a teletypewriter circuit. The machines used type on a transparent film, and enlarged images of the messages are projected on a screen as they are transmitted and received.

conference call, *n.* Call which interconnects three or more telephones and permits all parties to converse at random.

confidence, *n.* The degree to which a measurement (or statement) is believed to be true.

confidencer, *n.* Registered name of one brand of close-talking noise-canceling microphone, used to replace the telephone transmitter and permitting satisfactory transmission in the presence of high ambient noise.

configuration, conductor, *n.* The geometrical arrangement of a group of conductors including spacing between conductors and between conductors and earth.

confirmation signaling, *n.* A method of signaling on some intertoll trunks to ensure error-free transmission of dialed information. As each digit is sent over the trunk confirmation is accomplished by return of the same digit from the far terminal. If the wrong digit or no digit is received, the trunk is released and another is seized for a second attempt.

conflict, structure, *n.* A condition of a pole line such that if it overturns (pivoting at the ground line) its poles or conductors will contact the conductors of a second paralleling pole line. Lines are not considered to be in conflict under the following two conditions: (1) Where one line crosses another. (2) Where the two lines are on the opposite sides of a street or highway and are separated by a distance of not less than 60% of the height of the taller pole line and not less than 20 feet.

conjugate impedances. See "impedances, conjugate."

conjugate selection, *n.* The type of selection used in crossbar and matrix switching systems in which a path is selected across more than one switching stage at a time, and the switches in the several stages are positioned simultaneously.

conjunction, satellite, *n.* The apparent meeting or passing in space of two or more orbiting bodies *i.e.,* satellite and sun, satellite and moon, etc.) as viewed from a single observation point (on the earth).

connecting circuit, *n.* A circuit used to associate functional circuits for short periods of time, or to connect circuit inputs or outputs.

Connecting Company, *n.* An Independent Telephone Company having arrangements with a Bell Company for the interchange of telephone traffic.

connection, *n.* (1) A direct wire path for current between two points in the circuit. (2) The current-carrying junction which results when two conductors are clamped, wrapped, or wrapped and soldered into electrical contact.

connection, compression, *n.* A good electrical joint between two conductors made by means of a tightly crimped sleeve which covers them.

connection, delta, *n.* A method of connecting a three-phase primary power circuit in which each of the three transformer primaries are connected across a different pair of the three phase wires, so that the winding connection looks like the Greek letter "delta," an equilateral triangle.

connection, drainage, *n.* A wire connection which conducts stray currents to ground. See also "return, negative."

connection, loose, *n.* A contact between two conductors which is not tight, and therefore has resistance to the flow of current. Current flow through that resistance produces heat and electrical noise.

connection, parallel. See "parallel connection."

connection, permissive. See "permissive connection."

connection, rosin. See "joint, rosin."

connection, series, *n.* Elements in an electrical circuit are said to be connected in series when the same current flows through each of them in sequence.

connection, telephone, *n.* A two-way voice channel completed between two points by means of switching equipment, and capable of transmitting voice signals plus control, ringing, and supervisory signals.

connection, through, *n.* A telephone connection which is switched through an office, and does not terminate or bridge in the office.

connection, wye, *n.* A method of connecting a three-phase primary power circuit in which each of three transformer primaries are connected from a phase wire to a fourth wire which is grounded. Very often this grounded "neutral" wire is interconnected with the neutral of the secondary mains.

connection time, *n.* The time required by automatic telephone switching equipment to connect the calling line to the called line, measured in seconds from the time the last digit is dialed until the first ring of the called number.

connector, *n.* (1) An electrical multi-conductor connecting device consisting of a mating receptacle and plug. (2) An automatic switch which closes a large number of contacts simultaneously. (3) A two-digit automatic step-by-step switch which connects a trunk to a subscriber's line. It tests for busy before making the connection, and may be arranged to search (hunt) for an idle terminal within a group of terminals. (4) A type of central office MDF protector characterized by (a) plug-in protector units, factory wired stub cable, and (b) economy of space. (5) Any device for making a temporary or semi-permanent electrical connection. Many types are listed below.

connector, bridging, *n.* A screw fastener for connecting drop or bridle wires to open-wire conductors, or to provide an easily-opened connection between two open wires at a test point.

connector, cable, *n.* Multi-conductor receptacle used to terminate the end of equipment cables. Connectors

mate with similar multi-conductor plugs. Made in 12 and 25 pair sizes.

connector, cell, *n.* A lead-coated copper strap used to interconnect adjacent storage cells.

connector, coil-spring, *n.* A type of terminal, used instead of a screw-type binding post to enable the rapid connection of plastic-insulated conductors. Consists of a coil spring made of wire having a square cross-section. Connections are made by pulling the wire into the groove between adjacent turns of the coil where the corners of the square wire penetrate the insulation and contact is made.

connector, crossbar, *n.* A relay-type switching device for interconnecting, for a short interval of time, two equipment elements by a relatively large number of leads. The connector is named according to where the connected leads terminate. Example: The marker connector which connects a register to a marker.

connector, hermaphrodite, *n.* A cable connector in which the jack and plug are identically shaped.

connector, marker, *n.* A multi-contact (120, more or less) relay which connects a decoder to a marker upon command. Each connector serves one decoder and has access to all markers. (#4A TSS).

connector, master test frame, *n.* A connector by which markers and other equipment obtain access to a master test frame.

connector, PBX, *n.* A trunk-hunting connector. Frequently used to serve PBX trunk groups.

connector, pole strand, *n.* A small galvanized steel casting mounted to the pole with a through-bolt. Has two interlocking grooves which permit the suspension strand to be dead-ended both ways at the pole.

connector, pretranslator, *n.* A circuit which operates to call in a pretranslator after two or three dialed digits have been received by an originating register.

connector, recorder, *n.* A device for connecting a voice recorder to a telephone line on a high-impedance bridging basis. Provides a 1/5 second 1400 Hz "beep" tone to the line every 15 seconds to alert the distant party that the conversation is being recorded.

connector, solderless, *n.* A bolt-actuated clamp which permits making an electrical joint between heavy stranded conductors by clamping them together under considerable pressure. Used for power wiring in central offices.

connector, step-by-step, *n.* A two-motion electromechanical switch which operates on the last two digits of the telephone number to connect a trunk from a selector to any one of 100 (or 200) subscriber lines. The connector performs the following functions:

   a. Tests for a busy line.

   b. If busy, returns busy tone.

   c. If idle, rings the called line and returns ringback tone to the calling line.

   d. Provides reverse-battery supervision and trips the ring when the called subscriber answers.

   e. Provides talking battery to the calling and called lines.

   f. Disconnects when the subscribers hang up.

connector, test, *n.* (1) Automatic connector switch used by the operator or testman to connect to a subscriber's line, via his connector terminal. It will connect to busy or idle lines. (2) Clip device used to connect portable test equipment to circuits at terminal blocks or MDF's.

connector, 300 type, *n.* A protector mounting having a factory-connected stub cable, for use on central office main distributing frames. Available in 50 pair and 100 pair sizes.

connector, trunk and level hunting, *n.*

A step-by-step connector arranged to give access to any one of a group of 100 or less lines when the directory number of the first line in the group is dialed. The connector will step vertically to a level where there is an idle line, then cut into the bank and hunt horizontally to find the idle line.

connector, trunk block, *n.* In a #4 switching system, the connector terminates sleeve and select-magnet leads for 400 trunks, and gives all markers access to them so that the marker can make busy tests and identify the location of the trunk on the outgoing link frame. (#4A TSS).

connector, trunk-hunting, *n.* A step-by-step connector arranged to give access to any one of a group of ten or less consecutively numbered lines, listed in the directory by the first number of the group. When the first number of the group is dialed the connector hunts (steps) over the entire group until an idle line is found.

connector, wire, *n.* An insulated, pressure splicing device which strips and connects any 2 or 3 wires which are inserted and the connector crimped. Permits the splicing of cables by relatively unskilled labor.

Conservation of Energy, Law of. See "Appendix B."

console, *n.* A type of attendant's switchboard which uses push-button keys set on a sloping panel to control associated switching equipment. It reduces the operator's work and permits a greatly improved speed of service.

console, telephone, *n.* A multi-line key telephone set for desk use equipped with a plurality of six-button keys, a handset, a rotary or touch-tone dial, and a connector cable. Can optionally use an operator's tel set, and may be equipped with a NIGHT connection key, a power failure alarm lamp, an ATB lamp, and/or a station lamp field.

constant. See "attenuation constant," "dielectric constant," "phase constant," "propagation constant," and "time constant."

constant, dielectric. See "dielectric constant."

constant, phase. See "phase constant."

constant-k. See "filter, constant-k."

constant-voltage charge. See "charge, constant-voltage."

constrictor, cable sheath, *n.* Tool used to make the cable sheath smaller at one point for a gas plug. Squeezes or creases a ring in the cable sheath, pressing the sheath tightly against the conductors.

consultation call, *n.* A feature of some PAX's which enable a PAX station to hold a trunk call while calling another local station for consultation.

contact, *n.* The disc or bar of precious metal on a jack, key, or relay spring which touches another similar contact, thus making a temporary, low-resistance connection through which current can flow.

contact, back, *n.* The stationary contact of a pair of contacts which are closed when the relay or key is not operated.

contact, break, *n.* A back contact, which see.

contact, dry, *n.* A contact through which no direct current flows.

contact, front, *n.* The stationary contact of a pair of contacts which are normally open, but close when the relay or key is operated.

contact, make, *n.* A front contact, which see.

contact, moving, *n.* The portion of a relay or switch having a contact which moves toward or away from a fixed contact.

contact, normal, *n.* The stationary contact of a pair of contacts in a jack or key which are made when there is no plug in the jack, or when the key is non-operated.

contact, sealed, *n.* A ferreed, which see.

contact, wiping. See "wiping contact."

contact bounce, *n.* A rebound of a relay contact after closing, which momentarily opens the contact.

contact common, *n.* A solid segment in a contact bank assembly, on which a wiper rides to provide a common connection.

contact follow, *n.* The distance two contacts move together after they have made the first contact.

contact form, *n.* The configuration of a single-pole contact assembly, such as is used on a relay or key. See "form, contact."

contact noise. See "noise, contact."

contactor, *n.* In gas protection of cables, a bellows-operated contactor device which closes an alarm circuit to the central office when the cable gas pressure drops below normal.

contactor, gas pressure, *n.* A pneumatically operated electrical switch, connected to a pressurized cable by a pipe containing an alarm pair, which places a high resistance or a metallic short across the alarm pair when the pressure falls below a preset value, usually either 2 psig or 4 psig.

contactor, magnetic, *n.* A heavy-duty relay, capable of making and breaking electric power circuits.

contactor-terminal, *n.* A gas pressure contactor which also terminates the alarm pair used to transmit the gas alarm to a central test point.

contacts, *n. pl.* Conducting elements which act together to complete or to interrupt a circuit.

contacts, break, *n. pl.* Contacts which open when a key or relay is operated. See also "form, contact."

contacts, dissimilar, *n. pl.* To reduce contact erosion, relay contacts are usually made of dissimilar metals, one contact of the pair being made of silver and the other of palladium.

contacts, early relay. See "early relay contacts."

contacts, make, *n. pl.* Contacts which

close when a key or relay is operated. See also "form, contact."

contacts, make-before-break, *n. pl.* A set of three contacts on a key or relay, so arranged that contact A makes with contact C before breaking from contact B. See also "form, contact."

contacts, mercury-wetted, *n. pl.* Sealed contacts, used in relays and ferreed switches, which are constantly wetted by mercury, ensuring a reliable, resistance-free contact.

contacts, ordinary relay. See "ordinary relay contacts."

contacts, preliminary relay. See "preliminary relay contacts."

contacts, twin, *n. pl.* A feature which ensures reliable operation of relay and key contact springs. The ends of the contact springs are split, and each half is fitted with a contact. Thus each connection is made through two contacts in parallel.

contacts, wetted, *n. pl.* Relay contacts whose closed resistance is eliminated by either (1) coating the contacts with mercury or (2) superimposing a small (one milliampere) direct current.

continuity, *n.* The condition existing in a circuit when an electrical path is continuous and a current can flow.

continuous wave (CW) radiotelegraphy, *n.* A system of signaling on radiotelegraphy in which the radio carrier is transmitted for a mark signal and omitted for a space signal. At the receiver, the mark signals are beat against a local oscillator and the resulting audio tone is read by ear or rectified to operate a teletypewriter.

contrahelical, *adj.* Describing a multilayer cable in which each successive layer is spirally wrapped in the opposite direction to the preceding layer.

control, automatic frequency (AFC), *n.* (1) A circuit which maintains the frequency of an oscillator constant within specified limits. (2) In a radio receiver, a circuit which keeps the receiver accurately tuned by controlling the frequency of its local oscillator.

control, automatic gain (AGC), *n.* A property of some radio receivers which acts to maintain the intermediate frequency (IF) amplifier output constant, even with wide variations in the receiver input level.

control, automatic sensitivity (ASC), *n.* A circuit used for automatically maintaining receiver sensitivity at a predetermined level.

control, automatic volume (AVC), *n.* An automatic gain control which maintains the output level of a radio receiver or amplifier substantially constant although the input voltage varies over a wide range.

control, circuit, *n.* The authority to control and direct testing, repair, and maintenance of a toll circuit.

control, dynamic overload. See "dynamic overload control."

control, E&M lead. See "signaling, E&M."

control, high-traffic-day load. See "load control, high-traffic day."

control, line load, *n.* Selective denial of call origination capability to specified subscriber's lines when excessive demands for service are offered to a switching center. It does not affect the capability to receive calls. Normally, a central office is divided into three groups of lines and control is rotated, with one or two groups being denied outward service at a time.

control, remote, *n.* A system for electrically turning on and off and regulating a radio transmitter or other device from a distance, over wire or radio control circuits. See also "line, keying."

control, route. See "route control."

control, supervisory. See "supervisory control."

control, tech (nical), *n.* An activity or installation which controls circuit quality and patching. Also "technical control facility."

control, tilt. See "tilt control."

control, volume. See "volume control."

control grid, *n.* The grid in an electron tube that controls the flow of current from cathode to anode.

controlled re-ring, *n.* Capability of the equipment wherein the operator can ring back the telephone without redialing the number.

controlled ringing. See both "controlled start of ringing" and "controlled re-ring."

controlled start of ringing, *n.* Capability of equipment to permit dialing a telephone number and then delay machine ringing of the telephone until the operator operates the ringing key momentarily.

controller, recorder. See "recorder-connector."

control office, *n.* An office, testboard, or technical control facility which has responsibility for the establishment, rearrangement, and maintenance of circuits, trunks, and lines.

control point, dedicated plant. See "point, control."

controls, dynamic overload (DOC), *n. pl.* The automatic traffic control equipment in a regional toll center which senses growth of traffic congestion and cancels attempts to place multi-switched calls.

Control Switching Point (CSP), *n.* A toll switching center, which may be a Class 1, 2, or 3 office, at which intertoll trunks are connected to other intertoll trunks. At least one other office of lower rank homes on it, and it has the following capabilities:

    a. VNL operation of intertoll trunks.

    b. VNL + 2.5 db operation of toll connecting trunks.

    c. Meets terminal and through balance requirements.

    d. Provides automatic alternate routing.

    e. Translates 3 to 6 digits.

    f. Provides code conversion and variable spilling.

convection, *n.* The transfer of heat caused by the circulation of a heated liquid or gas.

convenience receptacle. See "receptacle."

convention, *n.* (1) A general agreement regarding the meaning of a symbol. (2) A symbol which is generally understood.

conversion, *n.* A change in form without a change in value.

conversion, code, *n.* The changing of a directory or toll directing code into an arbitrary code for controlling the selection of a trunk route at a distant switching point.

conversion, frequency, *n.* The changing of the carrier frequency of a received radio signal from its original value to an intermediate frequency (IF) in a superheterodyne receiver.

conversion, marker pulse, *n.* Feature of the #5 crossbar system which permits operator positions equipped only for MF pulsing, but colocated with the #5, to use direct trunks to reach offices which require the receipt of dial (DP) or revertive (RP) pulsing. (#5X Bar)

converter, *n.* A vacuum tube device in which two frequencies are mixed, producing the difference frequency.

converter, analog-to-digital, *n.* A converter, usually a sampling device, which converts an analog signal to a digital signal carrying equivalent information.

converter, code, *n.* (1) A unit of logic in a translator, consisting of a single-input or dual-input AND gate with its output connected to an inverter. It converts a negative voltage two-out-of-five code input to a single decimal output, also negative voltage. (2) A device that changes information expressed in one code system to equivalent information in another code system.

converter, DC-DC, *n.* An electrical device which converts direct current at one voltage to direct current at another voltage. Operation is as follows: (a) DC at 48 volts energizes a transistor oscillator, (b) AC from the oscillator is passed through a transformer to obtain the desired output voltage, and (c) AC from the transformer is rectified by silicon diodes and sent to the output.

converter, digital-to-analog, *n.* A device which converts a digital input signal to an analog signal carrying equivalent information.

converter, facsimile, *n.* A device which converts an amplitude modulated signal from a facsimile machine to a frequency modulated subcarrier for transmission over radio or line facilities and vice versa. The maximum FM swing is about 1000 Hz.

converter, frequency, *n.* (1) A circuit or device which changes a signal from one frequency to another. May either translate the frequency by heterodyne means, or multiply it as in a doubler. (2) In a superheterodyne receiver, the section consisting of the oscillator, mixer, and first detector stages.

converter, inverted rotary, *n.* A rotary machine identical with a rotary converter, but used to convert direct current to alternating current. Has only a single armature winding. See also "rotary converter" and "dynamotor."

converter, language and mode, *n.* A device providing an interface between teletypewriters operating at different speeds and/or with 5-level and 8-level codes. Consists of a receiver, a buffer store, and a transmitter for each direction of transmission.

converter, negative impedance. See "negative impedance converter."

converter, ringdown, *n.* A relay equipment used to change ringdown signals to E&M signals, and vice versa.

converter, ringing, *n.* (1) A signaling device at the terminal of a telephone line which converts the central office or switchboard ringing signal to the line ringing signal, and vice versa. Some examples are:

Switchboard	Line
E&M (DC)	SF (2600 Hz)
20 Hz	1000/20 Hz
20 Hz	135 Hz

(2) A device which converts DC to 20 Hz ringing power.

converter, rotary, *n.* A rotary machine which transforms alternating current to direct current by the rotation of a single armature winding through a magnetic field. The external alternating current system is connected to the armature winding through slip rings while the direct current system is connected through a commutator.

converter, serial-to-parallel. See "serial-to-parallel converter."

converter, signal, *n.* A device whose input and output signals contain the same information but employ different electrical systems for transmitting that information. Used at the terminal of a trunk to convert the equipment signals to the system used on the trunk. Examples are: (a) ringdown to SF, (b) E&M to SF.

converter, static, *n.* A converter which has no moving parts.

converter, synchronous. See "converter, rotary."

converter, tape-to-card, *n.* An electromechanical device that reads information from tape (magnetic or punched) and punches a data card with the same information in Hollerith code.

converter, touch-tone, *n.* A device which will receive dual-tone multifrequency address signals and convert them to 20 pps dial pulses into a subscriber sender or originating register. Required when converting a common control dial office to accept address signals from touch-tone telephones.

coordination, frequency, *n.* The cooperative selection and allocation of radio frequencies such that all systems can operate without giving or receiving interference.

coordination, inductive, *n.* (1) The

application of corrective measures to both communication and power circuits in order to reduce inductive interference. (2) The cooperative action of communication and power engineers to reduce inductive interference.

coordination, level, *n.* The assignment and maintenance of power levels on a multichannel system so that all channels operate without giving or receiving crosstalk.

coordination, structural, *n.* (1) The application of corrective measures to both power and communication pole lines in order to reduce the possibility of an accidental contact between power and communication conductors. It is concerned with adequate pole strength, proper guying, and adequate clearances both horizontal and vertical. (2) The cooperative action of communication and power engineers to provide adequate clearances and structural strength.

co-polymer, *n.* A long-chain chemical compound formed by the union of two or more monomers through polymerization.

copper, *n.* A soft, yellowish-red metal which is very ductile and malleable. When pure, it is an excellent conductor of electricity.

copper, soldering, *n.* A wedge shaped heavy (1 to 2 pounds) bar of copper fitted with a steel shank and heat-insulating handle. Is heated on the splicer's furnace and used for heavy soldering jobs.

copper-clad aluminum, *n.* Material used for telephone conductors, providing a light-weight inexpensive aluminum core cladded (covered) with high-conductivity copper.

copper-clad steel, *n.* Material used for telephone wire and strand, providing a high tensile strength steel core cladded (covered) with higher conductivity (30% or 40%) corrosion resistant copper.

copper-steel. See "copper-clad steel."

copper sulfate pentahydrate, *n.* A chemical ($CuSO_4$ $5H_2O$) used for pressure treatment of wooden poles to inhibit fungus, insects, and rot.

Copperweld, *n.* The name applied to copper coated steel products produced by a patented process which welds a cylinder of copper around a steel billet, then rolls this to rod, then draws it into wire, still with its uniform copper coating on a steel core.

copy, hard, *n.* The printed original copy of a message as it comes from a teletypewriter.

copy, page, *n.* A printed original copy of a message, page size, as it comes from a teletypewriter.

copy, tape, *n.* An original copy of a teletypewriter message as it was received on punched tape.

cord, *n.* A flexible insulated conductor or several such conductors under a common braided cover. Often equipped with a plug or plugs and used to make temporary connections to jacks on switchboards.

cord, answering, *n.* In a switchboard cord pair, the cord farthest from the operator (back cord) which is used for answering incoming calls.

cord, back, *n.* In a switchboard cord pair, the cord which is farthest from the operator and nearest to the jackfield. Also called the "answering cord."

cord, calling, *n.* In a switchboard cord pair, the cord nearest the operator (front cord) which is used in completing calls to the called line or trunk.

cord, closure sealing, *n.* Sealing compound supplied in the form of a cord, and used for the gasket around the edges between the two halves of a splice case closure.

cord, coiled. See "cord, retractile."

cord, completing. See "cord, calling."

cord, dial. See "dial cord."

cord, front, *n.* In a switchboard cord pair, the cord which is nearest to the operator. Also called the "calling cord."

cord, handset, *n.* The 3-conductor flexible cord used to connect a telephone handset to its mounting. This cord is usually a retractile type.

cord, line, *n.* The two or three conductor flexible cord used to connect a hand telephone set to the incoming line at a connecting block.

cord, nylon lacing, *n.* A cord of about 5,000 denier weight consisting of a flattened band of nylon filaments impregnated with wax. Because of the elasticity of nylon it produces a tight stitch. Used for lacing cable forms.

cord, patching, *n.* A flexible electrical cord having one to six conductors terminated on each end in a plug. Used for making temporary connections between circuits terminated on jacks.

cord, plugging-up. See "plugging-up cord."

cord, power, *n.* A two-wire insulated cord terminating in a two-prong plug, used to make connections to a source of AC power.

cord, retractile, *n.* Multiconductor flexible cable spirally wound so that it can be extended to its full length but upon release will shorten to the original spiral lenth. Used for telephone handset cords.

cord, sealing, *n.* Impregnated cord used to form a gasket for sealing the sides of splice cases.

cord, sounder test. See "sounder test cord."

cord, switchboard, *n.* A two (tip & sleeve) or three (tip, ring & sleeve) conductor flexible electrical cord terminated in a plug on one end which an operator uses to make rapid, temporary connections to the switchboard circuits which are terminated on jacks.

cord, telegraph facility patching, *n.* A cord pair on a telegraph testboard. The two cords are connected together through line (TGL) and equipment (TGEQ) jacks which permit testing the telegraph circuit while it is on a patched layout.

cord, telegraph leg patching, *n.* On a telegraph testboard, a circuit used to build up a concentration group on a patched layout. The circuit has a leg (L) plug, a concentration (C) plug, a hub (H) jack, and a trouble indicator (TI) jack, plus two relays.

cord, telegraph test signal, *n.* A cord pair on a telegraph test board, with associated relays, jack, and key. When the CONN SIG plug is patched to a test signal supply, the CONN LEG plug is patched to a leg of line or loop, and the ST SIG key operated, automatic test signals will be sent to the leg until interrupted.

cord, test, *n.* (1) A cord used for making temporary test connections. (2) Long cord at a distributing frame ending in a plug or shoe. Used by the test deskman for making temporary connection to a protector (cable pair) or a terminal block.

cord, tinsel, *n.* The type of flexible electrical cord used for switchboard and other telephone cords. The conductors consist of thin narrow copper tapes wrapped spirally around textile cords.

cord, toll. See "toll cord."

cord circuit, *n.* A pair of cords used to interconnect line and trunk jacks at a switchboard. One end of the two cords is terminated in plugs; the other ends are interconnected through a circuit which provides talking battery, ringing current, and supervision.

cordless switchboard. See "switchboard, cordless."

cord pair, *n.* The two cords, "answering" and "calling," which constitute one cord circuit on a switchboard.

cord shelf, *n.* The plug shelf of a switchboard.

cord-splitting, *n.* On a telephone switchboard, the act of opening the connections between the front cord and rear cord of the same cord pair, so that the operator may talk to either the called or the calling party separately.

cord test circuit, *n.* A test jack mounted on alternate switchboard positions and connected to a grounded repeating coil. By inserting the plug of a cord and observing noise and supervisory lamp action while twisting the cord, one can detect open tip, ring, or sleeve conductors in the cord.

core, *n.* (1) The magnetic material at the center of a relay or coil winding. (2) All of the conductors inside a cable sheath.

core, cable, *n.* The portion of a multiconductor cable lying inside the protective coverings and sheath.

core, closed, *adj. n.* The ferromagnetic core of a coil or transformer which forms a completely closed loop around the coil or transformer winding, thus providing a low reluctance path for the magnetic flux.

core, laminated, *n.* A magnetic core for a transformer or reactor, built up with stamped iron laminations, each of which is insulated with varnish. Such a core restricts the flow of eddy currents to within each lamination.

core, magnetic, *n.* (1) Ferromagnetic material placed inside of coils or transformer windings to provide a low reluctance path for the magnetic flux. This increases the inductance of single winding coils and increases the coupling between transformer windings. (2) A device which uses magnetic remanence to provide storage of binary information. Consists of a small doughnut-shaped core of a magnetic material having an open square hysteresis curve. Arranged in a matrix, each core is threaded with a vertical write wire, a horizontal write wire, and a sense (read) wire. Some types also have an inhibit (cancel) wire. Energizing the vertical and horizontal wires with a "half-write" current will switch the core at their intersection to the "one" state.

core, open, *n.* A magnetic core which is within a coil or winding, with the portion of the magnetic path external to the coil or winding being through air. Such a path has a high reluctance, and the magnetic flux is correspondingly low.

core, relay, *n.* The central metallic rod or strip on which a relay coil is wound.

core, tuning, *n.* A powdered iron or ferrite core that can be moved in or out of a coil to vary its inductance.

core hitch, *n.* Attachment of a pulling line directly to a cable core rather than to the cable sheath, to permit pulling it into a duct without damaging the sheath.

core loss, *n.* Iron loss, which see.

core storage. See "core, magnetic."

core tuning, *n.* Adjusting the frequency of resonance of a coil by moving a powdered iron or ferrite core in or out of the coil.

corner, *n.* In pole line construction, the point at which the pole line changes direction. The unbalanced pull at corners requires that the pole be guyed or braced.

corner pole, *n.* A pole which is located at a point where the pole line changes direction.

corner reflector. See "antenna, corner reflector."

corona, *n.* A bluish static discharge which forms on a conductor suspended in air when the electrostatic stress in the air exceeds about 75,000 volts peak per inch. Corona is accompanied by a hissing sound and the production of ozone.

correction, forward error. See "forward error correction."

correction, pulse. See "pulse correction."

corrector, impedance, *n.* An impedance network connected to a basic balancing network to improve its impedance match at low voice frequencies.

corrector, pulse, *n.* Relay or electronic

circuit associated with a pulse repeater which receives distorted pulses and re-sends them at the same speed but at the correct 61% break, —39% make ratio.

correed, *n.* A complete relay assembly consisting of a bobbin on which is wound the operating coil and within which are inserted one or more "reedcapsules." The reedcapsule is an hermetically sealed glass tube enclosing two flat ferromagnetic metal reeds supported at the ends and overlapping at the center of the tube. Current through the operating winding will cause these normally open reeds to move together and close the overlapping contact. Normally-closed reedcapsules can be made by adding a biasing permanent magnet whose small flux will be overcome by the flux from the operating winding.

correlation, reverse path, *n.* A check on a radio propagation path to determine that transmission is equally effective in both directions and that fading, if it occurs, is similar in the two directions.

correlation, signal, *n.* The relation between two radio signals at different frequencies when they exhibit fades at the same time, and possibly by similar percentage amounts. Signals with high correlation are useless for diversity reception.

correlator, *n.* A logic device which can recover intelligence signals which are masked by high level noise.

corrosion, *n.* The process or result of a material being eaten away gradually, usually by chemical action.

cost, annual operating, *n.* The annual cost of operating a communication facility, consisting of wages for operating, maintenance and administrative personnel, overhead charges, lease of building space, housekeeping costs, replacement parts, fuel, utilities, storm or other damages, etc.

coulomb, *n.* The basic unit for measuring the quantity (not intensity) of an electric current. The amount of electricity provided by a current of one ampere flowing for one second.

Coulomb's Law of Electrostatic Attraction. See "Appendix B."

count, *n.* The numerical sequence of pairs in a cable.

count, actual, *n.* The actual pair numbers, as determined by their position on a central office protector or in a terminal.

count, busy. See "busy count."

count, pair, *n.* The numerical designation of a cable pair, based on its position on the central office protectors or in a cross-connecting terminal. Example: Cable 5, Pair 16.—*n. pl.* The sequence of numbers which designates a group of pairs. Example: Cable 2501, pairs 1-101.

count, theoretical, *n.* The pair designation determined by the position of the pair in the cable, not by its use or termination. Thus, theoretical pairs 1-600 might have an actual count of cable 57 pairs 1-100, plus cable 62 pairs 1-400, plus 100 pairs dead.

count, usage, *n.* A count of the number of times a circuit tests busy. If tested every 100 seconds, the count will be in CCS.

counter, impulse noise. See "impulse noise counter."

counter, peg-count, *n.* (1) A small decade-dial odometer stepped by pushing a lever on top. Used at switchboard positions to make "peg counts," which see. (2) A message register.

counter, 3-type, *n.* A electromechanical timing device used on a traffic service position to remind the operator of the completion of the initial talking interval on coin calls or calls where the customer requests notice of completion. Adjustable to any of three initial periods from one to five minutes. Provides a flashing light six seconds before end of the initial period, changing to a steady light eighteen seconds later.

counter-electromotive force. See "force, counter-electromotive."

counter-EMF cell. See "cell, counter-EMF."

counterpoise, *n.* A network or radial system of wires just above the ground. Used to capacitively couple a radio transmitter to the ground when the ground resistance is high.

counting circuit, *n.* A circuit which is actuated by successive pulses and can be arranged to count either a definite number of pulses or to give a distinct indication corresponding to each individual pulse.

couple, *n.* (1) Two dissimilar metals in contact which form a galvanic couple or thermocouple. (2) A pair of opposing forces which tend to produce rotation.—*v.* To link two circuits together so that energy is transferred from one to the other through mutual capacitance or inductance.

coupler, antenna, *n.* (1) An RF transformer used to match impedances and transfer energy between a transmission line and transmitter or receiver. (2) An RF transformer used to transfer energy between an antenna and a transmission line.

coupler, directional, *n.* A device which can be inserted in a 75 ohm CATV cable to tap off the signal for local use. Its insertion loss is about 1 db; the loss to the tap is about 12 db.

coupler, multi-outlet TV, *n.* A splitter type device which permits serving several television receivers from the same CATV outlet.

coupling, *n.* The mutual relation between two circuits which permits the transfer of power from one to the other.

coupling, capacitive, *n.* (1) The coupling between two portions of a circuit which exists by virtue of mutual capacitance. (2) Interstage coupling in a multi-stage amplifier which employs a capacitor connected from the plate of one stage to the grid of the next stage.

coupling, close, *n.* Coupling between two circuits such that most of the power flowing in one is transferred to the other. Changes of impedance in one circuit profoundly affect the other.

coupling, conduit, *n.* (1) One of several types of cast iron fittings used for making connections between conduit pipe and bends. (2) A plastic sleeve having internal tapers, used to join lengths of asbestos-cement conduit.

coupling, critical, *n.* That degree of coupling which enables the maximum transfer of energy between two circuits.

coupling, crosstalk, *n.* The coupling (or loss) which exists between two circuits which crosstalk. See also "unit, crosstalk."

coupling, direct, *n.* Connecting two circuits, or stages in an amplifier, with a wire or resistor so that the coupling will pass all frequencies right down to zero (DC) with no discrimination. Direct-coupled amplifiers frequently have a resistor connected from the plate of one stage to the grid of the next stage.

coupling, ground rod, *n.* A heavy, bronze, internally-threaded pipe coupling used to couple two sections of sectional ground rod.

coupling, impedance, *n.* The coupling that exists between two circuits through a mutual impedance.

coupling, inductive, *n.* The coupling of two circuits through the mutual inductance of a transformer.

coupling, link, *n.* Coupling of two circuits through an intermediate link.

coupling, loose, *n.* Coupling between two circuits such that little power is transferred from one to the other, and such that an impedance change in one circuit has little effect on the other circuit.

coupling, magnetic, *n.* Coupling between two circuits by way of a magnetic flux which links coils in both circuits.

coupling, power-communication circuit, *n.* A summation of those factors which permit the transfer of noise induction from a power circuit to a communication circuit. These factors are:

a. The separation between the two circuits.

b. Their height above ground.

c. Shielding.

coupling, reference crosstalk, *n.* That degree of coupling between disturbing and disturbed circuits when there is a 90 decibel loss between the circuits.

coupling, resistance, *n.* (1) Coupling which transfers power between circuits through a resistor. (2) Coupling in which resistors are used as the output and input impedances of the circuits being coupled.

coupling, side-to-side antenna. See "side-to-side coupling."

coupling, unity. See "unity coupling."

coupling, variable, *n.* Inductive coupling in which one coil can be moved with respect to the other, thus varying the degree of coupling.

coupling factor, *n.* A number which combines the weighted contribution of those factors which permit the transfer of noise induction from a power circuit to a communication circuit.

coupling unit, telegraph. See "unit, telegraph coupling."

cover, *n.* (1) The distance from the surface of the earth to the depth at which a buried wire or cable is placed. (2) The type of surface material which covers underground conduit or buried cable, classified as "dirt," "sod," "concrete," "asphalt," etc.

cover, manhole, *n.* A heavy cast-iron circular plate supported by the manhole frame which gives access to the manhole. Designed to support vehicular loads.

cover, wall rack, *n.* Push-on cover for a wall relay rack.

coverage, *n.* The area that is effectively covered by a radio or television transmitter, and within which service is good. Also called "service area."

cradle, *n.* (1) A desk-type handset mounting. (2) The hookswitch portion of a handset mounting.

crank-back, *n.* The ability of a register-sender to obtain and use a new translation when the original translation results in call pocketing or is otherwise unuseable.

crank back, *vt.* To return a pocketed call (see "pocketing") to a register-sender with a mark to instruct the translator to select an alternate route. Avoids lost calls.

crash alarm system. See "system, crash alarm."

credit card call, *n.* A toll telephone call which is charged on a telephone credit card, requiring the operator to write a memo ticket.

creepage, *n.* In storage batteries or electrolytic cells, travel of the electrolyte by capillary attraction above the normal electrolyte level.

creosote, *n.* Oil obtained by the distillation of coal tar or wood tar. Used to preserve wood, particularly poles, from damage by fungus or insects.

crest factor of a pulse. See "factor, pulse crest."

crest value. *n.* Peak value.

crimping tool, connector. See "presser, connector."

crimp termination, *n.* A terminal lug which is applied by pressing it around the wire.

criteria, red/black. See "red/black criteria."

critical coupling. See "coupling, critical."

critical frequency, *n.* The limiting frequency below which a vertical radio wave will be returned to the earth by refraction from the ionosphere, Frequencies higher than the critical frequency will pass through the ionosphere into space.

critical load, *n.* That part of the total electrical power load which is required for synchronous communication equipment and automatic switching equipment.

crochet, *n.* A disturbance of the earth's magnetic field caused by eruption of a solar flare. Can be very disruptive to communications.

cross. *n.* An accidental contact between wires of different pairs.

cross-arm, *n.* A wooden member bolted at right angles to the pole top with wooden pins to hold glass insulators spaced across its top surface. Used to support open line wires. A standard 10-pin cross-arm is 3¼″ x 4¼″ x 10 feet long. Pin spacing is 12 inches, except for the pole pair which is 16 inches.

crossbar switch. See "switch, crossbar."

crossbar system, *n.* A switching system which uses crossbar switches. The dialed telephone address is received by a common-control unit which selects and closes a path through the switching equipment.

crossbar system. No 4A, *n.* A toll-switching system using 4-wire crossbar switches with common-control for interconnecting intertoll trunks, tandem trunks, toll-switching trunks, and miscellaneous terminating trunks. Provides up to 6-digit translation and automatic alternate routing.

crossbar system, No 5, *n.* A local switching system using two wire crossbar switches with common-control for interconnecting subscriber's lines with other lines or with interoffice or tandem trunks. Also used as a tandem office.

cross-connect, *adj.* Describing a device in which cross-connections are made.—*v.* To place or make a cross-connection.

cross-connections, *n.* Wire connections (paired, triples, or quads) run between terminals on the two sides

of a distributing frame, or between binding posts in a terminal.

cross-cut, *n.* A cross-connection. (Slang)

crossfire, *n.* (1) Interference from one telegraph circuit to another telegraph circuit. (2) The faulty operation of telegraph relays due to crossfire.

crossing, power. *n.* In pole line construction, a place where a communication line passes under a power line, requiring adequate clearance which depends on the voltage of the power line, and requiring adequate strength of the power line, depending on the importance of the communication line. Refer to the National Electrical Safety Code, Part 2.

crossing, railroad, *n.* In pole line construction, the place where a communication line passes over a railroad track, requiring special clearance (usually 27 feet) and adequate strength. For details, refer to the National Electrical Safety Code, Part 2.

cross modulation, *n.* A type of interference in which a carrier becomes modulated with an unwanted signal in addition to the desired signal.

crossover frequency. See "frequency, crossover."

crosspoint, *n.* A single inlet, single outlet switch used to construct a switching matrix.

cross-ring. *n.* The ringing of a second undesired party on a party line when one party is rung.

crosstalk, *n.* (1) Unwanted coupling from one signal path to another. (2) Faint speech or tone heard in one (disturbed) circuit, coming from an adjacent (disturbing) circuit.

crosstalk, direct, *n.* Crosstalk induced from the disturbing circuit directly into the disturbed circuit without involving an intermediate (tertiary) circuit.

crosstalk, equal-level, *n.* The crosstalk coupling that would be measured between equal level points on the disturbing and disturbed circuits.

crosstalk, far end, *n.* Crosstalk measured by application of tone to the far end of the disturbing circuit while measuring it at the near end of the disturbed circuit. It is a measure of the crosstalk coupling existing at the far end of the circuit.

crosstalk, indirect, *n.* Crosstalk which reaches the disturbed circuit over two paths in tandem, first from the disturbing circuit to tertiary circuits, and thence to the disturbed circuit.

crosstalk, interaction, *n.* Crosstalk caused by coupling between a carrier circuit and a non-carrier circuit, which may in turn be coupled to another carrier circuit.

crosstalk, near-end, *n.* Crosstalk measured by application of interfering tone to the near end of the disturbing circuit and measuring it at the near end of the disturbed circuit. It is a measure of the crosstalk coupling existing at the near end of the circuit.

crosstalk, runaround, *n.* Crosstalk in which a high-level signal from the output of a repeater couples to a tertiary non-repeatered circuit which in turn couples to a low-level circuit at a repeater input.

crosstalk coupling, *n.* The loss in db from a disturbing circuit to the disturbed circuit.

crosstalk level, *n.* The effective power in a crosstalk signal, expressed in decibels below one milliwatt.

crosstalk unit. See "unit, crosstalk."

crowbar, *n.* A low resistance short circuit.—*vt.* To place a low resistance short across the input to a circuit.

crown, cabinet, *n.* The top several inches of an equipment cabinet, above the racks and panels which mount equipment. This space has access from the top, and is usually used for terminal blocks which

form the interface between entrance cables and cabinet cables.

crypto-guard, *n.* A communication station designated to handle encrypted traffic to and from specified addressees.

crypto key. See "key, cryptographic."

crystal, *n.* A solid which has symmetry of its atomic structure. See also "crystal, piezoelectric" and "semiconductor."

crystal, piezoelectric, *n.* A crystal, such as quartz, which will convert pressure on a crystal face into electric charges, and vice versa. Used for precision frequency control of oscillators. See also "piezoelectric effect."

crystal, quartz, *n.* A piezoelectrical crystal cut from natural quartz, which is silicon dioxide.

crystal, X-cut, *n.* A crystal which is so cut that its major flat surfaces are perpendicular to an electrical (X) axis of the original quartz crystal.

crystal, XY-cut, *n.* A crystal which is so cut that its characteristics are between those of the X-cut and the Y-cut crystals. It has a very low temperature coefficient.

crystal, Y-cut, *n.* A crystal which is so cut that its major flat surfaces are perpendicular to a mechanical (Y) axis of the original quartz crystal.

crystal diode. See "diode, crystal."

crystallization, *n.* In lead cable sheaths, the condition in which the smooth amorphous consistency of the lead is changed to small sharp granules, due to age, movement, and temperature changes.

CSA, Communications Service Authorization (DCS), *n.* An order from the Defense Communications System to a commercial common carrier for a specific communication service. Issued from a DECCO office.

cupeth, *adj. n.* A type of telephone cable sheath having a 5-mil corrugated copper tape applied longitudinally with overlap under a polyethelene jacket. The low resistance copper tape limits the effect of power induction and of damage from lightning.

curb, manhole. See "shield, manhole."

curie point, *n.* The critical temperature at which piezoelectric materials lose their polarization, and therefore their piezoelectric properties.

current, *n.* (1) movement of electrons through a conductor. (2) The rate of transfer of electricity from one point in a circuit to another point. Usually measured in amperes, or fractional parts. thereof.

current, alternating, *n.* An electric current which continually varies in amount, and reverses its direction periodically. The plot of current versus time is usually a sine wave. Abbreviated "A.C." See also "frequency," "cycle," and "period."

current, average, *n.* The arithmetic mean of the instantaneous currents of a complex wave, averaged over one-half cycle.

current, charging, *n.* The current which flows to a capacitor when it is first connected to a source of electrical potential.

current, direct, (DC), *n.* An electric current which flows in only one direction.

current, eddy, *n.* A circulating current which is induced in conductors and transformer cores which are in a changing magnetic field. It produces heat, and is a loss of useful energy.

current, effective, *n.* That value of an alternating current which will cause the same heat in a resistor as an equivalent value of direct current. If the alternating current is a sine wave, the effective value is the peak value multiplied by 0.7071.

current, fault, *n.* A current which flows from a conductor to ground or to another conductor during an accidental short, cross or ground, including that caused by an arc.

current, ground fault, *n.* A fault current which flows to ground rather than between conductors.

current, ground-return, *n.* A current which returns to its source through the earth. It may be stray direct current from signaling or trolley bus circuits, or stray alternating current from the grounded neutral of an unbalanced three-phase power line.

current, holding. See "holding current."

current, lagging, *n.* In an alternating current circuit, a current wave which lags in phase behind the voltage wave which produced it. The current lags in a circuit in which the net reactance is inductive.

current, leading, *n.* In an alternating current circuit, a current wave which precedes in phase the voltage wave which produces it. The current leads in a circuit in which the net reactance is capacitive.

current, longitudinal, *n.* A current which travels in the same direction on the two sides of a wire communication circuit.

current, magnetizing, *n.* The current in a transformer which is just sufficient to magnetize the core and supply the iron losses, but which will not provide any current to a secondary load.

current, neutral, *n.* Residual current which flows in the neutral conductor of an unbalanced polyphase power circuit. See also "current, residual."

current, non-operate. See "non-operate current."

current, peak, *n.* The maximum value which a current which varies with time reaches during one period.

current, pickup, *n.* The maximum value of current at which a relay or circuit breaker just starts to operate.

current, plate, *n.* The current flowing in the anode (plate) circuit of an electron tube.

current, pull-in, *n.* Pickup current, which see.

current, pulsating, *n.* Current of varying magnitude but constant direction.

current, release. See "release current."

current, residual, *n.* In an unbalanced polyphase power circuit, the vector sum of the currents in the several phase wires.

current, reverse. See "reverse current."

current, sneak, *n.* An unwanted, extraneous current which is impressed on telephone conductors through a cross with foreign conductors. Implies a small current which would cause trouble only if prolonged.

current, space, *n.* The total current flowing between the cathode and all other electrodes in an electron tube, including plate current, control-grid current, screen-grid current, suppressor-grid current, etc.

current, stray. See "current, ground-return."

current amplifier, *n.* An amplifier having a low output impedance and capable of delivering a heavy current.

current flow test set. See "set, current-flow test."

Currents, Law of Induced. See "Lenz' Law" in "Appendix B."

current transformer, *n.* A highly accurate instrument transformer having a high-current low-resistance primary, often of only one-half turn, which is placed in series in a power conductor carrying a large alternating current. The low current secondary is connected to a low current ammeter having a scale indicating the current in the transformer primary. See also "instrument transformer."

curtain, antenna, *n.* (1) A vertical plane which contains a plurality of phased vertical or horizontal energized elements which radiate radio waves which combine in phase. (2) A vertical plane which contains a plurality of phased passive elements which reflect and reinforce the radio wave from the radiator curtain.

curve, gas pressure, *n.* Plot on graph paper of gas pressures read at selected valves in a pressurized cable system. The gas pressure is plotted vertically against a horizontal scale of cable length. Points of low pressure indicate leaks in the cable.

cushions, headset, *n. pl.* Vinyl foam cushions which cover the receiver cap and headband of an operator's telephone set and make it more comfortable to wear. See also "pad, receiver."

customer, telephone, *n.* A person who uses a telephone, either as a subscriber, with the permission of a subscriber, or as the user of a pay telephone.

cut, *n.* The orientation of the sides of a piezoelectric crystal with respect to the electrical and mechanical axes. —*v.* (1) To disconnect. (2) To open a circuit, and thereby interrupt communication. (3) To transfer a service from one facility to another.

cut, ring, *n.* An injury to an aerial cable sheath caused by rubbing on the supporting cable ring.

cut in, cut into, *vi.* To enter a switch bank, as the wipers on a selector switch cut into the bank.—*vt.* To operate a cord circuit key to the talking or listening position.

cut-in, *n.* The action of a step-by-step selector in rotating its wipers into the bank in search of a vacant terminal.

cut-off, *n.* (1) The premature severing of a connection. (2) The cut-off frequency, at which the transmission loss of a circuit exceeds by 10 db the loss at 1000 Hz.

cutoff, waveguide, *n.* The lowest radio frequency that a waveguide will carry without excessive attenuation. See also "waveguide."

cutoff, frequency, *n.* (1) The frequency at which the transmission loss exceeds by 10 db the loss at 1000. Hertz. (2) In an amplifier, the frequency at which the amplifier gain decreases sharply. (3) In a filter, the frequency at which the attenuation begins to increase sharply.

cutoff frequency, waveguide, *n.* The lowest frequency which will propagate through a waveguide while operating in a particular mode.

cut-off relay. See "relay, bridge cutoff."

cut out, *vt.* To operate a switchboard listening key to its normal (straight up) position.

cut-out, *n.* (1) A telephone protector is also known as an open-space cutout. (2) An intermittent open circuit. —*adj.* Said of pairs brought out of a cable and terminated at a location other than the end of the cable. —*vi.* Operating a switchboard talk key to the normal position so as to disconnect from the cord circuit.

cut-out, open space, *n.* A device to protect against over-voltage, consisting of an electrical gap in air between two conducting blocks, commonly of carbon. See also "block, protector."

cut over, *v.* To transfer from one system to another.

cutover, *n.* The act of transferring lines from one system to another, such as from manual service to dial service.

cutover device, *n.* A two-position toggle switch or relay which is wired into a circuit to permit the rapid transfer of a circuit from its present to a future termination. Facilitates pre-cutover testing, and the actual cutover.

cuts off *v.i.* Fails to permit satisfactory transmission above, or below, a specific frequency limit.

cuts out, *v.i.* Experiences a "come-and-go" interruption of communication.

cutter, cable, *n.* A pair of lopping shears having hardened jaws capable of cutting cables with copper conductors. See also "shears, lopping."

cutter, strand, *n.* A long-handled, compound, cutting plier with hardened jaws capable of cutting steel strand, bolts, etc. Also known as a "bolt cutter."

cutter, wire. See "pliers, diagonal" and "pliers, lineman's."

CW radiotelegraphy. See "continuous wave radiotelegraphy."

cybernetics, *n.* A comparative study of the similarities and differences between men and machines, with respect to their ability to communicate and control.

cycle, *n.* One complete sequence of values of an alternating wave; starting at zero, increasing to a maximum in a positive direction, reducing to zero, increasing to a maximum in a negative direction, then returning to zero. See also "dot-cycle," "duty cycle," and "sunspot cycle."

cycles, *n. pl.* Incorrectly used as an expression of frequency, when "cycles-per-second" is meant. See also "hertz."

cycles-per-second, *n.* The older unit of frequency, now replaced by the international standard "Hertz." Abbrev.: cps.

cycling, *n.* A periodic oscillation in an automatically controlled system between the high limit and the low limit at which the controls operate.

cylinder, propane, *n.* A steel cylinder for storing, transporting, and dispensing the liquid petroleum (LP) gas used as a fuel for cable splicer's furnaces, tent heaters, manhole blowers, and manhole pumps. Available in 20 lbs. capacity (Type B) and 40 lbs. capacity (Type C).

dam, *n.* A barrier within a cable, to prevent the flow of gas or air through the cable. Originally paraffin, but now usually some plastic compound which can be injected into the cable.

damped oscillation, *n.* (1) An oscillation in which the amplitude of each succeeding wave becomes less. (2) An oscillation which dies out because (a) the driving force has been removed and, (b) the oscillating circuit contains resistance.

damper, vibration, *n.* Any device used to prevent vibration of line wire or "dancing" and vibration of aerial cable. A spiral tube of polyethelene is used to damp open wire, and weights suspended by springs from the messenger to damp cable.

damping, *n.* The reduction of energy in a mechanical or electrical oscillating system by absorption, conversion into heat, or by radiation.

damping, magnetic, *n.* The slowing down of mechanical motion by the reaction between two magnetic fields. A common example is the metal disc which rotates between the poles of a permanent magnet in a watt-hour meter.

dancing, cable, *n.* Movement of an aerial cable above and below its normal position. A slow oscillation at resonant frequency built up by wind pressure.

daraf, *n.* The unit of electrical elastance, equal to the reciprocal of the capacitance in farads.

d'Arsonval movement, *n.* The movement in a millivollmeter which uses a moving coil in a permanent-magnet field.

dashpot, *n.* A cylinder and piston device using gas or a liquid to retard the movement of a relay or circuit breaker.

dash-pot relay. See "relay, dash-pot."

data, *n.* (1) Numbers, letters, symbols and facts that describe a condition or an object. (2) Basic element of information, usually numerically expressed, which can be processed by computers or machines.—*n. pl.* Plural of the term "datum," which is a basis for calculations.

data, raw, *n.* Data as received, which has not been processed by machine, and which may not yet be in the form which a machine can accept.

data card. See "card, data."

data inquiry-voice answer (DIVA) *n.* A computer inquiry system which uses an audio response mechanism to provide verbal answers to inquiries.

data link. See "link, data."

DATA-PHONE, *n.* Phone permitting making calls to other data subscribers over the DDD network, after which the equipment receives data signals from punched tape, punched cards, or magnetic tape and converts these into tone signals on the toll line. Permits the long distance exchange of information between business machines or other data processing equipment.

DATA-PLUS, *n.* A computer language which uses English words, and English syntax and semantics.

data rate, high speed, *n.* Data transmission at a rate between 2401 bauds and 500 kilobauds.

data rate, low speed, *n.* Transmission of data at any speed up to 150 bauds.

data rate, medium speed, *n.* Data transmission at a rate between 151 and 2400 bauds.

data set. See "set, data."

data sink, *n.* A memory or recording device in which data can be stored for future use.

date-time group, *n.* The date and time of filing a message, expressed in six digits and a letter suffix. The first two digits are the day, the next two the hour of a 24-hour day, the last two the minutes, followed by a letter suffix indicating the time zone.

db, or dB, *n.* Abbreviation for "decibel," which is one-tenth of a bel. A unit expressing the ratio of two voltages, currents, or powers. It is equal to 20 times the common logarithm of the ratio of the two voltages or two currents, and 10 times the common logarithm of the ratio of the two powers.

dba, or dBa, *n.* "Decibels adjusted." Describing the noise with F1A weighting. A noise meter having F1A weighting will read 85 dba when the input is 1000 Hz at a level of one milliwatt. White noise limited to 300-3400 Hz will give a reading of 82 dba.

dbaO, or dBaO, *n.* A reading of noise power in dba (using F1A weighting) at a test point, corrected to the equivalent noise power at the zero level transmission reference point.

dbk, or dBk, *n.* A unit of power. Decibels referred to a standard of one kilowatt.

dbm, or dBm, *n.* (1) The amount of power relative to that represented by a 1000 Hz signal which will feed one milliwatt of power into a 600 ohm resistive load. (2) A term used in CATV work to describe a signal level referred to an arbitrary zero level of one millivolt across 75 ohms.

dbm Al, or dBm Al, *n.* The dbm Al level is the maximum level (in dbm referred to the zero transmission level point) at which a long-term average of 70 noise peaks per hour can just be tolerated. Used to measure impulse noise.

dbm0, or dBm0, *n.* The power in dbm measured at, or referred to a point of zero relative transmission level.

dbr, or dBr, *n.* "Decibels relative level" used to define transmission levels at a point in a circuit, with respect to the level at the zero transmission level reference point.

dbRAP, or dBrap, *n.* A unit of acoustical power. Decibels above reference acoustical power, which is defined as 10^{-12} watts.

dbrn, or dBrn, *n.* "Decibels above

reference noise." Describing the power of a noise as seen through a "144 line weighting" network, corresponding to the frequency characteristics of deskstand telephone sets with #144 receivers. A 1000 Hz one milliwatt tone will give a reading of 90 dbrn. One milliwatt of white noise spread over the 300-3400 Hz band will give a reading of 82 dbrn.

dbrn C-message, or dBrnC, *n.* A measure of the interfering effect of noise when observed with a U-1 receiver, expressed as the "db above a reference noise" of —90 dbm at 1000 cycles. This reference noise is equivalent to —88.5 dbm of a 3 kc band of white noise.

dbv, or dBv, *n.* A unit of electrical pressure. Decibels referred to a standard of one volt.

dbw, or dBw, *n.* A unit of power. Decibels referred to a standard unit of one watt.

dbx, or dBx, *n.* Dbx means "decibels above reference coupling," and is a unit of crosstalk coupling. It is the numerical difference between 90 db. loss and the crosstalk coupling loss. If the coupling loss between the disturbing and disturbed circuit is 65 db, the coupling may be expressed as (90—65)=25 dbx.

dc or DC, *n.* Direct current. An electric current that flows in one direction.

"D" clip, *n.* An "S" shaped flat aluminum clip used to secure drop wire to itself for snub attachments. Clip is closed on drop wire by pressing with pliers.

dead, *adj.* (1) Not connected to any source of electric potential. (2) Having the same potential as the earth.

dead-end, *n.* The end of a cable, or of a wire pair on a pole.—*v.* To end a cable or wire pair at a pole.

dead-end, automatic. See "strandvise."

dead-end, false, *n.* A dead-end midway in a pole line where there is no unbalanced pull under normal conditions. Used as a safety measure, as a backup if the real dead-end were to be destroyed.

dead-end, preformed, *n.* A loop of several stainless steel wires, preformed into cylindrical shape. Can be spiraled onto a line wire, a distribution wire or steel strand to hold it without clamping, tightening as the pull increases.

dead-front, *adj.* Describing equipment, such as a powerboard, constructed so there are no exposed live parts on its front.

deadman, *n.* (1) A short pole having a wide steel fork at the upper end, used to temporarily support a pole while it is being raised. (2) A log or block of concrete, buried in the earth and used as an anchor.

dead pair, *n.* A cable pair which is not spliced through to the central office main distributing frame. It may, or may not, be continuous through the rest of the cable.

dead short, *n.* An electrical short circuit having a very low resistance.

deaf set. See "amplifier, hard-of-hearing" and "telephone, hard-of-hearing."

debug, *v.* (1) To eliminate the defects in a new circuit. (2) To remove clandestine listening devices.

decay, *n.* Expotential reduction in amplitude.—*vi.* To be reduced in an expotential manner, as the current in a circuit decays when the source of potential is removed.

decay time. See "time, decay."

decay time, pulse. See "time, pulse decay."

deci-. A prefix meaning one-tenth.

decibel, db, dB, *n.* A unit which expresses the ratio of two voltages, currents, or powers. Used to specify transmission loss, gain, or relative level. It is equal to 20 times the common logarithm of the ratio of two voltages or two currents, or 10 times the common logarithm of the ratio of two powers.

decimonic frequencies, *n.* Frequencies used for party line selective ringing which are in the series 20, 30, 40, 50, and 60 Hz.

deck, *n.* (1) A set of punched data cards. (2) A mechanical device for transporting magnetic tape past a recording or play-back head.

decode, *v.* (1) To translate digital data into alphanumeric characters. (2) In a translator, to provide an output signal which is logically derived from several input signals plus information in the translator's memory.

decoder, *n.* (1) An electro-mechanical device which selects the proper card from the card translator, reads the routing information, then provides the routing information to the marker and sender as required to complete the call. (#4A TSS) (2) A network or system in which a combination of inputs is energized at one time to produce a single output. (3) A device which provides a unique output for each of many sets of simultaneous inputs. (4) A branching network, tree shaped, which includes no meshes.

decoder, mobile radio, *n.* A circuit that responds to one particular coded signal while rejecting all others.

decoupling, *n.* The reduction or elimination of coupling between two electrical circuits.

decrement, *n.* In an oscillating system with damping (each oscillation has less amplitude than the one preceding it), the ratio of the peak values (voltage, distance, etc.) of two successive half-cycles. It is expressed as a decimal fraction less than one.

decryption, *n.* The technique by which messages which have been encoded to preserve their secrecy are returned to their original clear text form.

dedicated outside plant, *n.* A system of plant usage which avoids assignment, installation, and rearrangement costs on telephone subscriber's lines by permanently assigning a cable pair from the central office main distributing frame to each residence or business location within the area. Customers having key telephone or PBX service are allocated additional pairs. The system uses semi-permanent junction points called "control points" and "access points," which see. If party lines are involved they must be bridged at the central office, and require "bridge lifters" to avoid excessive bridged tap loss.

dedicated service, *n.* A communication service which is allocated for the exclusive use of a pair of users.

deductible time. See "time, deductible."

de-emphasis, *n.* The introduction of loss at the higher frequencies in the receiver of a communication system to compensate for earlier pre-emphasis in the transmitter, and produce an overall response which is flat with frequency. The customary emphasis is 6 db per octave.

de-energize, *v.* To stop the flow of current in a circuit or to remove electrical potential from a circuit, as by opening a switch.

deenergized, *adj.* Said of an apparatus or a system when all sources of power have been removed or turned off.

deflection, electrostatic. See "electrostatic deflection."

deflector, coin, *n.* A metal shield having a pyramidal top placed over the dial adapter on a coin telephone, which prevents coins which drop from the coin chute from lodging behind the dial.

degeneration, *n.* (1) Decay. (2) Negative feedback.

degradation, ultra-violet, *n.* Deterioration in the insulating qualities of a material caused by long-term exposure to sunlight or other short wavelength radiation.

degree, electrical, *n.* One 360th part of a cycle of alternating current.

dehumidifier, *n.* A mechanical refrigerating device which removes moisture from the air by cooling it.

deka-. A prefix meaning ten times.

delay, *n.* Some portions of a complex communication signal arrive at their destination later than other portions. The amount of time by which they are late (usually reckoned in milliseconds) is called the delay.

delay, absolute, *n.* The finite time interval required for transmission between the sending end and the receiving end of a circuit.

delay, call, *n.* The delay experienced by a call which arrives at automatic switching equipment such as a linefinder group and must wait because the equipment is busy handling another call. This delay is considered acceptable if not over 1½% of the calls are delayed by 3 seconds during the busy hour.

delay, differential, *n.* Envelope delay, which see.

delay, envelope, *n.* The time difference between the longest delay and the shortest delay for a given band of frequencies.

delay, hangover, *n.* In an echo suppressor, the length of time, proportional to circuit delay, that transmission in one direction is suppressed after the control signal has disappeared.

delay, posted. See "posted delay."

delay, propagation time. See "propagation time delay."

delay, relative, *n.* The difference in the absolute delay for a particular frequency compared with the absolute delay for a specific reference frequency. See "envelope delay" and "envelope delay distortion."

delay circuit, *n.* A circuit which introduces a time delay into a signal which passes through it.

delay dialing. See "signal, delay pulsing."

delay distortion, *n.* The distortion caused by the fact that some frequencies travel slower over the transmission path than others, and therefore arrive later. Numerically, it is the maximum difference in transmission time between any two frequencies in a specified frequency band, expressed in microseconds.

delay equalizer. See "equalizer, relative delay" and "equalizer, absolute delay."

delay line, *n.* A cable especially made to have a very low velocity of propagation. Used to electrically delay the signals which traverse it.

delay pulsing. See "signal, delay pulsing."

delay traffic table, *n.* Any of the telephone traffic tables designated T-8, T-10, T-20, etc. used for manual traffic handling, and based on an average delay (T-10 is 10 seconds delay, etc.) in seconds during the busy hour until an idle trunk becomes available. Each table relates three factors for a particular delay time:

a. Holding time of average call.

b. Traffic load, in CCS or call-minutes.

c. Trunks per group.

If any two factors are known, the third can be found from the delay table.

deletion, digit, *n.* The action of a register-sender which omits one to six digits of the 10-digit number it receives, by instruction from the translator. For example, if there are direct trunks to a central office within the same area, the sender can drop both the area code and the office code.

delta connection, *n.* A method of connecting a three-phase power circuit in which each of three transformer windings are connected across one of the three phases, so that the winding connection diagram looks like the Greek letter "delta," an equilateral triangle.

delta-matched, *adj.* Connected through a delta-matched transformer, a section of open wire radio-frequency transmission line in which the conductors are closely spaced at the low impedance end and get progressively farther apart toward the higher impedance end.

delta modulation. See "modulation, delta."

demand, power system, *n.* The total load of a power system, expressed in kilowatts or kilovoltamperes, averaged over a specified interval of time.

demand factor, power. See "factor, power demand."

demineralizer, water, *n.* A device which produces mineral-free water, suitable for use in a storage battery, by allowing tap water to percolate through a tank filled with pellets of an ion exchange resin.

demodulation, *n.* The act of recovering from a modulated wave the signal with which the wave was originally modulated.

demodulation, phase-lock loop, *n.* Demodulation used in satellite earth terminals which can detect extremely weak RF signals. Uses a signal-tracking filter which responds to only a narrow band centered about the instantaneous carrier frequency as it sweeps through its deviation.

demodulator, *n.* A semi-conductor or vacuum tube device which recovers the original intelligence signal from a modulated carrier wave.

demodulator, FM, *n.* An FM receiver fixed-tuned to a specific FM radio channel. Used at a CATV head end to obtain a music or other audio program from the air.

demodulator, SCA, *n.* Subsidiary carrier authorization demodulator. A low-frequency receiver tuned to a subcarrier signal broadcast by an FM radio station. It is connected to the multiplex output in an FM receiver and demodulates the subcarrier program carrying subscription music, stock reports, etc. See also "modulator, SCA."

demodulator, television, *n.* A television receiver minus the picture tube and its related circuits. It receives a complete television signal and demodulates it to two components:

(a) the video signal and (b) the 4.5 MHz FM sound signal. The FM sound signal may be further demodulated to provide an audio monitor output. Used at a CATV head end in conjunction with a television modulator, which see.

demonstration jacks, *n.* A group of jacks in the switchboard multiple to which are wired certain tones and signals such as dial tone, busy signal, NC signal, etc. for reference by the operator.

demultiplexer, *n.* A device that reverses the action of a multiplexer, and derives a group of separate channels from the complex multiplex signal.

denier, *n.* A unit of weight for threads or cords of silk, rayon, or nylon, equal to 0.05 gram per 450 meters.

density, power, *n.* Power in watts per hertz, or the total power in a band of frequencies divided by the bandwidth in hertz.

departure, frequency, *n.* The amount of variation of a carrier frequency from its assigned value or center frequency.

depletion layer, *n.* A zone, several atoms thick, at the junction of n-type and p-type semiconductor materials in which there are no current carriers, either free electrons or holes, unless biased by a direct voltage. Free electrons in the n-type material are repelled by negative charges in the p-type material, and the holes in the p-type material are repelled by the positive nucleous of atoms in the n-type material.

depolarizer, *n.* A chemical substance, usually manganese dioxide, added to a dry cell to remove the polarizing chemical products resulting from discharge, and thus to keep the discharge rate constant.

deposit, *v.t.* The placing of money in a coin telephone by the customer. —*n.* The money so deposited.

depository, after-hours payment, *n.* A receptacle, accessible from the lobby of the telephone business office, where subscribers may leave payments for their telephone bills when the office is closed.

derate, *v.* To use a device at a lower current or voltage than it is capable of handling in order to reduce the probability of failure, or to permit its use under a condition of high ambient temperature.

derating factor, wire, *n.* A factor by which the allowable current carrying capacity of a wire is reduced when it is used in an environment different from the environment for which the rating was established.

derivation equipment, channel, *n.* Equipment used to obtain a number of relatively narrow-band channels from a wider band facility, usually by dividing up the frequency band.

derive, *v.t.* To obtain a message channel by subdividing a transmission facility, either in terms of time or bandwidth.

derived filter. See" filter, m-derived."

derrick, gas cylinder, *n.* A small crane-type derrick which mounts on the rear of a cable splicer's truck, and is used with a block and tackle to transfer heavy gas cylinders from truck to manhole, and vice versa.

derrick, pole setting, *n.* A tripod of heavy steel poles, two of the legs being hinged to the back of a line construction truck, and having a large single-sheave block at the apex of the tripod. The truck's winch line is passed through the sheave and used to lift, lower, and support poles during the pole setting operation.

desensitization, receiver, *n.* A reduction of the sensitivity of a radio receiver through operation of the automatic gain control by a very strong interfering signal.

desiccant, *n.* A chemical with a great affinity for water, used for drying cable splices. Has a negligible vapor pressure at ordinary temperatures.

Common desiccants include the oxides of barium, calcium, and magnesium.

designation, *n.* (1) A distinguishing name and/or number. (2) A name plate or marker strip; also the information thereon.

designation strip, *n.* Narrow strip above switchboard jack or lamp strips, on which the name and number of the circuits are shown.

desk, information. See "information board."

desk, local test. See "test desk, local."

desk, special service, *n.* A switchboard having key-ended trunks which is used for handling special service calls, such as information, intercepting, and emergency.

deskstand, *n.* An obsolete type of desk telephone which mounts a transmitter at the upper end of a pedestal, a switchhook within the pedestal which supports a receiver, and a dial in the base.

despun, *adj.* Describing capability of an antenna to remain pointed at the same point in space even when carried on a vehicle (satellite) which is spinning.

destination code, *n.* The complete 10-digit number (3-digit NPA code + 3-digit CO code + 4-digit station number) which specifies the location of a particular telephone. Also called a "telephone address."

destructive readout. See "readout, destructive."

detached schematic drawing. See "drawing, detached schematic."

detect, *vt.* To rectify a modulated carrier wave and thereby recover the original modulating wave.

detection, *n.* The process by which a wave corresponding to the modulating wave is obtained from a modulated wave.

detector, *n.* That part of a radio receiver which demodulates the carrier wave.

detector, ANI, *n.* A transistor device which, with number networks, enables identification of the directory number of any line in an ANI central office.

detector, carbon monoxide, *n.* A glass ampoule in a cloth sleeve, which is crushed and suspended in a manhole before a cable splicer enters. The degree of discoloration of the sleeve indicates the percentage of carbon monoxide present in the manhole atmosphere, and whether it is safe to enter. If unsafe, the manhole is ventilated with a blower, and retested until found safe.

detector, coin level, *n.* A contact placed near the top of a coin receptacle in a coin telephone, used to provide a local or remote alarm when the receptacle is 70% full of coins.

detector, crystal, *n.* A germanium diode or similar rectifier which can be used to detect (demodulate) a modulated radio-frequency signal.

detector, first, *n.* The mixer stage in a superheterodyne radio receiver. It mixes the radio signal with a local oscillator signal to produce an intermediate frequency.

detector, gas leak, *n.* A device for finding a leak in a pressurized aerial cable, based on detecting the ultrasonic hiss of escaping gas. Consists of a microphone on a pole probe, an amplifier, and an heterodyne detector which produces an audio signal.

detector, ratio, *n.* The type of detector, or FM discriminator, commonly used in frequency modulation receivers. Uses a pair of diodes, one of which is reversed, and is preferred because it requires no limiter and provides an automatic volume control (AVC) voltage.

detector, second, *n.* In a superheterodyne radio receiver, the detector which derives the audio-frequency intelligence signal from the intermediate-frequency signal.

detector, ultrasonic leak, *n.* Device which can detect small leaks in gas-filled cables by translating the ultra-sonic hiss of leaking gas to a whistling sound within the audio range. Consists of a small microphone which can be mounted on a fishing pole and held close to the suspected aerial cable. Microphone output is fed thru a preamplifier to an oscillator/detector, whose output is fed to a loud speaker and/or output meter.

detector guard, *n.* A device associated with a signal detector which prevents speech-simulated signals from causing false operation of the signal detector, by requiring almost a pure tone to operate the signal detector. Operates by amplifying and rectifying all frequencies in the voice band outside of the 100 Hz signaling band, and using this error voltage to oppose that derived from the signal detector.

detent, *n.* (1) A mechanical element used to lock and unlock a rotary mechanism. Usually a toothed dog which drops into a depression (ratchet) in the moving member. (2) A notch or latch on a control knob which holds it in a fixed position until it is moved intentionally.

detent, double. See "double dog."

detune, *v.* (1) To adjust a circuit so that it does not respond to (is not resonant at) a particular frequency. (2) To change the inductance or capacitance of a tuned circuit so that it is not resonant at the frequency of the applied signal.

deviation, allowable, *n.* The permissible difference between any of a range of conditions and a reference condition.

deviation, carrier, *n.* The greatest instantaneous excursion of a frequency modulated carrier from its nominal value, eg: the highest instantaneous carrier frequency minus the nominal carrier frequency.

deviation, frequency, *n.* The measure of the percentage modulation of a frequency modulated wave. It is the peak difference between the instantaneous frequency of an FM modulated wave and the carrier frequency.

deviation, phase, *n.* In phase modulation, the peak difference between the instantaneous phase angle of the modulated wave and the phase angle of the sine-wave carrier, both expressed in radians.

deviation, standard, *n.* A measure of the variation (of one sample from a group) from the mean or average value of the group.

deviation ratio, *n.* In a frequency modulated wave, the ratio of the carrier deviation to the highest baseband frequency.

deviator, *n.* An FM modulator.

device, *n.* A single, discrete conventional electron device such as a resistor or transistor, or a microelectronic circuit.

device, analog, *n.* A device able to perform mathematical operations, such as summing or integration, on analog signals.

device, anti-singing. See "VODAS."

device, input/output, *n.* Any equipment which introduces data into or takes data from a data communication system.

device, semiconductor, *n.* Any electron device based on the use of conduction in a semiconductor, such as a crystal diode, transistor, thermistor, or photodiode.

device, warning, *n.* Flags, flashing lights, or signs such as "MEN WORKING," used to safeguard employees while at work.

dewpoint, *n.* The temperature at which moisture begins to condense out of a vapor. The relative humidity is then 100%.

diagonal brace. See "brace, diagonal."

diagram, block, *n.* A simplified circuit diagram, in which complex units of equipment are shown simply as a rectangle (block) bearing the appropriate name. Usually combined with a "single-line diagram."

diagram, schematic, *n.* A functional diagram of an electrical circuit in which the components are represented by conventional symbols, and the interconnecting wires by lines.

diagram, traffic, *n.* A block diagram in which the switching centers are represented by blocks and their interconnecting trunks by lines. Shows trunk quantities.

diagram, vector. See "vector diagram."

diagram, wiring, *n.* A circuit diagram that shows electrical components and all of the wires which interconnect them. The diagram shows the designation of the terminals, color coding of the wires, and whether the wires are singles, pairs, triples, or quads.

dial, *n.* A device which transmits a coded signal to actuate the central office switching equipment in accordance with the digit dialed. It may be either a rotary device which can be wound up and released to transmit open pulses (DC space pulses) or a touch-calling push button device (dual-tone, multi-frequency signals), —*vt.* Operating a dial or a keyset to transmit address information to automatic switching equipment.

dial, automatic, *n.* Device which will automatically dial any of a group of pre-selected telephone numbers.

dial, card-reader, *n.* An electromechanical device which provides an automatic dialing capability, using a repertory of punched cards on which the telephone numbers of frequently called stations are stored. The card is inserted into the reader and a "START" button pressed. The card punchings control a series of coded electrical breaks of the line current. These dial pulses transmit the telephone number information to the central office at the normal rate of ten pulses per second. Card reader dials which transmit DTMF signals are also available.

dial, partial. See "digits, partial."

dial, rotary, *n.* A rotary mechanism

having a ten-hole finger wheel which when wound up and released causes pulsing contacts to interrupt the line current and operate central office selecting equipment in accordance with the digit (1 thru 0) dialed.

dial, space-saver, *n.* A rotary telephone dial with a moveable finger stop which eliminates the need for the space between "1" and "0," thus permitting a smaller finger wheel.

dial, subscriber, *n.* A rotary dial intended for use on subscriber's telephones. Typical limiting performance of modern (1971) dials is 8-11 pps, 58-64% break during any portion of the rundown period.

dial, switchboard, *n.* A rotary dial for switchboard use which provides more accurate pulses than the average subscriber's dial. Typical performance is: (a) 9.7-10.3 pps, 62-66% break, (b) 17-21 pps, 62-66% break.

dial, telephone. See "dial, subscribers."

dial, touch-calling, *n.* A push-button device having ten or more non-locking push buttons designated 1 thru 0. Each of the buttons, when operated, generates a double-frequency signal distinctive to that button. See also "DTMF."

dial-back trunk, *n.* A trunk over which a calling subscriber in a community dial office (CDO) may reach an operator at the operator office, after which the operator may dial back over the same trunk to connect the calling subscriber to a called party served from the same CDO.

dial central office. See "office, dial central."

dial cord, *n.* Single separate cord which is inserted in the switchboard jack for the dialing operation only.

dialed number display. See "display, dialed number."

dialer, automatic. See "dial, card-reader" and "repertory dialing."

dialer, card. See "dial, card-reader."

dialer, Magicall, *n.* A magnetic recording repertory dialer unit having a capacity of either 400 or 1000 numbers, depending upon the length of the magnetic recording tape which is used. The tape is rotated by means of a manual selector wheel, and the desired number is selected by a red line on the tape which moves against an alphabetical index. The rear of the tape has a magnetic oxide coating, while the face has a typed list of names in alphabetical sequence. Scanning is across the tape, left to right.

dialer, repertory, *n.* Device which will automatically dial a complete telephone number after a single button is depressed. Its matrix of buttons can be pre-programmed for the desired telephone numbers.

dialing, abbreviated. See "abbreviated dialing."

dialing, direct distance (DDD). See "distance dialing."

dialing, direct inward. See "direct inward dialing."

dialing, direct outward. See "direct outward dialing."

dialing, intertoll, *n.* Dialing over intertoll trunks.

dialing, nationwide, *n.* The completion of long distance calls by either subscribers or operators dialing from their originating location directly to the called telephone without any assistance from intermediate operators.

dialing area, *n.* The area within which a customer may make calls by dialing.

dial-in-handset, *n.* Any of the several types of telephone handsets which include a small dial, either rotary or DTMF.

dial key, *n.* Key on a switchboard position which may be operated to permit dialing on any of the calling cords on which the "talk" key is operated.

dial key dialing, *n.* An arrangement at switchboards where, during the dialing operation, a common dialing circuit is connected to the cord in use by means of a dial key associated with each cord.

dial office, *n.* An automatic central office.

dial pilot lamp, *n.* A green signal lamp in the piling rail back of the dial on switchboards with listening key dialing. This lamp lights as soon as the dial is moved, and remains lighted until the dial release key is operated.

dial pulse. See "pulse, dial."

dial pulsing. See "pulsing, dial."

dial release key, *n.* A non-locking lever key mounted in front of the dial, which enables the operator to disconnect (release) the dial from the cord as soon as dialing is completed.

dial system "A" board. See "DSA board."

Dial Teletypewriter Exchange Service (DTWX), *n.* Subscriber dialing from any teletypewriter to any other teletypewriter, nation-wide.

dial tone, *n.* A tone indicating that automatic switching equipment is ready to receive dial signals. It is now a 600 Hz tone modulated with 120 Hz, but should be replaced with 350 + 440 Hz by 1972.

dial tone first, *n.* A method of operating pay telephones such that dial tone is received as soon as the handset is lifted, without depositing a coin. Enables dialing certain codes, such as the universal emergency code 911, even though the caller does not have a coin.

diamagnetic, *adj.* Describing a metal, such as antimony, bismuth, or zinc, which has a magnetic permeability less than one and is therefore repelled by a magnet.

diameter, pitch, *n.* Of a cable, the diameter of a circle passing through the centers of the conductors in any layer of a multiconductor cable.

diaphragm, *n.* A thin flexible sheet that can be vibrated by sound waves as in a microphone, or can be vibrated by magnetic waves to produce sound waves as in a telephone receiver.

diaphragm, damped, *n.* A diaphragm which is mechanically loaded so that it does not vibrate freely, thus eliminating resonant peaks and thereby reducing distortion.

dictation service, *n.* Feature of a dial PBX whereby dialing a code will connect the caller over a telephone dictation trunk to a dictation recorder at the central stenographic pool.

dictation service, remote, *n.* A service provided on some PABX's which enables a user to access a dictating machine by dialing an established number. After readying the machine, the user may exercise control by dialing additional digits.

dielectric, *n.* (1) A material which will not conduct electricity, but will contain an electrostatic field. (2) Insulating material used between the metal plates of a capacitor which can store electric charges in the form of dielectric stress.

dielectric constant, *n.* A measure of the ability of a dielectric material to store electrostatic energy, compared to air. Also called "specific inductive capacity." Some representative values of dielectric constant are:

Air	—	1.0
Paraffin	—	2.1
Mica	—	5.8
Glass	—	8.0

dielectric lens. See "antenna, lens."

dielectric phase angle, *n.* The angular phase difference in degrees or radians between the voltage applied to a capacitor dielectric and the alternating current through it.

dielectric strength, *n.* The maximum potential gradient that a dielectric material can withstand without puncturing.

dielguide, *n.* A dielectric feed assembly for an antenna.

difference, phase, *n.* The number of

electrical degrees (or radians) by which one electrical wave leads or lags another.

difference, potential, *n.* The algebraic difference between the voltages at two points in an electrical circuit.

differential, *adj.* Describing any device whose operation is dependent on the difference between two quantities.

differential gain, *n.* Variation in the gain of a transmission system with changing modulation.

differential phase, *n.* Phase distortion. Variation of the phase of a signal with modulation in an amplitude-modulated system.

diffraction, *n.* The bending of a wave, light or radio, as it passes the sharp edge of an object or through a grating.

diffuse, *v.* To broadcast. (British term)

diffuse reflection, *n.* The scattered reflection of light, radio, or sound waves from a rough surface. See also "specular reflection."

diffusion, *n.* The spreading or scattering of a wave, such as a sound wave.

digger, hydraulic, *n.* A pole hole auger with hydraulic drive and feed motors set in a steel frame which can be suspended from the pole derrick on a line construction truck. It uses hydraulic power furnished from the truck engine to bore pole holes.

digger, pole hole. See "auger, earth."

digger, trench. See "trencher."

digit, *n.* Any numeral from 0 to 9.

digit, check, *n.* A digit used for checking purposes, but which is otherwise redundant.

digit, language, *n.* On international toll calls, a digit automatically inserted and pulsed forward between the country code and the national code of the number dialed. It routes the call to an assistance operator speaking the same language as the originating operator.

digit, route control. See "route control digit."

digital, *adj.* Referring to the use of

digits to formulate and solve problems, or to encode information.

digital circuit switch, *n.* A switch used to interconnect circuits between users for the real-time transmission of digital signals.

digital data, *n.* Any data which is expressed in digits. Usually implies the use of binary digits.

digital signals, *n.* Signals made up of discontinuous pulses whose information is contained in their durations, periods, and/or amplitudes.

digitizing, *n.* The process of converting an analog signal to a digital signal.

digits, partial, *n.* A failure of an originating register to receive sufficient digits to complete the call.

digits, route control (RCD), *n. pl.* At a common-controlled tandem or toll office, the digits which specify the digits to be outpulsed as a function of the trunk route selected and the route control digits received.

dinkey, pole, *n.* A small pole trailer, not normally equipped with brakes or with an electric lighting system.

diode, *n.* (1) A vacuum tube which contains two elements: a cathode and a plate.* (2) A semi-conductor device which is the electrical equivalent of a vacuum-tube diode.

diode, crystal, *n.* A diode rectifier using a point contact on a silicon or germanium crystal. Because of its low capacitance it will rectify at ultrahigh and superhigh frequencies.

diode, germanium, *n.* A semiconductor diode which uses germanium as the rectifying element.

diode, junction, *n.* A semiconductor diode in which rectification occurs at a junction between n-type and p-type materials, rather than at a point contact.

diode, semiconductor, *n.* A two-electrode semiconductor device which conducts current more easily in one direction.

diode, tunnel, *n.* A heavily doped junction diode based on tunneling effect: the piercing of a potential barrier by a low-energy electron. Has a forward negative resistance, and is an excellent low-noise microwave amplifier. It has no upper frequency limitation.

diode, varactor, *n.* A low-loss silicon diode whose junction capacitance is a function of the voltage applied to its terminals. Since this capacitance can be made to vary at superhigh frequencies, the varactor diode is useful in a parametric amplifier.

diode, zener. See "zener diode."

diode bridge, *n.* A bridge configuration of diodes whose output polarity remains unchanged whatever the input polarity. Permits random bridging of polarity sensitive devices on a telephone line.

diplexer, *n.* A device which enables two radio transmitters operating at different frequencies to use the same antenna simultaneously.

diplex operation, *n.* (1) The simultaneous transmission or reception of two signals using a common feature, such as a single antenna or a single carrier. (2) The operation of two radio transmitters on different frequencies into the same antenna simultaneously.

dipole, *n.* A bi-directional antenna consisting of a straight wire one-half wavelength long which is cut at the center for connection to a coaxial feed line. Its impedance is 72 ohms.

dipole, wideband, *n.* A dipole antenna whose radiating elements are "fat," that is, have a much larger diameter than normal.

direct-burial *adj.* Said of telephone cable or wire which, because of its ruggedness, moisture protection, and resistance to rodent attack, is suitable for installation directly in the ground, without conduit or other protection.

direct circuit, *n.* (1) A circuit connecting two toll centers. (2) An intertoll trunk. (3) An interoffice trunk.

direct circuit call, *n.* A call involving the use of but one circuit between the originating toll center and the terminating toll center.

direct-control, *adj.* Describes an automatic telephone system in which the dial pulses from the calling telephone directly control the switches that establish the desired connection.

direct control office, *n.* A central office or switching center in which the switching equipment is actuated by dial pulses received from the subscriber's dial or from other central offices. Direct control equipment includes the following types:
   a. Step-by-step
   b. All relay
   c. Motor-switch

direct coupling, *n.* The interconnection of two stages of an electrical device, such as an amplifier, with a wire or resistor so that direct current can flow.

direct current (DC), *n.* An electric current that flows in one direction.

direct distance dialing (DDD), *n.* The dialing by the customer of all calls to which toll charges are applicable. Single and multi-unit calls within the local service area are not toll, and are therefore not classed as DDD calls. No operator assistance is used, other than by CAMA or TSP operators.

directing code, *n.* One or more digits dialed ahead of the telephone number which enable a customer or operator to dial numbers in an office contiguous to or near the local dialing area of the originating customer or operator. The digit "9" used in a PABX to access the city trunks is a directing code.

direct inward dialing (DID), *n.* (1) Dialing of a call from a city telephone directly to a PABX extension without help of the PABX operator. (2) The routing of a call from an automatic toll network directly to a telephone on a local system.

directional antenna. See "antenna, directional."

directional control, hub, *n.* A provision of a telegraph hub circuit which prevents a signal received from a particular telegraph leg from being sent back into the sending side of that same leg. Required for half-duplex operation.

directional coupler. See "coupler, directional."

directional filters. See "filters, directional."

directivity, *n.* Of a directional antenna, the value of its directive gain in the direction of its maximum value.

direct line service, *n.* Service which provides a direct line between two telephones, connected through a direct line equipment in the central office. Either party can call the other by merely lifting the handset of his telephone.

director, *n.* (1) A device which combines register-sender-translator functions to control automatic switching equipment. A registered trade mark of the Automatic Electric Co. (2) A parasitic element on a directional antenna which is on the major lobe side of the active element. See "element, parasitic."

directory, street address, *n.* A telephone directory which lists each telephone number alphabetically by street name and numerically by street address, but does not show the subscriber's name. Used by toll information operators to obtain a "nearby" telephone number, near to the desired address for the completion of emergency calls.

directory, telephone, *n.* A paperback book, revised at 6-12 month intervals, which lists the name of each telephone subscriber with his address and telephone number. Sometimes the directory also includes a Yellow Pages classified advertising section.

directory assistance, *n.* The furnishing of telephone numbers to users who are not able to find the listing in their directory. Formerly called "information service."

directory number. See "number, directory."

direct outward dialing (DOD), *n.* (1) Dialing of a call into the city system from a PAX/PABX extension without the help of an operator. Usually accomplished by first dialing the digit "9." (2) The dialing of a call from a local system into a toll network without the help of an operator.

direct triple, *n.* In automatic alternate routing of toll calls, the three most direct alternate forward routes available to the destination switching center. Does not include the direct (unswitched) route. See also "idle search."

direct voltage, *n.* A voltage which produces a direct current, which flows in only one direction.

direct wave. See "wave, direct."

disable, *v.* To perform some action on a circuit which will prevent it from operating.

disabler, echo suppressor, *n.* A device which disables an echo suppressor so that it will not interfere with transmission of full duplex data signals over the circuit. Operates upon receipt of a 2025 Hz signal over the four wire circuit for a period of 300 milliseconds.

disabler, tone, *n.* A tone operated device which will disable echo suppressors on a circuit whenever data signals are present on the circuit.

discharge, *n.* (1) Of a storage battery, the conversion of chemical energy into electrical energy. (2) Of a capacitor, the conversion of dielectric stress into an electric current.

discharge blocks, *n.* (1) A protector block. (2) A device which provides an accurately dimensioned gap between two discharge electrodes, used to provide the over-voltage control element in a protector.

discharger, *n.* A protector block.

disconnect, *vt.* To deenergize or disable an electrical circuit by the removal of connections.

disconnect-make busy, carrier, *n.* A feature of carrier systems which carry dial trunks. About ten seconds after system failure (loss of carrier, loss of battery voltage, or loss of synchronization) the trunks are automatically disconnected for about 500 milliseconds to release the switching equipment. All channels are then made busy by grounding the "C" leads to the switching equipment.

disconnect signal, *n.* The on-hook signal by which the calling and called terminals notify the switching equipment that an established connection is no longer needed and should be released.

discontinuity, *n.* A point of abrupt change in the impedance of a circuit, where wave reflections can occur.

discrete address, *n.* A separate and individual address for a particular communication terminal.

discriminate, *v.* (1) To restrict, as access to a trunk. (2) To detect which of two frequencies is present in a circuit.

discrimination, number, *n.* A means of differentiating, where necessary, between numbers in different office code groups but within the same number series group. Where required, separate rate treatment can be given to the three or less office code groups within one number series group.

discriminator, *n.* (1) A vacuum tube or solid-state device which converts an intermediate-frequency, frequency-modulated signal into a baseband amplitude-modulated signal. Serves as the "detector" in an FM receiver. (2) A device which provides a voltage output only if the input voltage exceeds a certain pre-set level. (3) A device which responds only to a pair of frequencies which have some characteristic in common, such as amplitude.

discriminator, FM, *n.* An electron tube or transistor device which is capable of detecting the frequency rate of change of an FM signal, and of converting this to a signal voltage identical with the original modulating signal.

dish, *n.* A parabolic antenna. (colloquial)

dispersion, *n.* (1) The scattering of microwave radio radiation by rain drops, or similar obstructions. (2) The separating of an electromagnetic wave into its components having different frequencies. (3) The distribution of a finely divided solid in a liquid, as graphite particles in oil.

dispersion, facility, *n.* The allocation of circuits between two points over more than one geographic or physical route, as a protection against interruptions.

display, *n.* A visual presentation of information, as on a cathode ray tube, digital register, or Nixie tube.

display, dialed number, *n.* A unit of face equipment on some switchboards and service observing boards, on which the number the subscriber dialed is visually displayed on a row of Nixie tubes.

dissipation factor, *n.* Of a dielectric material, the ratio of the energy lost in heat to the energy stored in the dielectric per hertz. Some typical values of dissipation factor at one kilohertz are:

Polyethelene	—	0.0002
Paraffin	—	0.0006
Mica	—	0.0006
Polyvinyl chloride	—	0.0185

dissipator, heat, *n.* A heat sink, which see.

distance, skip. See "skip distance."

distance dialing, *n.* The completion of long distance calls by either subscribers or operators dialing from the originating location without any assistance from intermediate operators. CAMA or TSP operators who may enter on the line for brief periods are not classed as intermediate operators. See also "direct distance dialing" and "operator distance dialing."

distort, *v.* To change the natural shape, particularly of a communication wave form during its transmission through a circuit.

distortion, *n.* Any difference between the wave shape of an original signal, and the wave shape after the signal has traversed the transmission circuit.

distortion, amplitude, *n.* Amplitude-frequency distortion, which see.

distortion, amplitude-frequency, *n.* The distortion which occurs when the various frequency components of a complex wave are not amplified, attenuated, or transmitted equally well.

distortion, attenuation, *n.* Amplitude-frequency distortion, which see.

distortion, bias, *n.* The distortion of telegraph or digital signals which causes lengthening of marking signals or shortening of spacing signals. See also "bias."

distortion, characteristic, *n.* Distortion of telegraph or digital signals which affects marking and spacing signals in the same manner, but is dependent upon the length of the signal element. In general, a short pulse will be distorted more than a long pulse.

distortion, delay, *n.* Distortion caused by the fact that the higher frequency components of a signal travel slower over the transmission facility than the lower frequency components, therefore arrive later and out of phase. Also called phase distortion.

distortion, envelope delay. See "envelope delay distortion."

distortion, fortuitous telegraph, *n.* Distortion of telegraph signals which does not follow any pattern, and is not predictable.

distortion, frequency, *n.* Distortion in which there is change in the relative magnitudes of the different frequency components of a complex

wave, providing that the change is not caused by non-linear distortion.

distortion, harmonic, *n.* A form of distortion in which harmonics of a fundamental frequency are generated by the non-linearity of a circuit.

distortion, intermodulation, *n.* The distortion caused by the addition of sum-and-difference modulation products when a complex wave (composed of two or more sine waves) passes through a non-linear circuit. When the modulation products are few, "distortion" is created; when they are many, "noise" is created.

distortion, linear, *n.* Changed waveform of a signal caused by unequal modification of the frequency components of the original wave, with the distortion increasing linearly with frequency.

distortion, non-linear, *n.* Distortion in an electrical system in which the ratio of voltage to current in the system varies as a function of either the voltage or current.

distortion, phase. See "distortion, delay."

distortion, phase-frequency, *n.* Distortion which occurs when phase-shift is not directly proportional to frequency.

distortion, single harmonic, *n.* The ratio, expressed in dB, of the power at the fundamental frequency at the output of a transmission system to the power of any single harmonic frequency in the output of the system, when a single frequency signal of specified power is applied to the input of the system.

distortion, speed, *n.* The apparent distortion which appears when there is a difference in speed between a sending device and the corresponding receiving device.

distortion, standard, *n.* A circuit which will transmit the frequencies in the band 250-3,000 Hz is considered to have zero distortion transmission impairment.

distortion, systematic, *n.* Distortion of a digital signal which is experienced repeatedly in accordance with a pattern, or system. It can be divided into two types: "bias distortion" and "characteristic distortion," which see.

distortion, telegraph signal, *n.* The deviation of telegraph signals with respect to the time of beginning and the time of ending of the individual signal elements, not including the average delay of the signals.

distortion, teletypewriter signal, *n.* The shifting of transition points of the signal pulses from their proper positions relative to the start pulse, expressed in percent of a perfect unit pulse length.

distortion, time-delay. See "distortion, delay."

distortion, total harmonic, *n.* The ratio, expressed in dB, of the power at the fundamental frequency at the output of a transmission system to the total power of all harmonics which appear at the output of the system because of system non-linearity, when a single frequency signal of specified power is applied to the input of the system.

distortionless line. See "line, distortionless."

distortion transmission impairment (DTI), *n.* The amount of attenuation which must be added to a distortionless circuit to produce the same transmission degradation as a specified reduction in bandwidth below 3,000. hertz.

DTI		Cutoff Frequency
0 db	—	3000 Hz
1 db	—	2900 "
2 db	—	2700 "
3 db	—	2500 "
4 db	—	2350 "
5 db	—	2200 "

distributed, *adj.* Describing the resistance, inductance, and capacitance of a transmission line which exist uniformly along the entire length of the circuit.

distributing frame. See "frame, - - - distributing."

distributing terminal assembly, *n.* An assembly of terminals in the center of a step-by-step selector bay on which the tip, ring, and sleeve leads of all levels of all selector shelves are terminated. Vertical straps permit grading each level to provide any desired number of trunks.

distribution, automatic call, *n.* A system for automatically distributing calls to a switchboard to an idle operator, in such a way that all operators receive a uniform traffic load.

distribution cable. See "cable, distribution."

distributor, *n.* The rotary stepping switch associated with a group of linefinders which automatically preselects (allots) the next idle linefinder of a group when the previously allotted linefinder has seized a calling line.

distributor, automatic call, *n.* Equipment which receives calls coming over a group of trunks and distributes each in sequence to the least busy operator.

distributor, CATV transmission, *n.* A directional coupler used with a bridging amplifier to supply signals to several branching CATV cables.

distributor, position, *n.* A circuit which makes automatic distribution of an incoming call to an idle switchboard position. See also "distributor, automatic call."

distributor, telegraph, *n.* An electrical or electromechanical time-division multiplex device which connects a single telegraph channel in rapid succession to several telegraph sending or receiving devices.

distributor, teletypewriter, *n.* On a start-stop teletypewriter, a circular commutator with a rotating brush which sequentially scans five leads from the keyboard or punched tape reader, corresponding to the five units of the Baudot code.

disturbance, *n.* (1) An interruption of

a quiet state. (2) Any form of interference with normal communications.

disturbance, sudden ionospheric (SID), *n.* A sudden and abnormally high ionization of the D region of the ionosphere caused by ultra-violet radiation from a solar flare. It may severely disrupt radio communication in the upper LF and lower MF frequencies, and may also severely disrupt grounded signaling and telegraph circuits. Radio communication on the dark side of the earth will not be affected.

dither signal, *n.* A rectangular noise signal of constant repetition rate and constant energy per cycle, but with a psuedo-random amplitude.

diurnal variation, *n.* A change in the propagation characteristics of a radio transmission path that repeats once a day. The variation between day and night.

DIVA, *n.* Data-Inquiry, Voice-Answer. A system wherein a computer is queried in digital language and provides a verbal answer by means of an audio response mechanism.

diversion, call, *n.* A feature of some PABX's, wherein direct inward dialed calls will be diverted to the attendant under certain conditions, such as:
  a. Call to the listed number.
  b. Call to a changed number.
  c. Call encountering a timed "don't answer."
  d. Call encountering a timed "line busy."

diversion, slumber time, *n.* A Centrex feature for hospitals which diverts calls for patients in the hospital to an operator between 10 PM and 7 AM.

diversion equipment. See "equipment, diversion."

diversity, *n.* A method of radio transmission and/or reception which counteracts the effects of fading by combining several signals, all bearing the same information.

diversity, angle, *n.* Polarization diversity.

diversity, cross-band, *n.* Frequency diversity in which the two radio frequencies used are in two frequency bands. Used only when the band is too congested for the assignment of a second frequency in the same band.

diversity, dual, *n.* The operation of combining two identical signals received over diverse paths to obtain an improvement of up to 3 db in signal-to-noise ratio.

diversity, frequency, *n.* Type of radio transmission in which the same information modulates two or more transmitters operating on frequencies separated by about one kilohertz. These signals are received on two or more receivers whose outputs are combined to produce one fade-free signal. See also "combiner."

diversity, polarization, *n.* A method of diversity radio transmission in which a single parabolic reflector is illuminated by two feed horns at angles to each other. The different polarizations of the transmitted wave results in two paths based on illuminating different scatter volumes in the troposphere.

diversity, quadruple, *n.* The operation of combining four identical signals received over diverse paths to obtain an improvement of up to 6 db in signal-to-noise ratio.

diversity, space, *n.* A method of diversity radio reception in which the receiving antennas are physically separated, vertically or horizontally, by 50 wavelengths or more.

diversity combiner, additive, *n.* A device for combining diversity radio signals in which the outputs of the several receivers are connected in series so that the signal-to-noise ratios are added.

diversity combiner, ratio-squared, *n.* A device for combining diversity radio signals in such a way that the contribution of any receiver to the combined output is proportional to the signal-to-noise power at the output of that receiver. To accomplish this the voltage signal-to-noise is squared, and the squared voltage used to control the receiver output.

diversity combiner, selective, *n.* A device for combining diversity radio signals in which only the signal from the receiver output having the greatest signal-to-noise ratio is selected and used.

diversity factor, power. See "factor, power diversity."

diversity gain, space. See "gain, space diversity."

diversity reception, *n.* Radio reception minimizing the effect of multipath fading by combining two or more received waves bearing the same modulation information. See "diversity, frequency" and "diversity, space."

diverter, call, *n.* A central office device which intercepts a call directed to a forbidden code and diverts it to an operator.

diverter-pole. See "generator, diverter-pole."

divided ringing. See "ringing, divided."

divider, frequency, *n.* A device whose output is of a frequency which is a sub-multiple of the input frequency.

divider, voltage, *n.* A resistor connected across a voltage and then tapped so as to provide a desired fraction of the total voltage.

D layer, *n.* A radio reflecting layer in the ionosphere which exists only during daylight at heights of 50-90 kilometers. It reflects very-low and low frequency waves, absorbs medium-frequency waves, and attenuates high-frequency waves.

domain, *n.* Region within a crystalline material in which all molecules have their electric fields oriented to be parallel.

domain, magnetic, *n.* A volume within a magnetic material where the direction of magnetization is everywhere the same.

donor, *n.* An impurity, usually antimony, arsenic, or phosphorus, which is added to a germanium or silicon semiconductor material to increase the number of free electrons. A material thus doped is called an n-type semiconductor.

doping, *n.* The addition of a "donor" impurity to a semiconductor to produce an n-type or a p-type material. See also "semiconductor, - - - type."

Doppler shift, *n.* The change in the frequency of a received radio signal caused by the radio transmitter moving toward (increased frequency) or away from (decreased frequency) the radio receiver. Important in satellite communications where satellite movement can cause an apparent shift in the frequency of its transmission as large as 210 KHz per megahertz. Doppler shift is a property of all waves, whether sound, radio, or light.

dot-cycle, *n.* One cycle of a periodic alternation between two signaling conditions, each condition having unit duration. A mark signal followed by a space signal constitutes one dot-cycle.

double dog, *n.* A double-toothed detent which fits into the rotary and vertical ratchets on a step-by-step switch shaft and holds the shaft in its operated position until released.

double-hop path, *n.* A path of a radio wave which is reflected from the ionosphere back to earth, where it is reflected from the earth's surface back to the ionosphere where a second reflection returns it to the earth and the receiving antenna.

double modulation. See "modulation, double."

double-pole, *adj.* Describing relay or switch contacts which simultaneously open or close both sides of the same circuit.

doubler, *n.* (1) Horizontals in a crossbar switch which make possible connection between verticals in the same switch. (2) A frequency doubler. (3) A voltage doubler.

doubler, frequency, *n.* An electron tube circuit in which the plate circuit is tuned to a frequency which is twice that of the frequency in its grid circuit.

doubler, voltage, *n.* An electron-tube rectifier circuit which has almost double the voltage output of a half-wave rectifier. It charges a capacitor during one half-cycle, then discharges it in series with the output voltage during the next half-cycle.

double sideband. See "sideband, double."

double space, telegraph, *n.* The condition in half-duplex telegraphy when two line or loop legs simultaneously transmit spaces to the receive hub, thus driving the hub potential to —60 volts instead of the normal spacing potential of —30 volts. In this case, the hub sends spaces towards all interconnected legs including those from which spaces are being received.

doublet, *n.* A dipole antenna, which see.

double-throw, *adj.* Describing relay or switch contacts which transfer circuit A from circuit B to circuit C.

dowel pin, conduit, *n.* A galvanized steel pin, $\frac{1}{4}''$D x $3''$ long, placed in holes in adjacent sections of multiple tile conduit when they are laid to ensure accurate alignment and a smooth bore.

downconverter, *n.* A converter whose input is a radio frequency and whose output is an intermediate frequency.

down-lead, *n.* A wire which connects an elevated antenna to a radio receiver or transmitter. Also called a "lead-in wire."

downlink. See "satellite downlink."

downtime, *n.* The time during which a system is not operating because a component has failed.

drain, *n.* (1) The current drawn from a voltage source by a load. (2) A drainage connection. (3) A negative return.

drain, busy-hour battery, *n.* (1) The maximum DC current drain measured at the power board during the busy hour. (2) To compute battery capacity required, the busy-hour drain is assumed to be the anticipated average current drain, in the tenth year from installation of the battery, during the busiest hour of a normal day during the busiest season.

drain, current, *n.* The amount of current drawn from a source of voltage.

drainage connection, *n.* A heavy wire connection from one or several interconnected cable sheaths to a galvanic anode or to a negative return. This wire drains current from the cable sheaths, leaving the cable sheaths negative to earth, and thereby protects them from electrolysis.

drawbar, *n.* A $3\frac{1}{2}$-inch steel channel 3 feet long, equipped on one end with a heavy cast steel towing eye which can be placed in the towing hook on a truck. The drawbar is bolted or bound to the top end of a pole which is to be towed on a pole trailer.

drawing, circuit description, *n.* A drawing, usually $8\frac{1}{2}''$ x $11''$ in size, which gives by narrative and simplified diagrams, a step-by-step description of the operation of a circuit.

drawing, circuit schematic, *n.* A representation of the components of an electrical circuit and their interconnections by symbols and lines.

drawing, detached schematic, *n.* A simplified (?) circuit or operation schematic drawing in which the relay coil and relay contacts are not combined, but may be scattered over the drawing. Break contacts are shown with a short bar across the wire, while make contacts are shown as a cross on the wire. The letter designation of the relay is shown beside each contact designation.

drawing, single line. *n.* A simplified circuit schematic in which a single line represents the 2, 3, or more wires which make up a single connection between two circuit components.

drawing, wire. *n.* In the manufacture of wire, pulling a metal rod through a series of dies to progressively reduce its size to a desired diameter.

drawing, wiring layout, *n.* A type of circuit diagram, made to show explicitly each wire, its gauge, its color coding, and its terminations.

dress. *v.* To arrange wire connections, cable ends, or cables so that they present a neat and orderly appearance.

dresser, cable, *n.* Maple or lignum vitae wood block with a handle, used by cable splicers for beating in the ends of lead sleeves to prepare them for wiping.

dresser, commutator, *n.* A device which can be fastened to a brush holder of an electric generator or motor and used to turn down the commutator while the machine is running. Not recommended for diverter-pole generators or ringing machines.

dressing, *n.* The process of arranging wires and skinners with respect to the terminals on which they terminate.

drift, *n.* (1) The movement of electrons or holes in a semiconductor. (2) A slow change in frequency or other parameter.

drift plug, *n.* A cylindrical wooden plug with tapered end. For driving into the end of deformed lead splicing sleeves to restore them to their normal cylindrical shape.

drift space, *n.* In a klystron tube, the space between the buncher grids and the catcher grids in which there is no electrostatic field and in which the electrons drift at their entering velocity. Since the electrons are traveling at varying velocities, the faster electrons will overtake the slower and form into groups

called "bunches" in the drift space.

drill, bell-hanger's, *n.* An extra-long (12″-18″-24″) twist drill having a hole through the drill flutes near the cutting head. Used to drill a hole through which wires can be fished when wiring wooden buildings. It is hardened so that it will cut through nails which may be encountered.

drill, cable, *n.* A small core drill having a 0.280 inch bit, and hand operated by means of a knurled wheel. Used to make a small hole in a lead cable sheath or splice sleeve over which a pressure testing flange and valve can be installed.

drill, concrete core, *n.* A fast-cutting, carbide tipped, hollow drill used with a slow-speed electric drill to make large round holes in concrete masonry. Cuts only an annular ring, leaving a core of masonry in the center. Available in sizes from 5/8 inch to 6 inches.

drill, masonry, *n.* A drill having a very hard carbide tip, and used in a hand drill or slow speed electric drill to make round holes in masonry. Available in sizes from 3/16 inch to 3/4 inch.

drill, star, *n.* A hardened steel chisel used with a hammer to make round holes in masonry or stone. The cutting edges of the drill, when seen from the end, resemble a four-pointed star. Available in sizes from 1/4 inch to 3/4 inch, in 1/16 inch increments.

drive, *n.* The signal applied to the input of a power amplifier. Also called "excitation."

driver, *n.* (1) A circuit which supplies the input to a high-power circuit. (2) The low-power oscillator-modulator-amplifier unit which supplies the excitation to a power amplifier. See also "exciter."

drop, *n.* (1) The central office side of a line repeating coil. (2) The central office side of test jacks. (3) A drop wire. (4) A subscriber's drop. (5)

A magneto drop. (6) A potential drop. (7) A switchboard drop.

drop, CATV subscriber, *n*. A flexible coaxial cable, often in figure-8 construction with an integral messenger wire, used to connect from the tap or directional coupler on the CATV cable to the subscriber's premises.

drop, clearing-out, *n*. An annunciator signal associated with a cord circuit or trunk circuit on a magneto switchboard which operates to indicate that the cord should be cleared out (taken down) when the subscriber or distant operator rings to signal completion of the call.

drop, magneto, *n*. An electro-magnetically operated shutter on a switchboard which gives visual notice to the operator of a call incoming from a magneto line.

drop, potential, *n*. The difference in potential between two ends of a resistance when a current flows through the resistance. The potential drop, in volts, is equal to the current flowing, in amperes, times the resistance, in ohms.

drop, resistance. See "resistance drop."

drop, subscriber's, *n*. Wire which runs from a cable terminal or an openwire bridging point to the subscriber's house.

drop, switchboard, *n*. (1) The annunciator-like device described under "drop, magneto." (2) In toll central office practice, all equipment on the "drop" side of the toll line repeating coil, including the jack, lamp, and relay equipment used to terminate the toll line circuit on the switchboard.

drop, voltage, *n*. (1) The decrease in voltage as a current traverses a resistance. (2) The voltage measured across a resistance through which a current is flowing.

drop-and-insert, *adj*. Referring to the capability to bring out, and to withdraw or add, carrier channels or carrier groups at a radio repeater point. Requires a baseband type repeater.

drop-back, *n*. The action of a step-by-step selector in dropping back to the first level rest position after reaching the level to which it was pulsed. Used for "digit absorption."

dropped channel, *n*. One or more channels of a multichannel system which are terminated (dropped) at some point intermediate between the end terminals of the system.

dropping resistor, *n*. A resistor whose specific purpose is to produce a drop in voltage.

drop-out value, *n*. The value of current or voltage at which an operated relay will release.

drop side, *n*. The side of equipment that looks toward a switchboard or central office.

drop wire, *n*. Paired insulated wires under a common cover, used to run a subscriber's line from the terminal on the pole to the protector at the house.

drum, manhole. See "shield, manhole."

drum factor, *n*. In facsimile transmission, the ratio of length to diameter of the scanning drum.

drum storage, *n*. A data storage unit consisting of a cylindrical drum coated with a magnetic material and continuously rotated. Data is recorded on and read from parallel tracks on the drum surface by a number of recording-playback heads.

drum storage, magnetic, *n*. A precisely-made cylindrical metal drum plated with a ferromagnetic cobalt-nickel alloy, and made to rotate at a constant speed between 3000 and 12,000 rpm. Read/write heads are arranged along the length of the drum, each associated with a track of stored data. The writing heads store data as magnetized spots on the drum surface. Reading is nondestructive.

dry, *adj*. (1) Said of circuits or contacts which do not carry direct current. (2) Free from water or humidity.

dry cell. See "cell, dry."

dry circuit, *n.* A circuit which carries only voice currents, and has no direct current flow.

dry contacts, *n. pl.* Contacts through which no direct current flows.

dry-disk rectifier. See "rectifier, dry disc."

dryer, air, *n.* A refrigeration unit which cools compressed air until its moisture condenses out, then uses that dry air (less than 2% R.H.) at 9 lbs. psig to pressurize telephone cables. Dry air is kept flowing into the cable, and escapes through minute leaks.

DSA board, *n.* Dial system "A" board. A switchboard used to provide operator assistance in a dial office.

DSA (Dial System "A") Operator, *n.* An "A" operator in a dial office who completes certain short-haul station calls, handles assistance calls, and generally assists the operator. The "A" Operator is usually reached by dialing "O."

DSA position, *n.* An assistance switchboard position in a dial office.

dual channel office, *n.* An office in which customers dial the code "O" to reach an operator for assistance, and dial "110" or "211" to reach an operator for toll calls.

dual-tone multifrequency. See "pulsing, DTMF."

duct, *n.* (1) A single pipe, tube, or conduit through which cables or wires can be passed. (2) One of several openings or tubes through a multiple duct conduit. (3) A layer of cold air under warm air which carries radio waves farther than they would normally travel.

duct, atmospheric, *n.* A layer in the troposphere formed under certain temperature conditions which traps microwave radio frequencies and carries them much farther than they would normally travel.

duct, metal floor wiring, *n.* A two-piece (base and cap) metal duct used to run wires over the surface of floors. The snap-on cap has tapered edges.

duct, multiple tile, *n.* A pre-cast clay tile unit made with 2, 3, 4, 6, 9, or 12 ducts (individual channels or holes for cables) and used to construct a multi-duct conduit system.

duct, radio. See "duct, atmospheric."

duct, rubber floor wiring, *n.* A hollow rubber duct used to cover and protect wires run on the surface of floors. About 3 inches wide x ½ inch high, with tapered edges.

duct, surface, *n.* An atmospheric duct whose lower boundary is the surface of the earth.

duct rod. See "rod, duct."

duct rodding. See "rodding."

duct run, *n.* (1) A system of underground ducts. (2) The path followed in the earth by a duct system.

duct sealing. See "sealing, duct."

dummy, *n.* (1) A device which can be substituted for another, but which has no operating features, such as a dummy heat coil or dummy fuse. (2) An artificial line simulating a customer's telegraph loop, which can be substituted for the loop when adjusting the telegraph repeater.

dummy antenna, *n.* A network device that simulates an antenna's impedance and power dissipation characteristics, but does not radiate or receive radio waves. Used for testing radio transmitters.

dummy load, *n.* A dissipative, impedance-matched network used at the end of a transmission line to absorb all incident power for conversion to heat. Permits testing under load conditions without the creation of any standing waves.

dump, *v.* To transfer information from a register word to a memory position.

duobinary coding, *n.* A three-level pulse coding arrangement which will permit transmission of twice the information in the same bandwidth as a simple binary signal. See also "coding, duobinary."

duplex, *adj.* (1) Two units in one. (2) Operating in both directions simultaneously.

duplex circuit. See "circuit, duplex."

duplex control (telegraph), *n.* The control exercised by a coupling unit on a half-duplex telegraph leg which does not permit spaces received at the receive hub to be sent to the repeater on the same leg, which would then interrupt the half-duplex transmission inward. See also: "double space."

duplex control circuit, telegraph, *n.* A circuit included in a telegraph loop repeater which prevents a spacing signal received from the loop being sent back to the same loop.

duplexer, *n.* A microwave device having dual cavity-tuned band-pass filters which permits the operation of a transmitter and a receiver on the same antenna, if spaced in frequency by at least two megahertz.

duplexer, antenna, *n.* A microwave device which permits simultaneous operation of one transmitter and one receiver on a common antenna. Consists of two or more coaxial line sections tuned to the frequencies of the transmitter and the receiver and acting as band pass or band rejection filters. Each filter presents a minimum loss to the through energy, from transmitter to antenna and antenna to receiver.

duplex operation, *n.* Simultaneous transmission and reception over the same circuit.

duplex signaling. See "signaling, duplex."

duration, pulse, *n.* The time interval between points on the leading and trailing edges of the pulse at which the instantaneous value has a specified relation to the peak pulse amplitude.

duty cycle, *n.* The ratio of operating time to total elapsed time of a device which operates intermittently, expressed in per cent.

duty ratio. See "duty cycle."

DX-1 signaling unit, *n.* A duplex signaling equipment which repeats signals from the E&M leads of a central office trunk to a duplex line, and vice versa.

DX-2 signaling unit, *n.* A duplex signaling equipment which repeats signals from the E&M leads of a signal converter (single-frequency, or other type) to a duplex line, and vice versa.

dynamic overload control. *n.* A control system used in regional toll centers which senses the growth of traffic congestion and, when a toll office reaches a predetermined level of congestion, automatically responds by cancelling or rerouting traffic.

dynamo, *n.* A dynamoelectric machine having an armature and a field, one rotating and one stationary. May be either a generator or motor, but usually the term is intended to mean a direct current generator.

dynamometer, *n.* An indicating instrument, about five inches in diameter, which can be placed between the chain hoist and the strand puller when tensioning guys or suspension strand. Reads tension 0-10,000 pounds, in 100 pound increments.

dynamotor, *n.* A rotary electrical machine used to convert from direct current to alternating current. The machine has a single field structure and a single rotating armature having two windings, one equipped with a DC commutator and the other with AC slip rings.

E&M leads. See "leads, E&M."

E&M signaling, *n.* An arrangement whereby signaling between a trunk circuit and an associated signaling unit is effected over two leads: an M lead to transMit signals to the signaling unit and an E lead which recEives signals from the signaling unit. Provides full-time, 2-way, 2-level supervision.

Early Bird, *n.* The first commercial communication satellite operated by COMSAT, launched 6 April 1965. A synchronous satellite parked over the mid-Atlantic, used for communications between Europe and the United States.

early relay contacts, *n.* Those groups of relay contact pairs which make or break before the "ordinary" contacts when the relay operates. See also "ordinary" and "preliminary" contacts.

earphone, *n.* An electroacoustic device which transforms electric waves into sound waves, and is intended to be closely coupled acoustically to the ear. The term "earphone" is preferred over the more ambiguous term "receiver."

earth auger. See "auger, earth."

earth potential compensation. See "compensation, earth potential."

EAS, optional, *n.* An extended area service plan (EAS) in which the subscriber is given an option to (a) retain his present exchange rate with toll charges to EAS points, or (b) pay higher exchange rates with the privilege of toll-free calling within the extended areas. See also "extended area service."

easement, *n.* A non-profitable interest in land which permits the holder the right to enter land owned by another for the purpose of installing or maintaining communications plant.

East terminal, *n.* An arbitrary designation for one terminal of a toll trunk or a carrier circuit. Usually the northern or eastern terminal. Enables designation of directions of transmission as "east-west" and "west-east," and facilitates record keeping.

eavesdropping, *n.* Listening secretly to what is said in presumed privacy on a telephone call.

eccentricity, conductor, *n.* The percentage amount by which a conductor strays from the exact center of the insulation which surrounds it.

echo, *n.* (1) An attenuated reflection of a talker's voice, separated from the primary wave by reflection at an electrical discontinuity in the circuit, and returned to him over the circuit on which he is talking and listening. If there is little delay between the original signal and the echo, the effect is increased sidetone. If the delay is appreciable, the effect is a disturbing "rain barrel" hollowness. (2) A delayed radio signal caused by multipath transmission. (3) A TV ghost.

echo, talker, *n.* The echo that the talker hears.

Echo I, *n.* The original communication satellite. It was a passive reflector, a 100-ft. diameter aluminum coated inflated plastic sphere at an altitude of 550 miles, traveling at a speed of about 17,000 miles per hour. It was launched 12 Aug. 1960 and lasted until 23 May 1968, although punctured by many micrometeorites.

echo path loss, *n.* (1) The total transmission loss that the echo encounters in its round trip. (2) The sum of the return loss at the distant hybrid and the round-trip loss in the four-wire toll circuit.

echo return loss. See "loss, echo return."

echo suppressor, *n.* A device which detects speech signals transmitted in either direction on a four-wire circuit, and introduces loss in the direction opposite to the direction of transmission for the purpose of suppressing echos.

echo suppressor, controlled, *n.* An

echo suppressor which is switched in or out of a circuit by a control lead—in on a via connection; out on a terminal connection.

echo suppressor, fixed, *n.* An echo suppressor which is enabled (operative) at all times.

echo suppressor, split, *n.* A suppressor which detects signals such as speech on one direction of a four-wire circuit and, when detected, introduces loss into (suppresses) transmission in the other direction.

echo suppressor, split controlled, *n.* A split echo suppressor which can be switching in and out of the circuit as required. In on via circuits, out on terminal circuits, etc.

echo tolerance, *n.* The amount of echo volume which can be tolerated on a telephone call by an average person. It depends upon the length of time the echo is delayed from the signal which produced it, as follows:

Round-trip Delay (milliseconds)	Minimum Loss in Echo Path in dB
0	1.4
20	11.1
40	17.7
60	22.7
80	27.2
100	30.9

EC lead, *n.* Extra control lead. The wire in a step-by-step central office which is used to control service restrictions or executive right-of-way service.

eclipse, satellite, *n.* Darkening or shadowing of one orbiting body due to the interpassing of another. When the Earth is between a satellite and the sun, the satellite is eclipsed and its solar battery power supply is cut off.

ecliptic, *n.* (1) The reference plane used to describe the orbits of all satellites. (2) The great circle on the celestial sphere where the plane containing the orbit of the Earth intersects.

eddy current, *n.* A circulating current which is induced within transformer cores or any conductor which is exposed to a varying magnetic field. It is a loss, and causes heating of the conductor.

Edison base, *n.* The coarse screw thread base used on common household electric lamps in the United States.

Edison storage cell. See "cell, nickel-iron storage."

Educational Television (ETV), *n.* Service providing transmission of a television signal from a centralized studio to outlying TV receivers, usually in schools.

effect, end, *n.* The effect of capacitance at the ends of a dipole antenna. Because of it, the actual length of a half-wave dipole is about 5% less than one-half wavelength, increasing to 6% less for frequencies above 50 megahertz.

effect, transit time. See "transit time effect."

effective loss. See "loss, effective transmission."

effective radius of the earth, *n.* The value of the earth's radius which must be used in calculating radio propagation losses to correct for the effect of atmospheric refraction.

effective resistance, *n.* The increased resistance shown by a conductor to the flow of an alternating current, as compared to direct current. It is due to the fact that, as the frequency increases, the current is not distributed uniformly throughout the conductor but tends to flow in the surface layer. See also "skin effect."

effective value, *n.* Of an alternating current or voltage, the square-root-of-mean-square value. Of an alternating current, that value which will cause the same heat in a resistor as the corresponding value of direct current. If the alternating current or voltage is a sine wave, the effective value is the peak value multiplied by 0.7071.

efficiency, *n.* Of an electrical device, the useful power output divided by the total power input, expressed in percent.

efficiency, ampere-hour, *n.* The number of ampere-hours obtained from a storage battery divided by the number of ampere-hours required to recharge the storage battery to its original condition.

efficiency, data transmission, *n.* The number of useable data bits delivered to the user at the receiving data terminal divided by the total number of bits that were transmitted. Also called the "throughput rate."

efficiency, plate circuit, *n.* In an electron tube amplifier, the ratio of signal power output to direct current power input.

efficiency, radiation, *n.* Of an antenna, the ratio of the power radiated to the total power supplied to the antenna, at a given frequency.

efficiency, voltage, *n.* Of a storage battery, the ratio of the average voltage during the discharge to the average voltage during the recharge.

efficiency, watthour, *n.* Of a storage battery, the ratio of the watthours output to the watthours required for recharge.

eight hundred cycle-miles. See "miles-of-standard-cable."

elapsed time, *n.* (1) The total time in seconds during which a circuit is usefully occupied. (2) The time printed on a toll ticket by a Calculagraph, for which charges will be made. See also "time, deductible."

elastance, *n.* A measure of the difficulty of placing an electric charge in a capacitor. It is the reciprocal of capacitance, and is expressed in darafs.

elasticity, modulus of. See "modulus of elasticity."

elastomer, *n.* Any elastic rubber-like substance, such as neoprene.

E layer, *n.* Lowest layer of ionization in the ionosphere, at about 65 miles above the earth. In the E layer, electron density is about 100,000. electrons per cubic centimeter during the day, but disappears at night.

E layer, sporadic, *n.* A layer of more intense ionization which occurs at times within the E layer and causes erratic propagation.

elbow, waveguide. See "waveguide bend."

"E" lead. See "signaling, E&M."

electric, *adj.* (1) Charged with or transporting electricity. (2) Producing or produced by electricity. (3) Operated by electricity. (4) Electrostatic.

electrical, *adj.* (1) Electric. (2) Concerned with the science or use of electricity.

electrical degree, *n.* One 360th part of a cycle of alternating current.

electrical length. See "length, electrical."

electrical metallic tubing (EMT). See "conduit, thin-wall metallic."

electric arc. See "arc."

electric field. See "field, electric."

electric gradient. See "gradient, voltage."

electricity, *n.* (1) A basic property of all matter, which consists of negative and positive charges (electrons and protons) which attract each other. (2) The potential energy of electrons at rest, and the kinetic energy of electrons in motion. (3) A manifestation of free electrons which can be generated by induction, by friction, or by chemical action. It is recognized by its magnetic, chemical, and radiant effects.

Electro-Acoustic Transmission Measuring System, *n.* New system for evaluating the performance of a transmission system, by giving the loss in db from the acoustical power (in millibars) into a transmitter to the acoustical power out of the receiver at the end of the circuit. It assumes that noise and bandwidth impairments are negligible.

electrocardiogram data set, *n.* A special data set that enables the acoustical coupling of any telephone handset to an electrocardiogram recorder for the transmission of the cardiogram over the telephone line. The data set provides a 2025 Hz signal for echo suppressor disabling, and modulates the 0-100 Hz EKG signal to the 1726-2250 Hz band for transmission over the telephone line. Designated a WECo type 603 Data-Phone.

electrode, *n.* (1) Either of the two terminals of an electric source, such as a battery. (2) A conducting element which emits, collects, or controls the movement of electrons in a vacuum tube. (3) A conducting element at whose surface electricity passes into another conducting medium.

electrode potential, *n.* The potential in volts which an electrode has when immersed in an electrolyte, compared to the zero potential of a hydrogen electrode. It depends upon the material of which the electrode is made. See also "electrode-potential series."

electrode-potential series, *n.* A series of chemical elements arranged in the order of their electrode potentials. Any metal will replace any other metal BELOW it in the series in a chemical or electrolytic action.

Electrode		Potential, volt
Magnesium	—	+2.400
Zinc	—	+0.762
Chromium	—	+0.557
Ferrous Iron	—	+0.441
Tin	—	+0.136
Lead (ous)	—	+0.122
Ferric Iron	—	+0.045
Hydrogen	—	0.000
Oxygen	—	—0.397
Copper	—	—0.470
Silver	—	—0.798
Mercury	—	—0.799
Lead (ic)	—	—0.800
Gold	—	—1.500

electro-luminescence, *n.* Light produced in a phosphor which is in an alternating electric field. Consists of a phosphor only a few mils thick placed between two metal films, one of which is transparent. Alternating current is applied to the plates through a current-limiting resistor. Used for luminous dial number plates.

electrolysis, *n.* (1) The production of chemical changes by passage of an electric current through an electrolyte. (2) The chemical destruction of the lead sheaths of underground cables caused by stray direct currents on the sheaths in the presence of a ground-water electrolyte.

electrolysis, solid-state, *n.* The migration of silver ions across a pair of silver contacts which are carrying current. The migration is from the positive contact to the negative contact.

electrolyte, *n.* A non-metallic electric conductor in which the current is carried by the movement of ions. Examples are (a) the sulfuric acid solution in storage batteries, (b) the sodium hydroxide solution in counter-EMF cells, and (c) ground water with dissolved salts.

electrolytic, *adj.* Said of an electrical device which contains an electrolyte.

electrolytic capacitor. See "capacitor, electrolytic."

electromagnet, *n.* A soft iron core which becomes a magnet temporarily when current flows through a coil of wire which surrounds it.

electromagnetic, *adj.* Pertaining to or caused by the combined electric and magnetic fields which are always associated with the flow of an electric current.

electromagnetic field, *n.* The field associated with radio or light waves, consisting of a magnetic and electric field at right angles to each other and to the direction of wave propagation.

Electromagnetic Systems, Law of. See "Appendix B."

electromagnetic wave. See "wave, electromagnetic."

electromotive force, *n.* The force that produces the movement of electric charges called current. Electromotive force is commonly called "voltage."

electron, *adj.* Containing, operated by, or producing electrons.—*n.* Any of the identical negative electric charges which form a part of all atoms. The smallest division of negative electricity.

electron, conduction. See "electron, valence."

electron, secondary. See "secondary electron."

electron, valence, *n.* Any of the electrons which comprise the outer shell of an atom, which can enter into chemical reactions and can move through influence of an electric field. It is the movement of valence electrons which constitutes the current flow in an n-type semiconductor.

electron emission. See "emission, - - -."

electron gun, *n.* A hot cathode that produces a finely focussed stream of fast electrons, as required in a cathode ray or television tube. Consists of a hot cathode electron source, a control grid, accelerating anodes, and usually focussing electrodes.

electronic, *adj.* Describing devices which depend upon the flow of electrons in vacuum or in semiconductors, such as electron tubes, transistors, etc.

Electronic Central Office (ECO), *n.* A modern central office using solid-state devices to accomplish switching of calls. There are two types: (a) time division, and (b) space division.

electronic data processing (EDP), *n.* Use of electronic memories to store, up-date, and read information automatically, and using that information in accounting, billing, traffic analysis, etc.

electronics, *adj.* Pertaining to the field of electronics.—*n.* That branch of science and technology which deals with the control and utilization of electron flow.

Electronic Secretary, *n.* One brand of telephone answering set, which see.

Electronic Sentry, *n.* A trade-marked electromechanical device which can be triggered by a signal from an alarm senser, then dials a preset telephone number, transmits a pre-recorded message, and repeats this until acknowledged.

electronic switching system (ESS), *n.* System using solid-state switching devices and computer-like operations to accomplish switching of telephone calls.

electron tube. See "tube, electron."

electron volt, *n.* The amount of energy gained by one electron in passing from a point to another point which is one volt higher in potential.

electroplate, *n. v.* The application of a metallic coating on a conductive surface by means of electrolytic action.

electropositive, *adj.* (1) Referring to an electrode having a more positive potential. (2) Referring to an element which is more positive than hydrogen in the electro-chemical series.

electrostatic, *adj.* Pertaining to electricity which is not flowing, and which exists only as a potential (voltage) and an electric field.

electrostatic deflection, *n.* In a cathode-ray tube, the deflection of the electron beam by means of pairs of charged electrodes on opposite sides of the beam. The electron beam is bent toward a positive electrode and bent away from a negative electrode.

electrostatic field, *n.* A volume within which there is electric stress, produced by stationary electric charges.

electrostatic induction, *n.* The process of inducing stationary electric charges on an object by bringing it near another object which has an excess of electric charges. A nega-tive charge will induce a positive charge, and vice versa.

electrostatic shield. See "shield, electrostatic."

element, *n.* (1) A component or basic part of the whole. (2) Units of telephone plant, such as a pole, a manhole, a foot of cable, etc.

element, circuit, *n.* Discrete units of resistance, inductance and capacitance which, when interconnected, form an electrical circuit.

element, code, *n.* One of the discrete conditions or events in a code, such as the presence or absence of a pulse.

element, driven, *n.* An element of an antenna, such as of a Yagi antenna, which is energized directly from the antenna feed line. See also "element, parasitic."

element, parasitic, *n.* An element of a directional antenna which has no electrical connection to the active element(s) of the antenna, but which reflects or directs the radio waves so that they are additive along the directional axis.

element, passive. See "element, parasitic."

element, radiating, *n.* A basic unit of an antenna which radiates or receives electromagnetic energy through radiation.

element, signal, *n.* Any of the parts of a data or telegraph signal, distinguished from other parts by its amplitude, polarity, or position in time.

eleventh rotary step, *n.* When a step-by-step switch fails to find an idle trunk after hunting over the ten bank contacts on a particular level, it continues to the eleventh rotary step, operating a cam switch which returns busy tone to the calling telephone.

eliminator, battery, *n.* A rectifier device equipped with sufficient filtering to provide a quiet DC output, so that it can be used as the battery supply for a PAX or PBX without the need for a paralleling storage battery.

ell, B pressure testing, *n.* A ⅛-inch bronze pipe ell having a branch for a pressure testing valve. Screws into a C flange, and connects to lead tubing for a gas by-pass.

elliptically polarized, *adj.* Describing an electromagnetic wave whose plane of polarization rotates through 360 degrees as the wave propagates in a forward direction. The magnitude of the wave varies constantly in a cyclical manner. See also "polarization, elliptical."

embedment, *n.* A process for enclosing an electronic part or assembly with a protective insulating material which completely fills all voids and requires a mold or container while it is hardening.

emergency, *n.* A sudden, generally unexpected occurrence or set of circumstances demanding immediate action, generally justifying extra effort and expense and the suspension of routine activity.

emergency engine generator. See "generator, emergency engine."

Emergency Reporting System, *n.* A network of manual street telephones dispersed throughout the city and connected to a central ERS PBX, to which any citizen can report any emergency: fire, police, ambulance, etc.

emergency route, *n.* Route not in the normal routing directions but authorized to complete an emergency call, at times of circuit congestion or equipment failure.

emission, *n.* (1) Radiation of electromagnetic waves, as from a radio transmitter. (2) Release of electrons from the cathode of a vacuum tube. In Europe known as "diffusion."

emission, primary, *n.* Emission of electrons from a body due solely to the high temperature or high negative potential of the body.

emission, radio, *n.* A designation, by Article 2 of the 1959 Geneva Radio Regulations, which classifies radio

transmissions by a three-character code. The first character, a letter, tells whether the carrier is amplitude (A), frequency (F), or pulse (P) modulated. The second character is a numeral designating the type of transmission, and the last character is a letter designating supplementary characteristics.

emission, secondary, *n.* Liberation of electrons from grids or plates in a vacuum tube due to bombardment by electrons from the cathode. An undesirable effect, since the net result is to reduce the flow of electrons from the cathode.

emission, spurious, *n.* Any emission from a radio transmitter outside of its assigned frequency band.

emission, thermionic, *n.* That portion of the radiation of electrons from a hot cathode in a vacuum tube which is due solely to the elevated temperature of the cathode.

emitter follower, *n.* A transistor circuit using a grounded collector to provide operation similar to an electron tube "cathode follower," which see.

emphasis, *n.* Pre-emphasis, which see.

empirical, *adj.* Based solely on experiment or observation, rather than on scientific theory.

emulsion, asphalt, *n.* A thin emulsion of asphalt used for painting cuts after tree pruning and trimming.

enable, *v.* (1) To allow to operate. (2) To remove restrictions. The opposite of "disable."

encapsulation, *n.* A process for encasing an electronic part or assembly with a protective insulating material which is usually not over 100 mils thick and does not require a mold or container.

enclosure, *n.* A housing such as a case, cabinet, cabinet racks, or console which is designed to provide protection and support to equipment.

encoder, *n.* A network or matrix in which only one input is energized at a time, and each input produces an unique combination of parallel outputs.

encryption, *n.* The conversion of a clear text signal to a coded signal, by the process of adding a crypto key to the clear digital information. Encryption makes it practically impossible for anyone not in possession of the crypto key to decipher the message.

encryption, bulk, *n.* The encryption of several communication channels by a single encryption device.

encryption, end-to-end, *n.* Encryption accomplished by compatible (identical keying material) cryptographic key equipment at the originating and terminating stations.

encryption, link, *n.* Encryption method whereby each link of a multi-switched or built-up circuit is encrypted separately.

encryption, super, *n.* The encryption of an already encrypted message. Occurs when an end-to-end encrypted message uses a link-encrypted circuit.

end cells, *n. pl.* Three reserve storage cells, identical with the 23 cells in the main central office battery, which are switched in series with the main cells if the battery charger fails, thus making a battery of 26 cells with a voltage of $50+$ volts.

end delay, *n.* The round trip time delay of a circuit between an echo suppressor and the point of echo reflection.

end effect. See "effect, end."

end instrument, *n.* A device which is connected at the end of a circuit and used to convert intelligence signals to electrical signals, and vice-versa. Examples: telephone, telegraph, data set.

end-of-dialing signal, *n.* Signal used with abbreviated dialing codes to inform the switching center that it has just received an abbreviated code, not an incompletely dialed number. In DTMF, the signal is 941 Hz $+$ 1477 Hz.

End Office (EO), *n.* (1) A Class 5 office in the Nationwide Distance Dialing Plan. (2) An entity of central office equipment where subscriber's loops are terminated for interconnection to each other, such as a common intermediate distributing frame in a step-by-step office, an originating marker group in #1 crossbar, a marker group in #5 crossbar, or a decoder group in a panel office. (3) The switching center in which a toll call is connected to the called telephone.

end of transmission signal (EOT), *n.* A standardized, uninterrupted sequence of characters or machine operations which are used to end a transmission and automatically disconnect the transmitting teletypewriter.

ends, clearing (cable), *n.* In cable splicing work, the operation of removing the sheath from the end of the cable, eliminating moisture (by boiling or with desiccant) and eliminating all crosses, grounds, and shorts in preparation for testing and splicing.

end section, *n.* (1) The distance from an end of a loaded cable to the nearest load point on the cable. (2) An additional position added to each end of a large multiple switchboard to enable the first and last operators to reach all jacks easily. The end positions contain jacks only, and do not have cords, keys, or an operator's telephone circuit.

end-to-end, *adj.* Describing similar circuit elements which are connected in series, or in tandem.

energize, *vt.* To provide power to.

energized, *adj.* (1) Connected to a source of energy. (2) Turned on. (3) Alive.

energy, *n.* The capacity for doing work and overcoming resistance.

energy dissipation factor. See "factor, energy dissipation."

energy storage factor. See "factor, energy storage."

engine, *n.* (1) A machine which converts heat energy into power to do work. (A machine which converts electricity into mechanical power is called a "motor"). (2) Loosely, any mechanical device which converts energy into motion.

engine, diesel, *n.* A high-compression internal combustion engine which burns fuel oil. Ignition is brought about by the heat resulting from air compression instead of by a spark, as in a gasoline engine.

engine, drum cable, *n.* A device used aboard a cable laying ship to pay out submarine cable as the ship proceeds. Consists of a ten-foot diameter sheave. Used with the older flexible repeaters.

engine, linear cable, *n.* A device used aboard a cable laying ship which grips a submarine cable and feeds it at proper rate as the ship proceeds. Consists of a pair of opposing flexible moving tracks driven by hydraulic motors. Made in linear form and about forty feet long to accommodate rigid repeaters.

engine, propane gas, *n.* A small engine powered by the same propane gas used to heat a cable splicer's furnace, and used to drive a blower for manhole ventilation.

engineer, communication, *n.* An electrical engineer who specializes in the design, construction, operation, or maintenance of communication circuits, equipment, or systems, whether by wire or radio.

engineer, professional, *n.* An engineer whose education and experience qualify him to be responsible for important engineering work, and who is registered as a professional engineer by a state authority.

engineered circuit, *n.* A standby or on-call circuit engineered and configured to meet a specific requirement.

engineering, circuit layout, *n.* The process by which a circuit, loop or trunk, is designed from one termination to another. Considerations include transmission levels, distor-

tion, stability, reliability, equipment compatibility, plant investment, and time schedules. The criterion is the highest quality of transmission consistent with economics, engineering standards, and system design.

engineering, electrical, *n.* A branch of engineering that applies a knowledge of the principles of electricity to the solution of practical problems for the benefit of mankind.

engineering, electronic, *n.* A branch of electrical engineering that applies the principles of electronics to the solution of practical problems. See also "electronics."

engineering, radio, *n.* Engineering which deals with the generation, transmission, and reception of radio waves, and of the design and production of radio equipment.

engineering, television, *n.* A branch of radio engineering which deals with the theory and practice of transmitting television programs and receiving the programs without loss of fidelity.

engineering, traffic, *n.* The art of and science of determining the minimum quantities of equipment and trunks which will carry the required traffic with an acceptable grade of service.

Enterphone, *n.* Patented system (AECo) for communication between the lobby of an apartment house and the apartments. It features dial service, automatic time-out, holding, and door unlocking by dialing.

ENterprise, *n.* A fictional exchange name used to identify automatic collect toll calls.

entropy, *n.* A measure of the amount of information in a communication signal, equal to the average number of bits per symbol.

enunciation, *n.* The act of pronouncing words clearly and distinctly. Articulation.

envelope delay distortion, *n.* The maximum difference in transmission time (absolute delay) between any two frequencies in a specified frequency band, expressed in microseconds.

ephemerides, *n. pl.* (1) The plural form of "ephemeris." (2) The computed positions which are listed in an ephemeris.

ephemeris, *n.* A collection of data listing the computed positions of a satellite, or several satellites, at particular times on each day for a period of days in the future.

ephemeris, satellite, *n.* Tables of data that indicate the predicted position of satellites or other celestial bodies at some particular time on each day for a period in the future.

epoxy, *adj.* Designating a two-part resin that polymerizes spontaneously when the two components are mixed, forming a strong, hard resistant adhesive. In an epoxy compound there is always an oxygen linked to each of two other connected atoms. See also "resin, epoxy."

epoxy resin, *n.* A flexible, usually thermosetting, resin made by polymerization of an epoxy compound. Much used in waterproof heat-resistant adhesives.

equalization, *n.* The process of reducing attenuation distortion and/or phase distortion of a circuit by introduction of networks which add compensating attenuation and/or time delay at various frequencies in the transmission band.

equalize, *vt.* To apply to a circuit an electrical network whose transmission characteristics are complementary to those of the line, so that when the loss (or delay) in the line and that in the equalizer are combined, the overall loss (or delay) is almost the same at all frequencies.

equalizer, *n.* A network, usually adjustable, which corrects the transmission-frequency characteristics of a circuit to permit it to transmit all the frequencies which it passes in a uniform manner. See also "attenuation equalizer" and "delay equalizer."

equalizer, absolute delay, *n.* Series lattice network(s) which equalize the absolute time delay of two or more circuits carrying the same signal to a single receiving terminal.

equalizer, adaptive, *n.* An equalizer which automatically and continuously readjusts itself so as to produce an equalized output signal from a distorted input.

equalizer, attenuation, *n.* An equalizer to correct the attenuation-frequency characteristic of a circuit, such as a non-loaded cable pair. It consists of a parallel-resonant circuit, resonant at a frequency just above the desired pass band, and whose bridged loss (when bridged on the circuit to be equalized) can be adjusted by means of a variable series resistance.

equalizer, bump, *n.* An equalizer consisting of a number of separate units, each of which can be varied to give adjustment over a small range of frequencies.

equalizer, delay, *n.* An equalizer inserted in a line to delay the higher frequencies, so that all useful frequencies will have almost equal delay, and therefore the minimum delay distortion. See also "equalizer, absolute delay" and "equalizer, relative delay."

equalizer, mop-up, *n.* A versatile, manually-adjusted equalizer which permits compensation for imperfect equalization which has occurred previously in the system.

equalizer, phase. See "equalizer, delay."

equalizer, program, *n.* A wide-band attenuation equalizer, permitting equalization of a band of frequencies to 10 kilohertz, or to 15 kilohertz.

equalizer, relative delay, *n.* A series lattice network having a delay characteristic which is the inverse of the line or equipment to which it is connected, and which therefore achieves a relatively constant delay over a given frequency band.

equalizer, slope. See "equalizer, attenuation."

equalizing charge, *n.* An overcharge given to a lead-acid storage battery to correct variations in the specific gravity of the individual cells. The voltage for an equalizing charge should be 2.30 volts per cell, and be maintained until all cells are fully charged.

equal-level point. See "bay, equal-level patching."

equipment, *n.* General term for telephone apparatus located indoors. See also "plant," "central office equipment," "line equipment," and "station equipment."

equipment, central office, *n.* Apparatus used in a telephone central office for the furnishing of communication services.

equipment, crossbar common control, *n.* In a crossbar office, all switching equipment exclusive of line link frames and trunk link frames.

equipment, digital subscriber terminal (DSTE), *n. pl.* Equipment for a terminal in the AUTODIN network, providing one or more of the following services:
1. Teletypewriter
2. Magnetic tape
3. Paper tape
4. Punched card

equipment, diversion, *n.* Equipment inserted in outgoing trunks from a PBX or DCO which analyzes the first digits dialed over a trunk and diverts unauthorized calls for toll, DDD, or EAS to busy tone, a recorded announcement, or operator intercept.

equipment, face. See "face equipment."

equipment, interface. See "interface equipment."

equipment, key telephone, *n.* Multibutton telephone sets with associated relay units which enable the user to pick up and hold PBX or central office lines, and provide flashing line, steady busy, and wink hold signals. Dial intercom service is also available. See also "set, key telephone."

equipment, line, *n.* Equipment located in a telephone office, associated with a particular line, and used when that line originates a call. Consists of a line relay and a bridge cutoff relay.

equipment, off-line, *n.* Communication equipment or devices which are not in direct communication with the distant terminal.

equipment, on-line, *n.* Communication equipment or devices which are in direct communication with the distant terminal.

equipment, peripheral, *n.* Equipment that works in conjunction with a communication system, but is not connected to it. For instance: a data card punch, or a tape perforator.

equipment, station, *n.* Equipment used on a subscriber's premises in connection with the furnishing of communication services.

equipment, subscriber's line, *n.* The equipment which operates when a subscriber lifts his handset to originate a call (line relay), or when his line receives a call (bridge cut-off relay).

equipment, terminal, *n.* The communication equipment in which the ends of a communication channel are terminated.

equipment, unitized power, *n.* A complete power system for a central office, consisting of three basic units: (a) a Power Unit which includes the rectifiers and power control devices, (b) a Station Signaling Rack, which includes the ringing and tone generators, and (c) the Equipment Supervisory Rack which includes the·distributing fuse panel, the visual and audible alarms and their associated control equipment.

equipment supervisory rack (ESR), *n.* The unit of central office power equipment which provides the major supervisory functions and the distribution fuse facilities.

equipotential, *adj.* Having the same voltage at all points.

equivalent, *n.* For any circuit containing resistance, transmission of a signal is accompanied by an energy loss. This loss is called its "equivalent." The term is an old one; dating back to the time when circuit losses were given in "equivalent miles of standard cable."

equivalent, circuit, *n.* The end-to-end 1000 Hz transmission loss of a circuit, expressed in decibels.

equivalent circuit, *n.* A simplified circuit which has the same response to changing voltage and frequency as a more complex circuit. Used to facilitate mathematical analysis.

equivalent circuits, *n. pl.* Two circuits are equivalent if they draw identical currents when they have identical voltages impressed on them.

equivalent networks, *n. pl.* Two networks are equivalent if one can replace the other in a circuit without any effect upon the external circuit.

erase, *v.* To remove all information from a register or a memory. Sometimes this consists of writing a zero into all memory positions.

erlang, *n.* A unit of telephone traffic widely used in Europe which is numerically equal to percentage occupancy. It is obtained by multiplying the number of calls by the length of the average call in fractions of an hour. One erlang is equal to 36 CCS. This unit was named for Agner K. Erlang of the Copenhagen Telephone Company, and in the United States is known as a "traffic unit" (TU).

error, *n.* (1) The difference between a computed, estimated, or measured value and the true value. (2) A deviation occurring during transmission such that a mark signal is received instead of a space signal, or vice versa.

error, aliasing, *n.* In a time division multiplex system, the generation of false low-frequency wave forms when the sampling rate is too low. In practice, the TDM sampling rate should be five times the information signal frequency, rather than two times which the Shannon information theory shows is the minimum sampling rate.

error, probable, *n.* That error which has a 50% chance of occurrence.

error, random, *n.* An error which is wholly due to chance, and does not recur periodically.

error, systematic, *n.* A statistical error that persists and cannot be considered as due entirely to chance.

error control codes. See "codes, error control."

error correction, *n.* Automatic procedure used on a duplex data circuit which has error detection equipment. If an error is received, the transmitter is instructed to re-send that message until it is correct.

error detection, *n.* The method of determining, at the receiving end of a data circuit, whether previously transmitted data is correct as received. This is usually accomplished by adding a "parity-checking bit" for every seven "signal" bits. Some codes, such as the duobinary, give error detection without the addition of a parity bit.

error rate, *n.* The probability of an error occurring during the transmission of a message. For digital transmission, one error in 100,000. bits is typical.

error signal. See "signal, error."

escape velocity, *n.* The minimum velocity required by a satellite to achieve and maintain a parabolic orbit. For the Earth, this velocity is 6.95 miles per second.

escutcheon, *n.* An ornamental plate or shield such as that around a telephone lever key, or a keyhole.

established connection, *n.* A connection on which all the necessary operating steps have been taken to connect the calling and called lines. An established connection is not necessarily a completed call.

estimate, *n.* (1) A calculation of the probable cost of doing a certain piece of work. (2) A written statement of proposed charges. (3) A formal plan, including an estimate of cost, for adding a sizeable amount of telephone plant, usually where cost exceeds $5,000 or $10,000 limits.

ether, *n.* A hypothetical medium without substance which some years ago was assumed to pervade all space and to be the medium through which electromagnetic radiations were propagated.

E-type repeater. See "repeater, negative impedance."

E-type signaling. See "signaling, E-type."

eutectic alloy. See "solder, eutectic."

event, *n.* A specific, definable accomplishment in a program plan, recognizable at a particular instant in time. See also "PERT."

exchange, *n.* (1) Properly an area within which there is a single, uniform set of charges for telephone service. (2) A telephone switching center. (Slang) (3) A telephone central office. (Slang and incorrect.)

exchange, all-relay. See "office, all-relay central."

exchange, crossbar. See "office, crossbar central."

exchange, dial. See "office, dial."

exchange, manual. See "office, manual central."

exchange, multi-office, *n.* A telephone exchange area in which there are several central office units.

exchange, private automatic (PAX), *n.* A small, unattended dial telephone office located on a subscriber's premises and serving only his stations with local and automatic trunked calls.

exchange, private automatic branch (PABX), *n.* A dial telephone office with an attendant's switchboard located on a subscriber's premises and providing local and trunked telephone service to his stations.

exchange, private branch (PBX), *n.* A small manual telephone switchboard located on a subscriber's premises, providing local and trunked telephone service only to the subscriber's own stations.

exchange, rotary. See "office, rotary central."

exchange, single-office, *n.* A telephone exchange area served by a single central office.

exchange, step-by-step. See "office, step-by-step central."

exchange, telephone, *n.* (1) An area within which telephone service is given without toll charges. (2) A telephone switching center (slang).

exchange, teletypewriter, *n.* A teletypewriter switchboard or switching center which provides teletypewriter stations with switched local and toll service.

exchange area, *n.* A geographical area within which there is a single, uniform set of charges for telephone service. The exchange area may be served by a number of central offices, each with its own service area.

excitation, *n.* (1) Current supplied to energize the field coils of a generator. (2) The signal applied to a power amplifier. (3) The signal applied to a transmitting antenna.

excitation, parasitic. See "parasitically excited."

excitation, separate. See "separately excited."

excitation, series, *n.* Obtaining the field current for a generator or motor by connecting the armature in series with the field.

excitation, shock, *n.* The sudden application of a momentary steep-wave-front voltage to a resonant circuit, resulting in a damped oscillation.

exciter, *n.* (1) The small generator which produces the field current for an alternator. (2) The radio-frequency oscillator that provides the carrier signal to a radio transmitter. (3) An element of a multi-element antenna which is connected directly to a source of radio-frequency energy.

exclusion, attendant, *n*. A feature of some PABX trunk circuits which prevents the PABX attendant from entering a busy trunk call unless recalled.

executive right-of-way, *n*. A feature of some dial connectors which enables a calling party to override a busy by pushing a button which grounds the tip side of his station loop circuit.

executive right-of-way service, *n*. A service provided to privileged telephones which permits them to call any phone in the same central office, even when the called phone is busy.

exempt materials, *n. pl*. Minor items of materials or property which are consumed in use or which lose their identity when installed, and which therefore need not be accounted for.

expandor, *n*. (1) An electrical device which expands the amplitude or volume range of an audio signal, particularly of a signal whose volume range had been compressed before transmission. (2) The expansion half of a "compandor."

expansion, *n*. A process in which a compressed voice signal is passed through an amplifier whose gain varies with the signal magnitude, amplifying large signals more than weaker signals.

expectancy, trouble. See "unit, trouble."

exploring coil, *n*. A coil of wire, with or without a magnetic core, which can be moved about and used to detect a stray-magnetic field. Small exploring coils are hand-held against aerial cables to detect the location of crosses and grounds. Large (bicycle wheel sized) exploring coils are used to trace the route of buried cables.

explosion-proof sets, *n*. Special hermetically sealed telephone station sets connected to a tight conduit system, so that they can be used safely in an explosive atmosphere.

exposed, *adj*. (1) Describing an aerial cable or other communication conductors which can be contacted by power conductors. (2) Describing current or potential carrying conductors which can be approached closer than a safe distance. (3) Not concealed from view.

exposure, *n*. A situation where communication circuits are in such proximity to electric power circuits that inductive interference could result.

expotential, *adj*. A variation which increases as the square, cube, or some other power (exponent) of a factor, instead of linearly.

expotential line. See "line, expotential transmission."

extended area service (EAS), *n*. Extension of a major exchange area to include other surrounding exchange areas. Toll-free dialing is permitted within the extended area in return for metropolitan area rates. See also "EAS, optional."

extender. *n*. Device consisting of a plug connected by a short cable to a receptacle of the same type. Used to keep a unit of equipment working while it is withdrawn from its mounting for test or repair.

extender, CATV line, *n*. A wideband amplifier for insertion in CATV cable lines serving remote subscribers.

extender, loop, *n*. A central office device which increases the signaling range on long subscriber lines by adding a series-aiding voltage to each side of the loop, thus effectively increasing the loop supply voltage. Operates from the 48 volt central office and can supply a boost of 24, 30, 48, or 60 volts. They maintain an additive loop voltage even after the battery reversal when the called party answers. Can be used as a substitute for or an additive to a long line adapter.

extender, loop signaling, *n.* A solid-state device placed in series with a subscriber's line at the central office which permits supervision and dial pulsing over a subscriber's loop longer than the normal 1000-1200 ohms. Some types include a booster battery source which provides an increased transmitter current.

extender, range, *n.* A device used in the central office to enable the use of 26 AWG station loops over 15,000 feet in length. It includes an amplifier with 5 dB gain, plus an increase in talking battery and an improvement in supervision range.

extension, *n.* (1) An additional telephone bridged on the same line with the main station. (2) A PBX station.

extension, bit, *n.* A steel rod 18 or 24 inches long having a thin chuck on one end for holding wood bits. Used for drilling at great depths in wooden partitions.

extension, cable rack, *n.* A bent galvanized steel bar used to mount underground cable racks away from the manhole wall, so as to avoid the moisture which causes rusting. Gives 3-inch or 6-inch wall clearance.

extension, off-premises, *n.* An extension telephone (or PBX station) located on property which is not contiguous with that on which the main station (or PBX) is located.

extension, PBX, *n.* A telephone station connected to a PBX station line.

extension, PBX off-premises, *n.* A primary station of a PBX, but located at premises distant from the PBX.

extension, pole top, *n.* A cross-arm or similar wooden member extending from the top of the pole to provide support and clearance for wires that cross the pole line.

extension, telephone, *n.* An additional telephone connected to the same central office line as the main station.

extension circuit, E&M lead, *n.* A DX type signaling circuit modified with an additional relay so it can be used as a pulse repeater for E&M lead signals. It converts E-lead conditions to M-lead conditions and vice versa.

extension station. See "station, extension."

extractor, lamp, *n.* A tubular sheet steel spring with handle, which can be slipped over a tubular switchboard lamp and used to pull it from its socket.

extractor, lamp cap, *n.* A small pair of pliers having hook shaped jaws which can be used to extract a switchboard lamp cap from the lamp socket.

extra pair, *n.* An additional pair in a cable, over and above the nominal number of pairs which are guaranteed to be good by the manufacturer. For instance: pair 26 in a 26 pr cable, pair 101 in a 101 pr cable. Extra pairs are seldom placed in cables manufactured today.

extrapolate, *n.* To estimate the values of a function which are less than or greater than those already known.

extremely low frequency (ELF), *adj.* Referring to any of the frequencies in the band between 30 and 300 hertz.

eye, pulling, *n.* A heavy metal eye sealed into the end of a cable and fastened to the cable conductors so it can be used to pull the cable into a duct.

eye dressing, *n.* A pack placed in first aid kits for the treatment of eye irritation. Consists of ⅛-oz tubes of boric acid ointment with sterile eye pads.

eyelet, *n.* A metal ring or short metal tube which lines and is crimped in a hole in a printed circuit board, which provides a connection from face to rear of board or a terminal into which a lead from a component can be soldered.

eye nut, *n.* A threaded nut extended into a thimble-shaped eye. Used to convert a standard threaded bolt into an eye bolt.

face, *n.* The side of a pole on which the crossarms are placed.—*v.* To set a pole in the ground so oriented that the crossarms will bear against the pole instead of pulling away from it.

face equipment, *n.* The jack and lamp equipment in the vertical panels of a switchboard or testboard.

facilities, *n. pl.* The elements of telephone plant which form a part of the complete end-to-end telephone connection. To avoid confusion, be specific: "outside plant facilities," "inside plant facilities," "radio facilities," etc. The term does not normally include the customer's equipment.

facilities, communication, *n. pl.* Installations, equipments, and personnel used to provide telecommunication.

facilities, transmission, *n. pl.* Facilities suitable for carrying communication intelligence, including wire (cable, open wire, paired wire), submarine cable, microwave, tropospheric scatter, HF radio, and satellite systems.

facility, *n.* Any one of the items of physical telephone plant which contribute to the giving of service.

facility, support. See "support facility."

facsimile, *adj.* Pertaining to facsimile transmission.—*n.* A system for the transmission of pictures, drawings, and written or printed documents by wire or radio. In common systems, the transmitter spirally scans copy fixed to a revolving drum.

facsimile receiver, *n.* A device which accepts an AM voice-frequency signal, converts it to a varying DC signal which is used to operate a recording stylus or to modulate a light for photographic recording of the received facsimile copy.

facsimile scanner, *n.* The portion of a facsimile transmitter consisting of a synchronously rotating drum on which a picture or other copy is placed. The copy is spirally scanned by a light beam to produce a varying direct current signal. The DC

signals go to a facsimile convertor which converts them to an amplitude-modulated voice-frequency signal for transmission.

factor, amplification, *n.* In an electron tube, the ratio of plate voltage change to grid voltage change under the condition that the plate current is held constant.

factor, dissipation. See "dissipation factor."

factor, duty. See "duty cycle."

factor, energy dissipation, *n.* For a capacitor, the ratio of the energy dissipated to the energy stored per cycle. Numerically, it is equal to the resistance of the capacitor leads and plates divided by its capacitive reactance.

factor, energy storage, *n.* For an inductor, the ratio of the energy stored to the energy dissipated per cycle. Numerically, it is equal to the inductive reactance of the inductor divided by its resistance.

factor, form. See "form factor."

factor, loss, *n.* A measure of the relative amount of heating which will occur in a dielectric material which is in an alternating electric field. Heating is directly proportional to frequency and the loss factor. Typical values of loss factor are as follows:

Hard rubber	—	0.015
Porcelain	—	0.044
Cellulose acetate	—	0.250

factor, power. See "power factor."

factor, power demand, *n.* The factor (less than unity) obtained when the actual maximum demand power load is divided by the connected power load.

factor, power diversity, *n.* The ratio of the sum of the individual demand power loads and the demand power load for an entire circuit or system. It is always less than unity because of time diversity, ie: some loads are used only in the daytime, others only at night, etc.

factor, pulse crest, *n.* The ratio of the

peak amplitude of a pulse to its root-mean-square value.

factor, shield, *n.* The ratio of noise or induced voltage on a shielded circuit to the noise or induced voltage on the same circuit when the shielding is absent.

factor, space, *n.* The percentage of the total volume of a coil which is occupied by the bare conductors which constitute the winding.

factor, telephone influence. See "Telephone Influence Factor (TIF)."

factor, via net loss. See "via net loss factor."

fade, *n.* A gradual change of signal strength.—*v.* To change the strength of a signal gradually.

fade margin. See "margin, fade."

fading, *n.* Variations in intensity of some or all components of a received radio signal due to changes in the propagation path. See also "multi-path fading."

fading, flat, *n.* Radio fading in which all frequency components of the received radio signal fluctuate in the same proportion concurrently.

fading, multipath. See "multipath fading."

fading, selective, *n.* Radio fading in which the various frequency components of the received signal fluctuate independently. See also "multipath fading."

Fahnestock clip, *n.* A spring terminal of the type commonly used on dry cells, permitting quick connection of a wire.

Fahrenheit, *adj.* Refers to one of several scales for designating temperatures. Under normal sea-level pressure, water freezes at +32 degrees F and boils at +212 degrees F.

fail-safe, *adj.* Describing a circuit or device which fails in such a way as to maintain circuit continuity or prevent damage.

failure, catastrophic, *n.* The complete and sudden failure of a complete communication system, or of an essential element of that system.

failure, partial, *n.* A serious trouble condition which results in a partial (not complete) loss of communication service.

failure, total, *n.* A complete loss of communication service resulting from serious trouble.

fan, also **fan out,** *vt.* To spread a group of conductors, such as a cable end, apart so that each can be individually tested or identified.

fanning strip. See "strip, fanning."

farad, or Farad, *n.* The basic unit of capacitance. That capacitance which permits the storing of one coulomb of electricity for each volt of applied potential difference. An impractically large unit. The unit commonly used is the microfarad, equal to one-millionth of a farad.

Faraday rotator. See "rotator, Faraday."

Faraday's Law. See "Appendix B."

far-end, *adj. n.* The opposite end of a circuit from the one referenced.

far-end crosstalk, *n.* A measure of the crosstalk which occurs at the far end of a toll circuit. To determine the far-end crosstalk between two pairs, 1 and 2, at station A standard crosstalk tone is transmitted on pair 1 while pair 2 is terminated. Then at the far station, B, the crosstalk level is measured on pair 2 with pair 1 terminated.

far-field region, *n.* The region beginning at a substantial distance from a transmitting antenna, where the antenna appears as a point source of energy and the power density of the electromagnetic field begins to decrease in proportion to the inverse square of the distance from the antenna.

farm, antenna, *n.* A large plot of ground (5-2000 acres) surrounding a radio transmitting or receiving station which provides space and adequate clearance for the installation of several large antennas, such as rhombic antennas.

far zone, antenna. See "zone, far."

fastener, *n.* A device for holding two or more items together to prevent their separation.

fastener, jack, *n.* A metal plate or butterfly washer used to hold a jack strip in place, on a switchboard or in a relay rack.

fastener, panel. *n.* A butterfly-shaped brass washer used to hold a removeable switchboard panel in place.

fastener, powder-powered, *n.* A hardened stud, or nail, or screw that can be propelled into wood, masonry, or steel by a properly sized gun powder charge.

fast link. See "link, fast."

fatigue, *n.* A sharp reduction in the strength of a metal, due to the formation of crystals within the metal from repeated flexing.

fault, *n.* (1) A fracture or break, such as in a cable sheath. (2) Any defect in an item of telephone plant which impairs its function. (3) A short or ground on a pair of wires. (4) A malfunction which occurs consistently under the same circumstances.

fault, intermittent, *n.* A defect in a transmission medium (cross, ground, short, etc.) which is not steadily present.

fault current. See "current, fault" and "current, ground fault."

fault finder, *n.* Any of several devices which enable one to identify and locate telephone faults.

fault to ground, *n.* A breakdown of the insulation between a communication conductor or equipment and ground.—*vi.* To rupture or break down insulation, and thus permit a conductor to become grounded.

Faure plate, *n.* A pasted storage battery plate, consisting of a grid of lead-antimony filled with a paste of lead oxide.

Federal Communications Commission, *n.* A board of seven commissioners, appointed by the President under the Communications Act of 1934, having the power to regulate all electrical communications systems originating in the United States, including radio, television, facsimile, telegraph, telephone, and cable systems.

feed, *n.* An antenna feed.—*v.* To supply energy to a line or antenna.

feed, antenna, *n.* The coaxial or wire transmission line that delivers energy to an antenna, or the dipole or horn that illuminates a reflector with radio frequency energy.

feed, current, *n.* The excitation of an antenna by connecting the feeder at a point of maximum current, as at the center of a dipole.

feed, series, *n.* The application of positive voltage to the plate of an electron tube through the same impedance in which the signal current flows. See also "series feed."

feed, shunt, *n.* The application of positive voltage to the plate of an electron tube through a choke in parallel with the signal circuit, so that the signal and DC plate voltage are kept separate.

feed, voltage, *n.* The excitation of an antenna by connecting the feeder at a point of maximum potential.

feedback, *n.* (1) The act of returning a portion of the output voltage of a circuit which includes amplification to the input of that circuit. (2) The signal which is thus fed back. See also "feedback, negative" and "feedback, positive."

feedback, acoustic, *n.* The feeding back of sound waves from a loudspeaker to a microphone in the same audio system. Creates distortion, and if excessive a "howl."

feedback, inverse, *n.* Negative feedback.

feedback, negative, *n.* The returning of a portion of the output of a device such as an amplifier to the input of the device, but 180 degrees out of phase with the normal input voltage. When correctly adjusted in amount, negative feedback will exactly compensate for any distortion or noise in the device, but will also reduce the gain.

feedback, positive, *n.* The return of a portion of the output signal of an amplifier to its input, with the signal fed back being in phase with the input signal. Increases amplification, and circuit instability. If the feedback circuit is frequency tuned, the combination becomes a variable-frequency oscillator.

feeder, *n.* A transmission line between an antenna and a radio transmitter or receiver.

feeder, cable, *n.* A flexible steel conduit, 4 inches ID and 9 or 12 feet long, used to feed cable being pulled in from the surface through the manhole to the duct entrance.

feeder, matched. See "feeder, non-resonant."

feeder, mismatched. See "feeder, resonant."

feeder, negative, *n.* In a street railway system, a heavy copper conductor, aerial or underground, which runs parallel to the tracks and periodically connects to the rails. It avoids the high resistance losses in the steel rails, and helps to prevent the current from leaving the rails to seek a more direct path through the earth.

feeder, non-resonant, *n.* A radio-frequency transmission line which is terminated in its characteristic impedance, and therefore does not have a standing wave on it. Also called a "matched feeder."

feeder, resonant, *n.* A radio-frequency transmission line which is not terminated in its characteristic impedance, and thus has a standing wave on it. Also called a "mismatched feeder."

feeder cable. See "cable, feeder."

feedhorn, *n.* A horn antenna consisting of the flared end of a waveguide, used to illuminate a parabolic reflector with microwave radio-frequency energy.

Fermat's Principle. See "Appendix B."

ferreed, *adj.* Describing any relay whose contact assembly is made up

of individual magnetic reeds sealed in an evacuated glass tube, operated by an external winding. Each tube contains one Form A, Form B, or Form C set of contacts. When operated, the contacts remain operated, held by magnetism until released by a current pulse.

ferrite, *n.* A magnetic core material consisting of powdered, compressed, and sintered ferric oxide combined with other oxides, such as of nickel, nickel-cobalt, and yttrium-iron. Has a high resistivity, so eddy-current losses at high frequencies are very low.

ferroelectric, *adj.* Said of a crystalline material in which the crystal electric domains can be reversed by application of an electric field, thereby making the material polar and thus piezoelectric.

ferromagnetic, *adj.* Describing a metal, such as iron, nickel, or cobalt, whose permeability greatly exceeds 1.0, and whose susceptibility increases as the magnetizing field increases. See also "paramagnetic" and "diamagnetic."

ferrule, *n.* The metal cap around the end of a cartridge fuse tube which serves as a contact for the fuse.

fidelity, *n.* The degree to which a transmission system faithfully produces at its output all of the essential characteristics of the signal which it received at its input.

field, card, *n.* A particular group of adjacent columns in a punched data card assigned for a particular item of information.

field, electric, *n.* (1) The region around an electrically charged body within which other electric charges are attracted or repelled. (2) The electrostatic component of a radio wave.

field, electromagnetic. See "electromagnetic field."

field, electrostatic, *n.* A volume within which there is electric stress produced by stationary electric charges.

field, jack, *n.* The area on the face of

a switchboard or test bay in which jacks may be installed.

field, magnetic, *n.* The region around a conductor or coil which is carrying a current within which moving electric charges will be acted upon by a magnetic force.

field, radiation, *n.* The electromagnetic field which surrounds a transmitting antenna.

field-effect transistor. See "transistor, field-effect."

field side, *adv., n.* The side of a pole away from the highway or street.

field strength, *n.* The strength of an electric, magnetic, or electromagnetic field. Electromagnetic (radio) field strength is expressed in microvolts per meter or millivolts per meter.

field telephone. See "telephone, field."

field wire. See "wire, field."

figure, noise. See "noise figure."

figures, metal. See "numerals, aluminum."

filament, *n.* In an electron tube, the directly-heated cathode consisting of a loop of resistance wire which emits electrons when heated by a current.

filament, mono, *n.* A single strand of wire or thread-like material, not made of braided or twisted filaments.

filament, thoriated, *n.* An electron tube filament made to emit electrons at a low (dull red) temperature by coating the filament with thorium oxide. Applied especially to electron tubes used in telephone repeaters.

file, no-test, *n.* In a crossbar office, the ten vertical units on a line switch bay in a line link frame, which are used for no-test calls.

file, vertical, *n.* In a crossbar office, the ten vertical units of a crossbar switch which are located one above another on a line link frame.

filing time, *n.* The time at which an operator accepts the call or order from the customer.

fill, *n.* (1) The number of lines working in a cable, a cable count, or a central office. (2) The percentage of working lines to total cable pairs or central office line equipments provided. (3) The percentage of the number of connected telephone stations on a line to the line capacity.

fill, cable, *n.* The percentage of working lines to total cable pairs.

fill, line, *n.* The ratio of the number of main stations connected to a telephone station line to the nominal station capacity of the line.

fill, percentage, *n.* Fill. expressed in per cent.

filler, *n.* (1) A material used to fill air voids in cables and electrical components. (2) A substance, usually inert, added to a compound to improve its properties or to decrease its cost.

filler, fibrous, *n.* A material consisting of fibers of cotton, jute, glass, etc., used to fill interstices in cables.

filter, *n.* A frequency selective network which transmits signals of desired frequencies while greatly attenuating all other frequencies.

filter, active RC, *n.* A filter which uses both negative and positive feedback, provided by solid-state amplifiers, to enhance its characteristics. Excellent selectivity can be provided at very low frequencies.

filter, band-elimination, *n.* A network which is designed to pass freely signals of all frequencies except those within a definite band.

filter, band-pass, *n.* A filter which passes, without appreciable attenuation or distortion, frequencies within a specified band while attenuating frequencies outside of that band.

filter, bandstop, *n.* A filter having characteristics opposite to those of a bandpass filter. The bandstop filter attenuates frequencies within a defined band, and offers low attenuation of frequencies outside this band.

filter, capacitor-input, *n.* A power filter in which the first element encountered by the voltage wave from the rectifier is a capacitor shunted across the circuit.

filter, carrier line, *n.* A filter placed in series with the line to separate the voice frequencies from the carrier frequencies, and to direct each into its proper path.

filter, cavity, *n.* A high-Q filter for microwave frequencies which uses a cavity as its resonant element.

filter, choke-input, *n.* A power filter in which the first element encountered by current from the rectifier is a series inductance.

filter, comb, *n.* A filter having a multiplicity of regularly-spaced narrow attenuation bands. For instance: the filter used to attenuate the carriers without attenuating the carrier sidebands.

filter, composite, *n.* A multisection network consisting of constant-k sections terminated with m-derived half sections. They have a uniform impedance over the transmission band, and a sharp cutoff.

filter, constant-k, *n.* A filter in which the series and shunt impedances are inverse elements (one inductive, one capacitive), and the product of the series and shunt impedances is a constant, independent of frequency.

filter, crystal, *n.* A low-loss and extremely sharp filter which uses quartz crystal resonant elements instead of inductor-capacitor elements. The Q of a quartz crystal is about 20,000.

filter, enhancement, *n.* A filter used with an amplifier to increase the transmission level of a particular signal over that of other signals on the same circuit, but without adding distortion.

filter, high-pass, *n.* A filter which passes, without appreciable attenuation or distortion, all frequencies above a specified cutoff frequency while attenuating all frequencies below the cutoff frequency.

filter, key click, *n.* A filter which smooths out the power circuit surges which result when a radio transmitter is keyed.

filter, LC, *n.* A filter consisting only of inductance (L) and capacitance (C).

filter, longitudinal suppression, *n.* A filter connected in series with a pair of wires for the purpose of suppressing longitudinal noise currents, those audio-frequency currents which travel in the same direction on both sides of a pair.

filter, low-pass, *n.* A filter which passes, without appreciable attenuation or distortion, all frequencies below a specified cutoff frequency while attenuating all frequencies above the cutoff frequency.

filter, m-derived, *n.* A filter configuration which is derived from the constant-k protype by operation of a factor "m."

filter, mechanical, *n.* An audio-frequency filter in which the resonant element is a magnetostriction device. See also "magnetostriction."

filter, notch, *n.* A filter which is designed to reject or attenuate one particular frequency.

filter, octave, *n.* A bandpass filter which passes one octave. That is, whose upper cutoff frequency is twice the lower cutoff frequency.

filter, power interference, *n.* A filter placed in the alternating current power feed to an electronic device which rejects high-frequency interfering signals which may be on the power line.

filter, prototype, *n.* A basic filter, of constant-k design.

filter, RFI, *n.* A small, 3-terminal filter mounted in telephone sets and connected to reduce radio frequency induction due to the dial pulses.

filter, roof, *n.* A low-pass filter.

filter, separation. See "separation filter."

filters, directional, *n. pl.* The pair of filters which are used to separate the east-to-west and west-to-east frequencies of a carrier system. A typical cable carrier system uses 40-140 kHz east-to-west, and 164-264 kHz west-to-east.

final group, *n.* A group of trunks which acts as an overflow or "last resort" route for traffic which finds a direct "high-usage" group to be busy.

final route, *n.* The last of several alternate routes.

final trunk group, *n.* A group of trunks to the next office which are liberally provided to give a good grade of service. The probability of being blocked by a busy condition is acceptably low.

finder, *n.* A switch arranged to find one input among many and to connect it to a single output.

finder, pull, *n.* A type of sighting protractor which can be set on the side of a corner pole and used to determine the angle of the corner in the line. It is calibrated in "feet of pull."

finder, trunk, *n.* A multiple inlet single-outlet switch which finds a particular trunk within a group, on which there is an incoming call, and connects it to a switchboard.

finger stop. See "stop, finger."

finger wheel, *n.* On a telephone dial, the circular plate with ten holes which is rotated to wind up the dial.

fire-reporting switchboard. See "switchboard, fire-reporting."

fire-reporting telephone. See "set, fire-reporting telephone."

first Fresnel zone. See "Fresnel zone."

fish, *vt.* To push a stiff steel wire or tape through a conduit, and then with it to pull through wires, cable, or a heavier pulling-in wire.

fitting, *n.* An accessory to an electrical wiring system which performs a mechanical rather than electrical function.

five-by-five, *adj.* Describing signals which are loud and clear. (Colloquial)

five-pair protector. See "protector, open wire."

fixed, *adj.* (1) Not subject to adjustment. (2) Not moveable.

fixed station, *n.* (1) A station (radio, etc.) which is not mobile. (2) A station which is permanently installed. (3) The base station in a mobile telephone system.

fixture, "A," *n.* A pole line support consisting of two poles with their butts spaced 5-6 feet apart and the tops bolted together, so the fixture resembles the letter "A." Provides additional lateral strength.

fixture, "H," *n.* A pole line support consisting of two upright poles spaced 8-9 feet, and tied together by bolted-on crossarms. May be placed either in line with the pole lead or across (at right angles to) the lead and resembles the letter "H." Used to provide either (a) additional lateral support or (b) a support for aerial loading cases.

fixture, loading, *n.* A reinforced "H" fixture in line with the pole lead on which a pair of steel channel beams are substituted for the crossarms. Used to support heavy loading cases at an aerial load point.

fixture, pole extension, *n.* A six-foot length of channel steel used when a light-duty extension of the pole top is necessary, such as the need for extra height for a drop wire attachment.

flag, danger, *n.* A 1-foot square flag of red muslin, usually on a 30-inch staff. Used by construction and repair forces to warn the public of a hazard.

flame-proof, *adj.* Said of insulated wire or other material which has been chemically treated so it will not aid the spread of flames.

flame-retardant, *adj.* Constructed or treated so as not to be able to convey flame.

flange, ceiling, *n.* A metal strap having two holes for mounting and an offset center, used for suspending ⅜ inch or ½ inch hanger rods from the ceiling of a central office.

flange, C pressure testing, *n.* A tinned bronze flange for soldering to lead cables or lead splice sleeves. Has an internal ⅛-inch pipe thread into which an F pressure testing valve can be screwed.

flange, D, *n.* A tinned bronze flange having a ½-inch male pipe thread on one end by which it can be screwed into a cable sheath or splice sleeve and then soldered. The upper end has a ⅛-inch female pipe thread into which a resin pressure gun or a ⅛-inch pipe plug can be screwed.

flange, pressure testing, *n.* A brass disk which can be sweated onto a cable sheath and, by means of a threaded hole continued through the sheath, may be used to attach a valve stem or pipe plug for gas pressure protection.

flanking, filter, *n.* The use of band-pass filters, such as carrier channel filters, in parallel. When operating in parallel, each filter has an effect on the susceptance of the other filters, particularly those on adjacent channels. Removal of a channel filter may severely degrade the adjacent channels unless it is replaced by a susceptance annulling network.

flash, *n.* (1) A flashing signal. (2) A succession of on-hook and off-hook intervals. Flashing signals are outmoded, and no longer specified.

Flash (F), *n.* The second highest ranking message precedence. See "precedence."

flash, hookswitch, *n.* A repeated operate-and-release sequence of the telephone hookswitch, long enough to flash switchboard supervisory lamps but not long enough to release the circuit.

flashing jack, *n.* Jack on which the equipment is such that the operator can flash on the trunk by plugging into this jack.

flashover, *n.* The discharge of high voltage electricity across the surface or around an insulator.

Flash Override (FO), *n.* The highest ranking message precedence. See "precedence."

flat-rate, *adj.* Describing a telephone line which receives unlimited local service in return for the payment of a fixed charge per month.

flat response, *n.* A uniform response over a specified frequency band.

F layer(s), *n.* The upper layers of ionozation in the ionosphere. The F-1 layer is at about 130 miles above the earth, with about 1,000,000 electrons per cc. during the day, greatly reduced during the night. The F-2 layer height varies from about 250 miles during the day to about 150 miles at night, and with ionozation varying from 1,000,000 electrons per cc. during the day to 100,000 per cc. during the night.

Fleming's Rule. See "Right-Hand Rule" in Appendix B.

Flexiduct, *n.* A rubber duct used to cover and protect wires on the surface of floors. About 3 inches wide x ½ inch high, with tapered edges.

flex life. See "life, flex."

flicker noise. See "pink noise."

flink, *n.* A galloping lamp signal which combines a "wink" and a "flash." Timing for the complete cycle is: 0.25 second on, 0.03 second off, 0.25 second on, 0.50 second off.

flip-flop, *n.* A bi-stable device, which can be switched to either of two states.

float, *v.* To operate a storage battery in parallel with a charger and a load, at such a voltage that the charger supplies the load current and the battery supplies only transient peaks above the normal load.

floating battery, *n.* A direct current supply from a constant voltage source (generator or rectifier) paralleled with a storage battery. If the constant voltage source is interrupted, the storage battery maintains power to the load. If there are minor variations in the load current, they are supplied from the battery.

floating neutral. See "neutral, floating power."

floor, raised, *n.* A type of floor used in most computer rooms and in some communication equipment rooms, in which the floor consists of individually removeable 3 foot square panels supported above a sub-floor by leveling jacks at the panel corners. It permits rapid access to the sub-floor cabling space and permits that space to be used as a plenum for cold air to cool the equipment racks.

floor-wall distributing frame, *n.* A single-sided distributing frame designed to rest on the floor but mount against a wall.

Florduct, *n.* A two-piece (base and cap) metal floor duct used to extend wires over the surface of floors. Snap-on cap has tapered edges. About 1⅛ inch wide x ⅜ inch high.

Flotrol, *n.* Registered name of one brand of power rectifier which has close voltage regulation and thus is able to "float" charge a central office storage battery.

flow chart, *n.* A graphical representation of a procedure or process.

flow system, continuous, *n.* System for the dry air pressurization of cables, based on providing a continuous supply of dry air to the cable at a central point and tolerating small leaks as long as the far end of the cable has a minimum pressure of 2 psi.

fluid, leak detecting. See "solution, pressure testing."

fluorescence, *n.* The property of some chemical elements particularly gases, to emit light of a longer visible wavelength than the light with which they are illuminated.

flutter, *n.* Rapid variation of the transmission loss of voice telephone circuits due to the saturation of re-

peating coil or loading coil cores by superimposed DC telegraph circuits. Rarely encountered today.

flux, *n.* (1) The flow of electric or magnetic lines of force. (2) Soldering flux.

flux, leakage, *n.* Magnetic flux which by-passes windings where it could do useful work.

flux, magnetic. See "magnetic flux."

flux, noncorrosive soldering, *n.* A soldering flux which is free from acid and will not corrode the work if not removed after soldering. Rosin is the only truly practical noncorrosive flux for soldering copper wires.

flux, residual, *n.* The magnetic flux which remains in a magnetic circuit after the magnetomotive force is removed.

flux, soldering, *n.* Any of the substances, such as rosin, borax, or ammonium chloride, which are used to remove oxide films from metals to prepare them for soldering.

fly wheel motor-generator diesel unit, *n.* A motor-generator with fly wheel on a common shaft, clutch-coupled to a diesel engine. Normally, primary AC power to the motor drives the generator which feeds the load. Interruption of the primary AC power engages the clutch to start the diesel unit from fly wheel-supplied inertial energy. The load is supplied from the generator without interruption.

fly wheel motor-generator unit, *n.* A motor-generator unit with a large fly wheel on the same shaft. Interruption of primary power initiates action to transfer the motor to an alternate AC source. The fly wheel ensures continuous power from the generator to the load.

foil, *n.* A very thin sheet of metal, such as tin, aluminum, etc. Used in the construction of fixed capacitors.

foil-electret, *n.* A polymer plastic film about one mil thick with a very thin metal layer evaporated on one surface, and having a permanent electrostatic polarization created by electron bombardment or by heating while exposed to a powerful electric field. Used to make condenser microphone diaphragms.

folded-dipole. See "antenna, folded-dipole."

force, back electromotive, *n.* A voltage developed in an inductive circuit when the current through the circuit changes. The polarity of the back voltage is at each instant opposite to and less than that of the voltage which produces the current.

force, counterelectromotive, *n.* A voltage generated in an inductive circuit by a change in current in the same circuit. The counter EMF is opposite in polarity to the voltage which produces the current in the circuit.

force, electromotive (EMF), *n.* The force that produces a movement of electric charges resulting in a "current" flow. Electromotive force is commonly called "voltage."

force, magnetomotive. See "magnetomotive force."

forced dialing, *n.* The act of forcing the rotary telephone dial to return to normal faster than it would automatically, thus increasing the dialing speed and aggravating wrong numbers.

forced disconnect, *n.* The automatic release of a telephone connection when the calling station does not disconnect within a specified period after the called party disconnects.

foreign area. See "area, foreign."

foreign attachment, *n.* Equipment, apparatus, circuit, or device not furnished by the Telephone Company which is attached or connected to the facilities of the Telephone Company, whether physically, by induction, or by other means. May or may not be legally acceptable.

form, cable, *n.* (1) The ends of equipment and tipping cables in central offices where the wires are fanned and formed to fit equipment terminals, and then are laced in that position. (2) A formation of wires not enclosed in a covering or sheath, but held in formation either by sewing with twine or by fanning rings or other wire retaining devices. Cable forms may be made from bulk wire or from the formed end of a switchboard cable.

form, contact, *n.* The configuration of a single-pole contact assembly. The different forms are designated by letter, as follows:

A — Make. Single-pole, single-throw, normally open.

B — Break. Single-pole, single-throw, normally closed.

C — Transfer. Single-pole, double-throw.

D — Transfer. Make before break.

E — Break-make-break.

K — Single-pole, double-throw, but normally open.

U — Contact A makes with contacts B and C.

V — Contact A breaks from contacts B and C.

W — Contact A breaks from contacts B and C, and makes with contacts D and E.

X — Double make. Contact B makes with contact A which makes with contact C.

Y — Double break. Contact B breaks with contact A which breaks with contact C.

Z — Same as form W, except that contact A terminal is not brought out for connection.

form, fanned, *n.* An arrangement whereby wires are brought directly from the butt of a cable, or from the point where the wires leave a sewed cable form through a fanning strip or fanning rings, and thence to the terminals where they are terminated.

form, loose wire, *n.* Wiring which is held in cable formation by the use of fanning rings rather than by lacing.

form, manhole, *n*. Metal or wooden sections which can be assembled to the size and shape of an underground manhole. Serve as a form for a cast-in-place concrete manhole, with cast-in pulling irons and bolt anchors for cable rack mounting. Form is easily disassembled after the concrete has hardened.

form, sewed, *n*. A formation of bulk wires or cable wires compactly sewed into a cable form so that the wires are brought out approximately opposite their associated terminals.

form, soldering, *n*. A form which confines solder to a small area and makes it possible to solder a neat patch around a pressure testing fitting. Consists of a length of gummed kraft paper with a felt washer glued to the under side. Available to make a ⅞-inch square patch or a 1½-inch round patch.

form factor, *n*. (1) Of a complex wave, the effective value divided by the mean value during one-half period. (2) A factor which influences the inductance of coils, and depends upon the ratio of their diameter to length.

fortuitous, *adj*. Occurring by chance, without any predictable pattern. A characteristic of telephone traffic and some types of noise.

forward error correction (FEC), *n*. A system of data transmission in which redundant bits generated at the transmitter are used at the receiving terminal to detect, locate, and correct any transmission errors before delivery to the data sink. Its advantage is that it does not require a feedback channel, and can therefore be used with a one-way transmission system.

forwarding, call, *n*. (1) A service available in some dial offices whereby a subscriber can have calls to his number forwarded to another phone by dialing the forwarding number to the equipment. All incoming calls are then forwarded automatically. The forwarding can be discontinued at will, by command from the base telephone. (2) A service available in centrex offices in which incoming calls to busy lines, or to lines which do not answer within a prescribed interval, are automatically routed to the centrex attendant.

forwarding, customer-selective call, *n*. Capability of a common-controlled central office which allows a customer to activate equipment which will route calls directed to his telephone number to any other desired number.

forward propagation ionospheric scatter (FPIS). See "scatter, ionospheric."

forward propagation tropospheric scatter (FPTS). See "scatter, tropospheric."

forward routing, *n*. (1) Advancing a toll call into a home grid from a switching center outside of the home grid. (2) A call advanced toward its destination by a specified distance improvement factor.

Fourier analysis, *n*. The process of analyzing a complex wave by separating it into a plurality of component waves, each of a particular frequency, amplitude, and phase displacement.

four-party line. See "line, party."

four-thirds earth radius, *n*. A value of 8,500 kilometers, or 4/3 of the earth's actual radius. Used to correct for atmospheric refraction under normal conditions of pressure and temperature when calculating radio propagation losses.

four-wire circuit. See "circuit, four-wire."

four-wire line, *n*. A two-way transmission circuit which uses four conductors, one pair for the transmitting direction and the other pair for the receiving direction.

four-wire repeater. See "repeater, four-wire."

four-wire terminating set. See "set, four-wire terminating."

fox test, *n.* The traditional message used to test teletypewriter circuits and equipment: "THE QUICK BROWN FOX JUMPED OVER A LAZY DOG'S BACK 1234567890."

Frahm frequency meter. See "frequency meter, vibrating reed."

frame, *n.* (1) A distributing frame. (2) A switch frame. (3) A trunk board. (4) One complete television picture, transmitted 30 times per second.

frame, combined distributing (CDF), *n.* A distributing frame which has main distributing frame verticals on one end and intermediate distributing frame verticals on the other end. A combined distributing frame must be free to grow in both directions.

frame, crossbar district junctor, *n.* The frame which mounts the relay equipment which provides talking battery and supervision for the calling subscriber. It is intermediate between the line link frame and the district link frame. (#1 X Bar)

frame, crossbar district link, *n.* A frame terminating district junctors (from the line link frame) on the horizontals of primary switches and office junctors on the verticals of secondary switches. (#1 X Bar)

frame, crossbar line link, *n.* A frame containing crossbar switches, used to connect the subscriber's lines, which are assigned to verticals of the primary switches, with district junctors for outgoing calls and with line junctors for incoming calls. (#1 X Bar)

frame, crossbar office link, *n.* A frame of 10 primary and 10 secondary 200 point switches. Office junctors (from the district link frames) terminate on verticals of the primary switches. Outgoing trunks appear on the horizontals of the secondary switches. (#1 X Bar)

frame, crossbar trunk link, *n.* A frame which mounts junctor switches, trunk switches, and relays for marker access to the frame. Junctors from the line link frame are connected to horizontals of the junctor switches. Trunks and originating registers are connected to the trunk switches. (#5 X Bar)

frame, distributing, *n.* A rectangular bar steel framework having "verticals" on which protectors and terminal blocks may be fastened, and open shelves, "horizontals," on which terminal blocks may be mounted. Used in telephone central offices to enable the placing of semipermanent "cross-connections" to permanent equipment.

frame, double-sided distributing. See "frame, floor-type distributing."

frame, facsimile, *n.* A rectangular area, the width of which is the "available line," and the length of which is determined by requirements.

frame, floor-type distributing, *n.* A free-standing distributing frame which is floor-supported, and which has access on both vertical and horizontal sides. Also called a "double-sided distributing frame."

frame, floor-wall distributing, *n.* A distributing frame which mounts against the wall, but is supported from the floor.

frame, incoming link, *n.* Frame in a #4A toll switching system which terminates incoming toll and intertoll trunks on the horizontals of primary crossbar switches, and outgoing link junctors on the verticals of secondary crossbar switches.

frame, intermediate distributing (IDF), *n.* A distributing frame having terminal blocks on both sides. One side terminates the telephone number (line multiple or connector terminal) while the other side terminates the subscriber's line circuit, permitting any telephone number to be associated with any line circuit.

frame, junctor grouping, *n.* (1) In a crossbar office, a frame which distributes the 100 junctors from each line link frame over all link frames so that each line link frame will have equal access to all trunk link frames. (2) In an electronic switching office, a distributing frame to which all link networks are cabled, for crossconnection as required by traffic flow.

frame, line intermediate distributing (LIDF), *n.* A distributing frame on which the subscriber line multiple (telephone number) appears on blocks on one side, and the subscriber's line circuits on blocks on the other side. Allows the crossconnecting of any telephone to any line equipment for traffic load balancing.

frame, line link, *n.* In a crossbar office, a frame containing line links with their associated equipment and the customer line relays.

frame, main distributing (MDF), *n.* A distributing frame at which outside plant cables terminate on vertical protector strips, from which they crossconnect to central office line equipment terminated on horizontal blocks. See also "frame, type-A main distributing" and "frame, type-B main distributing."

frame, manhole, *n.* The cast iron structure which caps the manhole chimney at ground level and provides a support for the manhole cover.

frame, master test, *n.* In a crossbar office, a unit of equipment which provides means for testing the equipment units of a marker group.

frame, number group, *n.* In a crossbar office, a frame containing 1,000 consecutive line numbers that can be associated with one, two, or three office code groups. A maximum of 40 number groups may be associated with one marker group.

frame, outgoing link, *n.* Frame which terminates junctors from the incoming frame on verticals of the primary crossbar switch and outgoing trunks on horizontals of this secondary cross bar switch. (#4A TSS)

frame, outgoing sender, *n.* Frame containing senders used only to offices requiring revertive pulsing (RP) or to manual offices arranged for panel call indicator (PCI). They do not have register capabilities. All routing information is received from the incoming sender on a DC key pulsing basis.

frame, sender link, *n.* Frame containing crossbar switches which connect incoming senders to incoming trunks and outgoing senders to outgoing trunks, as required. (#4A TSS)

frame, sender make-busy, *n.* Frame which provides a means to remove senders from service, for maintenance or test. (#4A TSS)

frame, sender test, *n.* Frame containing equipment for making routine and trouble location tests on senders, both automatically and manually. (#4A TSS)

frame, single-sided distributing, *n.* A distributing frame which mounts terminal blocks on only one side, either only on verticals or on both verticals and horizontals. There are three general types: (a) a one-foot deep frame which mounts in a switch-bay line-up, (b) a wall-type distributing frame, and (c) a floor-wall type distributing frame.

frame, switch, *n.* An open framework of channel or angle steel on which switch shelves are mounted in a dial central office.

frame, toll connecting trunk test, *n.* Frame provided with the means to test toll connecting trunks on an automatic or manual basis. (#4A TSS)

frame, trouble recorder, *n.* Equipment which indicates by means of a punched card or printed record exactly where, in the course of switching a call, the switching equipment encounters trouble. Also provides a means of testing common-control equipment. (#4A TSS)

frame, trunk intermediate distributing (TIDF), *n.* A distributing frame on which trunk repeaters, interoffice two-wire trunks, and intra-office three-wire trunks terminate on terminal blocks for crossconnection. Facilitates trunk rearrangements to meet changing traffic patterns.

frame, type "A" main distributing, *n.* An obsolete type of main distributing frame at which outside plant cables were terminated on horizontal blocks from which they were crossconnected to equipment cables terminated on vertical protectors. Used fewer protectors than a type "B" frame.

frame, type "B" main distributing, *n.* The standard main distributing frame at which outside plant cables terminate on vertical protectors, from which they crossconnect to equipment cables terminated on horizontal blocks. Provides a protector on every exposed outside plant pair.

frame, wall-type distributing, *n.* A distributing frame which is mounted against and supported by a wall. Its verticals may mount either protector strips or terminal blocks. It is not normally equipped with shelves for horizontal terminal blocks.

framing, *n.* The operation of cutting a pole to make it suitable for its intended use, including cutting a roof, cutting crossarm gains, and boring holes for through-bolts.

Fraunhofer region, *n.* The far-field region, which see.

frayed, *adj.* Said of wrapped or braided insulation on wires when the cut ends become ragged by rubbing.

fraying, *n.* The unraveling of a fibrous braid.

free-running, *adj.* Describing an oscillator or multivibrator which operates without a synchronizing input.

free space loss. See "loss, free space."

free space transmission, *n.* Straight-line transmission of a radio wave through a vacuum or an ideal atmosphere, without absorption, reflection, or diffraction of energy by near-by objects.

free space wave, *n.* That portion of a radio wave which travels in a direct path between transmitting and receiving antennas, without reflections or refractions.

frequency, *n.* For a periodic wave, such as alternating current, the number of complete cycles per unit of time. The unit of time is usually a second. The number of cycles can be expressed in cycles, kilocycles, megacycles, etc. See also "hertz," and "spectrum, frequency."

frequency, audio, *n.* Any of the frequencies in the range 20 to 20,000 hertz.

frequency, beat. See "beat frequency."

frequency, center. See "frequency, resting."

frequency, critical radio. See "critical frequency."

frequency, critical singing, *n.* The frequency at which the singing margin is lowest, and at which singing first occurs when gain is added. Usually occurs in the range 250-500 Hz or 2500-3400 Hz.

frequency, crossover, *n.* Of a dividing network, the frequency at which equal powers are delivered to the higher band and the lower band when both are terminated in their normal load.

frequency, cutoff. See "cutoff frequency."

frequency, effective, *n.* The frequency in a broad-band radio radiation chosen such that the total energy in the band at lesser frequencies equals the total energy in the band at greater frequencies.

frequency, extremely high (EHF), *n.* Any of the radio frequencies in the band 30,000 MHz-300,000 MHz.

frequencely, extremely low (ELF), *n.* A radio frequency below 300 hertz.

frequency, facsimile frame, *n.* The number of times per second that a facsimile frame is transmitted or received.

frequency, high (HF), *n.* Any of the radio frequencies in the band between 3,000 and 30,000 kilohertz.

frequency, image. See "image frequency."

frequency, intermediate, *n.* In a superheterodyne radio receiver, the frequency produced by combining the incoming radio signal with that from a local oscillator. Allows amplification to be at the lower intermediate frequency, which gives superior selectivity. The intermediate frequency is commonly 455 kHz for a broadcast receiver, 45.75 MHz for the TV picture channel, and 41.25 MHz for the TV sound channel.

frequency, low (LF), *n.* Any of the band of radio frequencies between 30 and 300 kilohertz.

frequency, lowest useful (LUF). See "lowest useful frequency."

frequency, maximum usable (MUF). See "maximum usable frequency."

frequency, medium (MF), *n.* Any of the radio frequencies in the band 300-3000 kilohertz.

frequency, natural, *n.* (1) The lowest frequency at which there is a standing wave on an antenna. (2) Any frequency at which a body will oscillate freely.

frequency, optimum working, *n.* The frequency at which long-distance radio transmission via the ionosphere can be most effectively maintained at a particular time of day. Sometimes assumed to be a frequency 15% less than the maximum usable frequency (MUF).

frequency, penetration. See "penetration frequency."

frequency, pilot. See "pilot frequency."

frequency, pulse repetition (PRF), *n.* The number of pulses per second in a pulse train.

frequency, radio. See "radio frequency."

frequency, resonant. See "resonant frequency."

frequency, resting, *n.* Of a frequency modulated wave, the frequency of the carrier before modulation.

frequency, super high (SHF), *n.* Any of the radio frequencies in the band 3,000-30,000 megahertz.

frequency, ultra-high (UHF), *n.* Any of the radio frequencies in the band between 300 and 3,000 megahertz.

frequency, very high (VHF), *n.* Any of the radio frequencies in the band between 30 and 300 megahertz.

frequency, very low (VLF), *n.* Any of the radio frequencies between 3000 hertz and 30 kilohertz.

frequency, voice, *n.* (1) Any of the frequencies within the band 32-16,000 Hz which are audible to the human ear. (2) Any of the frequencies within the band 300-3500 Hz which are normally used for telephone communication.

frequency allocation. See "allocation, frequency."

frequency band, high-group, *n.* The upper of two frequency bands which are used for E to W and W to E directional transmissions on a carrier system. Example: The WECo N2 carrier uses a high-group band of 172-268 kHz, and a low-group band of 36-132 kHz.

frequency band, low-group, *n.* The lower of two frequency bands which are used for E to W and W to E directional transmission on a carrier system. Example: The WECo N2 carrier uses a low-group band of 36-132 kHz and a high group band of 172-268 kHz.

frequency changer, *n.* A device for changing power at one frequency to equivalent power at another frequency. For instance: 25 Hz to 60 Hz, 50 Hz to 60 Hz, 60 Hz to 400 Hz, and vice versa. Used to interface power systems operating at different frequencies. May be either rotary (motor-generator) or static (mercury-arc, or electron tube) devices.

frequency conversion. See "conversion, frequency."

frequency converter. See "converter, frequency."

frequency coordination. See "coordination, frequency."

frequency deviation. See "deviation, frequency."

frequency distortion. See "distortion, amplitude-frequency."

frequency diversity. See "diversity, frequency."

frequency divider. See "divider, frequency."

frequency-division multiplex, *n.* Arrangement where several message channels share a single transmission facility, each having its own frequency band.

frequency doubler. See "doubler, frequency."

frequency-frogging, *adj.* Describing a carrier repeater which is arranged to interchange the low-group and high-group frequency bands.—*n.* The process of modulating the signal input to a carrier repeater so that both high-group and low-group signals are inverted, converting the incoming high-group to low-group outgoing and vice versa. This practice provides self-equalization of the cable loss-frequency characteristic, reduces crosstalk, and reduces the total repeater gain required.

frequency meter, vibrating reed, *n.* A meter consisting of a series of steel reeds excited by an electromagnet fed by the alternating current whose frequency is to be measured. The reeds are mechanically tuned, by adjusting length and weight, one to the exact desired frequency, two others to a frequency one-half hertz above and below the desired. The reed showing the greatest amplitude of vibration will indicate the supply frequency. These Frahm meters are used to check and adjust harmonic ringing frequencies.

frequency modulation. See "modulation, frequency."

frequency multiplier, *n.* A device whose output frequency is some exact multiple of the input frequency. A frequency doubler or frequency tripler.

frequency of resonance. See "resonant frequency."

frequency service, standard. See "service, standard frequency."

frequency-shift. See "keying, frequency shift."

frequency-shift carrier, *n.* Narrow band frequency modulated carrier used for telegraph channels, in which one frequency is transmitted for a mark signal, and a second frequency 70 Hz lower for the space signal. Channels are spaced 170 Hz.

frequency-shift keying. See "keying, frequency-shift."

frequency-shift pulsing. See "pulsing, frequency-shift."

frequency translation. See "translation, frequency."

fresnel, *n.* A unit of frequency equal to one million megahertz.

Fresnel region, *n.* The region close to an antenna, extending outward to the Fraunhofer region. See also "near-field region."

Fresnel zone, *n.* The unit by which the clearance of a line-of-sight radio path over the earth is described. The first Fresnel zone is that volume containing all points from which a wave could be reflected with a delay of not over one-half wavelength. Similarly, the boundary of the nth Fresnel zone consists of all the points from which the delay is n/2 wavelength. A good line-of-sight radio path will have a clearance over earth of not less than 0.6 Fresnel zone.

fringe area, *n.* An area beyond that in which reliable standard service is given. Applies to telephone transmission, radio reception, and television reception.

frogging, *n.* At an intermediate carrier repeater, changing low-group frequencies on the input to high group frequencies on the output, and vice versa, as a means of reducing crosstalk.

frogging repeater. See "repeater, frogging."

front contacts, *n. pl.* Make contacts.

front cord, *n.* That cord of a pair which is nearer the operator.

front-to-back ratio, antenna, *n.* The ratio of the power received by (or transmitted from) the front side of a directional radio antenna to the power received by (or transmitted from) the back side of the antenna, expressed in decibels.

front-to-back ratio, effective antenna, *n.* The front-to-back ratio measured on an actual antenna, which is less than ideal because of reflections.

front-to-back ratio, ideal antenna, *n.* The front-to-back ratio which would exist if the antenna were isolated in free space.

fuel cell, *n.* A chemical cell which produces low-voltage, high direct current electricity when supplied with a gaseous or liquid fuel. Early fuel cells used hydrogen with oxygen as a fuel. Later fuel cells use methane, alcohol, gasoline, or kerosene. These devices are useful to provide energy to remote radio relay stations.

full adder. See "adder, full."

full availability. See "availability, full."

full-duplex operation, *n.* A method of operation which provides simultaneous, 2-way communications between two points.

full-float, *adj.* Floating. Describes a battery operating as a "floated battery."

full-period, *adj.* Full-time, 24 hours per day.

full trunk group, *n.* A trunk group which would ordinarily be a high usage group, except that no alternate route is provided and therefore enough trunks must be provided to give an acceptable grade of service.

full-wave rectifier. See "rectifier, full-wave."

function, *n.* A nontyping operation of a teletypewriter such as line feed, carriage return, space, letters shift, figures shift, unshift on space, and motor stop.

fundamental frequency, *n.* The lowest frequency component of a complex sound or electrical signal.

Fundamental Plans, *n. pl.* A statement of basic Telephone Company objectives, and proposed ways of achieving them.

1. Objectives would include:
   a. Service for new customers.
   b. Increased use of service by present customers.
   c. New and improved services.
   d. Replacement of inadequate, obsolete, or worn out plant.
   e. Achievement of overall economical operation.

2. Anticipated revenues would be spread properly over:
   a. Capital expenditures.
   b. Operating costs.
   c. Good service.
   d. Improved services.
   e. Long-range objectives.

furnace, *n.* A cable splicer's portable, high-temperature stove used for melting paraffin or wiping solder. Uses gasoline, propane, or butane for fuel.

fuse, *n.* A device used for protection against excessive currents. Consists of a short length of fusible metal wire or strip which melts when the current through it exceeds the rated amount for a definite time. Placed in series with the circuit it is to protect.

fuse, alarm and indicator, *n.* Cartridge type fuse about 1¾" long, consisting of a tube of insulating material containing a fusible link attached to a metal cap on one end and to a coil spring and metal cap at the other end. When the fuse operates, the spring forces the cap against the alarm contact of the fuse block.

fuse, cartridge, *n.* A short tube of fibre containing a fusible link or wire which is connected to metallic ferrules at the ends of the tube. Serves to interrupt excessive currents by melting of the fusible link.

fuse, dummy, *n.* A device the same size and shape as a fuse, but composed of insulating material. For use on fuse panels or fuse blocks for circuits which are not active.

fuse, grasshopper, *n.* A small fuse having a spring-loaded fusible wire. When the wire fuses to open the circuit, the spring shows a visible signal and closes an auxiliary circuit to acuate an alarm.

fuse, heat coil, *n.* A slow-blow, thermally actuated heat coil made to fit a fuse block in place of a fuse. Used to interrupt low fault currents of long duration which are not large enough to operate a fuse.

fuse, indicator alarm, *n.* A flat fuse with 1¼ inch mounting centers having a spring-loaded open fuse wire. Operation of fuse releases springs which (1) close battery to the fuse alarm bus-bar, and (2) extend a colored glass bead indicator. Typically rated at 1-1/3, 2, and 5 amperes.

fuse, non-alarm, *n.* A flat fuse, typically with 1-inch mounting centers, consisting of exposed fuse wire between metal ferrules on a flat fibre body. Typically rated at 1/2, 3/4, 1-1/3, or 5 amperes, continuous.

fuse, plug, *n.* A fuse of small rating (5-30 amperes) having a screw thread like that on an electric lamp base, and used in a standard screw receptacle.

fuse, power rated, *n.* A fuse which will carry its rated current indefinitely and will blow within 5 minutes on 1.5 times its rated current.

fuse, protector, *n.* A tubular fuse, having a 7/16 inch fibre or ceramic body containing the fuse wire or strip, 3 to 4 inches long, and fitted with ferrule, threaded stud, or binding post ends. Made in 1, 3, 5, or 7 ampere capacities.

fuse, quick-break. See "quick-break fuse."

fuse, sneak current. See "sneak current fuse."

fuse, terminal, *n.* A tubular fuse used in a fuse-protected cable cross-connecting terminal. See also "fuse, tubular."

fuse, tubular, *n.* Insulating tube about 4 inches long with screw terminals at each end. Contains fuse wires enclosed in asbestos sleeving. Available in 1 thru 8 amperes capacities, but usual capacity is 7 amperes.

fuse alarm, *n.* A lamp and bell indication that a fuse has blown. The lamp indicates the location by bay and fuse panel.

fuse block. See "block, fuse."

fuse chamber. See "chamber, fuse."

fuse clip. See "clip, fuse."

fused station protector. See "protector. fused station."

fuseholder, extractor, *n.* A panel-mounting holder for a small cartridge fuse in which the fuse is removed when the holder cap is unscrewed.

fusestat, *n.* A fusetron having a socket adapter which prevents insertion of a fusetron having an incorrect current rating.

fusetron, *n.* A time-delay fuse which will carry 150% of its rated current for a short time without operating.

fuze. See "fuse," which is the preferred spelling.

gaff, *n.* The spur on a lineman's climber.

gain, *n.* (1) In pole line work, the squared notch on the upper part of a pole into which a cross-arm fits. (2) The increase in power obtained from an amplifier. (3) In transmission, the condition of being better, or at a higher energy level, than the reference standard.

gain, antenna, *n.* The ratio, expressed in decibels, of the signal level received (or transmitted) by an antenna to the signal level which would be received (or transmitted) by an isotropic antenna at the same location (and fed with the same power).

gain, insertion. See "insertion gain."

gain, loop. See "loop gain."

gain, net, *n.* The sum of all repeater gains minus the sum of all losses in a multi-repeatered telephone circuit.

gain, notch, *n.* A cut at the top of a pole, 4¾″ high and ½″ deep, into which a cross-arm fits.

gain, obstacle, *n.* A reduction in loss on a long radio path due to the radio wave being diffracted back down to earth by a hill or other obstruction which is midway in the radio path.

gain, pole, *n.* A notch or slab cut on one face of a pole at the top, used to hold cross-arms in alignment.

gain, power, *n.* The ratio of the power at the output from a device to the power input to the device, expressed in decibels.

gain, radio system, *n.* The difference, expressed in dB, between the transmitter output power and the signal power required by the distant radio receiver at its practical threshold.

gain, reflection, *n.* The condition existing when the power transferred from one circuit (#1) to another (#2) is greater than it would be if the driving circuit (#1) and the driven circuit (#2) had matched impedances. Reflection gain occurs when the impedances are conjugate.

gain, slab, *n.* A type of pole gaining in which the upper 6-8 feet of the pole has a ½-inch deep flat surface cut on one face. Used to keep the cross-arms in alignment.

gain, space diversity, *n.* The improvement in radio reception, expressed in dB, obtained by combining the signals from two receiving antennas physically separated by not less than five wavelengths.

gain, steel pole, *n.* A galvanized steel fitting used when it is impossible to cut a crossarm gain in a pole, such as on a concrete or steel pole.

gain, transmission, *n.* The increase in the power of an electrical signal from one point in the circuit to another.

gain, voltage, *n.* The ratio of the voltage at the input to a device to the voltage at the output from the device, expressed in decibels.

gain enhancement, *n.* The ratio of the output pilot level variation to the input level variation, either for a single repeater or for a system, expressed in db.

gain margin, *n.* The amount of additional gain which could be added to a repeatered circuit before the repeater would start to sing.

galactic radio noise, *n.* A continuous radio-frequency radiation from outer space, much of which originates in the Milky Way. Only the portion between 30 MHz and 30,000 MHz reaches us through the "atmospheric window."

gallium arsenide, *n.* A semiconductor material used both in tunnel diodes and lasers.

galvanic, *adj.* Describing any substance from which, or through which, direct current flows as a result of chemical action.

gang capacitor, *n.* A multi-unit variable capacitor in which all moving plates are mounted on a single common shaft, so that all can be adjusted simultaneously by a single control. Circuits are designed to place the rotor plates at ground potential.

ganged, *adj.* Describing a group of devices, such as variable capacitors, which are coupled mechanically so that all are adjusted simultaneously from one control.

gang meet, *n.* A meeting of the construction gangs of two or more utility companies to do work on jointly used poles.

gang switch, *n.* A multi-unit wafer switch in which all lever contacts are fastened to a single shaft to enable simultaneous operation.

gang tuning, *n.* The tuning of several circuits simultaneously using a single control knob.

gap, *n.* (1) The space between a pair of relay contacts in their non-operated condition. (2) The space between a relay armature and its pole piece.

gap, residual. See "residual gap."

garbled, *adj.* The condition of a message, particularly one sent by teletypewriter, in which there are so many letters in error that the message tends to be unintelligible.

gas-filled, *adj.* Describing apparatus, such as reed switches, which is filled with an inert gas (helium, or 97% nitrogen plus 3% hydrogen) to increase the voltage breakdown limit of contacts, and to improve the arc-quenching qualities.

gas pressurization. See "system, gas pressure."

gas tube. See "tube, gas."

gate, *n.* A circuit having several inputs and one output. The output is blocked unless an input is energized (OR gate), or unless all inputs are energized (AND gate).

gate, AND. See "AND gate."

gate, time, *n.* A transducer which has an output only during selected time intervals.

gateway office, *n.* A toll office through which calls to and from another country pass. New York and Oakland are typical gateway offices.

gating, *n.* The process of selecting for use only those portions of a wave between selected time intervals or between selected amplitude limits.

gating pulse, *n.* A pulse which causes operation (opening) of a gate for the period of the pulse.

gauge, *n.* (1) An instrument for measuring or testing dimensions. (2) A measure of the diameter of wire or the thickness of sheet metal.

Gauge, American Wire (AWG), *n.* A standard system for measuring and specifying the diameter of non-ferrous wires. The standard for gauging copper wires. Also known as the Brown & Sharpe (B&S) gauge.

gauge, Birmingham Wire (BWG), *n.* An English standard system for measuring and specifying the diameter of ferrous wires. In Great Britain it is known also as the Stubs' Iron Wire Gage, and is used only for soft iron wires. In the United States it is used for both iron and steel wires.

gauge, Brown & Sharpe (B&S), *n.* A system for measuring and specifying the diameter of non-ferrous wires. Now called the American Wire Gauge (AWG).

gauge, feeler, *n.* A flat strip of hardened steel, marked with its thickness in thousandths of an inch. Usually assembled in sets of graded thickness. Used for adjusting the air gap of relay armatures.

gauge, pressure, *n.* In gas pressure work, a device to measure gas pressure having a dial calibrated in pounds per square inch.

gauge, spring tension, *n.* Device used to measure the tension of relay springs. Consists of a handle holding a flexible leaf spring whose deflection against a scale indicates the tension in grams.

gauge, wire, *n.* (1) A small circular disc of hardened steel having graded slots around the periphery, each marked with the gauge of round wire which it matches for size. (2)

A system for specifying the diameter of wire.

gauges, thickness, *n.* A set of hardened steel strips, each of a different thickness, and each marked with its thickness in thousandths of an inch.

gauges, wire, *n. pl.* Two systems or scales for the measurement of wires are in common use today. The American Wire Gauge (AWG) specifies the size of non-ferrous (copper, bronze, etc.) wires, while the Birmingham Wire Gauge (BWG) specifies the size of ferrous (iron and steel) wires. The diameters, in decimal parts of an inch, corresponding to the gauge numbers are as follows for common sizes of wire:

| Gauge No. | Diameter-Inches | |
	AWG	BWG
4	.204	.238
6	.162	.203
8	.128	.165
9	.114	.148
10	.102	.134
12	.081	.109
13	.072	.095
14	.064	.083

gauss, *n., n. pl.* The cgs electromagnetic unit of magnetic induction. Now replaced by the "oersted."

Gaussian distribution, *n.* A distribution of random variables characterized by a symetrical and continuous distribution decreasing gradually to zero on either side of the most probable value.

Gaussian noise, *n.* A random noise signal whose frequency components have a Gaussian distribution centered on a specified frequency.

generator, *n.* A rotating machine which converts mechanical energy into electrical energy.

generator, alternating current, *n.* A rotary machine which generates alternating current when its rotor, which may be either the armature or the field, is rotated by an engine or a motor. Also called an "alternator."

generator, direct current, *n.* A rotary machine having a commutator, which generates direct current when its armature is rotated in a magnetic field by an engine or motor. The commutator reverses the alternating current generated in the armature winding to produce direct current at the machine's output terminals.

generator, diverter-pole, *n.* A DC generator particularly suited to the float-charging of storage batteries because of its inherent capability to maintain a constant output voltage, regardless of fluctuations in the load or the AC power supply to its driving motor.

generator, electrical, *n.* A machine which converts mechanical energy into electrical energy.

generator, emergency engine, *n.* A diesel or gasoline engine driven alternating current generator which is used to supply alternating current power to a central office or other communication facility when the commercial power fails. Usually includes automatic-start and automatic load transfer features.

generator, frequency. See "generator, sub-harmonic."

generator, hand. See "generator, magneto hand."

generator, magneto hand, *n.* A two-pole alternating current generator, cranked by hand, used to produce 20 Hz ringing current. A part of a magneto telephone, and sometimes placed on switchboard positions to provide emergency ringing power. See also "magneto."

generator, milliwatt, *n.* An oscillator which produces 1000 hertz power at a level of one milliwatt for use in transmission testing.

generator, noise, *n.* An electronic device which generates wide-band white noise for use in testing. The generator output is obtained by amplifying low-level white noise obtained from a source such as a photo-multiplier.

generator, receiver-off-hook, *n.* A generator designed to replace the "howler" as a means of getting off-hook telephones hung up. Consists of 50 milliseconds each of 1400 Hz, 2060 Hz, 2450 Hz, and 2600 Hz tones repeated sequentially at 300 IPM. Its single frequencies do not interfere with multifrequency signaling systems.

generator, ringing, *n.* (1) A rotary converter driven from the 48 volt central office battery, whose output is 20 hertz ringing power. Usually has interrupter contacts. (2) A sub-harmonic generator. (3) A transistor ringing generator.

generator, signal, *n.* A portable test oscillator which can be adjusted to provide a test signal at some desired frequency, voltage, modulation, or waveform.

generator, spectrum, *n.* A test tone generator which reduces testing time by placing a series of test tones, covering a complete frequency spectrum, on the transmission facility simultaneously. These test tones are measured at the receiving end with a tuneable detector or a spectrum analyzer. In some generators this spectrum of tones is obtained by passing a square pulse through a band-pass filter.

generator, square wave, *n.* A signal generator whose output is a square wave, useful for testing the frequency response of wide band devices. See also "square wave testing."

generator, standby power, *n.* An alternating current generator, commonly a diesel engine-generator, held in reserve and used to supply the necessary AC power requirements of a communication facility when there is failure of commercially-supplied AC power.

generator, sub-harmonic, *n.* A transformer or auto-transformer whose secondary is capacitance-tuned to a sub-harmonic of the supply frequency. Used to obtain 20 Hz or

30 Hz ringing power from a 60 Hz supply.

generator, sweep-frequency, *n.* An oscillator which generates an audio or radio frequency which is repetitively swept, low to high or high to low, over a pre-set band of frequencies. Provides a test signal for wide-band devices.

generator, thermoelectric, *n.* A semiconductor device using thermocouple action to convert heat directly into electricity. When heat is applied to a p-n junction, electrons migrate to the cooler end of the n-type material and holes to the cooler end of the p-type material. To provide a useful voltage, a number of such junctions are connected in series, forming a "thermopile."

generator, tone, *n.* A generator, either rotary or transistor, which supplies busy and dial tone to a central office. If a rotary machine, it is often combined with the tone interrupter. See also "alternator, tone" and "tone generator."

generator, transistor ringing, *n.* A transistor generator, either 20 hertz or any of the five harmonic frequencies, with a power amplifier, in sizes from that required for a small PBX to that for a large central office. Requires a separate ringing interrupter.

generator-heater-blower, *n.* An LP-gas powered unit used for supplying electrical power and for ventilating manholes with fresh heated or unheated air. Consists of a single cylinder, 4-cycle LP-gas engine, an AC generator, a belt-driven multiblade centrifugal fan, and a propane furnace with heat exchanger. Supplies 800 watts of 110 volt, 60 Hz power, plus 600 CFM of air at a maximum temperature of 120 degrees Fahrenheit.

geodesic, *n.* The shortest distance between two points on the surface of the earth. A great circle.

geomagnetism, *n.* The earth's magnetism. It is a factor in the positioning of the ionized belts which affect radio communication.

germanium, *n.* A brittle, light gray metal which is a semiconductor, extensively used in making transistors and crystal diodes.

germanium diode, *n.* A semiconductor rectifier which uses germanium as the rectifying element.

getter, *n.* A metal such as sodium, magnesium, or potassium which is placed inside an electron tube during manufacture, then vaporized after the tube has been evacuated. The getter combines with any residual gases within the tube and prevents them from impairing the operation. Some getters leave a mirror coating on the inside of the glass.

Gfeller unit. See "concentrator, line."

ghost, *n.* An undesired duplicate image in a television picture, fainter and to one side of the normal picture. Due to multipath transmission.

giga-, *adj.* A prefix representing one billion, or 1,000,000,000.

gigacycles-per-second, *n.* Gigahertz.

gigahertz, *n.* One billion (1,000,000,-000) cycles per second.

gilbert, *n.* The unit of magnetomotive force in the centimeter-gram-second electromagnetic system. The value of the magnetomotive force in gilberts in any magnetic circuit is equal to the line integral around the circuit of the magnetic intensity in oersteds, with length being in centimeters. One gilbert is equivalent to 0.7956 ampere-turn.

gimmick, *n.* A very small capacitance formed by twisting two insulated wires together.

gin pole, *n.* A pole which is used, together with ropes and pulleys, as a derrick for lifting heavy loads and for erecting poles or towers.

glare, *n.* The blocking of a call by the simultaneous seizure of a trunk at both ends, also the blocking of a call by two subscribers who call each other simultaneously.

G-line, *n.* A single insulated wire

which can be strung in the open and used as a surface wave radio-frequency transmission line. Acts like a coaxial cable without the outer tubular conductor.

glove, rubber, *n.* A heavy rubber glove worn by linemen and repairmen when handling telephone plant which may be crossed with low-voltage power conductors. Rated at 10,000 volts. Always worn with outer leather gloves which protect the rubber gloves from mechanical damage.

glow discharge, *n.* The luminous glow in some electron tubes caused by ionization of gas within the tube.

glow lamp, *n.* A small lamp having two electrodes and filled with a gas which ionizes easily. When energized the negative electrode will be covered with a glow, orange-red if the gas is neon, and blue if the gas is argon. Widely used as indicator lamps.

Glyptal, *n.* The trade name of an insulating varnish much used on coil windings. It is both heat and oil resistant.

go cipher, *v.* The instruction to change a plain language transmission to encrypted transmission.

goggles, safety, *n. pl.* Goggles with clear plastic lenses which can be worn over personal eyeglasses to protect both the eyes and the eyeglasses from injury.

gong, loud-ringing. See "bell, loud-ringing."

goodnight plug, *n.* A single (Type 347) plug having the tip and sleeve strapped, used at a telegraph testboard. When placed in a HUB jack it sends a space signal outward over all interconnected telegraph legs.

go plain, *v.* The instruction to change encrypted transmission to plain language transmission.

go signal. See "signal, go."

governor, *n.* An automatic attachment to a motor for controlling the speed of rotation.

grade, *v.* To arrange, or rearrange, the multipling between selector banks so that the number of outgoing trunks may be greater than ten.

grade, data, *adj.* Said of a circuit which has transmission characteristics (low delay distortion and low impulse noise) which enable it to carry data signals.

grade, special, *adj.* Said of a circuit which has special transmission characteristics which enable it to carry special intelligence, such as program material, secure voice, etc.

grade, voice, *adj.* Said of a circuit which is suitable for transmitting voice.

graded multiple, *n.* An arrangement whereby the bank terminals of several selector shelves are connected together so that the number of trunks is greater than ten, with each selector having access to ten trunks.

grade-of-service, *n.* The probability of a call being blocked by busy trunks, expressed as a decimal fraction, and usually meaning the busy-hour probability. The probability for the overall connection is equal to the sum of the individual probabilities at each switching stage. One busy per 100 attempts is shown as: $P = 0.01$.

gradient, voltage, *n.* (1) The voltage drop per unit length of a conductor. (2) The voltage impressed across a unit thickness of dielectric.

grading, *n.* The act of arranging, or rearranging, the multipling of selector bank terminals. Usually accomplished by restrapping of the selector distributing terminal assembly (DTA).

grading terminal assembly (GTA), *n.* A terminal assembly on an X-Y selector bay that serves the same purpose as a "distributing terminal assembly" on a Strowger selector bay.

graphics, *n.* A method of transmitting visual intelligence via telecommunications. A broader term than "facsimile."

gravity, specific. See "specific gravity."

Gray code. See "code, Gray."

grazing path, *n.* A radio transmission path from transmitting to receiving antenna which barely has an optical line-of-sight clearance over the intervening terrain, and does not have the first Fresnel zone clearance needed for good transmission.

great circle route, *n.* The path taken by a radio wave, which is a portion of the great circle (whose diameter is the diameter of the Earth) formed if one stretched a string over the terrestial globe from the transmitting station to the receiving station. If the latitude and longitude of the two stations are known, the length of the great circle path and the proper azimuth of the two antennas can be found by spherical trigonometry.

green circuit, *n.* A physically protected, electrically-shielded, tamper-proof circuit which is approved for the transmission of classified information in the "clear," or without encryption.

Greenwich mean time (GMT), *n.* The time at the meridian of Greenwich, Great Britain (just outside of London), used as a world-wide reference time. Also called zulu time, because of the Z time zone.

grid, *n.* Any of the one or more wire mesh electrodes located between the cathode (filament) and the anode (plate) in a vacuum tube, which by its potential (relative voltage) controls the flow of electrons between the cathode and the anode.

grid, control, *n.* A grid in an electron tube that controls the flow of current from cathode to anode.

grid, screen, *n.* A grid between the control grid and plate of an electron tube held at a stable positive potential so that it shields the control grid from changes in plate potential.

grid, suppressor, *n.* A grid placed between the plate and other grids in an electron tube which suppresses the emission of secondary electrons from the plate.

grid bias, *n.* The negative voltage applied to a grid of an electron tube, with respect to the cathode potential.

grip, cable, *n.* A tube braided of bronze wire which can be slipped over a cable end. When pulled from an eye at one end of the tube the tube contracts with a firm grip on the cable, and permits the cable to be pulled into a duct.

grip, flexible pulling. See "grip, cable."

grip, strand, *n.* A steel grip having two parallel jaws which tighten when the grip is pulled. Used to tension guys and suspension strand.

grommet, *n.* (1) An eyelet of rubber or neoprene placed in a hole in sheet metal, such as a terminal entrance, to insulate and protect wires which pass through. (2) A brass eyelet placed on the edge of a canvas to enable it to be tied with rope.

ground, *n.* A conducting connection through which a circuit or electrical equipment is connected to the earth or to a conducting body which is at earth potential. A ground may be accidental or intentional.—*vt.* To connect to a ground.

ground, solid, *n.* A connection to ground which does not have any inserted resistance.

ground clamp, *n.* A metal clamp used to connect a ground wire to a ground rod or to a cold water pipe.

grounded, *adj.* Connected to the earth, or to a rod or pipe which makes a good electrical connection with the earth.

grounded, resistance, *adj.* Grounded through a resistance, so as to limit the current which will flow in the event of a ground fault.

grounded system. See "system, grounded."

grounding, *n.* The act of connecting an electric circuit or equipment to earth, or to a conductor connected to earth. A safety measure to avoid electric shock.

grounding device, *n.* An impedance through which an electrical system is connected to ground, and which serves to limit ground fault currents.

grounding outlet, *n.* An alternating current receptacle which has a third contact connected to ground. Used with three-wire plugs and cords to safely ground portable electric tools and appliances.

ground loop, *n.* The condition created when a circuit is grounded at several points. Results in circulating ground current if there is a difference in potential between the several grounding points.

ground potential, *n.* Having the same (zero) potential as the earth.

ground reflected wave, *n.* That portion of a radio wave which is reflected from ground or water in its path between transmitting and receiving antennas.

ground return, *n.* (1) A conductor which drains currents to ground. (2) A common conductor which returns the current from several circuits back to the grounded (positive) side of the central office battery. (3) A conductor which connects the lead sheaths of all the cables entering an office to the central office ground.

ground-return circuit, *n.* A circuit using the earth as one side of the complete circuit.

ground rod, *n.* A pointed round metal rod for driving into the earth to obtain a ground connection.

ground wave, *n.* That portion of a radio wave traveling between transmitting and receiving antennas which is associated with currents induced in the ground or water surface of the earth. It is important only below about ten megahertz.

ground wire, *n.* A heavy copper conductor, usually insulated, which is used to connect protectors or other equipment to a ground rod or cold water pipe.

group, *n.* A number of voice channels, usually 12, processed as a unit in carrier systems.

group, binder, *n.* A group of pairs in polyethelene insulated cable which have the same color code and are under a single binder string.

group, carrier, *n.* A group of twelve voice-frequency channels translated ·by modulation with carriers so as to be stacked one above the other in the band 60-108 kHz.

group, carrier line, *n.* The entire group of carrier channels as they appear on the carrier line. The frequency allocation, for two different sizes of line groups, is as follows:
60 channel line group—
    12 to 252 kHz
600 channel line group—
    60 to 2540 kHz

group, code. See "code group."

group, crossbar horizontal, *n.* The 19 to 69 lines having access to the horizontals of one line link primary switch.

group, crossbar number, *n.* Equipment which translates subscriber directory numbers into subscriber's line locations on the line link frame. (#5 Crossbar).

group, date-time. See "date-time group."

group, final trunk. See "final trunk group."

group, full trunk. See "full trunk group."

group, high-usage. See "high-usage group."

group, junctor, *n.* In a crossbar office, the junctors which extend from a particular line link frame to a trunk link frame. The size of the junctor group depends upon the number of trunk link frames.

group, line, *n.* In an electronic central office, a switching unit controlled by a marker which provides access to and from line circuits.

group, marker, *n.* A common group of markers which serve one or more central offices. A marker group is arranged to handle a maximum of six office code groups spread over six number series with a maximum of 40,000 numbers. The term "marker group" is also used to refer to the group of equipment served by a single marker group.

group, master carrier, *n.* A group of 600 carrier channels, occupying the band 60 to 2540 kHz.

group, number series, *n.* Thirty thousand or less telephone numbers that are associated with three or less office code groups. There may be two number series groups, designated group A and group B.

group, office code, *n.* In a crossbar office, one or more office codes which are given the same rate or number treatment, and therefore are grouped together to operate the same local completion relay in the marker.

group, phantom, *n.* A group of three voice circuits: a phantom circuit, and the two side circuits from which the phantom was derived. See also "phantom."

group, trunk, *n.* A group of trunks between the same two points, which are electrically similar and are used for the same purpose.

group, vertical, *n.* In a crossbar office, the five vertical files making up the left or right half of a column of lines.

Group Alerting and Dispatching System, *n.* A service for Volunteer Fire Depts., Civil Defense Units, etc. enabling one controlling telephone to alert as many as 480 phones simultaneously. If any of the called lines are busy, the equipment camps until it is free, then rings and plays the tape recorded message.

grouping, position, *n.* The switching together of the circuits of two adjacent switchboard positions, enabling an operator to use also the cords at an adjacent vacant position.

grouping circuit. See "circuit, grouping."

group modulation, *n.* Translation of a 12-channel carrier group from the band 60-108 kHz to one of the five 48 kHz bands which form a 60-channel supergroup in the band 312-552 kHz.

group relays, *n.* A set of relays, associated with a group of linefinders, which controls the action of each linefinder in the group.

growler, *n.* An electromagnetic device consisting essentially of two field poles arranged as in a motor, energized with A.C. and used for locating short-circuited coils in a generator or motor armature. A growling noise indicates a short-circuited coil.

guard, *n.* Any device which restricts access or prevents damage or injury.—*v.* (1) To hold a circuit busy for an interval after its release to make sure equipment has been disconnected before the circuit is seized again. (2) To monitor constantly a specific radio band.

guard, detector. See "detector guard."

guard, guy, *n.* A one-piece colored plastic tube, slit longitudinally, used to slip over the bottom 8 feet of an anchor guy to make it more visible and less harmful to pedestrians.

guard, manhole, *n.* A three-section pipe frame, 32 inches high, which can be opened and placed around a manhole opening as a guard.

guard, plastic tree wire, *n.* A spirally slit plastic tube, 3 feet long, which can be wound onto a drop wire to protect it from the abrasion of tree branches.

guard, pressure. See "contactor, gas pressure."

guard, timed, *n.* A feature of some toll translators which senses an approaching all-trunks-busy condition, and places a timed delay on translations to any trunk group which has only one (or two) idle trunks. Avoids call pocketing, which see.

guard, tree, *n.* A two-piece wooden or slotted plastic tubing placed around a cable suspension strand to prevent the strand and cable from rubbing on tree limbs.

guard, trolley, *n.* A wooden guard which encloses aerial cable and strand where it passes over an electric trolley. Prevents contact if the cable should sag onto the trolley conductor, and prevents mechanical damage to the cable if the trolley should come off the wire and allow the trolley pole to fly upward.

guard, "U" cable, *n.* A semi-cylindrical steel protector placed over a cable riser on the side of a pole. The cross-section of the guard is similar to the letter "U."

guard, wire, *n.* A helically-slit plastic tube, 36 inches long and 1¼ inches in diameter, placed over multiple line wire and multiple drop wire to protect it against abrasion, and against contact with metallic conduits and electric service wires.

guard action, *n.* In an in-band signaling system, the use of energy in the voice-frequency spectrum but outside of the narrow signaling frequency band to generate a voltage which opposes the voltage generated by the 2600 Hz components of speech. This opposing voltage guards against production of false signals during talking.

guardband, *n.* A narrow frequency band provided between adjacent channels to prevent inter-channel crosstalk and to permit economical channel filters. Typical guardbands are: V.F. Carrier—500 Hz, Broadcast—3 kHz, Television—250 kHz.

guard circuit, *n.* (1) A circuit which prevents leakage across insulators from effecting the accuracy of measurements with sensitive galvanometers. Operates by surrounding the insulator with a metal ring kept at the highest potential to which the measuring circuit is connected. (2) A circuit which prevents the circuit which it guards from operating due to noise or other false signals.

guarding, *n.* The act of holding a circuit busy after disconnections, for an interval long enough to ensure its release.

guard lead, *n.* A wire which extends from each switch in a group to control equipment, and which is marked (with ground, etc.) when it becomes busy to guard it from intrusion.

guard period, busy, *n.* The 750 millisecond time period that a trunk circuit must be held busy after its release to prevent wrong connections caused by slow release of equipment in the connecting office.

guard ring, *n.* A annular ring-shaped terminal which surrounds the insulator on which a megger or potentiometer terminal is mounted. See also "guard circuit."

guards, gaff, *n. pl.* Leather sheaths which cover and protect the gaffs on lineman's climbers when they are not in use.

guided wave, *n.* An electromagnetic wave which is transmitted entirely within a round or rectangular pipe or tube of metal or a dielectric. See also "waveguide."

gun, electron, *n.* The portion of a TV picture tube, or cathode ray tube, which produces the stream of electrons, and may also focus and center the stream.

gun, pressure, *n.* A screw-actuated cup-type gun operated by a ratchet handle, and having a ⅛-inch pipe nozzle. Used for injecting resin plugging compound into cables to be pressurized.

gun, soldering, *n.* A pistol-shaped soldering tool having a trigger switch to turn it on. Operates from 117 volts AC, and has an integral stepdown transformer with a single turn secondary which heats the soldering loop.

gun, stapling, *n.* A hand gun which can be loaded with a strip of staples. Steady pressure on a trigger trips a spring-loaded hammer which drives a staple. Used to staple wire and inside cable to a supporting surface.

guy, *n.* A steel strand used to hold a pole upright and straight against unbalanced pulls.

guy, anchor, *n.* A stranded steel wire which transfers stress from a pole or stub pole to an anchor rod which is attached to an anchor buried in the ground.

guy, crossarm, *n.* A guy placed to the end of a crossarm from the adjacent pole to offset unbalanced stress caused by deadending a portion of the conductors carried by that crossarm.

guy, dead-end, *n.* An anchor guy which takes the unbalanced pull on a pole at the end of a cable or open wire line.

guy, down, *n.* A guy from a pole to an anchor. May be either a "head guy" or a "side guy."

guy, head, *n.* A guy which is parallel to the direction of the pole line.

guy, overhead, *n.* A guy from pole to pole, or from pole to guy stub, which has standard clearance above ground.

guy, pole-to-pole, *n.* A guy used to transfer stress in the direction of the pole line from one pole to the next. Used when it is not possible to place a down guy on the first pole.

guy, pole-to-stub, *n.* A guy used to transfer stress from a pole to a stub pole, where it can be anchored.

guy, side, *n.* A guy which is at an angle to the direction of the pole line.

guys, storm, *n. pl.* Anchor guys on a pole line, usually placed in pairs and at right angles to the direction of the line, which provide strength to resist transverse wind loading.

guy wire, *n.* A stranded wire used to transfer stress from a pole to an anchor, or from a pole to another pole or stub pole.

gyrator, *n.* A negative impedance device which can change the sign of a reactance, thus allowing a capacitor to act as an inductor. Usually consists of a ferrite section in a wave guide.

half adder. See "adder, half."

half-duplex, *adj.* Describes a system in which communication can be in either direction, but only one way at a time.

half-power frequency, *n.* Either of the two frequencies on an amplifier or filter response curve where the output is 0.7071 times that at midband.

half-tap, *n.* A bridged connection made to a circuit without disturbing its continuity.—*v.* To make a bridged connection.

half-wave dipole, *n.* The common dipole antenna, whose overall length is approximately one-half wavelength.

half-wave rectifier, *n.* A rectifier whose output current flows during alternate half cycles.

ham, *n.* An amateur radio operator. (Slang)

hammer, lineman's, *n.* A heavy hammer, usually with a 40-ounce head and a 14-16 inch handle. Several types are used, usually either a double-face, round-head striking hammer or a cross-pein blacksmith's hammer.

hand generator. See "generator, magneto hand."

handhole, *n.* A sub-surface box of concrete, usually not less than 12″ x 12″ x 18″ and having a cover flush with the ground, into which small conduits enter. It provides a place where wires can be pulled into conduits and where wire and small cable splices can be made.

handhole, pre-cast, *n.* A factory made concrete handhole for installation where needed. Not constructed in place.

handi-talkie, *n.* A two-way radio communication unit small enough to be carried in the hand.

handline, *n.* A 75-foot length of ½-inch rope having a snap hook on one end. Used by linemen to hoist materials to a pole top.

handline, aerial, *n.* A 60-foot ½-inch

rope having a ring and hook on one end and a ring on the other end, with the rope threaded through a single-sheave block with a clamp for fastening to a cable strand. Used by cable splicers for hoisting solder pots, tools, etc.

handling, call, *n.* The total process by which a telephone call is received, recorded, completed, and timed.

handover, satellite, *n.* The act of relinquishing the control of a satellite at one earth station, and picking up control at another earth station from which the satellite is visible at a higher altitude.

handset, *n.* That portion of the telephone containing the transmitter and receiver which is hand-held when the telephone is in use. Consists of a receiver and transmitter about six inches apart at the ends of a common handle, connected by an electrical cord to the handset mounting. Sometimes includes a dial.

handset, sound booster, *n.* A telephone handset having a transistor amplifier inserted in the hollow handset handle. Provides about 28 dB of gain for the received signal, adjustable by a volume control through the back of the handle. Used by hard-of-hearing subscribers.

hands-free telephone, *n.* A desk telephone containing a microphone and voice-switched amplifiers with a separate loudspeaker unit, permitting telephone conversation without use of a hand-held handset.

hand telephone set. See "set, hand telephone."

hanger, figure-8 cable, *n.* A two-piece clamp placed over a through-bolt and used to support integral messenger cable on the side of a pole. Usually includes a hook to hold the cable during stringing operations.

hangover, *n.* In an echo-suppressor, the period of time during which suppression continues after speech has ended.

hangover delay. See "delay, hangover."

hangover time, *n.* The length of time that a voice-operated device, VOGAD or echo-suppressor, continues to operate after the voice has ceased. Usually set between 100 and 150 milliseconds.

hangup, *n.* The act of placing the handset on the cradle of the telephone to signal completion of the call.

hang up, *vi.* (1) To replace a telephone handset in its cradle. (2) To replace a receiver or handset in its hook-switch. (3) To disconnect from a line.

hard, *adj.* (1) Having high strength and difficult to bend, as a "hard-drawn" wire. (2) Describing an electron tube which has been highly evacuated and contains no residual gases.

hard copy, *n.* A tangible, printed copy of a message, such as that obtained from a teletypewriter.

hard-drawn, *adj.* Describing a wire which was not annealed after the final steps in the wire drawing process, and thereby has a higher tensile strength and is more difficult to bend.

hard-drawn copper wire. See "wire, hard-drawn copper."

harden, *v.* To construct communication facilities in such a manner that they will survive and be operable following a nearby bomb blast.

hardened, *adj.* Constructed in such a manner as to avoid damage from overpressure, air blast, heat, or debris fallout following a bomb blast. The transcontinental L3 and L4 coaxial cable systems are designed to resist 50 psi overpressure.

hardness, *n.* (1) A measure of the capability of a communication facility to withstand external blast or explosion. (2) A measure of the evacuation of a vacuum tube. The more perfect the vacuum, the harder the tube.

hard tube, *n.* An electron tube which has been evacuated to such a high degree of vacuum that the residual gases which remain do not affect the characteristics of the tube.

hardware, *n.* (1) The screws, nuts, anchors, angles, clamps, etc. used in installing telephone plant. (2) Components, repair parts, sub-assemblies of telephone equipment.

hardwire, *v.* To wire or cable directly between units of equipment, without passing through test jacks or cross-connect points.

harmonic, *n.* In electrical usage, an alternating voltage or current whose frequency is some integral multiple of the fundamental frequency. The third harmonic of 20 Hz is 60 Hz. The fifth harmonic of 100 Hz is 500 Hz.

harmonic, even, *n.* Any harmonic whose frequency is the fundamental frequency multiplied by an even number. The even harmonics of 60 Hz are 120 Hz, 240 Hz, 360 Hz, 480 Hz, etc.

harmonic, odd, *n.* Any harmonic whose frequency is the fundamental frequency multiplied by an odd number. The odd harmonics of 60 Hz are 180 Hz, 300 Hz, 420 Hz, 540 Hz, etc.

harmonic, third. See "third harmonic."

harmonic analysis, *n.* The defining of a complex wave as the sum of several harmonics of the fundamental wave, each harmonic having a specified magnitude and phase.

harmonic analyzer, *n.* A measuring device having tuneable circuits which can identify the frequency of each of the components of a complex wave, and with a meter measure their amplitudes separately.

harmonic distortion, *n.* (1) The ratio, expressed in decibels, of the power at the fundamental frequency, to the power of a harmonic of that fundamental. (2) A form of non-linear distortion in which harmonics of a fundamental frequency are generated by the nonlinearity of a circuit.

harmonic ringing, *n.* A system of selectively signaling the several parties on a party line by using a different frequency and a specially tuned ringer for each party. The frequencies are harmonics of 16-2/3 Hz and 25 Hz as follows: 16-2/3, 25, 33-1/3, 50, and 66-2/3 Hz. See also "synchromonic" and "decimonic."

harmonics, non-triple, *n. pl.* Odd harmonics in a power system which are not multiples of three, such as the 5th, 7th, 11th, 13th, etc.

harmonics, triple, *n. pl.* Power harmonics that are odd multiples of three, such as the 3rd, 9th, 15th, 21st, etc.

harness, wiring, *n.* A group of coded insulated wires, cut to length, bent to shape, and laced together. Installed as a unit to form the back-of-panel wiring for a unit of equipment.

Hartley, *n.* A unit of "information content" containing the information needed to identify one of ten equally likely choices. It is equal to 3.3219 bits.
$$H = \log_2 10 \text{ bits} = 3.3219 \text{ bits.}$$

Hartley's Law. See "Appendix B."

hash, *n.* Wide-band high frequency audio noise such as that produced by the contacts of a vibrating ringing generator.

hash mark stripe. See "stripe, hash mark."

hat, safety, *n.* A light-weight but strong metal or plexiglass helmet with a chin strap. Used to protect workmen from objects dropped from above, or from any blow to the top of the head.

haul, *n.* An arbitrary classification of toll calls, as follows: short haul—less than 30 miles; medium haul—30-1000 miles; long haul—over 1000 miles.

hazard, *n.* Any condition which imperils the safety of telephone plant, employees, or the public. Report it to your supervisor at once.

hazard, fire, *n.* Any condition which

may cause a fire to start, or which would make a fire difficult to control, once started.

hazard, high voltage, *n.* Any potentially dangerous exposure of telephone plant or workmen to voltages above 5,000 volts AC or 750 volts DC.

hazard, radiation, *n.* The possible harmful effect of powerful electromagnetic radiation on the human body or on electrically detonated explosives. A level of 0.01 watts per square centimeter is the maximum average power considered safe for continuous exposure to human beings. Frequencies above 5 GHz are especially dangerous.

head, pruner, *n.* A pruning shears which can be attached to the top of a long pole and operated from the ground by a rope. Used by telephone installers for light tree trimming.

headband, *n.* A light-weight, wire, over-the-head band used to hold a telephone receiver or an operator's telephone set.

head end (CATV), *n.* The equipment which receives the television and FM radio signals from the antennas and processes and amplifies the signals before applying them to the CATV distribution cable, is known as the "head end."

header, message, *n.* The first portion of a radio-telegraph message which contains the name of the office of origin, date-time group, message number, and class of message.

head guy. See "guy, head."

headphone, *n.* A telephone receiver held against the ear by a headband.

headset, *n.* (1) An operator's head telephone set. (2) A dual headphone, consisting of two receivers on a headband.

headset, operator's. See "set, operator's telephone."

hearing loss, *n.* The difference in level, expressed in decibels, between the weakest sound a particular human ear can hear and the weakest sound

heard by an average normal ear.

heat coil. See "coil, heat."

heat coil, indicating, *n.* A sneak current fuse which gives a visual indication when it has operated.

heat coil fuse, *n.* A sneak current fuse designed to carry 0.35 ampere indefinitely, to sustain short overloads, but to open within five minutes when carrying 0.53 ampere. Looks like a tubular fuse, 3 inches long, with ferrule ends.

heater, *n.* The electric heating element in the center of an indirectly heated cathode of an electron tube. Permits using alternating current to heat the cathode without causing AC hum.

heater, tent, *n.* Small cylindrical kerosene stove used to heat a splicers tent in winter-time.

heat exchanger, *n.* A device somewhat like a tube boiler which can be used to transfer heat from one medium to another—steam to hot water, hot water to air, etc.

heat loss, *n.* The loss of useful power in an electrical device due to its being converted to unwanted heat, caused by resistance in wires and hysteresis in iron cores.

heat seal, *n.* A method of sealing plastic, such as the tape wrap jacket on a cable, by the use of thermal fusion.

heat-shrinkable tubing. See "tubing, heat-shrinkable."

heat sink, *n.* A mass of metal, often with fins, mounted on or under a circuit component which produces heat, such as a silicon rectifier, electron tube, etc. Absorbs and radiates the heat to maintain a safe working temperature.

Heaviside layer, *n.* Any of the ionized layers in the ionosphere.

hecto-. A prefix meaning one hundred times.

heel piece, *n.* The base of a relay, upon which one or more contact spring assemblies are mounted, and to which the core of a relay is fastened.

height, virtual. See "virtual height."

helical stripe. See "stripe, helical color."

helix, *n.* A spiral, formed as though on the surface of a cylinder.

helmet, safety. See "hat, safety."

henry, *n.* The cgs unit of inductance. The inductance of a coil is one henry when a current change of one ampere per second produces a drop of one volt across the coil.

heptode, *n.* A seven-electrode vacuum tube, containing an anode, a cathode, a control grid, and four other electrodes which may be diodes or extra grids.

hermaphrodite connector, *n.* A cable connector in which the jack and the plug are identically shaped.

hermetically sealed relay, *n.* A relay which is permanently sealed inside its metal or glass can. Usually has dual mercury-wetted contacts and is enclosed with an inert nitrogen atmosphere.

Hertz, hertz, *n.* International standard unit of frequency. Replaces, and is identical to, the older unit "cycles-per-second." Abbrev: Hz.

Hertz antenna. See "antenna, Hertz."

heterodyne, *v.* To shift an incoming radio signal to a different frequency, often to a much lower "intermediate frequency."

heterodyne amplifier. See "amplifier, heterodyne CATV."

heterodyne frequency, *n.* Either of the two frequencies, the sum or the difference, which result from an amplitude modulation process.

heterodyne repeater. See "repeater, heterodyne."

heuristic, *adj.* Empirical. Referring to knowledge or procedures determined by experience, but difficult of proof.

hexode, *n.* A six-electrode vacuum tube, containing an anode, a cathode, a control grid, and three extra electrodes which may be grids.

H fixture. See "fixture, H."

high-density carrier, *n.* A carrier system capable of transmitting a large number of carrier telephone and signaling channels over a single transmission medium. Usually implies a 600-channel capability.

hi-fi, *adj.* High fidelity.—*n.* A monophonic radio broadcast receiver and/or record player.

high fidelity, *n.* The reproduction of audio sounds so perfectly that a listener is not aware of any loss of naturalness.

high frequency (HF), *adj.* Referring to the band of radio frequencies between 3,000 and 30,000 kilohertz.

high-group frequencies. See "frequency band, high-group."

high-low repeater, *n.* An intermediate carrier repeater which receives signals in a high-frequency band, amplifies and translates them, and transmits the amplified signals in a low-frequency band. See "frogging."

high-pass filter, *n.* An electrical network which passes all frequencies higher than a certain designed cutoff frequency, and greatly attenuates all lower frequencies.

high Q, *adj.* The condition of an inductance or capacitance when the ratio of its reactance to its resistance is high. A high Q inductance or capacitance ensures sharper tuning of the circuit in which it is used, and lower circuit losses. See also "Q-factor."

high quality, *adj.* Having the inherent capacity to transmit sounds or signals without objectionable distortion.

high tension, *adj., n.* High voltage. This is an ambiguous slang term having no accepted meaning. It can mean over 2400 volts, over 4000 volts, over 5000 volts, or over 13,200 volts. See also "high voltage joint use."

high tone. See "tone, high."

high-usage group, *n.* A group of trunks which is the primary direct route between two points, and is engineered to carry the maximum traffic at all times. To provide an acceptable grade of service an alternate 'final group" must be provided for the overflow traffic.

high usage trunk group, *n.* A group of trunks for which an engineered alternate route has been provided. The HU trunk group is heavily loaded with traffic, and has a high percentage of busies.

high-voltage alarm, *n.* A bell alarm in a dial central office which is activated when the DC voltage being supplied to the equipment rises above 53 volts.

high voltage joint use, *n.* Joint utilization of a pole by the telephone company and a power company when the power circuit carries 5,000 volts or over (Bell System); or when the power circuit carries 8,700 volts or over (National Electrical Safety Code).

highway, common, *n.* An intra-office communication circuit which is used on a time-division basis by many channels.

hit, *n.* An impulse noise having a duration of about one millisecond.

hitch, core, *n.* The attachment of a pulling line directly to a cable core rather than to the cable sheath. Permits pulling the cable without over-stressing the sheath.

hit indicator, *n.* A lamp on a telegraph testboard, associated with a particular working circuit. It lights to indicate a prolonged open (space) condition on the circuit.

hi-valve assembly, *n.* An assembly of five gas pressure testing valves which can be mounted below the manhole rim and piped to individual cables in the manhole, thus enabling the testing of cable gas pressures without entering the manhole.

hoist, chain, *n.* Small ratchet lever hoist used in outside plant construction work to tighten line wires, guy wires, etc. Consists of a ratchet

body with hook, operating lever, and roller chain with hook. Light enough (15-35 lbs) for use on a pole, and capable of 1500-6000 lbs pull.

hoist, Coffing, *n.* Popular brand of chain hoist used in outside plant construction. See "hoist, chain."

hold, *v.* To maintain an established telephone connection, possibly while disconnecting to answer another call.

hold button. See "key, hold."

holder, directory, *n.* Device used in telephone booths, etc., to hold the telephone directory in a convenient position for use while protecting it from maltreatment or pilfering.

holder, purse, *n.* A large spring clip which can be mounted on the back of an operator's chair to hold the operator's purse where it will not interfere with her work at the switchboard.

holder, receiver, *n.* Moulded plastic case designed to hold a receiver unit, and to terminate the 2-conductor cord. Converts a receiver unit to a telephone receiver which can be hand-held or headband supported.

holding bridge, *n.* A direct current shunt path across a circuit, having a resistance low enough to operate supervisory relays and an impedance high enough not to degrade transmission.

holding circuit, *n.* An alternate circuit which, when completed, holds a relay in the operated position and enables it to remain operated after the initial operating winding is de-energized.

holding current, *n.* The minimum current which will hold a relay in its operated position. The holding current is less than the operating current.

holding jack, *n.* A jack to which an operator can connect the front cord of a pair when she wishes to hold a line so that she can cut out from that cord. The holding jack extinguishes the supervisory lamp and provides a termination to prevent the circuit from singing while being held.

holding time, *n.* The total time in seconds that a circuit is held busy.

hold lamp. See "lamp, hold."

hole, *n.* (1) A pole hole. (2) A vacancy in the valance band of an atom, where an electron once was. In a semiconductor, holes act as positive charges having mass. Sometimes called a "positron."

holes, feed, *n. pl.* The central row of small holes in a punched paper tape, used to feed the tape past a tape reader mechanism.

Hollerith code, *n.* A 12-level (twelve bits per character) code which defines the relation between an alphanumeric character and the punched holes in an 80-column data card.

hollow, *adj.* Said of a repeatered voice circuit which is on the verge of singing, resulting in echos as though one were speaking into an empty barrel.

hollow circuit, *n.* A repeatered voice circuit which is unstable, because of poor hybrid balance, in the 200-500 Hz range. Speaking over this circuit is like talking into an empty barrel.

holly strip, *n.* In a switchboard face equipment, a strip of white holly wood the same length as a strip of jacks but 1/16-inch thick. Used as a divider between a jack strip and the associated lamp strip.

holster, tool, *n.* A leather pocket for a single tool, made to hang from a tool belt.

home, *v.i.* To be connected by a final trunk group to an office of higher rank (to an office with a lower class number).

home area. See "area, home."

home area toll, *adj.* Toll (calls) to telephones having the same area code.

home grid, *n.* In a polygrid toll switching network, the set of switching centers which surround, and are directly connected to, the destination switching center.

home on, *vi.* (1) To be connected to a central office for service. (Said of a telephone subscriber). (2) To be connected by a direct trunk to an office of a higher class. (Said of an office of a lower class.)

home position, *n.* The normal, or initial rest position, to which the wipers of homing-type stepping switches return after the switch is released.

homing, *n.* (1) Returning to the starting position, as in a rotary stepping switch. (2) Connected with or trunking to a particular central office or toll center.

homing, dual, *n.* (1) The capability of a tributary office to trunk to either of two toll centers. (2) The capability of a telephone or a PBX to receive service from either of two central offices.

homing arrangement (of toll switching centers), *n.* An office of any class may home on (be connected by direct trunks to) an office of any higher class.

homing type switch, *n.* An automatic stepping switch which always restores to its normal at-rest position when not in use.

honeycomb coil, *n.* An air-core radio-frequency inductance wound in a crisscross lattice to reduce its distributed capacitance. Also called a "lattice-wound coil."

hook, cable suspension, *n.* A heavy forged steel hook used in catenary cable construction to provide the connection between the catenary strand and the cable messenger strand.

hook, cant, *n.* A tool used for rolling and carrying poles. Consists of a 40-inch wooden handle having a long curved steel hook hinged one foot from the end.

hook, drive, *n.* A heavy screw hook having threads which permit it to be driven into the pole. Used to support drop wire clamps.

hook, guard-arm, *n.* A ½-inch eye bolt having a partially open eye. Mounts through a guard-arm to provide support for drop wire clamps.

hook, house, *n.* A 5/16″D x 4″ long screw hook, used to attach drop wires to buildings.

hook, manhole cover, *n.* Heavy steel hook, 2 feet long with handle, used for lifting and pulling off manhole covers.

hook, pulling, *n.* Device used to temporarily connect the hook of a chain hoist to an automatic dead-end. Used for tensioning the guy or strand.

hook, receiver. See "hookswitch."

hook, screw, *n.* A wire hook having a wood screw shank.

hook, shave, *n.* A hand scraper having a sharp-edged oval blade, used by a cable splicer to shave oxidized lead from the cable sheath and sleeve preparatory to making a wiped joint.

hook, underground cable, *n.* A steel step, of "T" cross-section, which can be hooked into an underground cable rack and used to support cable in manholes or cable vaults. Available in 4, 7½, 10, and 14-inch lengths.

hooklatch, *n.* Device used on hookswitch of telephones on party lines. When the handset is removed from the hookswitch, it travels only far enough to enable the subscriber to listen on the line without interrupting a call in progress. If the line is free, the hooklatch can be tripped to permit full travel of the hookswitch and the placing of a call.

hooks, *n. pl.* A pair of lineman's climbers. (Slang)

hookswitch, *n.* The device on which a telephone receiver hangs or on which a telephone handset hangs or rests when not in use. The weight of the receiver or handset operates a switch which opens the telephone circuit, leaving only the bell connected to the line.

hookswitch, mercury, *n.* A type of hookswitch with mercury pool contacts used on pay telephones to protect against fraudulent use. If the hookswitch is operated rapidly to simulate dialing, the mercury breaks up into droplets which do not bridge the contacts.

hookup, *n.* An interconnection of circuit components for a particular purpose.

hookup wire, *n.* Tinned solid or stranded copper wire with varnished braid insulation used for interconnecting circuit components. Available in most gauges from 24 AWG to 12 AWG.

hop, radio, *n.* In high frequency radio, the number of reflections from the ionosphere encountered by the radio wave in traveling from transmitter to receiver. See also "double hop" and "single hop."

horizon, *n.* The line where the sky seems to meet the earth as seen from an antenna. The limit of the "line-of-sight."

horizon, radio. See "radio horizon."

horizontal, crossbar, *n.* The horizontal path selected by a single select magnet of a crossbar switch.

horizontal, distributing frame, *n.* The horizontal steel bar at the edge of a distributing frame shelf, on which terminal blocks are mounted.

horizontal polarization, *n.* Transmission of radio waves in such an orientation that the electric field vector is horizontal. Television signals in the United States are transmitted with horizontal polarization.

horizontal stripe. See "stripe, longitudinal color."

horn, launching, *n.* A conical metallic horn that forms the transition between a coaxial cable and a G-line waveguide.

horn, signaling. See "howler, signaling."

horn antenna, *n.* A microwave antenna formed by flaring the end of a waveguide into the shape of a horn.

horn feed, *n.* A small horn antenna used to illuminate a parabolic reflector antenna.

horn gap, *n.* A high-voltage lightning arrester, having a gap between two wire horns. Heat causes the arc discharge to rise on the horns, which lengthen the arc until it is extinguished.

horn loudspeaker, *n.* A very directional loudspeaker in which the driver unit is fed into a metal horn, whose flare is usually an expotential curve.

horn throat, *n.* The small, or input end of a horn.

horsepower, *n.* A unit of mechanical power equivalent to 550 foot-pounds per second, or to 745.7 watts.

hose, blower, *n.* An 8-inch diameter x 15 feet long hose used to convey air from a blower or heater unit into a manhole. Made of yellow vinyl coated fiberglass fabric stitched over a helical coil of spring steel wire.

hose, suction, *n.* A wire-reinforced 1½ ″ or 2-inch rubber hose which can be attached to a pump and the other end placed in a manhole to remove water.

hot, *adj.* Energized. Implies a high voltage. (Slang)

hot dip, *adj. n.* The covering of a metallic surface by dipping into a molten bath of the coating material. Steel is hot dip galvanized by being dipped into a bath of molten zinc.

hotel service codes. See "codes, hotel service."

hot-standby operation, *n.* A method of achieving reliable operation of a radio link by the use of two fully energized transmitters fed through a waveguide hybrid to a common antenna. A switch in the waveguide allows the output of only one transmitter to reach the antenna. If one transmitter fails, the second is substituted instantly. A variation of this operation which switches both the radio frequency and baseband signals permits a single hot-standby transmitter to provide standby protection for a group of transmitters.

hour, busy. See "busy hour."

house, pole, *n.* A pole-mounting cabinet with hinged doors, used to provide a weatherproof housing for binding post chambers, etc.

house hook, *n.* Stainless or galvanized steel formed wire hook. Screws to the house, and is used to support the bail of a drop wire clamp.

houseline, *n.* A small twine of three strands laid counterclockwise, usually tarred, and used for temporary lashing or seizing.

housing, *n.* A box for containing equipment, or a removable protective cover over equipment.

housing, outdoor telephone, *n.* A weatherproof cast aluminum housing, 12″ wide x 17″ high x 6″ deep, with a spring loaded hinged door held closed by a magnetic latch. Intended to house a standard wall telephone. Has screened openings in the bottom to vent ringer signals.

howl, *n.* A loud wailing sound caused by electrical or acoustic feedback.

howl, repeater, *n.* A very loud "sing" or sustained oscillation of a telephone repeater, caused by extreme unbalance of the hybrid coil terminations. See also "singing."

howler, *n.* Electrical device which emits a howling signal. Used at the local test desk where it is connected to permanent (off-hook) subscriber lines in the hope that the loud howl will be heard and the telephone hung up. The device starts the howl at low intensity with a high audio frequency and gradually builds up to the maximum intensity at a low frequency.

howler, signaling, *n.* A device similar to an auto horn, and operated by 60 Hz AC through a control relay. Puts out a loud 120 Hz signal and substitutes for a telephone bell in extremely noisy locations.

hub, full duplex telegraph, *n.* Four bridging points providing the interconnecting point for full duplex (simultaneous transmission in two directions) telegraph loops and lines. The four points are:

   (a)   receive leg, West
   (b)   send leg, West
   (c)   receive leg, East
   (d)   send leg, East

hub, half-duplex telegraph, *n.* A pair of busses, or common connection points, one called the "receive hub" and the other the "send hub" where all receive legs and all send legs of a particular half-duplex telegraph circuit can be connected together on a bridging basis. See also "hub, full duplex telegraph."

hub, telegraph, *n.* A large type of interconnection in which a large number of telegraph loops can be bridged together on a high impedance basis. The hub marking condition is normally +60 volts and the spacing condition —30 volts.

hub, telegraph receive, *n.* A bus, or common connection, to which all receive legs of a particular telegraph system are connected on a bridged basis. Incoming signals (+60 volts mark, —30 volts space) are then transferred, through a hub link or regenerative repeater to the send hub for distribution to all send legs of the system, except that of the loop from which the signal was received.

hub, telegraph send, *n.* The bus, or common connection point, to which all send legs of a particular telegraph system are bridged. Signals (+60 volts mark, —30 volts space) coming from the receive hub via the hub link or regenerative repeater are distributed to send legs of the system, except to the loop whence the signal originated.

hub directional control. See "directional control, hub."

hub link. See "link, telegraph hub."

hub operation, *n.* A method of interconnecting telegraph legs where the signals are transferred between legs on a voltage basis.

hub potentiometer. See "potentiometer, telegraph hub."

hub voltages, telegraph. See "voltages, telegraph hub."

hue, *n.* In color TV, one of the three characteristics of color. Defines color on the basis of its position in the frequency spectrum, ie: whether red, blue, green, or yellow, etc. See also "luminance" and "saturation."

hum, *n.* Audio frequency interference which is at the frequency of the power supply or its harmonics.

humidity, relative, *n.* The ratio of the amount of water vapor the air contains to the maximum amount it could hold at the same temperature and pressure, expressed in percent.

humming, *n.* A low-pitched droning sound. Humming at 120 hertz is sometimes produced by transformers energized at 60 hertz if the iron laminations in the transformer core are free to vibrate.

hundred call-seconds. See "CCS."

hunting, *n.* The operation of a selector, or like mechanism, in searching from one terminal to another until an idle terminal is found.

hunting, preferential. See "preferential hunting."

hybrid, *adj.* Made up of several different components.—*n.* A hybrid coil, which was originally a combination of two different repeating coils.

hybrid, coil, *n.* A hybrid consisting of a three-winding tapped transformer used with a balancing network to convert a four-wire line to a two-wire line.

hybrid, resistance, *n.* A hybrid circuit made up solely of resistances. Cheaper than coil hybrids, but requires amplification to compensate for its high loss.

hybrid balance. See "balance, hybrid."

hybrid coil, *n.* A three-winding repeating coil having four pairs of terminals: (1) four-wire line IN, (2) four-wire line OUT, (3) two-wire line, and (4) balancing network. Used to connect a four-wire line to a two-wire line, or to terminate it on a two-wire switchboard.

hybrid junction, *n.* Any network or device which provides a low-impedance path and impedance-matching between adjacent circuits, but a high degree of isolation between opposite circuits. Several types are common: (a) A three-winding "hybrid transformer," (b) a resistance bridge circuit, and (c) a waveguide device known as a "hybrid tee."

hybrid loss, *n.* The transmission loss incurred when a signal goes through a hybrid coil. This loss is about 3.6 db, consisting of 3 db because the current divides into two equal halves, and 0.6 db for coil loss.

hybrid tee, *n.* A section of rectangular waveguide with both E-plane and H-plane tee junctions. It is provided with an internal post and iris for matching, so that energy may be fed into the junction from any arm without reflection if the other three arms are terminated.

hydrometer, *n.* An instrument for determining the specific gravity of liquids, especially of storage battery electrolyte. It consists of a weighted glass float having a graduated stem which sinks into the liquid to a point determined by the specific gravity of the liquid. The float is usually contained in a glass and rubber syringe which can be used to withdraw a sample of the liquid. See also "specific gravity."

hygrometer, *n.* An indicating instrument which measures the relative humidity of the atmosphere.

hygroscopic, *adj.* Capable of absorbing moisture from the air.

hygrostat, *n.* A device for closing a pair of contacts when the air humidity reaches a predetermined level.

hysteresis, *n.* A property of all magnetic materials which causes the value of magnetic flux density to lag behind the change in value of the magnetizing force which produces the flux. It is caused by the reluctance of the molecules to change their orientation. The work done to move the molecular magnets is a loss, and appears in the form of heat.

hysteresis, dielectric, *n.* A lagging of an electric field in a dielectric behind the alternating voltage which produces it. It causes a loss similar to that of magnetic hysteresis.

hysteresis, magnetic. See "hysteresis."

hystereis loop, *n.* For any magnetic material a graphical plot of magnetizing current versus magnetic flux density will appear as a loop, with one value of flux when the current is increasing and a second value when the current is decreasing. The area within the loop is proportional to the power loss due to hysteresis.

hysteresis loss, *n.* The power loss in a magnetic core, such as in a transformer energized by an alternating current, which is due to hysteresis.

identification on outward dialing (AIOD), *n.* The capability of some CENTREX PBX's which enables the telephone company to provide the customer with an itemized statement of toll charges or message unit charges on directly dialed calls. Provided by automatic number identification (ANI) equipment installed in the CENTREX PBX and connected over a data link to the serving AMA central office. See also "ANI" and "AMA."

idle, *adj.* (1) Not in use. (2) Not busy. (3) Available for use. (4) In the "on-hook" condition.

idle-line indicating. See "indicating, idle-line."

idle line termination, *n.* A bridged impedance placed on a 2-wire line or trunk during its idle condition which prevents connected voice repeaters from singing during establishment of a call.

idle search, *n.* In alternate route tables, the portion of the search pattern consisting of (a) the direct trunk group to the destination switching center, and (b) the three most direct forward routed alternate trunk groups. This type of search is used for routine calls.

idle trunk indication, *n.* A small lighted signal lamp associated with a trunk jack, indicating to the operator that the trunk is idle and that she may plug into it without testing.

ignore, *n.* A punched tape code which indicates that no action should be taken.

illegal state, *n.* A condition of a switching circuit such that "you shouldn't have been able to get here from where you started."

illuminate, *v.* To cover with radio-frequency energy, as a parabolic reflector antenna from a feed horn, or a passive reflector from a parabolic reflector.

image, *n.* One of the two groups of sidebands generated in the process of modulation, so called because one is the reverse (mirror image) of the other with respect to frequency.

image antenna, *n.* A hypothetical antenna which is a mirror image of the real antenna. Of the same size and configuration, it is as far below the ground as the real antenna is above ground. Where the real antenna has a positive charge, the image antenna has a negative charge, and vice versa. Any wave from the real antenna which is reflected from the earth proceeds in a direction and phase which it would have had if it had originated at the image antenna.

image frequency, *n.* In heterodyne frequency convertors, an undesired input frequency which can beat with the local oscillator to produce the intermediate frequency, and thus appear in the receiver output.

image impedances. See "impedances, image."

image ratio, *n.* The ratio of the field strength at the image frequency to the field strength at the desired frequency, each of which will produce equal outputs if applied to the input of a superheterodyne radio receiver.

image rejection, *n.* The action of a superheterodyne receiver in suppressing signals at the image frequency, which see.

image response, *n.* The action of a superheterodyne receiver in responding to an undesired signal which is separated from the desired signal by twice the intermediate frequency.

Immediate (I), *n.* The third highest ranking message precedence. See "precedence."

immediate ringing. See "ringing, immediate."

impact meter. See "meter, impulse noise."

impairment, distortion transmission (DTI), *n.* The reduction in intelligibility of a telephone transmission resulting from (a) transmission of a voice bandwidth less than 250-3000 Hz, or (b) unequal transmission of the various frequencies within the 250-3000 Hz band. Expressed in db DTI, which is the number of db of transmission loss which must be added to a distortionless circuit to give the same impairment.

Cutoff	DTI
3600 Hz	0 dB
3000 Hz	1 dB
2600 Hz	2 dB
2400 Hz	3 dB
2200 Hz	4 dB

impairment, noise transmission (NTI), *n.* The reduction in intelligibility of a telephone transmission due to the presence of noise on the circuit, expressed in decibels NTI. The db NTI is equal to the loss one must add to a noise-free circuit of 250-3,000 Hz bandwidth to produce the same impairment.

impedance, *n.* The total opposition (resistance and reactance) of a circuit to the flow of an alternating current. Expressed as the vector sum of resistance and reactance $(R+jX)$ or as a vector of magnitude "Z" at an angle "theta." (Z,θ)

impedance, average central office, *n.* The impedance of an average local central office is assumed to be that of a 900 ohms resistor in series with a 2.16 microfarad capacitor.

impedance, blocked, *n.* The impedance at the input of a transducer when the impedance at the output is made infinite, as by mechanically blocking the diaphragm of a telephone receiver.

impedance, characteristic, *n.* The impedance that a transmission line would have if it were infinitely long. Often called "iterative impedance," which see.

impedance, driving point. *n.* The input impedance of a transmission line or of an antenna.

impedance, free, *n.* The impedance at the input of a transducer when the impedance of its output is made zero.

impedance, input, *n.* The impedance looking into the input terminals of a circuit or device.

impedance, iterative, *n.* The impedance that will terminate the output of a line or network such that the impedance then measured at the input of the line or network will be equal to the (iterative) terminating impedance.

impedance, line, *n.* The impedance measured at the input to a transmission line.

impedance, loaded, *n.* The impedance at the input of a transducer when its output is connected to its normal load.

impedance, mechanical, *n.* The impedance, for simple harmonic motion, obtained by dividing force by velocity.

impedance, mid-series, *n.* The impedance looking into a repetitive symmetrical network, if measured at the mid-point of one of the series elements.

impedance, mid-shunt, *n.* The impedance looking into a repetitive symmetrical network, if measured looking at a shunt element which has an impedance double that of the other shunt elements in the network.

impedance, motional, *n.* That part of the impedance of a telephone receiver or loudspeaker which is due solely to the motion of the diaphragm or voice coil. Obtained by subtracting the damped, motionless impedance of the receiver from the total impedance with the diaphragm moving and loaded.

impedance, mutual, *n.* The impedance existing between the primary and secondary of a transformer. It is numerically equal to the secondary voltage divided by the primary current.

impedance, natural. See "impedance, surge."

impedance, negative, *n.* A property of some circuits containing induc-tance in which the current increases as the voltage is decreased.

impedance, non-linear, *n.* An impedance which is not constant, but varies in some manner with the voltage impressed on it or the current through it. A sine-wave voltage impressed on a non-linear impedance will result in a current containing harmonics of the voltage wave.

impedance, office, *n.* The nominal impedance of a switching center, to which all trunk terminal impedances are matched. It is assumed to be either 600 ohms (toll) or 900 ohms (local) in series with a 2.16 microfarad capacitor.

impedance, open-circuit, *n.* The input impedance of a line or four-terminal network when the far end or output terminals are open.

impedance, output, *n.* The impedance looking into the output terminals of a power source, a circuit, or device.

impedance, reflected, *n.* An impedance such that if inserted in the primary of a transformer it would alter the primary current by the same amount as a particular impedance connected as a load on the transformer secondary.

impedance, self. See "self-impedance."

impedance, sending end. *n.* The impedance looking into the input of a transmission line.

impedance, short-circuit, *n.* The input impedance to a line or four-terminal network when the far end or output terminals are shorted.

impedance, surge, *n.* The impedance of a line equal to the square root of the quantity consisting of the line inductance in henries divided by the line capacitance in farads. If the resistance and leakage are assumed to be negligible, then the surge impedance is equal to the characteristic impedance.

impedance, terminal, *n.* The complex impedance looking into the unloaded input or output terminals of an equipment or line which is otherwise in operating condition.

impedance, transfer, *n.* The impedance obtained by dividing the voltage at the input to a network by the current at the output of the network.

impedance bridge. See "bridge, impedance."

impedance characteristic, *n.* A graphical plot of the impedance of a circuit versus frequency.

impedance compensator. See "compensator, impedance."

impedance corrector, See "corrector, impedance."

impedance irregularity, *n.* A discontinuity in the impedance of an electrically smooth transmission line, such as that caused by addition of extra resistance, omission of a loading coil, substitution of high-capacitance for low-capacitance cable, etc.

impedance matching, *n.* Making the load impedance equal to the source impedance, in order to obtain maximum power transfer. Implies that the impedances must be equal in magnitude, but not necessarily equal or opposite in sign. See also "impedances, conjugate."

impedance-matching transformer, *n.* A transformer whose chief function is to match the impedances of two dis-similar circuits, and thus attain maximum power transfer at their junction.

impedances, conjugate, *n. pl.* Impedances which have equal resistances, and reactances which are equal in amount but opposite in sign, ie: capacitive versus inductive. The conjugate of the impedance $R+jX$ is $R—jX$.

impedances, image, *n. pl.* The impedances which will simultaneously terminate each pair of terminals of a network or transducer in such a way that at each pair of terminals the impedances in both directions are equal.

impedances, reciprocal, *n. pl.* Two impedances are said to be reciprocal

if their product is equal to the square of a specified resistance.

impregnated, *adj.* Said of a porous material which has all voids filled with an insulating oil, varnish, or wax.

impulse, *n.* A surge of electricity having a single polarity.

impulse noise, *n.* An unwanted signal characterized by a steep wave front and short time duration. Its level is taken to be the highest level which recurs 70 times per hour, and is designated the dbm A1 level.

impulse noise counter, *n.* An instrument to measure the relative interfering effect of impulse noise. Consists of an electro-mechanical counter (message register) which will operate not oftener than one count each 150 milliseconds, with an input circuit which can set a noise level threshhold below which the counter will not operate. A typical requirement is: "Not more than 288 counts in 8 hours having a level greater than —19 dbm."

impulse ratio, *n.* Pulse ratio.

impurity, *n.* Atoms of a foreign chemical introduced into semiconductor material to increase the number of free electrons. Also called a "donor."

in-band signaling, *n.* Using the entire 200-3700 cps bandwidth of a carrier channel to carry the voice signal, and transmitting supervisory signals at 2600 cps. Supervisory signals are not required during the talking period. Sometimes known as "tone on when idle" operation.

inboard channel, *n.* In SSB or ISB radio transmission, the voice channel nearest in frequency to the carrier frequency. See also "outboard channel."

incidence angle, *n.* The angle at which a radio wave strikes a plane reflecting surface, measured by the angle between the wave and a perpendicular to the surface.

inclination, satellite orbit, *n.* The angle formed between the plane of the satellite's orbit and the plane of the ecliptic.

incoming, *adj.* Describing a trunk which is used only for calls coming in from another office.

increment, *n.* A small change, either positive or negative, in the value of a variable quantity.

independent sideband (ISB) modulation, *n.* A form of amplitude modulation of a radio signal in which the carrier is suppressed or reduced and each sideband is modulated independently with separate information.

index, modulation, *n.* A measure of the degree of modulation. For frequency modulation, it is the ratio of the frequency deviation to the frequency of the modulating wave.

indexer, AMA call identity, *n.* Device which supplies a 2-digit number identifying the trunk used on an AMA call. (#5 XBar)

index of cooperation, *n.* In facsimile transmission, the product of the scanning drum diameter in inches and the number of scanning lines per inch.

index of refraction, *n.* The ratio of the velocity of a wave in a specified medium to the velocity of the same wave in a vacuum.

in-dialing, network, *n.* Telephone dialing which proceeds from a commercial network into a private network, or from a toll network into a local network.

indicating, idle-line, *n.* A lamp indication system for toll switchboards which lights only the lamp associated with the next available outgoing trunk in each group, rather than lighting the lamps of all busy trunks. Conserves power and keeps the switchboard cooler.

indicating instrument, *n.* Any instrument in which the value of the quantity being measured is shown visually, as on a meter scale.

indicator, B flow, *n.* An inclined alcohol manometer which, when connected to a pair of pressure testing valves, can indicate very accurately small differences in gas pressure between two points and the resulting direction of gas flow. See also "manometer, mercury."

indicator, call. See "call indicator."

indicator, dial speed, *n.* A portable test set or a component of a local test desk used to measure the pulse speed of telephone dials.

indicator, direction of gas flow, *n.* A section of glass tubing containing a light weight plastic ball. When the tubing is connected, by rubber hoses, to two pressure testing valves the movement of the plastic ball will show the direction of gas flow between the two valves.

indicator, end-of-message, *n.* A standardized, uninterrupted sequence of characters and machine functions used to terminate a teletypewriter transmission, and to shut down the receiving teletypewriter.

indicator, gas. See "detector, gas."

indicator, idle trunk. See "idle trunk indication."

indicator, lamp, *n.* A holder for switchboard lamps which provides wall or desk mounting with colored lamp caps or beehive lenses. Available for 1, 2, 3, or 4 lamps with white, red, green or amber caps or lenses.

indicator, level. See "volume indicator."

indicator, routing, *n.* A group of letters assigned to identify a communication station, and to facilitate the routing of traffic through the communication network to that station.

indicator, start-of-message, *n.* A group of characters used on teletypewriter messages to activate automatic switching equipment.

indicator, start signal, *n.* A wink, dial tone, or key pulse tone signal.

indicator, tuning, *n.* A small voltmeter in a radio receiver, used to indicate when the receiver is tuned accurately.

indicator, volume, *n.* An indicating meter of special dynamic construction, read in a carefully prescribed manner, which indicates that the program level is a certain number of "volume units" above standard program, defined as one milliwatt steady-state power into 600 ohms resistance.

individual line, *n.* A line which provides telephone service for the exclusive use of one subscriber.

induced, *adj.* Produced as a result of exposure to a changing electric or magnetic field.

induced charge, *n.* An electrostatic charge produced on a conducting body when it is brought near to or connected to another body which bears an electric charge.

induced current, *n.* Current which flows in a conductor because of an induced voltage.

induced voltage, *n.* The voltage produced in a coil of wire either (a) when the coil moves through a magnetic field or (b) when the magnetic flux through the coil is varied.

inductance, *n.* The property possessed by a coil of wire of opposing any change in a current which flows through it. It is a measure of the electromotive force which will be generated as a result of a given rate of change of current in the circuit.

inductance, distributed, *n.* The inductance which is spread uniformly along the entire length of a conductor, as distinguished by "lumped inductance" which is concentrated at a point.

inductance, mutual, *n.* The common inductance of two coupled electrical circuits which determines, for a given rate of change of current in one of the circuits, the electromotive force that will be induced in the other.

inductance, self, *n.* The property of an electrical circuit which determines, for a given rate of change of current in the circuit, the electromotive force which is induced in the same circuit.

inductance, variable, *n.* A coil whose inductance can be varied, either by (a) moving a portion of the coil, (b) by a tap switch, or (c) by inserting a ferrite or powdered-iron slug.

induction, *n.* The process by which a change in current in one circuit causes a corresponding change in an adjacent circuit due to magnetic coupling, or by which a voltage on one conductor causes the opposite voltage to appear on another conductor with which there is electrostatic coupling. See also "self induction."

induction, electrostatic. See "electrostatic induction."

induction, low-frequency, *n.* Induction of power at its fundamental frequency (usually 60 Hz in the USA) from a power circuit to a communication circuit.

induction, noise, *n.* The transfer of noise into a communication circuit through magnetic coupling or electrostatic coupling with some other circuit, which may be power, street lights, telephone, telegraph, or even earth currents.

induction, power, *n.* Induction which, because of its sound or frequency, is identifiable as coming from commercial power lines. It may be noise induction at harmonics of the power frequency, or low-frequency induction at 60 Hz, 120 Hz, or 180 Hz.

induction, ringing, *n.* (1) Noise which, because of its sound or frequency, is identifiable as ringing current induced from another circuit. (2) That small portion of the ringing current which is returned to the calling subscriber as an indication that the called party is being rung. Ringback tone.

induction, self, *n.* The production of a counterelectromotive force in a conductor when its own magnetic field expands or collapses with a change of current in the conductor.

induction coil. See "coil, induction."

induction field, *n.* The magnetic field which is predominant in the near zone of a radio transmitting antenna, and which is directly proportional to the current in the antenna.

induction motor, *n.* A machine which converts electrical power in its stator winding to mechanical power. The current in the rotor winding is obtained solely by induction from the stator winding. Its speed is less than that of a synchronous machine, and depends on its load.

inductive, *adj.* (1) Having inductive reactance. (2) Having coupling with another circuit through mutual inductance.

inductive circuit, *n.* A circuit having a net inductive reactance, that is a higher value of inductive reactance than of capacitive reactance.

inductive coordination. See "coordination, inductive."

inductive coupling, *n.* (1) The coupling that exists between two circuits through a mutual inductance, such as that in a transformer. (2) Coupling between two circuits through an inductance that is common to the two circuits. Direct inductive coupling.

inductive interference. See "interference, inductive."

inductive kick, *n.* The voltage surge that is induced in an inductance when the current through it is interrupted and the magnetic flux collapses suddenly.

inductive load, *n.* An electrical load that has a significant inductive reactance.

inductive reactance, *n.* The reactance of a circuit which is due only to the presence of inductance. The inductive reactance in ohms is equal to 6.283 times the frequency in hertz times the inductance in henries.

inductometer, *n.* An inductor whose inductance can be varied, sometimes by a calibrated amount.

inductor, *n.* A coil of wire, usually with a highly permeable core, having an inductive reactance which (at its working frequency) is high compared to its resistance. Used to add lumped inductance to a circuit.

inductor, saturable, *n.* A coil having two balanced, low-resistance windings on a toroidal magnetic core. Used to reduce bridged tap loss when creating a party line with two pairs bridged at the central office. One saturable inductor is connected in series with each pair at the central office. When the telephone is "on-hook" and no current flows, the inductor has a high impedance and low bridging loss. When the telephone is "off-hook" the line current saturates the core of the inductor, greatly reducing its impedance and series transmission loss.

inert, *adj.* (1) Describing equipment which does not require a local source of power. (2) Inactive.

inertance, *n.* The inertia displayed by the air, and vibrating objects, to a sound wave. It is the acoustical equivalent of electrical inductance.

infinite line, *n.* A transmission line which has no reflections from its far end. It can either (a) be of infinite length, or (b) be terminated in its iterative impedance.

influence, *n.* The tendency of a power system to cause noise or low frequency induction in a telephone system. Influence is determined by (1) power voltage, (2) power system balance, (3) harmonic content of the power voltage and current waves, and (4) power circuit transpositions. See also "telephone influence factor," "coupling," and "susceptiveness."

influence, power circuit, *n.* A summation of the characteristics of a power circuit which determines how much inductive interference it will create in a neighboring communication circuit. The characteristics which contribute are:

    a. Voltage.

    b. Circuit connection, wye or delta.

c. Unbalanced loads.

d. Harmonic content of the voltage and current waves.

e. Wire configuration and spacing.

f. Power circuit transpositions.

influence factor, *n.* A number which combines the weighted contribution of all power circuit characteristics which cause inductive interference.

information, *n.* (1) Information service, (2) An information operator, (3) News or intelligence which cannot be inferred or predetermined from data already on hand.

information bit. See "bit."

information board, *n.* A switchboard or turret at which calls for information are handled. Often used also to handle intercepting calls.

information operator, *n.* One who furnishes telephone numbers to customers and operators upon request.

information position, *n.* A desk or switchboard position at which incoming Information trunks terminate, and at which records for furnishing the telephone numbers of subscribers in the local exchange and other selected points are provided.

information processing, *n.* Data processing.

information retrieval, *n.* The recovery of data which has been stored at a particular address in a memory.

information theory, *n.* The mathematical theory that deals with the transmission of information, and the effects of bandwidth, distortion, and noise.

infrasonic, *adj.* Pertaining to a sound wave which is too low in frequency to be audible to the human ear. Below about 20 hertz.

inhalant, ammonia, *n.* A crushable glass ampoule filled with spirits of ammonia and enclosed in a knitted sleeve. Found in first-aid kits, and used in the treatment of fainting and shock.

inhibit, *v.* (1) To hold in check. (2) To prevent from operating.

inhibiting input, *n.* An input, as to a gate circuit, which prevents operation of a circuit.

inhibit pulse, *n.* A pulse into a memory element which occurs simultaneously with a drive pulse, and cancels its effect.

initial period, *n.* On a toll call, the period for which a minimum charge is made, usually 3 minutes.

inlet circuit, group selector, *n.* In an electronic central office, an access circuit to the switching stages of the "group selector."

in phase, *adj.* Describing waves which have the same frequency, and which pass through their maximum, zero, and minimum values simultaneously.

input, *n.* (1) The signal which is fed into a circuit. (2) The terminals which receive the input signal. (3) The power which energizes an electrical device.

input impedance, *n.* The impedance which is seen looking into the input terminals of a line or electrical device when the input signal source has been disconnected.

input-output device, *n.* Any equipment which introduces data into or receives data from a data communication system.

input transformer, *n.* A transformer used to transform the impedance of a signal source to the impedance of the device of which it is a part.

insert, concrete, *n.* Device for providing threaded holes in concrete. A fixture which can be cast in the wall of a concrete manhole as the manhole is being poured. Has internal threads for ⅜-inch or ½ machine bolts used to secure cable racks.

insertion gain, *n.* The increase in power level at the receiving terminal of a circuit caused by inserting a gain including device in the circuit, expressed in decibels.

insertion loss, *n.* The transmission loss

caused by insertion of a component or network in a circuit. The ratio of power received at a load before insertion to that received at the load after insertion, expressed in decibels.

inside plant. See "plant, inside."

inspection, pole, *n.* The inspection at regular intervals, in the field, of poles over a certain minimum age to determine whether they have deteriorated to the point of needing replacement or reinforcement. See also "borer, increment."

inspector's ring-back switch, *n.* A reverting-call switch, specifically for the use of telephone installers and repairmen.

installer, telephone, *n.* A workman who installs subscriber's telephone equipment, including the drop wire, and then tests its operation with the local test desk.

instantaneous value, *n.* The value at some particular instant in time of any of the parameters (voltage, current, etc.) of a time-varying wave, such as a sinusoidal electrical wave.

instrument, telephone, *n.* A complete subscriber's telephone set.

instrument shunt, *n.* An ammeter shunt. See "shunt."

instrument multiplier, *n.* A voltage multiplier, which permits measuring a high voltage with a voltmeter having a lower voltage range.

instrument transformer, *n.* A highly accurate low-power transformer having negligible leakage flux which can be used to transform high voltages or high currents to low ranges so they may be measured on low voltage or low current meters. See "voltage transformer" and "current transformer."

insulate, *vt.* To separate from conducting bodies by means of nonconducting material to prevent the transfer of electricity.

insulated, *n.* Covered or separated by a dielectric material which prevents passage of current to other conductors.

insulated, paper, *adj.* Said of a conductor which is insulated with a spiral wrapping of paper tape, or with a coating of paper pulp.

insulating joint. See "joint, insulating."

insulation, *n.* A material which will not conduct electricity and which is suitable for surrounding conductors to prevent the loss of current.

insulation, low, *n.* A condition in which the normal insulation is impaired and there is a leakage of current.

insulation, primary, *n.* The layer of material which supplies the electrical insulation, usually the first layer of material applied over a conductor.

insulation resistance. See "resistance, insulation."

insulator, *n.* (1) A material such as glass or a ceramic which is a very poor conductor of electricity. (2) A cup shaped glass or porcelain device, which may be screwed onto wooden or steel pins which are pole or cross-arm mounted, used to support line wires at poles.

insulator, double petticoat, *n.* A medium sized (3⅝"D x 4" high) glass pin insulator having two skirts to provide a longer leakage path. The standard insulator for toll open wire lines without carrier circuits.

insulator, exchange line, *n.* A small (2-7/16"D x 3-1/4"" High) glass single petticoat pin insulator suitable for common-battery open-wire exchange lines.

insulator, glass. See "insulator, double petticoat," "insulator, exchange line," "insulator, pin," "insulator, pony," and "insulator, transposition."

insulator, guy, *n.* A strain insulator placed in a guy to ensure that the portion of the guy which can be reached from the ground will not carry lethal voltages.

insulator, metallic, *n.* A metal support for a narrow-band radio-frequency transmission line, constructed to be one-quarter wavelength long overall and therefore to look like an open at the operating frequency.

insulator, pin, *n.* A cap-shaped insulator having internal threads so that it can be screwed onto a pin in a crossarm, and having an external groove to which a line wire can be tied. Used to insulate line wires in open construction.

insulator, pony, *n.* A small (2¼″D x 3⅜″ High) glass single petticoat pin insulator for use on rural open wire lines.

insulator, porcelain knob. See "knob, porcelain."

insulator, standoff, *n.* An insulator used to support a high voltage lead, such as an antenna feeder, at a distance from the mounting surface.

insulator, strain, *n.* A porcelain insulator shaped so it will withstand a considerable pull. Used to couple two sections of guy strand mechanically while separating them electrically.

insulator, transposition, *n.* A medium size (3¼″D x 3⅞″ high) glass double petticoat pin insulator having two wire grooves separated by two annular ridges. Enables tying the two wires of a pair on the same insulator at transposition points, without the use of a transposition bracket.

integrated circuit, *n.* A complete circuit consisting of transistors, capacitors, resistors, diodes, etc., which is formed in or on a single semiconductor substrate.

integrated circuit, film, *n.* An integrated circuit whose elements are films formed in place by plating, printing, sputtering or etching upon an insulating substrate. The conducting film may be thin to form a capacitor plate or resistor, or thick to form an interconnecting lead.

integrated circuit, hybrid, *n.* An integrated circuit consisting of several types of integrated circuits, or of an integrated circuit and conventional semiconductor elements.

integrated circuit, monolithic, *n.* An integrated circuit whose elements are formed on or within a silicon semiconductor substrate.

integrated circuit, multi-chip, *n.* An integrated circuit whose elements are formed on or within silicon semiconductor chips which are then attached to an insulating substrate.

integrated telephone recorder. See "recorder, integrated telephone."

integrity checking, signaling, *n.* A feature whereby the continuity in both directions on four-wire facilities is checked before signals are passed. Accomplished by a timed (150 millisecond) off-hook signal which must be returned by the receiving office before the sending office is permitted to outpulse.

intelligence, *n.* Information, or data.

intelligence signal, *n.* Any signal containing information, regardless of whether it is in analog or digital form.

intelligibility, *n.* The capability of being understood. The capability of transferring information. It does not necessarily imply the recognition of a particular voice. See also "articulation."

INTELSAT, *n.* International Telecommunications Satellite Consortium. A group of companies in 68 countries (1969) which jointly own the global satellite system. COMSAT represents the United States in INTELSAT, has 53% ownership in the system, and acts as its manager.

Intelsat satellites. See "satellite, Intelsat."

intensity, radio field, *n.* The strength of the electric field caused by a radio wave at a particular point in space, measured in rms microvolts per meter. Usually taken in the direction of the maximum field intensity.

intensity, sound, *n.* The sound energy transmitted per unit of time through a unit area normal to the direction of transmission. It is commonly expressed in watts per square centimeter.

intercept, *vt.* To stop a telephone call directed to an improper telephone number, and redirect that call to an operator or a recording. (Note: INTERCEPT is a verb, never an adjective. The adjective form is "intercepting.")

intercepting, *adj.* Pertaining to the practice of diverting an improperly addressed call to an operator or to a recording.—*n.* The routing of a call placed to a disconnected, re-used, or non-existing telephone number to an operator, or to a recorder-announcer answering device.

intercepting, dual, *n.* A system giving a choice of "operator intercepting" or "machine intercepting" by reversing the cross-connection to the intercepting equipment.

intercepting, machine, *n.* Answering an intercepting call with a machine, as with a message recorded on a magnetic tape or belt.

intercepting, matched pulse, *n.* A system for intercepting calls to party lines in a terminal-per-line office. Operates on a ground pulse which is matched in time with the intercepted station's particular ringing period.

intercepting, operator, *n.* The act of answering an intercepted call by an operator who asks, "What number did you call, please?", and then gives instructions on completing the call.

intercepting operator, *n.* One who gives information to customers and operators regarding changed numbers, disconnected numbers, no such numbers, etc.

intercepting position, *n.* A desk or position to which calls are routed for numbers which have been changed, disconnected, temporarily disconnected, etc. since the latest directory issue, and at which suitable records of such information are maintained.

interceptor, *n.* One company's designation for a fuseless substation protector.

intercom, *n.* (1) An intercommunication system. (2) An intercommunication station.

intercom, home extension, *n.* A reverting-call service enabling intercom service between extension phones in a residence. Any one of ten different ringing codes may be sounded by dialing a two-digit code.

intercom, telephone, *n.* An intercommunication system for use with key telephone systems. The most common version allows nine stations to be bridged on to a common talking pair, with each of the nine stations signaled individually by dialing a single digit. Other more elaborate systems add stations in multiples of nine, and signal by dialing two digits. Two links, permitting two simultaneous intercom conversations, are also available. See also "unit, intercom selector."

intercom station, master. See "master intercom station."

intercommunication system, *n.* A system which permits selective loudspeaker voice communication via wires between any pair of several stations, usually in the same building. The stations may be either "master stations" which may initiate calls to any of a group of stations, or "slave stations" which may initiate calls only to their master station. See also "master intercom station" and "slave intercom station."

inter-digital pause, *n.* The pause, or interval of about 600 milliseconds, between the dialing of two successive digits of the telephone number. During this pause the calling telephone's loop is closed, and loop current flows.

interdigital time, *n.* When dialing a sequence of digits, the time interval from the end of the last on-hook pulse of one digit train to the beginning of the first on-hook pulse of the next digit train. Usually not less than 600 milliseconds.

interface, *n.* The junction or point of inter-connection between two systems or equipments having different characteristics. They may differ with respect to voltage, frequency, speed of operation, type of signal, and/or type of information coding. —*v.* To interconnect two different systems with care to resolve their incompatibilities.

interface equipment, *n.* Equipment used between two other equipments which would otherwise be incompatible. It converts the terminal voltage, power level, impedance, or type of signal of one equipment to match those of the second equipment. Examples are: transformers, amplifiers, pads, and convertors.

interference, *n.* (1) Noise or crosstalk on a communication circuit which acts to reduce the intelligibility of the desired signal or speech. (2) Wave interference.

interference, inductive, *n.* The interference to a communication circuit by the transfer of noise voltages from a neighboring power circuit, through the electric field or the magnetic field, or both.

interference, intersymbol, *n.* The distortion in pulse code transmission caused by the spreading of some of each pulse's energy into the time slots of adjacent pulses.

interference, radio-frequency (RFI). See "radio-frequency interference."

interference, selective radio, *n.* Radio interference whose energy is concentrated in a narrow band of frequencies.

interference, wave, *n.* The variation of wave amplitude with distance or time caused by the addition or subtraction of two waves having very nearly the same frequency.

interference filter. See "filter, power interference."

interlace, *n.* The action of the scanning beam in a television (CRT) tube, in which for each frame the beam scans left to right 262 times from top to bottom of the picture then repeats this, with the beam tracing between the previously scanned lines.

interleaving, pulse, *n.* The process by which the pulses from two or more time division multiplex systems are transmitted in time division sequence over a single transmission path.

interlock, *n.* (1) The latch on a multi-key telephone which releases any key which may be locked operated when another key button is depressed. (2) An automatic switch on a door giving access to high-voltage equipment which operates to de-energize the equipment whenever the door is opened.

interlock, key, *n.* On multibutton key telephones, a latch bar which holds a depressed key in the "down" position, but releases it when another key is depressed.

intermediate dialing center, *n.* An intermediate toll center office equipped for operator distance dialing, which completes calls originating at ringdown or non-dial offices by dialing direct to the called telephone at a distant office.

intermediate distributing frame. See "frame, intermediate distributing."

intermediate frequency. See "frequency, intermediate."

intermediate repeater. See "repeater, intermediate."

intermediate toll center, *n.* Any office, other than the originating toll center and terminating toll center, which assists in establishing a built-up toll connection.

intermediate toll operator, *n.* Any operator, not in the originating toll center or terminating toll center, who assists in establishing a built-up connection.

intermittent, *adj.* Not continuously present; disappearing and reappearing.

intermittent fault. See "fault, intermittent."

intermodulation, *n.* The production, in a nonlinear circuit element, of frequencies corresponding to the sums and differences of frequencies which are transmitted through the circuit element.

intermodulation distortion. See "distortion, intermodulation."

internal resistance, *n.* The resistance of a voltage source, such as a generator, which acts to reduce the terminal voltage of the source as current is drawn.

international Morse code, *n.* The code used for radiotelegraphy. Consists of a sequence of dots and dashes in which the dashes are three times the length of the dots. Characters vary in length from one dot (the letter "e") to five dashes (zero).

International Telecommunications Union (ITU), *n.* An international civil organization with headquarters at Geneva, Switzerland which makes recommendations for standardization of telecommunications.

interoffice, *adj.* Between two telephone offices or switching centers.

interoffice trunk, *n.* Trunk connecting two local central offices.

interpolate, *n.* To estimate the values of a function which are intermediate between those already known. Can be estimated by making a smooth graph of known values.

interpolation, speech, *n.* On a multichannel voice transmission system, the practice of assigning a speech path to a subscriber only when his speech requires it. See also "Time Assignment, Speech Interpolation."

interpole, *n.* An auxiliary pole placed between the main poles of a rotary electrical generator or motor which has a commutator. It produces a flux which assists to reverse the current in the armature coil which is short-circuited by the brush at the instant of commutation.

interposition trunk. See "trunk, interposition."

interpret, *v.* To print on a punched card a translation of the punched information in standard letters, numbers, and symbols.

interpreter, data card, *n.* A device which will accept a punched 80-column data card and print its interpretation of the punched code along the edge of the card.

interrogator, *n.* Device which triggers a transponder. Its use is to establish the identity of a signal, particularly that emitted by an unidentified aircraft. Only the transponders of friendly aircraft would respond to the coded interrogation.

interrupted, self. See "self-interrupted."

interrupted continuous wave (ICW). See "wave, interrupted continuous."

interrupter, *n.* A set of eight contact spring assemblies which open and close periodically, under the control of cams driven from the ringing machine, or other motor. They provide the various timing pulses required in a dial central office. Five are used to provide interrupted ring cycles (1 second ring, 4 seconds off). One operates momentarily once every five seconds to provide alarm delay time. One breaks the line busy tone circuit at 60 IPM, and the last breaks the trunk busy tone circuit at 120 IPM.

interrupting capacity, *n.* The rating of a fuse or circuit breaker, being the maximum current that it can interrupt at its rated voltage.

interstate, *adj.* Between states, or crossing a state line.

interstice, *n.* In the construction of cable, an air void left between the conductors or pair groups.

intertoll dialing, *n.* Dialing over intertoll trunks.

intertoll trunk, *n.* A toll trunk, ie: a trunk between toll offices over which toll calls are passed.

interval, character, *n.* The total number of unit intervals (including synchronizing, intelligence, error checking, or control bits) required to transmit any given character over a communication system.

interval, charge-delay, *n.* An extended interval of time (2-5 seconds) maintained in the control of message charging to ensure that there will not be false charging due to transients or other short-term conditions.

interval, pulse, *n.* The time from start of one pulse until the start of the next pulse in the train.

interval, ringing, *n.* The one-second length of time during which interrupted ringing current is applied to a subscriber's line. The ringing intervals are normally separated by four-second or three-second silent intervals.

interval, silent, *n.* Any of the periods, usually about 4 seconds long, between ringing intervals during which ringing current is flowing to the called telephone.

interval, transposition, *n.* Any of the 32 equal segments of a transposition section.

interval, unit, *n.* The unit of time such that the theoretical duration of the significant intervals of a telegraph modulation are all whole multiples of the unit interval.

interzone call, *n.* A call between two of the zones into which a large metropolitan exchange area is divided.

Intrafax, *n.* A Western Union leased facsimile system.

intra-office, *adj.* Within the same telephone office or switching center.

intrastate, *adj.* Within the boundaries of a single state.

intrinsic noise. See "noise, intrinsic."

inverse feedback, *n.* Negative feedback, which see.

inverse-neutral telegraph. See "telegraph, inverse-neutral."

Inverse Square Law. See "Appendix B."

inverse voltage, *n.* The effective value of the alternating voltage that exists across a device which conducts current in only one direction during the half-cycle when current is not flowing.

inversion, *n.* (1) The changing of direct current to alternating current. (2) Changing a positive pulse to a negative pulse, and vice versa. (3) Changing the phase of an alternating current by 180 electrical degrees. (4) Temperature inversion.

inversion, temperature, *n.* An unusual atmospheric condition in which moist warm air overlays cool dry air. This can create a "duct" which carries radio waves much farther than normal. See also "duct, atmospheric."

inverter, *n.* (1) Any of several devices used to convert direct current to alternating current. They are of three types, as follows: a. Electromechanical. The vibrating pole changer previously used to convert battery power to 20 Hz ringing current. b. Electrical. Devices in which the pole changing is done by thyratron gas tube or thyristor semi-conductor circuits. These are now available in large (over 5 KVA) sizes to supply emergency 60 Hz, 3-phase power. c. Rotary. A motor-generator in which the AC and DC sections have a common magnetic circuit and field winding, and a single common armature having one winding tapped for both commutator and slip rings. Note that a "dynamotor" serves the same purpose, but has two armature windings. (2) A single input, single output device which changes the polarity of (inverts) a signal when passing it from input to output. A negative signal at the input becomes positive at the output, and vice versa.

inverter, phase. See "phase inverter."

inward toll. See "toll, inward."

INWATS, *n.* Service which allows a customer to place a direct dialed call (free of charges) to a company for the purpose of placing an order or to make a reservation.

ion, *n.* An electrically charged atom or group of atoms, resulting when a neutral atom or group of atoms gains or loses one or more electrons. See also "anion" and "cation."

ionization, *n.* The process of giving net charge to a neutral atom or molecule by adding or subtracting an electron. Can be accomplished by radiation, or by creation of a strong electric field.

ionized, *adj.* Describing an atom or molecule which has more or less electrons than normal and therefore possesses a net charge, and is capable of being attracted by other charges or being moved in the presence of a magnetic field.

ionized layer. See "D layer," "E layer," or "F layer."

ionosphere, *n.* That region of ionized atmosphere beginning about 50 miles above the earth and extending to a height of about 300 miles. See also "E layer" and "F layer."

ionospheric disturbance. See "disturbance, sudden ionospheric."

ionospheric scatter. See "scatter transmission, ionospheric."

ionospheric sounding. See "sounder, ionospheric."

ionospheric storm. See "storm ionospheric."

IR drop, *n.* The voltage drop that exists across a resistance of R ohms when a current of I amperes is flowing through it.

iris, *n.* A conducting plate which restricts the opening in a waveguide and, by varying its position, acts as a capacitive or inductive susceptance.

iron, break, *n.* A strip of flat steel with holes for two steel insulator pins. Used on a cross-arm for dead-ending a wire in each direction.

iron, pulling-in, *n.* A fitting of 7/8-inch galvanized rod, bent into an eye and set into the concrete end wall of a cable vault or manhole. Used to attach pulling-in pulley blocks when installing or removing cable.

iron, soldering, *n.* A copper-tipped tool, usually electrically heated, which enables heating of the work and melting of a solder to make a soldered joint.

irradiation, *n.* The exposure of a material to high energy emissions, such as x-rays or radium emanations, so as to favorably alter its molecular structure.

irregularity, impedance, *n.* (1) A point along an otherwise uniform transmission facility where the impedance changes abruptly. (2) The irregularity which caused that change, such as (a) a change to a cable having a different unit capacitance, (b) a missing or extra loading coil, (c) a cross with another conductor, etc.

isochronous, *adj.* (1) Equal in length of time. (2) Occurring at equal intervals of time.

isolation, *n.* (1) The condition which exists between two circuits which prevents their interacting with each other. Isolation can be achieved in several non-equivalent ways: (a) by increasing the loss between two circuits, (b) by inserting a transformer or capacitors to prevent the flow of longitudinal current, (c) by applying decoupling to joint branches of the circuits, or (d) by inserting a one-way amplifier between the circuits. (2) The degree of de-coupling between two circuits, expressed in decibels.

isolation time. See "time, isolation."

isolation transformer. See "transformer, isolation."

isolator, *n.* A passive microwave device, which permits RF transmission in only one direction, absorbing energy in the opposite direction. It therefore eliminates echoes and reflections.

isolator, ringer, *n.* A device consisting of a pair of p-n-p-n thyristors which effectively opens the circuit to ground of a party line telephone ringer, and thus prevents longitudinally induced voltages from causing metallic noise. Replaces the older gas tube relay for party line ringing.

isolator, switching, *n.* A waveguide switch consisting of two Faraday rotators (which see) controlled by electromagnets. By reversing the magnetic fields a radio wave can be passed through the waveguide or blocked.

isolator, waveguide resonance, *n.* A microwave device placed in a waveguide which enables low loss forward transmission but causes a high loss (150 times greater) in the reverse direction. Consists of a magnetically biased ferrite vane placed in a section of waveguide.

isotropic, *adj.* Having the same properties in all directions.

I^2R loss, *n.* The power which is lost in electrical conductors due to their resistance. The lost power in watts is equal to the square of the current in amperes times the resistance in ohms.

ITA #2. See "code, ITA #2."

iterative, *adj.* Recurring an infinite number of times. Said of a network with an infinite number of identical sections, or of the impedance looking into such a network.

iterative impedance, *n.* The impedance which will terminate the output of a network in such a way that the impedance then measured at the input of the network will be equal to the (iterative) terminating impedance.

IT product, *n.* A measure of the influence of an electric power supply circuit expressed in terms of the product of its rms current in amperes (I) times its Telephone Influence Factor (TIF).

jack, *n.* A connecting device having springs which make electrical contact with mating contacts of a plug.

jack, answering, *n.* A line jack. See also "answering jack."

jack, cable bending. See "bender, cable."

jack, flashing. See "flashing jack."

jack, holding. See "holding jack."

jack, line, *n.* A jack on a switchboard on which a subscriber's line terminates.

jack, out-of-service, *n.* A jack which is connected to remove the associated circuit from service when a shorted plug is inserted.

jack, patching, *n.* A jack on a patch panel used to make temporary circuit rearrangements by by-passing or replacing faulty circuit components.

jack, pin, *n.* A single-contact connecting device into which a pin plug can be inserted to make temporary circuit connections. The pin contact is $1/8''$ diameter.

jack, pipe-pushing, *n.* A flat steel bed holding a racket-operated traveling carriage fitted with quick-release pipe jaws. Can be set up in a roadside excavation and used to push a pipe conduit under the road.

jack, pole, *n.* A mechanical lifting device, similar to but larger than an auto jack, used to pull pole butts from the hole. Facilitates pole removals by avoiding digging.

jack, preferential. See "preferential jack."

jack, telegraph splitting, *n.* A set of telegraph looping jacks, with one end of the loop appearing in a single jack (for a Type 347 plug) and the other end in a dual jack (for a Type 241 plug).

jack, test, *n.* (1) Any jack on which a circuit or circuit component appears, to facilitate access for testing. (2) Any of the jacks on a "Test and Control Switchboard," identical in appearance to the operator's switchboard, where circuits can be operation-tested and busied.

jack box. See "box, jack."

jack circuit, full duplex, *n.* A four-jack circuit for the WECo #2 telegraph test board, consisting of "STATION," "LINE," "COUPLER," and "HUB" jacks.

jack-ended, *adj.* Said of a circuit or trunk which terminates at a switchboard on a jack with associated line and busy lamps. It therefore requires the use of a cord circuit to connect it to another circuit. See also "key-ended" and "plug-ended."

jacket, *n.* An outer covering on an insulated wire or group of wires. The jacket on a cable is usually called a "sheath."

jack field. See "field, jack."

jacks, cable, *n. pl.* Heavy duty jacks, similar to auto jacks, which permit lifting full reels of cable by a pipe through their center, and allow them to rotate for the feeding of cable.

jacks, primary, *n. pl.* A set of four jacks in the primary section of a toll testboard. One pair of jacks looks toward the toll line (LINE), the other pair toward the office equipment (EQUIP).

jacks, secondary, *n. pl.* A set of eight jacks found in the secondary section of older toll testboards, labeled LIST (listening across the drop), LPX (line of phantom coil), DPX (drop of phantom coil), and DROP.

jacks, telegraph turnover, *n.* A pair of looping jacks with the tip of one connected to the ring of the other, and vice versa. Used to reverse a telegraph line.

jacks, test, *n. pl.* Jacks on a testboard, used to give access to a circuit for testing.

jacks, tone. See "tone jacks."

jamming, *n.* The deliberate radiation, reradiation, or reflection of electromagnetic energy with the object of impairing the use of electronic devices, equipment, or systems.

jar, *n.* Of a storage cell, the glass or

plastic container which holds the electrolyte surrounding the active plates.

jitter, *n.* Short-term instability of the amplitude or phase of a signal, or both.

jitter, pulse, *n.* A short-term variation of the pulse spacing of an otherwise regular pulse train.

job, *n.* A specific function assigned to a marker.

job, marker, *n.* A single marker usage, from seizure to release, involved in completing just one of its designated functions. These include the:

    (a) Dial tone job.
    (b) Intraoffice trunk job.
    (c) Outgoing trunk job.
    (d) Incoming trunk job.
    (e) Reverting trunk job.
    (f) Tandem trunk job.

joint, *n.* (1) A connection of two or more conductors. (2) The soldered connection of a conductor to a terminal. (3) The union of two lead cable sheaths by wiping.

joint, high resistance, *n.* A connection between conductors or conductor and terminal which is faulty, resulting in (a) a reduction in current flow, (b) a drop in voltage at the connection, (c) heat at the connection, and (d) possibly circuit noise.

joint, insulating, *n.* A gas-tight union of two cable sheaths made in such a manner that current cannot flow from one cable sheath to the other.

joint, pressure, *n.* A good electrical connection between two conductors made by means of a tightly crimped bronze sleeve.

joint, rolled, *n.* An end-to-end union of two wires by means of a bronze sleeve which is compressed around the wires by a pair of concave rollers.

joint, rosin, *n.* An electrical connection which appears to be securely soldered, but which is held in contact only by the rosin which was used as a flux in soldering. Caused by insufficient heating of the parts to be soldered.

joint, rotating, *n.* A joint in a section of circular waveguide which permits rotation without interfering with the transmission of radio-frequency energy.

joint, soldered, *n.* A good electrical connection which is held in place and protected against corrosion by covering with a frozen low melting point alloy. See also "solder."

joint, twisted, *n.* Union of two conductors which are overlapped, then twisted tightly about each other. See also "joint, Western-Union."

joint, Western Union, *n.* The most popular of twisted wire joints, made as follows: (a) overlap the wires at right angles, (b) make one long twist, (c) make five tight turns of each end around the other wire.

joint, wiped, *n.* A gas-tight union between the cable sheaths of two or more lead-sheathed cables made by placing a lead sleeve over the splice, beating down the ends of the sleeve, and closing the joint by wiping with molten solder.

joint use, *n.* Two or more utility companies (telephone, power, street light, CATV) using the same poles by mutual agreement.

joint use, higher voltage, *n.* Joint use with power circuits of 5,000 volts or over (Bell System); with circuits of 8,700 volts or over (National Electrical Safety Code).

joule, *n.* An international unit of work or energy. The work required to maintain a current of one ampere through one ohm for one second. A watt-second.

Joule's law, *n.* The rate at which heat is produced in an electric circuit is proportional to the product of the resistance by the square of the current.

juice, *n.* Electric current (slang).—*vt.* To feed electric current to a circuit (slang).

jumper, *n.* A cross-connection, on a distributing frame or in a cross-connecting terminal.—*vt.* To make a cross-connection.

junction, *n.* (1) The point where two pole lines meet. (2) The plane of transition between two different regions of a semi-conductor device. (3) A fitting used to join two sections of waveguide.

junction, hybrid. See "hybrid junction."

junction, N3-L, *n.* Interface equipment which permits the interconnection of N3 carrier and L carrier on a 24-channel group basis, rather than on a voice frequency channel basis. There are three types of junctions as follows: (a) Type A junction is used at the interface of the N high-frequency line and the broadband L facility, (b) the Type B junction serves as a terminal for the L portion, and (c) the Type C junction sends only one group of 12 channels of the N system over the L carrier system. The other 12 channels are converted to voice frequency.

junction, thermoelectric. See "thermoelectric junction."

junction box, *n.* A sheet steel box, normally 3¼ or 4 inches square, with a cover, into which low-voltage (117V) power cables are led and where splices and taps are made.

junction diode, *n.* A semiconductor diode in which the rectifying action takes place at a junction between n-type and p-type material.

junction loss. See "loss, junction."

junction pole. See "pole, junction."

junction transistor. See "transistor, junction."

junctor, *n.* An intra-office trunk in a crossbar office. A trunk between switch frames, terminating on a crossbar switch in each frame. The junctor takes the name of the frame to which it leads.

junctor, insertion, *n.* A junctor which includes the equipment required to render a particular special service. When a special service is required, the call is looped through a suitable insertion junctor.

junctor, originating, *n.* In an elec-tronic central office, a circuit which provides a temporary path from the "line group" matrix to a register-sender, then, under direction of the register-sender, advances the call through an inlet circuit to the "group selector" matrix.

junctor, register, *n.* In an electronic central office, the circuit which connects to the calling line and performs register functions, such as: pulse repeating, party identification, dial tone control, coin detection, and coin refund.

junctor, terminating, *n.* In an electronic central office, the circuit which advances the call from the "group selector" to the "line group," and performs functions such as ringing, ring trip, and battery feed.

junctor group, *n.* The 16 junctors, contained in one patch cord, which interconnect a pair of link networks in an ESS office.

junctor grouping frame. See "frame, junctor grouping."

junior-multiple, *adj.* Type of cabinet used for a multiple switchboard intended for not over 1200 lines on a 3-panel multiple basis. Consists of one or more 1-position, 2-panel sections.

jute, *n.* A strong glossy fiber much used for making burlap and rope. It is often saturated with tar and wound as a protective layer over lead cable sheaths intended for direct burial in the earth.

Kelvin temperature (K degrees), *n.* A scale of temperatures which uses Centigrade degrees, but dropped so that absolute zero is 0 degrees Kelvin. Water freezes at 273 degrees K and boils at 373 degrees K.

Kennelly-Heaviside layer, *n.* The E layer of the ionosphere.

Kepler's Laws of Satellite Motion. See "Appendix B."

kettle, melting, *n.* A double-boiler type kettle, used for melting insulating compound.

key, *n.* (1) A type of multiple-contact switch intended for use on switchboards. Only the operating handle, a lever or turn-button, protrudes through the key shelf or escutcheon. (2) A key signal. (3) A hand-operated switch for sending code signals on a telegraph system.—*v.* To cause a transmitter signal to change in amplitude or frequency.

key, busy. See "busy key."

key, cam. See "key, turn button."

key, collect, *n.* The key which an operator depresses to collect the deposit in a prepay coin telephone.

key, cryptographic, *n.* A pseudo-random key signal generated by a shift-register which produces a binary signal having a logical pattern which may not repeat for 1000 hours, and therefore approximates a random signal. This key signal is combined with a digital intelligence signal, making it unintelligible until decoded by subtracting the key signal.

key, function, *n.* One of the keys on the keyboard of a teletypewriter which cause an operation but not the printing of a character, such as "letters," "figures," "carriage return" and "line feed."

key, lever, *n.* Telephone-type multipole electrical switch, hand-operated by a lever projecting above the keyshelf which is moved backward or forward. May be two-position or three-position, and locking or non-locking. Used on switchboard keyshelves.

key, listening. See "key, talk."

key, monitoring, *n.* One of the keys of a cord circuit (or of a position circuit) which, when operated, makes it possible for an operator to listen in on a circuit without being detected and without impairing the through transmission.

key, pole, *n.* An expanding steel plate or creosoted wooden plank buried against a pole butt to increase its effective area, enabling it to better resist an unbalanced force.

key, position transfer, *n.* A key which bridges a switchboard position onto the adjacent position, so that one operator can use cords on both positions.

key, push-button, *n.* A telephone-type hand-operated multipole electrical switch which is actuated by an axial push-button. The button may be locking or non-locking.

key, refund, *n.* The key with which an operator returns the deposit in a prepay coin telephone.

key, register. See "register key."

key, ringing, *n.* A key on a switchboard used by the operator to connect signaling (or ringing) current to a line.

key, splitting, *n.* Key used by a switchboard operator to connect her telephone set to either the front or the back cord. At the same time it "splits" the connection, ie: disconnects the front cord from the back cord. Operates only in conjunction with the "talk key."

key, talk, *n.* One of the keys associated with every switchboard cord circuit, used by the operator to connect her telephone set to that cord circuit.

key, talk-ringing, *n.* A key in a switchboard cord circuit which has two positions, a locking position away from the operator which connects the operator's telephone circuit to the cord, and a non-locking position toward the operator which rings on the cord.

key, telegraph, *n.* A single-pole, single-throw switch made so that it can be operated rapidly by hand so as to form the dots and dashes of telegraph code signals.

key, transfer, *n.* (1) A key which transfers circuit A from circuit B to standby circuit C. (2) A key which connects together two adjacent switchboard positions, enabling an operator to use also the cords on the adjacent vacant position.

key, turn button, *n.* Telephone-type electrical switch, hand-operated by turning an axially-mounted button, the bottom of which is cut into a cam which operates the contact springs.

key, two-forward-motion, *n.* A lever-type key having one normal and two operated positions, both of which are on one side of the normal position, at 30 degrees and 60 degrees from the normal.

keyboard, *n.* The set of keys on a teletypewriter or key punch at which an operator can translate alphanumeric characters into Baudot code or Hollerith code.

key change, *n.* The changing of the encryption key to a different cipher key.

key-ended, *adj.* Said of a trunk, such as those to a repair desk, which terminates on a lever key with associated line and busy lamps. The key is operated to connect the attendant or operator to that trunk.

keyer, *n.* A device which causes a radio transmitter to change the amplitude or frequency of its signal in response to keying signals.

keying, *n.* (1) The act of transmitting telephone address information by using a keyset. (2) The forming a signal by an abrupt change of the output of a direct current or alternating current source, by interrupting it or by suddenly changing its amplitude or frequency.

keying, frequency-shift, *n.* Transmission of coded intelligence by varying the carrier frequency by a small amount—using one frequency for a "mark" signal and another for a "space" signal. The resulting signal is characterized by continuity of phase during the frequency transitions.

keying, phase-shift, *n.* The encoding of digital information as different phases of signal elements having constant amplitude and frequency.

keying, two-tone. See "keying, frequency-shift."

keying line. See "line, keying."

key-pulse, *vt.* To send address, precedence, or route information using a keyset.

key-pulsing, *n.* The sending of address, precedence, and routing information using a keyset instead of a rotary dial.

key pulsing keys (KP), *n.* One or a pair of keys at the right of the keyshelf which associate the keyset with either cord of a pair while cut in, leaving the operator's telephone set connected to the other cord of the pair. If only one KP key is provided, it is associated with both cords and does not split the connection.

key pulsing signal, *n.* A green lamp signal associated with the key pulsing key. This lamp lights as soon as the KP key is operated and goes out when the keyset is released.

key pulsing start key (ST), *n.* A nonlocking key by which the pulsing is started as soon as the correct number has been set up with the keyset.

keypunch, *n.* A machine controlled by a typewriter-like keyboard which enables an operator to punch data in Hollerith code into data cards.

keysender, *n.* Device which stores the digits which are keyed from a pushbutton keyset and automatically DC-pulses the succeeding switch train. (Accomplishes DTMF to DC dial pulse conversion) Usually operates under the control of an operator's keyset.

keyset, *n.* A set of 10, 12, or 16 pushbutton keys which may be punched

in sequence for sending address, precedence, or routing signals. The buttons are designated 1, 2, 3, 4, 5, 6, 7, 8, 9, 0, *, A, FO, F, I, and P.

key shelf, *n.* The front hinged part of the lower horizontal member of a switchboard. Mounts the keys (lever switches), a dial, and the supervisory lamps for the cord circuits.

key signal, *n.* A pseudo-random sequence of two-level pulses used to accomplish enciphering or deciphering processes.

keys, interlocked, *n. pl.* Mechanically locking keys, commonly in sets of six, arranged so that operation of any locking button releases any other button which is already locked.

key telephone. See "set, key telephone."

key telephone equipment. See "equipment, key telephone."

key telephone set, *n.* Telephone set having six button keys and used with relay equipment to provide call holding, multi-line pickup, signaling, intercommunication, and conference services.

killer, noise, *n.* A filter or wave-shaping network connected into a communication circuit, particularly a DC telegraph circuit, to reduce its interference to other communication circuits.

killer, spark, *n.* A network, usually a capacitor and resistor in series, connected across a pair of contacts to absorb and reduce sparking.

kilo-, *adj.* A prefix meaning "one thousand."

kilobaud, *n.* One thousand bauds.

kilobit, *n.* One thousand bits.

kilocycle, *n.* (1) One thousand cycles. (2) One thousand cycles per second, now properly termed "kilohertz."

kilohertz (kHz), *n.* (1) One thousand hertz. (2) One thousand cycles per second.

kilohm, *n.* One thousand ohms.

kilomega-, *adj.* A prefix indicating

"one thousand million." Now superseded by "giga-".

kilovar, *n.* One thousand volt-amperes, reactive.

kilovolt, *n.* One thousand volts.

kilovolt-ampere, *n.* One thousand volt-amperes.

kilowatt, *n.* One thousand watts.

kilowatt-hour, *n.* One thousand watt-hours, which see.

Kinescope, *n.* A cathode ray tube of the type used in television receivers.

Kirchoff's Laws. See "Appendix B."

kit, anti-stuffing coin return, *n.* A kit of parts required to convert a coin telephone to provide an anti-stuffing feature. After conversion, when the coin return is opened to remove refunded coins, access to the coin chute is blocked.

kit, digit-absorbing conversion, *n.* A kit of parts required to convert a regular selector to a digit-absorbing selector.

kit, dual access conversion, *n.* A kit of parts to convert a 200-line three-digit connector to a two-digit connector accessed from two selector levels.

kit, first aid, *n.* Weatherproof metal boxes carried in all telephone company vehicles, containing as a minimum

Bandages and compresses
Triangular bandage
Tourniquet and forceps
Merthiolate swabs
Ammonia inhalants
Tannic acid jelly for burns.

kit, 5-cent to 10-cent conversion, *n.* A kit to convert a coin telephone for 10-cent local service. After conversion it will accept either two nickels or one dime for a local call.

kit, slug-proof coin, *n.* A kit containing a modified 25-cent coin channel and a permanent magnet. If a magnetic slug is dropped in the 25 cent slot, the magnet pulls the slug away from the gong.

kit, touch calling, *n.* A kit for the conversion of rotary dial coin telephones to DTMF dialing.

klystron, *n.* A velocity-modulated electron tube in which the electron beam is fed into a tuneable cavity resonator. Used as an ultra-high frequency amplifier or oscillator.

klystron, reflex, *n.* A klystron having a single resonant cavity in which the electrons traverse the cavity, then are reflected in phase back through the cavity by a negative repeller electrode, thus extracting the maximum energy from the electron beam. An efficient microwave oscillator, adaptable to automatic frequency control.

knee, *n.* The region of maximum curvature.

knife, cable sheath splitting, *n.* A heavy knife, looking somewhat like a small meat cleaver, used to split and remove cable sheath. The blade is thick, allowing the use of a hammer to drive it.

knife, lineman's, *n.* A heavy-duty jack-knife, having a single hooked blade. Used for skinning the insulation from heavy electrical conductors.

knife, skinning, *n.* A lineman's knife having a fixed blade which cannot be closed into the handle.

knob, *n.* (1) A cylindrical porcelain insulator, grooved on the outside for attachment of a wire, and with a hole through the center for a mounting screw. (2) A two-piece knob. (3) A knob-shaped handle on a control shaft.

knob, porcelain, *n.* A cylindrical porcelain insulator having an axial mounting hole and one, two, or four circumferential grooves in which drop wires can be tied. Mounts on a clevis, or with a wood screw.

knob, two-piece porcelain, *n.* A Type C knob. A pair of rectangular porcelain blocks held together and to their mounting surface by a screw through both blocks. The blocks have matching grooves to hold a pair of wires in surface wiring.

knocked-down, *adj.* Not assembled.

knockout, *n.* A metal disc punched in the side of a metal terminal, junction box, or outlet box which can be punched out to allow entry of cable or conduit.

koken, *n.* A ring circuit containing an odd number of bistable flip-flops.

Korduct, *n. adj.* One brand of thin wall asbestos-cement conduit used where the conduit is to be encased in concrete. See "conduit, thin wall asbestos-cement." Now known as Transite "B" conduit.

KvT product, *n.* A measure of the influence of an electric power circuit expressed as the product of its rms voltage in kilovolts (kv) times its Telephone Influence Factor (TIF).

lace, *v.* To draw together and fasten by means of a cord or ribbon which goes around the whole.

lacing cord, nylon, *n.* A cord consisting of a flattened band of nylon filaments, impregnated with wax. Used to lace cable conductors. Because nylon is elastic, it produces a tighter stitch than a linen cord. Made in 5,000 denier weight.

lacing twine, *n.* A 6-ply or 8-ply waxed linen cord used to lace cable conductors. See also "cord, nylon lacing."

lacquer, *n.* A liquid resin applied to fibrous insulation to prevent fraying, moisture absorption, or wicking.

ladder, A, *n.* A ladder shaped like the letter A, hinged at the apex of the A and rolling on wheels at the bottom of the ladder rails. Used between the equipment bays in central offices.

ladder, manhole, *n.* A light-weight galvanized steel ladder intended to be left in underground manholes to provide access for cable splicers and electrolysis testers. Has ⅝-inch rod rungs. Available in 6½, 8, 10, 12, 14, 16, and 18-foot lengths.

ladder, rolling, *n.* A ladder giving access to high bays of equipment in a central office, suspended from a track under the top of bay channel braces and rolling on the floor.

laddic, *n.* A magnetic core logic structure which physically resembles a ladder. It has windings both on the rungs and on the side rails.

ladle, pouring, *n.* A heavy steel ladle with an air-cooled wooden handle. About 3½-inch diameter, with a capacity of ¼ pint. Used by a cable splicer to pour molten solder while wiping a lead sheath joint.

lag, *n.* The difference in phase, expressed in electrical degrees, between a current and the voltage which produced it.—*v.* To follow behind, as a current wave follows a voltage wage in an inductive circuit.

lag, cable reel, *n.* Any of the several wooden strips, about 2 x 4 inches in cross-section, which are used to cover the cable reel and protect the cable during shipment.

lagging current, *n.* Current in a circuit containing only inductive reactance. In such a circuit the current lags 90 electrical degrees behind the voltage which produces it.

lag-stud. See "screw, cable suspension."

laminate, *n.* A thin strong sheet material made by bonding together several layers of the same or different materials. Plywood is an example. —*v.* (1) To construct a laminated material. (2) To interleave laminations.

lamination, *n.* Any of the multiple stamped pieces of sheet iron which are interleaved to make a magnetic core. They are individually insulated with varnish to reduce eddy current losses.

lamp, answer, *n.* The supervisory lamp associated with the answering cord of a cord circuit.

lamp, ballast, *n.* A lamp placed in series with the power supply to an item of equipment which is sensitive to power supply changes. The ballast lamp maintains almost a constant current by increasing in resistance as the current increases.

lamp, busy, *n.* A lamp in the face equipment of a switchboard which indicates that the associated line or trunk is busy.

lamp, charge. See "charge lamp."

lamp, dial pilot, *n.* A lamp on the pilot rail of a switchboard which remains lighted during the time the operator is dialing. If a "stop dial" condition is encountered the lamp will be extinguished.

lamp, electric, *n.* A device for producing light from electricity, either by the heating of a wire filament in a vacuum or by a current discharge through a gas, as in a fluorescent lamp.

lamp, fuse alarm, *n.* A red lamp on a fuse panel, and at the end of a bay containing a fuse panel, which lights to indicate that a fuse on that panel has blown.

lamp, glow. See "glow lamp."

lamp, group busy, *n.* A lamp used on a switchboard to indicate that the entire group of trunks with which it is associated, is busy.

lamp, hold, *n.* A lamp which remains lighted to indicate that a telephone connection is being held.

lamp, line, *n.* A lamp used on a switchboard to indicate an incoming call on the line with which it is associated.

lamp, message-waiting, *n.* A small lamp on a telephone set which can be lighted or flashed from the switchboard (or call waiting panel) to notify a hotel/motel guest that a message is being held for him.

lamp, neon, *n.* A small 117 volt lamp having two metal electrodes in an envelope filled with neon gas. Produces a red glow due to ionization of the neon gas. Useful in (a) an indicator lamp, (b) a relaxation oscillator circuit, or (c) in a voltage regulator circuit.

lamp, pilot, *n.* A centrally located lamp with a large lamp cap which lights to call attention to another smaller lamp signal on the same switchboard panel, position, or on a relay rack.

lamp, precedence busy, *n.* A lamp associated with a switchboard line jack which indicates that line is busy with a precedence call.

lamp, resistance, *n.* A tungsten filament incandescent lamp used as a current-limiting device. Placed in series with a low-current load, any great increase in load lights the lamp, greatly increasing its resistance and thereby limiting the current.

lamp, slide-base, *n.* A switchboard lamp having a slide (push in, pull out) base. See "lamp, switchboard."

lamp, supervisory, *n.* A switchboard lamp associated with each cord of a pair, which indicates that the cord is no longer in use, ie: that the line or trunk to which it was connected has "hung up" or disconnected.

lamp, switchboard, *n.* Small (5/16″ diameter x 1-11/16″ long) incandescent lamp with slide base (push in, pull out) used for switchboard lamp signals. Provides approximately 200 end foot-candles. Available in ratings of 4, 6, 8, 10, 16, 18, 24, 30, 36, and 48 volts.

lampholder, *n.* A device which supports an electric lamp and connects it to an electric supply circuit.

lamps, call-waiting, *n. pl.* A set of lamps in a wall-mounted display panel in an operating room which informs supervisors and chief operators how many incoming calls of each class are being held awaiting assignment to an idle operators position. Part of an automatic call distribution system.

lamps, cord, *n. pl.* Cord supervisory lamps.

landline, *n.* A circuit between two ground locations which is in wire or cable.

language, machine, *n.* The symbols and rules used to express information to be handled by computers or data processing equipment.

language, plain, *n.* (1) Text or language which conveys an intelligible meaning in the language in which it is written, with no hidden meaning. (2) Not encrypted.

language digit. See "digit, language."

language media format, *n.* A two-character sequence in a data-formatted message header. The first character indicates the method used by the originator in preparing the message, the second character indicates the preferred form of delivery.

larynx, artificial, *n.* A development by the Bell Telephone Laboratories which enables persons who have had their vocal cords removed to speak and use the telephone. It consists of a buzz-hiss oscillator whose sound output is fed through a tube into the mouth, where the lips and teeth modulate it into speech.

laser, *n.* Acronym for "Light Amplification by Stimulated Emission of Radiation." A laser is a maser which operates at optical frequencies. A device which produces an intense beam of visible or infrared coherent light by pumping atoms to ever higher energy levels and allowing them to oscillate in an optical resonator until the energy level is high enough that a constant stream of photons is emitted.

lash, *vt.* (1) To fasten together with a lashing. (2) To fasten an aerial cable to its supporting strand with a spiral wire lashing.

lashed cable, *n.* Aerial cable which is fastened to its supporting strand with a long pitch (17 inches) spiral of lashing wire.

lasher, cable, *n.* A machine which is towed along an aerial cable suspension strand and lashes the cable to the strand by spirally wrapping a 0.045 inch steel wire around both. The pitch of the wrapping is about 17 inches.

lashing, *n.* (1) A fastening with a cord which is wound around the objects to be fastened together. (2) A spirally wrapped wire around an aerial cable and its supporting messenger.

lashing tape. See "tape, lashing."

last trunk busy (LTB), *n.* The condition where the last choice trunk of a group or sub-group is busy.

latch, hookswitch, *n.* A catch on the hookswitch of party-line telephones which allows the hookswitch to operate far enough to permit monitoring but not far enough so that dialing or conversation would be interrupted if the line were busy.

lateral, *adj.* Toward the side.—*n.* (1) A lateral cable. (2) A lateral conduit. Specify which is meant.

lateral conduit. See "conduit, lateral."

lateral routing, *n.* In a polygrid toll switching network, any acceptable routing not classed as forward routing. Lateral routing may permit a limited "back-haul."

lattice network. See "network, lattice."

lattice-wound, *adj.* Describing a coil which is wound in a criss-cross manner to reduce its distributed capacitance. Also called "honeycomb-wound."

launch, *v.* (1) To transfer energy from a coaxial cable to a surface-wave guide or waveguide. (2) To lift a communication satellite into orbit.

launch, satellite establishment, *n.* Placement of satellites into orbit for the establishment of a system.

launch, satellite replenishment, *n.* Launches after the first to replace those satellites which are no longer operable.

launcher, *n.* A launching horn for a G-line wave guide.

Law Enforcement Teletypewriter Service (LETS), *n.* Service providing state-wide private line teletypewriter service for the dissemination of criminal alarms and police messages.

LAWS. See Appendix B for a statement of the following laws:
Coulomb's
Conservation of Energy
Electric Charges
Electromagnetic Systems
Electrostatic Attraction
Faraday's
Hartley's
Induced Current
Inverse Square
Joule's
Kepler's
Kirchoff's
Lenz'
Magnetic Poles
Networks
Newton's
Ohm's
Stefan-Boltzmann
Volta's

lay, *n.* (1) The fashion in which wires are twisted together to form a cable. (2) The axial distance along the cable that a conductor advances in one spiral turn around the cable core.

lay, direction of, *n.* The direction, either right-hand (clockwise) or left-hand (counterclockwise), in which a conductor or group of conductors spiral around a cable core as they travel away from the observer.

layer, cable, *n.* Self-powered machine to install buried cable. Usually a track-type tractor equipped with a carrier for a reel of cable, a cutting wheel to cut a narrow slot in the earth and a plow share to follow and lay the cable in the slot.

layer of the ionosphere. See "D layer," "E layer," and "F layers."

layout, *n.* An assignment of facilities and equipment, with related information, for any type of communications. (2) A preliminary drawing showing a proposed arrangement.

layout, current facility, *n.* A record of all of the toll transmission facilities in use or available for circuit assignment, such as L units, R units, MUR's, groups and supergroups.

layout, patched, *n.* A temporary circuit configuration set up by the use of patch cords.

LC ratio, *n.* The ratio of inductance to capacitance, equal to the inductance in henrys divided by the capacitance in farads.

LD terminal, *n.* Long distance terminal, which see.

lead (rhymes with "need"), *n.* (1) A pole line. (2) A wire used as a terminal for an electrical component. (3) In an alternating current circuit, the amount by which the voltage (or current) leads the current (or voltage), expressed in electrical degrees.—*v.* To precede, as a voltage wave precedes the current wave it creates in an inductive circuit.

lead (pronounced "led"), *n.* A heavy, soft, malleable, bluish-gray metal used for cable splicing sleeves, and as an ingredient in solder.

lead, pull, *n.* Wire which connects to

a relay or operate winding which sets up a connection. See also "pull."

lead, test, *n.* A short flexible, insulated wire with a test clip or test prod on one end, used to make temporary connections between test instruments and the circuit to be tested.

lead-acid battery. See "cell, lead-acid storage."

lead-calcium battery. See "cell, lead-calcium storage."

lead covered cable. See "cable, lead covered."

lead-in, *n.* A single wire which connects an elevated antenna to a radio receiver or transmitter.

leading edge, *n.* The first part of a pulse or electromagnetic wave, during which the current or voltage rises rapidly from zero to a relatively steady-state value.

leads, E&M, *n. pl.* A pair of leads which carry signals between a trunk equipment and a separate signaling equipment unit. The M lead transmits battery or ground signals to the signaling equipment, and the E lead receives open or ground signals from the signaling equipment. The E&M leads are limited to 25 ohms, and if greater length is required a signal lead extension circuit must be used.

lead zirconate titanate, *n.* A ferroelectric ceramic consisting of a solid solution of lead zirconate and lead titanate. A desireable piezoelectric material, having a high Curie point, and strong piezoelectric properties.

leak, *n.* A condition of low insulation which permits a current to leak (drain off) from its conductor.

leakage, *n.* (1) Current which drains from a conductor through shunt resistance. (2) The shunt resistance (conductance) through which a leakage current drains. (3) Magnetic flux which by-passes a path on which it can do useful work.

leakage, magnetic, *n.* Magnetic flux

which by-passes a path on which it could do useful work.

leakage, surface. See "surface leakage."

leakage flux. See "flux, leakage."

leakage reactance. See "reactance, leakage."

leakage resistance, *n.* The resistance of a path over which a leakage current flows. Normally of a high value, measured in megohms.

leak detector. See "detector, ultrasonic leak."

least-replaceable-unit, *n.* An electronic or electromechanical component, part, or sub-assembly which is removed and replaced by a repairman when it fails.

Lecher wires, *n.* A section of radio-frequency transmission line consisting of a pair of parallel wires on which standing waves are set up, usually for the measurement of wavelength.

Leclanche cell, *n.* A dry cell.

left, *adj.* Describing equipment which is on the left side of a switchboard, shelf, frame, or rack when viewed from the front.

Left-Hand Rule. See "Appendix B."

left-in, *adj.* Describing telephone equipment which is disconnected but left in place after a subscriber moves out.

leg, balanced telegraph, *n.* A telegraph leg which is connected to positive battery at the telegraph, or teletypewriter end. At the central office repeater, a mark signal connects negative battery to the leg for maximum current flow, while a space signal connects positive battery for rapid collapse of the current in the leg.

leg, butt, *n.* The leg nearest the butt or main body of a cable form which has two or more legs or branches.

leg, cable, *n.* A branch cable from a main cable.

leg, composite, *n.* The terminal on a telegraph composite set which is connected to the telegraph set, or to other DC signaling equipment.

leg, dial, *n.* The terminal on a circuit which is brought out for connection to a dial, or to other DC signaling equipment.

leg, telegraph, *n.* (1) The tip of a telegraph loop to subscriber's telegraph equipment. The ring side of that loop is connected to positive ($+$) telegraph battery. (2) Either of the two single-wire legs (receive leg or send leg) from a "loop repeater" or "coupling unit" installed on a telegraph loop.

leg, terminal, *n.* The stub cable of a cable terminal. (Slang)

leg, tip, *n.* The leg farthest from the butt or main body of a cable form having two or more legs.

legs relay circuit, telegraph, *n.* The circuit in a telegraph service position which terminates each line leg or loop leg. The legs jacks permit the facilities to be patched out for testing or substitution.

length, electrical, *n.* (1) The length of an electrical circuit, expressed in wavelengths or electrical degrees of phase shift. (2) The effective length of a loaded cable circuit which has been built out with capacitances to simulate a circuit which is longer than its geographical length.

lens, microwave, *n.* A lens, usually of a dielectric material such as polystyrene, used to collect and focus divergent microwave radiation into a parallel beam by refraction, in the same way that an optical lens focuses a light beam.

lens antenna, *n.* An arrangement of dielectric or metal elements arranged in a lattice of varying thickness, and placed in front of a microwave antenna to concentrate the beam.

Lenz' Law of Induced Current. See "Appendix B."

level, *adj.* Designates the number of bits per character in a code, such as (a) an eight-level ASCII code, or a twelve-level Hollerith code.— *n.* (1) The difference between a quantity, such as voltage, power, or sound volume, and a specified reference quantity. This difference is usually specified in decibels. (2) An expression of the relative signal strength at a point in a communication circuit, compared to a standard level such as "zero dbm" or to the level at a reference point on the same circuit such as the "zero transmission level point."

level, crosstalk, *n.* The effective power of crosstalk, expressed in decibels below one milliwatt.

level, group selector, *n.* In an electronic central office, any of the several "group selector" outlets which lead to the same destination.

level, high, *adj.* Said of digital transmission equipment using line currents of 20 or 60 milliamperes at potentials of 60 volts (polar) or 130 volts (neutral).

level, low, *adj.* Said of digital transmission equipment using line currents of 100 microamperes at potentials of 6 volts, polar.

level, noise, *n.* A volume of noise energy, specified as so many decibels above a reference level. See also "dba," "dbrn," "dbrnc."

level, peak, *n.* The maximum instantaneous level of electrical power or sound, usually as indicated on a meter of carefully specified dynamic characteristics, such as a "VU meter."

level, precedence, *n.* A relative degree of importance assigned to a message which determines its priority for transmission. These designations in descending order of priority are Flash Override, Flash, Immediate, Priority, Routine, and Deferred.

level, slicing, *n.* Of a signal representing a binary digit, the signal level below which the bit is judged to be a space, and above which it is judged to be a mark.

level, sound, *n.* The pressure level in the atmosphere due to a sound wave, given in decibels above a 1000 hertz sound that can just be heard by a young person. It must be measured in a manner specified by the American Standards Association.

level, speech, *n.* The energy of speech measured in "volume units" on a meter called a "volume indicator" which has certain specified dynamic characteristics.

level, speech interference (SIL), *n.* The speech interference level of a noise is the average, in decibels, of the sound pressure levels of the noise in three octave bands, the centers of which are at 500, 1000, and 2000 hertz.

level, speech power, *n.* The level of acoustic power in human speech. The range of a loud talker is from —30 dBm to +10 dBm; of a soft talker from —60 dBm to —20 dBm. Speech power therefore ranges from —60 dBm to +10 dBm.

level, testing, *n.* The normal transmission test level, being one milliwatt of 1000 Hz power.

level, transmission, *n.* The ratio of the power of a test signal at a particular point to the test signal power applied at some other point in the system chosen as a reference point. The level is NOT a measure of absolute power.

level, volume, *n.* The energy level of speech or music as measured in "volume units" on a "volume indicator," a meter having closely specified dynamic characteristics.

level, zero, *n.* (1) The transmission power at a reference point in a circuit, to which all other power measurements in the circuit are compared. (2) Zero decibels above one milliwatt, or one milliwatt of power.

level coordination. See "coordination, level."

lever, armature, *n.* The metal arm connected to a relay armature which transmits armature movement to the relay springs.

L group, *n.* A one-way 48 kHz bandwidth transmission path between two points, established over coaxial cable facilities, and having terminal frequencies of 60-108 kHz.

life, flex, *n.* A measure of the ability of a cable, wire, or spring to withstand repeated bending.

life, service, *n.* (1) Of a storage battery, the number of years before the battery ampere-hour capacity will drop an unacceptable amount. (2) Of a dry cell, the period of useful service before its working voltage drops to an unacceptable level. (3) The life expectancy under normal conditions of use.

life, shelf, *n.* The life, when not in service, of electrical components which deteriorate with time, such as batteries and electrolytic capacitors.

life cycle, *n.* A test performed on a material or device to determine the length of time before failure. Conducted in a controlled, sometimes accelerated, environment.

light, *n.* An electromagnetic wave motion propagated at a speed of 186,284 miles per second, having wavelengths from 4000 angstroms (extreme violet) to 7000 angstroms (extreme red), and evidenced by its visual effects. The term light is also applied to the non-visible radiations in the ultra-violet (20-4000 angstroms) and infra-red (7000-3,000,000 angstroms) regions which overlap the X-ray and sub-millimeter radio regions respectively.

light, coherent, *n.* Light in which all waves are of exactly the same frequency and exactly in phase. It can therefore be modulated for the transmission of information.

light, fuse alarm pilot, *n.* A light, usually red, on the face of a switchboard which lights to indicate to the operator that a fuse associated with the switchboard has blown.

light, pilot, *n.* A lamp which lights to call attention to any of several indicators or conditions in a particular bay or panel of equipment.

light, supervisory pilot, *n.* A light,

usually green, on the face of each switchboard position which lights to call attention to the fact that one of the supervisory lamps on that position is lighted.

light, velocity of. See "velocity of light."

lighthouse tube, *n.* A type of electron tube designed to have low inter-electrode capacitance and low transit time, thus making it suitable for frequencies up to 3000 MHz. Its electrodes are closely spaced discs.

lightning arrester. See "protector, - - -" and "arrester, - - -."

lightning rod. See "rod, lightning."

limiter, *n.* A circuit which limits its output waveform to a specific maximum level, even though the input voltage exceeds the corresponding amount.

limiter, call, *n.* A central office device which times a call and either interrupts the call or superimposes warning tone if the call exceeds a preestablished length of time. Seldom used today.

limiter, noise, *n.* A circuit which cuts off noise peaks which are greater than the signal peaks.

limiting, *n.* The action of a limiter, which see.

limiting, hard, *n.* Limiting action which occurs very abruptly once the limiting level is reached.

line, *n.* (1) A pole line. (2) A subscriber's line. (3) A toll line. (4) Any set of conductors with their supporting poles.

line, artificial, *n.* A network of inductances, capacitances, and resistances which closely simulates the impedance of a particular actual line. See also "network, precision."

line, cable, *n.* A pole line whose primary purpose is the supporting of aerial cables.

line, delay, *n.* A transmission line, radio frequency or ultrasonic, so constructed that the propagation time through it is considerable. If the signal to be delayed is digital, the delay line can be a shift register.

line, dissipation, *n.* A spaced open wire line which is connected to a transmitting rhombic antenna at the vertex opposite the antenna feeder, and which terminates the rhombic and provides a means for dissipating the power which flows in the termination.

line, distortionless, *n.* A transmission line in which the product of its inductance and susceptance is equal to the product of its capacitance and resistance. Under such conditions propagation is at the speed of light. Attenuation is at a minimum, the impedance is a high pure resistance, and both are independent of frequency.

line, expotential transmission, *n.* A transmission line whose inductance and capacitance vary expotentially with distance along the line. Can be made by varying the wire spacing expotentially. An expotential line has a cutoff frequency, and the impedances at the two ends are different. Used for impedance-matching at radio frequencies.

line, four-wire, *n.* A two-way transmission circuit using separate paths for the two directions of transmission. If the transmission is at voice-frequency, this requires two pairs (4 wires).

line, individual, *n.* A line which provides public, switched telephone service for the exclusive use of one subscriber.

line, keying, *n.* (1) A wire or radio circuit used to key a remote radio transmitter with a telegraph signal. (2) A wire or radio circuit which carries a voice signal used to modulate a remote radio transmitter. (3) A wire or radio circuit which carries the output of remote radio receivers to a central control point. Keying lines may also serve as remote control lines. See "control, remote."

line, lossless, *n.* A transmission line which has no series resistance or

leakage conductance has no loss. Its characteristic impedance is the same at all frequencies.

line, lossy, *n.* A transmission line, usually a coaxial cable, which is designed to have a very high transmission loss per unit length.

line, message, *n.* A type of multiparty telephone line used for railway dispatching. Utilizes local battery telephones equipped with Gill selectors. See also "waystation" and "selector, Gill."

line, multiparty, *n.* A central office line which serves more than one customer. May be a 2-party, 4-party, or 6-10 party (rural) line.

line, off-premises, *n.* A station line connecting a remote station to its PBX.

line, open wire, *n.* A pole line whose principal function is the supporting of "open wire" lines.

line, party, *n.* A telephone line which serves two or more parties. Usually means either a "two-party" or a "four-party" line. Lines serving more than four parties are called "rural lines." Provision is made for ringing which discriminates between the several parties on the line.

line, PBX tie, *n.* A telephone circuit between two PBX's, over which stations of one PBX may be connected to stations of the other.

line, pole, *n.* A series of poles in a line, used to support cables or wires.

line, power, *n.* A pole line carrying wires or cable for the transmission or distribution of electric power.

line, private, *n.* (1) A telephone line which serves only one party. An individual line. (2) A communication line which is used only for communication between two points, and which does not connect with a public telephone system.

line, radio-frequency transmission, *n.* A pair of spaced copper wires which will transfer radio-frequency energy from a transmitter to an antenna without appreciable radiation. A pair of #12 AWG wires spaced six inches apart would have a line impedance of 600 ohms.

line, rural, *n.* A subscriber's line in rural territory which is designed to serve from five to ten parties per line.

line, slotted, *n.* A section of coaxial line or waveguide having a slot in the grounded conductor through which a probe can be inserted to determine voltage nodes in a standing wave. Used for precision measurements of wavelength.

line, subscriber's, *n.* A telephone circuit from the central office to the subscriber's telephone.

line, surface wave, *n.* A radio-frequency transmission line consisting of a single insulated wire strung in the open without bends. Acts like a coaxial cable without the outer tubular conductor.

line, telegraph, *n.* A communication circuit for passing telegraph or teletypewriter signals.

line, telephone, *n.* (1) A pole line which carries telephone circuits. (2) The conductors and related outside plant which comprise a single telephone circuit.

line, toll, *n.* (1) A circuit between toll switchboards which carries toll telephone traffic. (2) A toll pole line.

line, toll pole (TPL), *n.* A line of poles between two toll centers which carries toll telephone circuits, either in cable or on open wire, as physical circuits or carrier circuits.

line, transmission, *n.* Any circuit: open wire, paired cable, or coaxial cable, used to transfer energy from one point to another. A power transmission line must transfer energy with maximum efficiency. A telephone transmission line must transfer the maximum signal power (at 50% efficiency) with acceptable fidelity.

line, twin. See "twin-line."

line, two-wire, *n.* A two-conductor metallic circuit used for one-way or two-way transmission.

line, unbalanced, *n.* A transmission line having one side at ground potential, such as a coaxial line.

line, uniform, *n.* A line which has identical electrical properties distributed throughout its length.

linear, *adj.* Describing a device in which the signal output voltage is directly proportional to the signal input voltage.

linearizer, *n.* A passive waveguide device which uses negative feedback to ensure that the output of a klystron modulator is linear. Consists of a short section of waveguide containing a broadband filter and adjustable waveguide transformer which reflects a portion of the energy back to the klystron at the proper phase and amplitude to cancel distortion products.

line balance, *n.* The degree of similarity between the two conductors of a communication line. Balance implies equal resistance, equal inductance, equal capacitance to ground, and equal leakage to ground. A balanced line will be free of noise and crosstalk.

line bank, *n.* The lower bank, or banks, of Strowger-type step-by-step switches, comprised of the contacts of the line or talking circuit.

line building-out unit. See "unit, line building-out."

line conductor, *n.* Any of the wires running between poles on a telephone or power line, but not including lateral or vertical connecting wires.

line fill. See "fill, line."

line filter, *n.* A filter associated with a transmission line, such as a filter used to separate speech frequencies from carrier frequencies.

line filter balancing network, *n.* A network designed to maintain phantom group balance when one side of the group is equipped with a carrier line filter.

linefinder, *n.* A switching mechanism which finds a calling line out of a group of 100 or 200, and connects it to an intra-office trunk, usually to a local first selector.

line group, carrier. See "group, carrier line."

line-load control. See "control, line-load."

line loss, *n.* The total of the several energy losses occurring in a transmission line, expressed in decibels.

lineman, *n.* A workman who climbs and works on poles while constructing telephone outside plant. The work includes setting poles, placing anchors and guys, stringing strand, cable, and open wire.

line of force, *n.* A line drawn in an electric or a magnetic field so that its direction at every point is the direction of the electric or magnetic force at that point.

line-of-sight path, *n.* A radio path from the transmitting antenna to the receiving antenna which clears the intervening terrain so that there is an optical path from one to the other. To be practically useable, a line-of-sight path must have additional clearance at least equal to the first Fresnel zone radius.

line side, *n.* The side of equipment that looks toward the transmission path.

line signal, *n.* A lamp signal associated with a subscriber line or toll circuit which lights to announce an incoming call.

lineswitch, *n.* An automatic switch which connects a (subscriber's) line to an idle trunk within a group of ten. If used as a "primary lineswitch" it has associated with it the "subscriber's line equipment."

lineswitch, plunger, *n.* An electromechanical switch which is associated with the line equipment of each subscriber's line and operates when the subscriber lifts his handset to dial. It connects the subscriber's line to an idle trunk within a group of ten trunks to first selectors. Plunger lineswitches are provided in groups of 25, controlled

by a "masterswitch." Plunger lineswitches are obsolescent today.

lineswitch, primary, *n.* A lineswitch which is directly connected to a subscriber's line equipment.

lineswitch, rotary, *n.* A 25-point, nonnumerical, rotary stepping switch connected to each telephone line, used in the older, smaller dial central offices. When its connected telephone initiates a call, it rotates its wipers to select an idle trunk to the next switch, a selector or a connector.

lineswitch, secondary, *n.* A second lineswitch connected between the primary lineswitch and the local first selectors which gives the subscriber 100 outlets to a first selector instead of only ten outlets.

line-up, *n.* (1) The procedure used in adjusting the components of a communication circuit so that it will have the desired (a) transmission loss, (b) echo return loss, (c) band pass, and (d) freedom from delay distortion. (2) A row of rack mounted equipment, in a central office or in a radio station.

line up, *v.* To adjust the components of a communication circuit so that it will have (a) the proper transmission loss, (b) echo return loss, and (c) delay distortion.

line voltage, *n.* The voltage of an alternating power source at its point of utilization. The average A.C. line voltage in the United States is 117 volts.

link, *n.* (1) One of a series of interconnecting circuits which comprise a long built-up circuit. (2) In an automatic central office, a circuit consisting of two selecting switches connected back-to-back, such as a linefinder cabled directly to a connector. (3) A trunk or junctor with a selecting switch on each end. Selection is outward from the link. (4) The portion of a radio relay system between adjacent radio stations. (5) A small metal strap used as a removeable connection between two adjacent screws on a connecting block.

link, auxiliary pulse. See "pulse link, auxiliary."

link, cable reinforcing, *n.* A closed link of ½-inch steel rod, 6-8 inches long, fastened to the two sides of the pole on either side of the cable suspension clamp at corners in the pole line. Relieves the side stress and sharp bending of the cable messenger.

link, centrex data, *n.* A two-way time-division digital circuit between a central office and the customer's centrex equipment. It carries control signals to the centrex attendant's console, and information regarding the state of the console's keys back to the central office.

link, coin supervisory, *n.* In a crossbar office, a switching arrangement for connecting originating dial equipment to coin supervisory circuits.

link, connecting, *n.* A small flat metal strip which provides a removeable connection between two terminal screws.

link, crossbar, *n.* A connection between the primary and secondary switch on the same frame.

link, data, *n.* A circuit designed to carry digital information, usually by time-division multiplex techniques. Often used to transfer information from one register to another.

link, fast, *n.* A link designed for very fast action, and liberally provided so that access to a common register-sender can be given rapidly such that pulsing can be received one-tenth second after the link is seized. Used to avoid second dial tone.

link, fusible, *n.* The current carrying portion of a fuse which is designed to melt when the rated current is exceeded for a specified length of time. Some fuses are made so that the fusible link can be replaced.

link, incoming register, *n.* Trunk and associated single crossbar switch which connects incoming trunks to incoming registers. This connection

is made without the assistance of a marker. (#5 XBar)

link, line, *n.* In a crossbar office, a switching arrangement for connecting customer lines to junctors on originating calls, and junctors to customer lines or trunks on terminating or through calls.

link, outgoing sender, *n.* Trunk and associated single crossbar switch which connects an outgoing or intermarker group sender to an outgoing trunk. (#5 XBar)

link, radio, *n.* A single-hop radio system which directly connects two locations. May be part of a multi-hop radio relay system.

link, sender, *n.* A switching arrangement for interconnecting outgoing senders and trunks.

link, strand. See "strandlink."

link, telegraph hub, *n.* The metallic connection between the receive hub and the send hub by which a marking potential ($+60V$) on the receive hub reaches the send hub and causes a mark to be transmitted outward over the facilities which are connected to the send hub. If a regenerative repeater is required, it replaces the hub link.

link, terminating, *n.* A toll connecting trunk; the trunk which connects a toll office to a local end office.

link, trunk, *n.* A switching arrangement for connecting originating registers and trunks to junctors.

linkage, flux, *n.* The product of the magnetic flux in maxwells and the number of turns in a coil or winding with which it is linked.

link encryption, *n.* The application of on-line encryption to each link of a relay system so that all messages passing over the link are encrypted, whether classified or not.

link lamp, *n.* A lamp provided on certain "B" and tandem boards in a dial system, which lights to indicate that the position has been seized and connected to an incoming call.

link terminal, *n.* The earth terminal of an earth-to-satellite communication link.

Lissajous figure, *n.* The pattern appearing on a cathode ray oscilloscope when the horizontal plates are fed one alternating frequency, and the vertical plates are fed another alternating frequency.

listed number trunk. See "trunk, listed number."

listening key, *n.* A key associated with a cord pair which, when operated, allows the operator to talk or listen on that cord pair.

listing, private, *n.* Telephone service where the telephone number is kept private, not listed in the directory or with information service.

listing, reference, *n.* A telephone directory listing of an alternate number to be called if no answer is received at the regular number. The alternate number may be a telephone answering service number.

listing, semi-private, *n.* Variety of non-listed telephone service where the telephone number is listed at "information," but not listed in the directory.

Litz wire, *n.* Litzendraht wire. A braided stranded wire of individually insulated very fine strands. It has a reduced skin effect, and thus a lower resistance at radio frequencies than other wires of equivalent size.

live, *adj.* (1) Energized. (2) Connected to a source of an electrical voltage. (3) Charged to an electrical potential different from that of the earth. (4) Reverberant, as a room in which there are reflections of sound.

live-front, *adj.* Describing an equipment, such as a power board, which has exposed live parts on the front.

live parts, *n.* Metallic portions of equipment which are at a potential different from that of the earth.

live room, *n.* (1) A room in which sound reverberates. (2) A room in which sound is not excessively absorbed.

L network. See "network, L."

load, *n.* (1) A circuit component that consumes electric power. (2) A device that receives the useful output of an electric generator, oscillator, or other signal source. (3) The amount of electric power that is drawn from the source.

load, artificial, *n.* A device which can dissipate energy (into heat) without radiating it. Used to test radio transmitter, engine generators, etc.

load, balanced polyphase, *n.* A load to which symmetrical currents will be supplied if it is connected to a power source having symmetrical voltages.

load, connected power, *n.* The sum of the rated capacities of all equipment, motor, lamp, etc. loads connected to a power circuit. It is the load which would occur if all individual loads were turned "ON" simultaneously.

load, demand power, *n.* The maximum load which occurs on a power circuit over a long period.

load, matched, *n.* A load having an impedance such that there is maximum power transfer from the generator or signal source.

load, technical. See "technical load."

load, utility power. See "utility power load."

load coil. See "coil, loading."

load control, high-traffic-day, *n.* Feature of some toll translators which diverts hard-to-reach (multiswitched) area traffic to a delay recorded message whenever a trunk-busy monitoring circuit detects a pre-determined high percentage of trunk busies.

load control, subscribers. See "control, line load."

loading, *n.* (1) A system for adding regularly spaced inductance units to a circuit to improve its transmission characteristics. (2) The amount of ice and wind pressure which must be assumed in designing a pole line. (3) Overhead expense above direct charges, such as supervision, exempt material, and motor vehicle expense. (4) The amount of power carried by the channels on a carrier system.

loading, antenna, *n.* The use of a series inductance to tune an antenna to a frequency lower than its natural frequency.

loading, carrier, *n.* Lumped inductive loading to improve transmission characteristics, specifically designed for application to a cable for carrier frequencies.

loading, CCITT standard system, *n.* The CCITT has specified a standard system loading as follows:

Average talker volume (VU)	—12.0
Standard deviation (VU)	5.0
Upper limit of talker volume for 1% of time (VU)	0.5
Talker activity factor (percentage talking simultaneously)	0.25
RMS Power per Channel (dBm)	—15.0
RMS Power per Group (dBm)	— 4.2
RMS Power per Band (dBm) (System load)	+ 4.8

loading, conductor, *n.* The combined mechanical loading per unit length of conductor due to the weight of the wire plus wind and ice loads.

loading, inductive, *n.* The application of lumped series inductance at regular intervals along a cable circuit in order to reduce its attenuation over a limited frequency band. See also "system, loading" and "spacing, load coil."

loading, lumped, *n.* Inductive loading in which inductance is inserted at intervals along a cable circuit.

loading, storm, *n.* The combined stress imposed on a pole line by wind, low temperature, and perhaps ice on the wires. See also "area, light loading," "area, medium loading," and "area, heavy loading."

loading, system, *n.* The total intelligence signal power carried by a multi-channel communication system, which is a summation of the instantaneous average power on all of the channels. Usually expressed as the per channel load which can be carried by all channels.

loading, uniform, *n.* A process of adding inductance distributed uniformly along the line by wrapping the conductor with a continuous high permeability metallic tape. Used on some of the older submarine cables.

loading area. See "area, light loading," "area, medium loading," and "area, heavy loading."

loading coil. See "coil, loading."

loading section. See "section, loading."

loading system. See "system, loading."

load line, *n.* Of an electron tube, a straight line drawn across a family of plate current-plate voltage characteristic curves which shows the relationship between grid voltage and plate current for a particular plate load resistance.

load point. See "point, load."

load sharing. See "paralleling."

load spacing. See "spacing, load coil."

lobe, *n.* One of the three-dimensional petals representing the radiation or reception efficiency of a directional antenna. There is one "major" or "main" lobe, and several "minor" "side" and "back" lobes.

lobe, back, *n.* The three-dimensional petal representing antenna directional response which is pointing away from the intended direction.

lobe, front, *n.* The major lobe of a directional antenna. The lobe in the direction of preferred reception or transmission.

lobe, major, *n.* The largest of the several lobes, or three-dimensional petals, which represent the radiation pattern of a directional radio antenna. The lobe in the direction of preferred reception or transmission.

lobe, minor, *n.* Any of the lobes, except the major lobe, which represent the radiation pattern of a directional antenna.

lobe, side, *n.* Any of the three-dimensional petals representing the radiation efficiency of a directional antenna except the front lobe and the back lobe.

local, *n.* A PBX station.

local, long-distance, *n.* An off-premises PBX station.

local action, *n.* Localized currents within a primary or secondary cell caused by impurities in the plates.

local automatic message accounting (LAMA), *n.* Automatic message accounting equipment combined in the same office with automatic number identification equipment, so that a customer dialed toll can be completely processed automatically without the assistance of an operator.

local battery, *adj.* Describes a system or station in which the talking battery is supplied by a dry-cell battery located at the subscriber's station.

local call, *n.* Any call (attempted or completed) within the local service area of the calling telephone.

locality, *n.* A place within an exchange area which has a different name, but the same rate center and routing instructions.

localization time. See "time, localization."

local message, *n.* A completed local call.

local multiple connection, *n.* A connection established by an "A" operator in the subscriber multiple appearing before her.

local service area, *n.* The area within which are located the stations which a customer may call at local rates.

locating circuit, *n.* A circuit used to choose one functional circuit out of many.

locator, gas leak. See "detector, gas leak."

locator, ultrasonic gas leak. See "detector, gas leak."

locking, *adj.* Capable of remaining in

an operated position after operation. The lock may be electrical or mechanical.

locking relay. See "relay, locking."

lock-on, *n.* (1) The act of a satellite ground station in tracking a communication satellite automatically. (2) The instant when a satellite ground station antenna starts automatic tracking.

lock-out, *n.* (1) Treatment of a subscriber's line which is permanent or in trouble, in which it is automatically disconnected from the switching equipment so that the equipment is not held busy. (2) An effect caused at echo suppressors when parties at both terminals of the circuit talk at once.

lockout, echo suppressor, *n.* The condition existing when two echo suppressors at opposite ends of a circuit act together to block transmission in both directions. Can be avoided by the use of a "split echo suppressor."

lock-out circuit, *n.* A circuit which permits but one out of several competing functional circuits to act or to have access to a common part of the system.

lockstitch, *n.* (1) Lacing twine. (2) The stitch used for lacing cable forms.

lock-up, *n.* False operations of an echo suppressor caused by high received noise.

log, *n.* (1) A report in narrative form of routine maintenance performed or trouble activities. (2) A logarithm.

logarithm, *n.* The logarithm of a number is the power to which a "base" (usually 10) must be raised to equal the number. Facilitates computations, because two numbers can be multiplied by adding their logarithms, and divided by subtracting one logarithm from the other.

logarithm, natural, *n.* A logarithm using the base 2.71828183, instead of the base 10. Much used in electrical calculations.

logarithmic scale, *n.* Meter scale in which the displacement of the meter needle is proportional to the logarithm of the quantity which it measures.

logic, *n.* (1) That portion of a computer or common-control equipment which can provide a "yes" or "no" answer based on its ability to compare data furnished it with pre-programmed data. (2) An organized procedure for going wrong with confidence and certainty.

logic, symbolic. See "Boolean algebra."

logic, wired, *n.* Any logic device, such as a group of relays, in which the logic is determined by wired interconnections. Any change in the program therefore requires that the logic device be rewired. See also "program, stored."

log-periodic antenna. See "antenna, log-periodic."

long distance, *adj.* Pertaining to toll telephone service.—*n.* (1) The toll operator. (2) A toll call.

long distance call, *n.* (1) Any call beyond the local or multi-message unit calling area. (2) A toll call other than one handled as an "A" board toll call.

long-distance local, *n.* An outside (off premises) PBX station.

long distance operator, *n.* A person who works at a toll switchboard and completes toll calls.

long distance terminal, *n.* A customer's line which terminates directly on a long distance switchboard.

long haul, *adj.* A term of indefinite meaning describing circuits spanning considerable distances and requiring special techniques, such as repeatering, echo suppression, etc. Generally applied only to four-wire transmission facilities, inter-state or overseas.

long-haul carrier, *n.* Carrier system designed for use over distances of 200-4,000 miles.

longitudinal balance. See "balance, longitudinal."

longitudinal circuit. See "circuit, longitudinal."

longitudinal current, *n.* Current that travels in the same direction on both sides of a pair.

longitudinal stripe. See stripe, longitudinal color."

Long Lines Department, *n.* The department of the American Telephone and Telegraph Company which operates all interstate toll circuits.

long line unit. See "adapter, long line."

long wave, *n.* Having a wavelength above about 600 meters.

loom. See "tubing, flexible nonmetallic."

loop, *n.* (1) The closed path in an electrical circuit. (2) A subscriber's loop. The pair of wires from a central office out to the subscriber's telephone.

loop, effective polar telegraph. See "loop, balanced telegraph."

loop, ground. See "ground loop."

loop, L.D., *n.* Line from a subscriber's phone or PBX directly to the toll switchboard. Used for placing toll calls expeditiously.

loop, local, *n.* A circuit connecting an end instrument to a switching facility or distribution point.

loop, open wire, *n.* (1) Subscriber's loop which is run in open wire. (2) A single circuit open wire branch line.

loop, polar telegraph, *n.* Telegraph loop in which equal currents of opposite polarity are used for the mark and space signals. At the receiving (printer) end of the loop a polarized relay is used to receive the signal and translate it into a neutral signal.

loop, program supply, *n.* A circuit from the point of a broadcast program pick-up back to the radio broadcasting station. Usually "equalized" to improve its transmission characteristics.

loop, radio, *n.* A circuit used for program supply.

loop, subscriber's, *n.* The pair of wires from a subscriber's telephone into the central office.

loop, Varley, *n.* An arrangement of a Wheatstone bridge circuit which gives in a single measurement the difference in resistance between the two wires of a loop. To make this measurement the far end of the loop must be shorted and grounded.

loop extender. See "extender, loop."

loop gain, *n.* The total amplifier gain around a closed loop such as a two-wire repeater or a carrier terminal. Loop gain is limited by unbalance which may cause the circuit to sing.

loop-mile, *n.* A mile of two-wire line.

loop options, *n. pl.* The different D.C. circuit arrangements that can be made between a carrier telegraph terminal and a teletypewriter. For instance: neutral, polar, half-duplex, and full-duplex.

loop pulsing. See "pulsing, loop."

loop resistance, *n.* The resistance in ohms of the pair of line wires which extend from a subscriber's telephone to the central office. Does not include the resistance of the telephone.

loop signaling. See "signaling, loop."

loop wire, *n.* A piece of color-coded switchboard wire which runs from terminal to terminal of the same or adjacent components, but is laced into a cable form instead of being run directly.

loose coupling. See "coupling, loose."

loran, *n.* Acronym for "LOng RAnge Navigation." A navigation system with which planes and ships can obtain a very accurate estimate of position by measuring the delay and phase of radio pulses from scattered master and slave stations. The position is at the intersection of two hyperbolic lines of position.

loss, *n.* (1) Power that is dissipated in a circuit without doing useful work.

(2) The drop in energy in traversing a circuit. (3) Transmission loss, expressed in decibels.

loss, attenuation, *n.* The reduction of energy which occurs as a wave travels through space, through a waveguide, or over a line. Generally expressed in decibels, or decibels per unit distance.

loss, bridging, *n.* The loss resulting from bridging an impedance across a transmission circuit. Unless the impedance is a pure resistance, the loss will vary with frequency.

loss, copper. See "I^2R loss."

loss, dielectric hysteresis, *n.* The energy which is dissipated in alternately reversing the electric field in the dielectric of a capacitor, or of an insulator, when these are stressed by an alternating voltage.

loss, diffraction, *n.* The loss suffered by radio waves traveling a path which is longer than line-of-sight, caused by the bending of the wave around the earth's curvature or around an obstruction.

loss, echo return, *n.* The loss which must be in the echo path to reduce echo to a tolerable amount. The normal telephone off-hook has a return loss of about 11 db, and can therefore tolerate a round-trip echo delay of 20 milliseconds. If the circuit were longer so that the delay was 60 milliseconds, the return loss would need to be increased to 23 db for equal user tolerance.

loss, eddy-current, *n.* The energy loss represented by the flow of eddy-currents through the resistance of a magnetic core.

loss, effective transmission, *n.* An overall loss for a telephone message channel which includes the impairments caused by attenuation, noise, and bandwidth restriction.

loss, expected measured (EML), *n.* The 1000 hertz loss that is expected to be measured between specified test points.

loss, free space, *n.* The theoretical transmission loss between two isotropic radio antennas dependent only upon distance and frequency, with all variable factors eliminated.

loss, hearing. See "hearing loss."

loss, hybrid insertion, *n.* The undesired loss between the two-wire line and four-wire line of a hybrid junction. See also "hybrid loss."

loss, hysteresis. See "loss, dielectric hysteresis" and "loss, magnetic hysteresis."

loss, inserted connection (ICL), *n.* Of a trunk, the net equivalent 1000 hertz loss inserted by switching the trunk into an actual operating connection.

loss, insertion, *n.* The loss at a particular frequency caused by the insertion of apparatus or a network into a communication system. It is the ratio, expressed in db, of the power at that frequency delivered beyond the point of insertion before and after the insertion.

loss, iron, *n.* The power loss in the iron core of an inductance or transformer due to hysteresis or eddy currents.

loss, junction, *n.* The transmission loss due to the mismatch of impedance between two types of transmission facilities.

loss, line, *n.* The total of the several energy losses occurring in a transmission line, expressed in decibels.

loss, magnetic hysteresis, *n.* The energy lost in alternately reversing the magnetic field of a ferromagnetic material such as the core of a transformer.

loss, net, *n.* (1) In a transmission circuit, the sum of all the losses minus the sum of all the gains. (2) The loss of a toll circuit in its terminal arrangement or simulated terminal arrangement.

loss, obstruction, *n.* That portion of the loss encountered by a radio wave when its path is not through free space, but has a finite clearance over the terrain. Obstruction loss varies from zero at free-space, to about ten decibels with a grazing

path (zero clearance over terrain at some point). Obstruction loss is a function of Fresnel zone clearance.

loss, polarization, *n.* A loss suffered by a plane-polarized wave when the receiving antenna does not have the same angle of polarization as the incoming radio wave.

loss, power, *n.* The ratio of the total power delivered to a line or transducer to the power from the line or transducer into the load, expressed in decibels.

loss, reflection, *n.* The loss in transferring power from one circuit to another which occurs when the driven impedance does not equal (in magnitude and angle, including sign) the driving impedance, expressed in db.

loss, return, *n.* A measure of the dissimilarity between two impedances, expressed in db. Numerically equal to "reflection loss."

loss, shadow, *n.* The loss suffered by radio waves when they encounter objects such as hills, buildings, and trees which shade the receiving antenna.

loss, terminal net (TNL), *n.* Of an intertoll trunk, the sum of the "via net losses" plus the losses of the switching pads which are a part of the circuit in its terminal condition.

loss, toll terminal, *n.* That part of the overall transmission loss on a toll telephone connection caused by the facilities from the toll center through a tributary office, if any, to and including the subscriber's telephone equipment.

loss, transformer, *n.* The ratio, expressed in decibels, of the power that an ideal transformer would deliver to the load to the power that an actual transformer of the same impedance ratio would deliver to a load of the same impedance.

loss, trans-hybrid, *n.* The loss (isolation) between the transmit and receive branches of a four-wire line.

It is directly dependent upon the degree of balance achieved between the two-wire line and its balancing network.

loss, transition, *n.* The ratio of the power that is transferred from one circuit to another under actual circuit conditions to the power which would be transferred if the load impedance and the source impedance were conjugates, expressed in dB.

loss, transmission, *n.* The ratio of the power at the input to a transmission line to the power at the output, expressed in decibels.

loss, tributary, *n.* The transmission loss between the users telephone and the toll center. It includes the loss of the station loop and of the tributary trunk.

loss, trunk, *n.* That portion of the overall loss assignable to the trunk used in a telephone connection.

loss, via net, *n.* The lowest loss at which telephone trunk facilities can be operated, as limited by their inherent characteristics and achievable return losses. See also "via net loss factor."

loss, wet weather, *n.* The transmission loss of an open wire pair increases considerably when wet due to two effects: (a) The conductance increases, allowing more current to be by-passed through the shunt leakage paths, and (b) skin effect causes the current to leave the conductor and flow in the high resistance water film covering it.

loss factor. See "factor, loss."

lossless line. See "line, lossless."

lossy, *adj.* A term indicating that the transmission loss per unit length is much greater than normal.

lossy cable, *n.* A single-circuit cable (frequently of coaxial construction) deliberately constructed to have high transmission loss so that it can be used as an attenuator, an artificial load, or a termination.

lost call, *n.* A call which arrives at automatic switching equipment and finds all trunks leaving the equipment to be busy.

loudness, *n.* A subjective auditory sensation by which a listener can estimate the intensity of sounds, from soft to loud. Loudness depends upon sound pressure, but also upon the frequency and wave form of the stimulus.

loudness, sound, *n.* The magnitude of the sensation produced in the brain of the listener by sound. It is dependent on both the intensity and the frequency of the sound.

loudness contour, *n.* A graph showing the relationship between sound pressure, frequency, and loudness sensation for a typical listener.

loudness level, *n.* The loudness level, measured in phons, is numerically equal to the sound pressure level, in decibels above 0.0002 microbar, of a pure 1000 Hz tone which is judged by listeners to be equivalent in loudness.

loudspeaker, *n.* A transducer that converts audio frequency electrical power into acoustic (sound) power, and then radiates that sound effectively through the air.

louver, *n.* (1) An arrangement of slots or holes in a housing or cabinet which provides mechanical protection while permitting sound to pass. (2) Slots in a cabinet or housing to provide ventilation.

lower sideband, *n.* The lower of two bands of frequencies which are produced by an amplitude modulation process. The sideband containing frequencies below the carrier frequency.

lowest useful frequency (LUF), *n.* The lowest frequency in the high-frequency radio band which can be used at a particular time of day for ionospheric propagation between two specified points.

low frequency (LF), *adj.* Referring to any of the band of radio frequencies between 30 and 300 kilohertz.

low-frequency induction. See "induction, low-frequency."

low-group frequencies. See "frequency band, low-group."

low-high repeater, *n.* An intermediate carrier repeater which receives signals in a low-frequency band, amplifies and translates them, then transmits the amplified signals in the high-frequency band. See "frogging."

low-loss, *adj.* Describing circuits or devices in which little energy is lost in heating resistances. See also "high-Q."

low-pass filter. See "filter, low-pass."

low tension, *adj. n.* Low voltage. (British).

low tone. See "tone, low."

low-voltage, *adj.* (1) Describing an electrical supply system having an operating voltage less than 750 volts. (2) Describing an electrical control system having an operating voltage less than 100 volts.

low-voltage alarm, *n.* A bell alarm in a dial central office which is activated when the DC voltage being supplied to the equipment falls to 45 volts.

L pad. See "network, L."

LR group, *n.* A one-way 48 kHz 12-channel group between two points, established over coaxial cable facilities connected in tandem with radio facilities.

L supergroup, *n.* A permanently associated continuity of coaxial cable units arranged to provide a 60-channel one-way transmission path.

LTB, last trunk busy, *n.* The condition where the last choice trunk of a group, or a sub-group, is busy.

lubricant, cable pulling, *n.* A mixture of powdered soapstone or colloidal silica with a heavy, non-corrosive grease used to reduce the tension required to pull a cable into a duct. The cable is liberally painted with the lubricant as it enters the duct.

Lucite, *n.* Du Pont's brand of transparent acrylic resin products.

lug, *n.* An ear-like projection of a terminal, to which an electrical connection can be made by soldering, crimping, or wrapping.

lug, solder, *n.* A 1½-inch (more or less) piece of copper tubing having one flattened end with a hole through it. The wire is fastened into the tubing end with molten solder, then the flattened end is bolted to a circuit terminal.

lug, solderless, *n.* A terminal lug which holds the conductor it terminates by compressing it under a screw.

lug, spade, *n.* A solder lug which has an open end so that it can be slipped under the head of a binding screw.

lug, terminal, *n.* In a terminal box, a threaded stud fitted with nuts under which a wire can be clamped.

lumen, *n.* The amount of light which falls on a unit surface, all points of which are at a unit distance from a source of one candle. A 100-watt incandescent lamp (circa 1971) emits about 1650 lumens.

luminance, *n.* An attribute of light or color. Luminous intensity or brightness, as measured by a photometer instead of by the human eye.

lumped, *adj.* Located at a point, opposite to being distributed. Said of inductance, capacitance, and resistance.

lumped constant, *n.* A resistance, inductance, or capacitance which is connected at a point, rather than being distributed uniformly throughout the circuit.

lump loading, *n.* The normal type of inductive loading, in which inductance is inserted in lumps at intervals along a cable circuit.

lumpy, *adj.* Describing a line in which the inductance, capacitance, or resistance are concentrated in discrete units rather than being distributed.

Luneberg lens. See "antenna, Luneberg lens."

L unit. See "unit, L."

machete, *n.* A large, 18-24 inch, knife having a heavy wide blade. In action, it is swung like an axe. Originally used to cut sugar cane, but useful in clearing brush.

machine, cable lashing, *n.* A cable lasher, used to lash aerial cable to its supporting strand.

machine ringing, *n.* Ringing which continues automatically at regular intervals until the called telephone answers or the call is abandoned.

Magicall, *n.* Trade-marked name of a repertory dialer.

magic tee. See "hybrid tee."

magnesium anode. See "anode, galvanic."

magnet, *n.* An object that produces a magnetic field external to itself, and can attract iron and attract or repel other magnets. A "permanent magnet" has a permanent magnetic field. An "electromagnet" produces a magnetic field only when current flows through its winding.

magnet, electro. See "electromagnet" (one word).

magnet, permanent, *n.* A bar of hardened steel, or other magnetic material, whose molecules are all oriented in one direction so that their magnetic moments are additive and an external magnetic field is produced.

magnet, release, *n.* On a step-by-step switch, a magnet whose armature trips a pawl or detent, and thus allows the switch shaft and wipers to return to normal.

magnet, stepping, *n.* Either of the electromagnets which actuates the stepping motion of a step-by-step switch. There are two: the vertical magnet and the rotary magnet.

magnetic amplifier. See "amplifier, magnetic."

magnetic circuit. See "circuit, magnetic."

magnetic core. See "core, magnetic."

magnetic core storage. See "core, magnetic."

magnetic field. See "field, magnetic."

magnetic flux, *n.* The field produced in the medium surrounding electric currents or magnets. Magnetic flux is to the magnetic circuit as current is to an electrical circuit.

magnetic hysteresis. See "hysteresis."

magnetic leakage, *n.* Magnetic flux which by-passes a path on which it could do useful work.

magnetic pole, *n.* (1) One of the two centers or spots on a magnet where magnetic attraction is the strongest. These spots are where the magnetic lines of force enter and leave the magnet. (2) Either of the earth's two magnetic poles.

Magnetic Poles, Law of. See "Appendix B."

magnetic storm, *n.* A violent random variation in the earth's magnetic field, caused by the solar activity that results in sunspots.

magnetic tape. See "tape, magnetic."

magnetism, *n.* A property possessed by iron and certain other materials called magnets by which they can produce and maintain an external magnetic field which will attract magnetic materials, and will either attract or repel other magnets.

magnetism, residual, *n.* The magnetism that remains in an electromagnet after its energizing circuit is opened.

magnetization, *n.* The degree to which a magnetic material has been magnetized.

magnetizing force, *n.* The force that produces magnetization of a substance, expressed in oersteds or ampere-turns per meter.

magneto, *adj.* Describes any device which includes a magneto generator.—*n.* An AC generator which uses several permanent magnets to produce its magnetic field. In telephone practice, a two-pole, hand-cranked generator used in a telephone or switchboard to produce ringing signals of approximately 16-20 Hz AC.

magneto line, *n.* Subscriber's line with magneto telephones.

magnetomotive force, *n.* The force which tends to produce lines of force in a magnetic circuit. It has the same relation to a magnetic circuit as voltage has to an electrical circuit. Its practical unit is the "ampere-turn," equal to 1.257 gilberts.

magneto office. See "office, magneto central."

magneto operation, *n.* Type of operation in which telephones use local battery supply and magneto hand generators for signaling the operator. From the operator's viewpoint the salient feature is the absence of automatic station supervision.

magneto signaling. See "signaling, magneto."

magnetostriction, *n.* The contraction of a ferromagnetic rod, particularly one of iron or nickel, when placed in a longitudinal magnetic field having a strength of over about 250 oersteds. When the magnetic field is removed, the rod returns to its original length.

magneto switchboard. See "switchboard, magneto."

magneto telephone, *n.* Telephone which uses local dry cell battery for talking current supply, and a magneto hand generator for signaling.

magnetron, *n.* A high-power ultra high frequency electron tube oscillator which uses the interaction of a strong electric field between anode and cathode with a strong permanent magnet field to cause oscillatory electron flow through multiple internal cavity resonators. Operation is in the range 3-30 gigahertz.

main distributing frame. See "frame, main distributing."

main station. See "station, main."

maintainability, *n.* A characteristic of design and installation, expressed as the probability that an item will be retained in, or restored to, an acceptable operating condition within a stated period of time when maintenance is performed in accordance with prescribed procedures and resources.

maintenance, *n.* All of the work required to keep telephone plant, circuits, and service up to standards. This includes testing, trouble clearing, repairing and replacing defective elements.

maintenance, preventive, *n.* The systematic inspection, cleaning, adjustment, and minor repair of equipment or outside plant to correct troubles before they develop into major defects or cause outages.

major relay center, *n.* A tape relay center is one which has two or more trunk circuits connected which provide alternate routes for traffic.

make, *n.* The closing of a contact or contacts, on relays, keys, jacks, or other device.—*v.* To close a contact.

make, per cent, *n.* In pulse testing, the time contacts remain closed as a percentage of the total time open and closed.

make-before-break contacts. See "contacts, make-before-break."

make-break ratio. See "ratio, make-break."

make contacts, *n. pl.* Pairs of contacts which meet and close a circuit when a key or relay is operated.

manganin, *n.* An alloy of 85% copper, 10% manganese, and 5% nickel which has high resistivity but low change in resistance with temperature. Used in making precision wirewound resistors.

manhole, *n.* A concrete vault underground, large enough for a man to work in, into which cables enter through conduits. Divides conduit runs into sections permitting easy pulling-in of cables, and permits the splicing together of the cables as desired. See also "cover, manhole" and "frame, manhole."

manhole chimney. See "chimney, manhole" and "collar, manhole."

manhole frame and cover. See "frame, manhole" and "cover, manhole."

manifold, dry air, *n.* A device for distributing dry air from a pipeline to one to five cables. Provides individual shutoff of air to each cable, individual pressure testing valves for reading the pressure in each cable, and a valve for reading the manifold pressure.

manometer, *n.* An instrument, usually a U-shaped glass tube filled with a liquid or mercury, and enabling the accurate measurement of gas pressures.

manometer, mercury, *n.* A U-shaped Pyrex glass tubing partially filled with mercury, with one leg of the U connectable to a pressure testing valve by rubber tubing. The rise of mercury can be read on a scale under the opposite leg of the U to determine the gas pressure, from 0 to 15 pounds, by tenths of a pound.

mantissa, *n.* The decimal fraction part of a logarithm, which depends only upon the significant figures in the number without regard to the decimal point location.

manual, *adj.* Operated with the hands.

manual office, *n.* A telephone office in which the switching is done at manual switchboards.

manual ringing. See "ringing, manual."

manual start, *adj.* Said of systems (such as standby power) in which operation personnel must take action to start units and transfer loads.

manual switchboard. See "switchboard, manual."

map, topographic, *n.* An accurately scaled map having contour lines which show the elevation above sea level. Used in preparing profiles of microwave radio propagation paths. Available from the U.S. Geological Survey in quadrangles covering (a) 7½ minutes of latitude and longitude in scales 1:24,000 and 1:31,-680, (b) 15 minutes in the scale 1:62,500, and (c) 30 minutes in the scale 1:125,000.

Marconi antenna. See "antenna, Marconi."

margin, *n.* (1) In repeatered voice circuits, the db of repeater gain which can be added, above the normal operating gain, before the repeater sings. Singing margin. (2) In teletypewriter circuits, the amount of marking bias or spacing bias which can be added before teletypewriter errors are produced. (3) In radio transmission, the number of db the field strength can be reduced, below the normal level, before the circuit fails.

margin, fade, *n.* The extra radio signal strength which must be available during normal propagation to insure that even with signal fading an adequate signal will reach the receiver for an adequate percentage of the time, usually 99.9%. Depending on the frequency and the radio path, the fade margin may be 10-40 dB.

margin, singing, *n.* The gain in decibels which, if added to a circuit containing a hybrid junction, will just cause the circuit to sing.

marginal, *adj.* Operating at the borderland of permissable limits of voltage, current, distortion, etc. When operation is marginal, a very small impairment can cause the device to fail.

marginal relay, *n.* A relay having a small difference (margin) between its "non-operate" current value and its "operate" current value.

margining, *n.* The act of testing the pulsing relays of selectors or repeaters under conditions of maximum loop resistance, maximum shunt leakage, or maximum shunt capacitance, to determine whether they will operate correctly under extreme (marginal) conditions.

margining, relay, *n.* The checking, or testing and adjusting, of a relay for satisfactory operation at the "operate" and "non-operate" current values.

mark, *n.* (1) The closed-circuit condi- tion in telegraph or teletypewriter operation. The opposite of "space." (2) In digital transmission, the binary state "one," when any of the following conditions exist: (a) Loop closed, (b) current flowing, (c) tone on, (d) positive voltage, line to ground, (e) lower frequency of an FSK system, (f) hole punched in paper tape. (3) The presence of ground, battery, or resistance-battery potentials on one or more of a large group of leads.—*v.* To place a marking potential on a terminal or lead.

mark, class-of-service, *n.* A connection, or a signal, which provides information regarding the class of service to which a particular subscriber is entitled. These service classes include:

Flat-rate residential
Message-rate residential
Flat-rate business
Message-rate business
Flat-rate PBX business
Message-rate PBX business
Public coin
Semi-public coin

marker, *n.* (1) A switch in a crossbar office which (a) locates the calling line or trunk, (b) tests paths between the calling and called lines or trunks, then (c) marks an idle path before setting up the connection. See also "mark." (2) A monument or post placed to indicate the location of plant which is hidden, as a buried cable.

marker, buried cable, *n.* A 4-inch square post of concrete with designation, placed over a buried cable to indicate its location.

marker, combined, *n.* Marker which can be used for either originating calls (dial tone marker) or terminating calls (completing marker).

marker, completing, *n.* A marker which performs all marker operations except the dial tone job. See also "job, marker."

marker, crossbar, *n.* The heart of common-control crossbar central office equipment. It (a) determines terminal locations of calling lines, incoming trunks, called lines, and outgoing trunks in the equipment, (b) determines the proper route for the call, establishes the connection, and passes routing information to the senders, (c) determines the calling line class-of-service, and provides charge classification, (d) recognizes line busy, trouble, intercept, and vacant line conditions.

marker, defective pair, *n.* An orange plastic tube which is slipped over a pair at the end of a cable while at the factory to indicate that the pair is defective or irregular.

marker, dial tone, *n.* A marker which performs only the dial tone job. See also "job, marker."

marker, group selector, *n.* In an electronic central office, the common equipment which controls the switching paths within the "group selector" section of the office.

marker, line group, *n.* In an electronic central office, the common equipment which controls the switching paths within the "line group" section of the office.

marker, tandem, *n.* Marker which has the capability of denying access to specific outgoing routes for some groups of incoming trunks while permitting other trunk groups to complete calls to these routes. (#5 XBar)

marker, test, *n.* Marker equipped with special features for the use of operators and test men: (a) No-test calls, (b) no hunting in trunk-hunting group, (c) special hunt calls from the test desk. (#5 XBar)

marker, trunk group, *n.* In an electronic central office, the common equipment which controls the switching paths within the "trunk group" section of the office.

marker group. See "group, marker."

marking, multiple. See "multiple marking."

marking bias. See "bias, marking."

mark-sense, *adj.* Describing the cards,

equipment, or process by which conductive pencil marks on data cards are used to control a card punch to punch the same information on the same card in Hollerith code.—*n.* A process using special pencils whose mark will conduct electricity to mark 80-column pre-printed data card toll tickets with all the information needed for automatic billing of toll calls.

marline, *n.* A small cord of two loosely twisted strands, used for lashing or lacing.

MARS, *n.* Military Affiliated Radio System. A world-wide network of amateur radio stations, sponsored by the Army and Air Force for their potential usefulness during emergencies.

maser, *n.* Acronym for "Microwave Amplification by Stimulated Emission of Radiation." A low-noise microwave amplifier used to amplify very weak radio signals. Operates by using the microwave signal to trigger release of a much larger local signal, created by exciting molecules of a substance such as ammonia gas to ever higher energy levels until there is self-sustaining oscillation at millimeter wavelengths. Modulation of the microwave signal can be accomplished in a traveling wave tube.

mask, *v.t.* To hide, to obscure, to make less noticeable, as noise masks crosstalk.

mast, *n.* A vertical metal pole used to support antennas, or to support drop wires entering free-standing pay telephone booths.

mast, service, *n.* A vertical metal pole used to support the power service wire and telephone drop wire entering a free-standing pay telephone booth.

master busy jack, *n.* The first of five jacks which provides, by tone or signal, an indication that all five trunks are busy.

master carrier terminal. See "terminal, master carrier."

mastergroup, *n.* Ten carrier super-groups, or 600 channels. See also "group, master carrier."

master intercom station, *n.* An intercom station capable of receiving calls from and initiating calls to any of a group of stations. Consists of a desk cabinet containing (a) an amplifier, (b) a loudspeaker which also acts as a microphone, (c) a group of station keys (6, 12, 18, 24, 36, or 48), (d) sometimes annunciators to identify incoming calls, and (e) a buzzer or chime to announce incoming calls.

master office, *n.* A central office which serves a sub-office or a satellite office, and to which all of their trunks come.

master oscillator, *n.* (1) An oscillator which provides the basic frequency for a number of carrier systems. (2) An oscillator that establishes the carrier frequency of a radio transmitter.

masterswitch, *n.* An electromechanical switch associated with a group of 25, 50, 75, or 100 plunger line-switches which keeps the plungers of all idle lineswitches standing in front of an idle trunk outlet, ready for operation.

match, impedance, *n.* The condition existing between two circuits when electrical waves passing between them do not suffer any reflection loss. This condition is satisfied when the impedances of the two circuits are alike, both in magnitude and angle, including sign.

matched pulse, *adj.* Describing any of the central office equipments which depend on synchronization obtained from the ringing interrupter ground pulses. Typical uses are: (a) synchronizing ringback tone with ringing current, and (b) intercepting the calls of a particular party on a party line.

matching, *n.* Connecting two circuits together through an impedance transforming device so that there is maximum power transfer.

matching, antenna, *n.* The process of adjusting the impedance of an antenna so that it matches the impedance of its transmission line.

matrices, *n. pl.* Plural of matrix, which see.

matrix, *n.* A rectangular array of horizontal and vertical input or output leads with diode or correed crosspoints at the intersections, used as a means of switching from any input to any output.

matrix, antenna switch, *n.* A crosspoint network of coaxial switches with which it is possible to connect any one of several radio transmitters (or receivers) to any of several antennas. The coaxial switch is usually a relay which can be remotely operated.

matrix, EAX switching, *n.* A group of correed switches mounted on a printed wiring card and connected so that every matrix inlet can be connected to a matrix outlet. Cards having inlet-outlet or outlet-inlet configurations of 10X4, 10X5, 10X6, and 10X8 are used.

matrix, nonblocking, *n.* A switching matrix through which a connection can always be found, even to the point where all the matrix terminals are in use.

matrix, translation. See "decoder."

maximum power transfer, *n.* The condition in which the maximum amount of power is transferred from a generator or signal source to a load. This occurs when the load impedance is a conjugate of the source impedance.

Maximum Power Transfer Theorem. See "Appendix B."

maximum useable frequency (MUF), *n.* In HF radio communications which uses waves reflected from the ionosphere, the highest frequency which will be reflected back to the receiver under ionospheric conditions which then prevail. A higher frequency would penetrate the ionosphere and be lost in space.

maxwell, *n.* The unit of flux density, equal to the number of lines of force, assumed to be one line per square centimeter normal to a field of one gauss.

Maxwell's equations, *n. pl.* Fundamental mathematical equations which state the condition at a point under the influence of varying electric and magnetic fields.

meaconing, *n.* The clandestine generation or retransmission of a radio navigation signal in order to confuse navigation.

mean, *n.* The arithmetic middle point of a range of values, obtained by adding the smallest value to the largest value and dividing that sum by two.

mean-time-to-repair (MTTR), *n.* On a particular item or system, the total corrective maintenance time divided by the total number of corrective maintenance actions during a given period of time.

measured-rate, *adj.* Describing a telephone line which receives measured service; service for which a charge is made in accordance with a measured amount of usage.

measured service, *n.* Telephone service for which a charge is made in accordance with the number of calls or "message units" during the billing period.

mechanical intercepting. See "intercepting, machine."

median, *n.* A point below which there are as many instances as there are above.

meet-me. See "conference, meet-me."

meg, *n.* Megohm (slang).

mega-. A prefix meaning "one million."

megabit, *n.* One million binary digits.

megacycle, *n.* One million cycles.

megahertz, *n.* One million cycles per second.

megawatt, *n.* One million watts.

Megger, *n.* Registered name of the James G. Biddle Company's brand of ohmmeter containing a hand-cranked generator as its source of testing power. Loosely, any ohmmeter with a hand-generator power

source. The word "megger" inplies a meter reading in megohms.

megger, ground resistance, *n.* A meter reading ground resistance in ohms and having a hand-cranked generator power supply. It has three terminals, one for the ground being measured plus two reference grounds.

megohm, *n.* One million ohms. The unit used when measuring insulation resistance.

megohm miles, *n.* Megohms per mile.

megohms per mile, *n.* The insulation of a telephone cable conductor, measured from the conductor to the sheath and to all other conductors grounded, equal to the resistance to ground in megohms divided by the conductor length in miles.

mel, *n.* A subjective unit of pitch, related to a scale on which a pitch of 1000 mels is produced by a pure 1000 hertz tone at a level 40 dB above the listener's threshold of hearing.

memory, *n.* That portion of a translator, register, or computer in which information in the form of binary digits can be stored for later use.

memory, permanent, *n.* (1) Memory which contains information which is likely to be needed over long periods of time. (2) Memory which is not erased when it is read.

memory, random-access, *n.* A memory system which requires that a memory address be specified with each command to read or write.

memory, scratch pad, *n.* A memory intended to temporarily store a small amount of information which may be needed often, and without delay.

memory, semi-permanent, *n.* A memory unit in a common-controlled switching center used for the stored program and translation information.

memory, temporary, *n.* A memory unit used for the storage of transient information required in processing telephone calls.

memory core. See "core, magnetic."

memo ticket, *n.* A special-instruction toll ticket used for "credit card" and "bill-to-third-number" calls. On it is recorded the "bill to" number, calling number, called number, ticketer number, date, and clock time.

memo ticket call. See "special-instruction call."

mesh, *n.* A set of branches forming a closed path in a network, provided that if any one branch is omitted from the set, the remaining branches of the set do not form a closed path, or loop.

message, *n.* (1) A completed telephone call. (2) A teletypewriter message.

message, multiple address, *n.* A message which is to be delivered to several addressees.

message, service, *n.* A message between communication personnel concerning the problems of providing communication service.

message, straggler. See "straggler message."

message, toll, *n.* A completed toll call.

message register. See "register, message."

message switching, *n.* A method of handling digital messages at a switching facility where incoming messages are stored pending availability of an outgoing circuit, and then transmitted onward. The method may be manual, semi-automatic, or automatic.

message unit, *n.* A unit of measurement used in charging for local messages, based on time and distance.

message waiting service, *n.* A service provided at stations on hotel or motel PABXs, which indicates visually, by a flashing lamp on the telephone, that someone has called and left a message with the attendant. Requires special telephones and a panel of locking keys at the attendants switchboard.

messenger, *n.* (1) One who carries a message. (2) A steel strand that carries an aerial cable. See "strand, suspension."

metallic circuit, *n.* A circuit which is completely in wire, not via the earth or via carrier or radio.

metallic Varley. See "Varley, three-wire."

meter, *n.* An instrument for measuring pressures, rates, or quantities.

meter, field strength, *n.* A portable radio receiver, calibrated in microvolts or millivolts per meter when used with a standard antenna, used to measure the strength of a radio signal at a point in the field.

meter, frequency. See "frequency meter."

meter, noise. See "set, noise measuring."

meter, VU. See "volume indicator."

meteor, *n.* The total phenomena which accompany a rocky body (meteoroid) which falls toward the Earth from space: the flash, streak of light, and ionized trail.

meteor burst transmission, *n.* The theory which states that scatter radio transmission is made possible by the reflection of radio energy from ionized trails left by the many meteors which strike the atmosphere each second. Meteor trail reflections probably add to reradiations from the E layer scattering region.

meteorite, *n.* A metallic or stony body from outer space which enters the earth's atmosphere at about 45 miles per second and becomes incandescent about 60 miles above the earth. Causes additional ionization in the ionosphere, and thus affects radio communications.

meter, *n.* (1) The basic unit of length in the metric system, equal to 3.281 feet or 39.37 inches. (2) An instrument for measuring the value of some quantity. Unless specifically designated to be a recording meter it is assumed to be an indicating meter. See also "ammeter," "bias meter," "frequency meter," "milliammeter," "ohmmeter," "vacuum-tube voltmeter," "volt-ohm-milliam-meter." "voltmeter," and "watt-hour meter."

meter, ampere-hour, *n.* A meter which measures and registers the integral, with respect to time, of the current which passes through it.

meter, ATB, *n.* A message register so connected to the "C" leads of all trunks in a group that it registers the number of times all trunks in this group are busy.

meter, bias, *n.* A direct current zero-center milliammeter used on tele-typewriter circuits to measure signal bias directly in percent. A positive reading indicates marking bias; a negative reading indicates spacing bias.

meter, field strength, *n.* (1) A cali-brated portable radio receiver hav-ing an output meter, used with a standard antenna to measure the strength of the radio frequency electromagnetic field at a particular point due to radiation from a par-ticular radio transmitter. (2) A tune-able radio-frequency voltmeter used to measure the signal strength along a CATV distribution or feeder cable. It is usually connected at an amplifier location.

meter, gas volume, *n.* A double-dia-phragm displacement-type totalizing gas meter which measures the total volume in cubic feet of gas or dry air passing through the meter and registers the total volume on a decimal dial. Used to indicate the total volume of dry air flowing into a pressurized cable system. Ex-cessive usage of gas indicates a leak in the system.

meter, LTB, *n.* A message register so connected to the "C" lead of the last-choice trunk in a trunk group that it counts the number of times this last trunk is busy.

meter, overflow, *n.* A message regis-ter connected to count the number of calls received which cannot be forwarded because all trunks are busy. Overflow meters are common-ly used on linefinder circuits. See also "lost call."

meter, peg-count, *n.* A message regis-ter connected in a circuit to count the number of calls offered. See also "register, message."

meter, pipe alarm, *n.* Device which monitors the pressure and volume of dry gas delivered to a pipe which supplies gas to a pressurized cable.

meter, running-time, *n.* An electric clock which runs during the period that a circuit is energized, and shows the total length of time it is in use. Usually made with a digital register dial showing hours.

meter, usage, *n.* A device for measur-ing telephone traffic consisting of a scanner which scans one or more groups of circuits each 100 seconds to determine if they are busy. The busy count is tallied on a register in CCS, and sometimes printed out each hour or half-hour.

metering, periodic pulse, *n.* A method of metering toll calls used in Europe in which a message unit meter steps periodically, with a frequency depending upon the distance be-tween the two subscribers in con-versation. In the United States it is known as "zone registration."

metering service, message, *n.* A service provided with hotel and motel PABXs where a message register associated with each station counts the number of completed trunk calls, for which a charge will be made.

meter panel, dry air, *n.* A panel in-cluding the following components: (a) An indicating gas meter showing the number of cubic feet of dry air used by all cables fed from the panel. (b) A manifold which dis-tributes the dry air to individual cables, and for each one provides: an individual air shut-off valve, an individual pressure testing valve, and an individual air flow rate indicator.

meter panel, gas pipe alarm, *n.* A panel which monitors a dry gas pipeline, and (a) Adjusts and indicates gas pressure to the pipeline. (b) Indicates gas flow rate and total volume of gas used. (c) Provides an alarm when the gas usage rate increases.

MF 2/6. See "signaling, multifrequency, 2/6."

mho, *n.* The unit of conductance or admittance. It is the measure of the resistance or impedance in ohms. Note that "mho" is "ohm" spelled backwards.

mica, *n.* A naturally occurring crystalline form of aluminum-potassium-silicate which can be split into thin somewhat flexible sheets, translucent or transparent. Heat-resistant, and an excellent insulator. Sometimes called "isinglass."

micro-. A prefix meaning "one millionth part of."

microammeter, *n.* A meter calibrated to read microamperes.

microampere, *n.* One-millionth of an ampere.

microbar, *n.* The metric unit of sound pressure, equal to one dyne per square centimeter.

microcircuit, *n.* Any very small circuit, such as an integrated circuit.

microelectronics, *n.* Electronics construction in the form of semiconductor integrated circuits, thin film circuits, and combinations of these. Excluded is circuitry constructed mainly of discrete active and passive electronic devices.

microfarad (mf), *n.* A unit of capacitance equal to one millionth of a farad. Most capacitances used in telephone equipment are of sizes which can be conveniently stated in microfarads.

micromicro-. Obsolete prefix meaning "one millionth of one millionth of," now replaced by the prefix "pico-."

micromicrofarad (mmf), *n.* One millionth of one millionth of a farad, now properly known as a picofarad (pf).

micron, *n.* The unit used for specifying the wavelength of light, equal to one millionth of a meter.

microphone, *n.* A transducer which accepts sound waves and converts them into electric waves. A fairly high degree of fidelity is implied. See also "transmitter, telephone," which is not high fidelity.

microphone, carbon, *n.* A microphone in which sound waves compress loosely packed carbon granules, causing their resistance and the current through them to vary in step with the sound wave.

microphone, close-talking, *n.* A microphone designed to be held close to the mouth of the speaker, so that ambient noise will not degrade the speech.

microphone, crystal, *n.* A microphone in which sound waves generate a complex voice current by deforming a piezoelectric crystal.

microphone, foil-electret, *n.* A microphone having high fidelity, good sensitivity, and high reliability. Consists of an electrically charged plastic foil stretched over a perforated metal backplate. Vibration of the charged foil generates an electric field between the foil and the backplate, and thereby an AC voltage in an external circuit. See also "foil-electret."

microphone, moving-coil, *n.* A microphone in which sound waves generate a complex voice current by moving a small coil through a permanent-magnet flux field.

microphone, moving-conductor, *n.* A microphone in which sound waves generate a complex voice current by moving a ribbon conductor through a permanent-magnet flux field.

microphonic, *adj.* Likely to produce circuit noise as a result of mechanical movement. The resultant noise is termed "microphonics."

Micro Switch, *n.* Honeywell's trademarked name for their brand of small switches having toggle contact springs which can be operated by a very small movement of the actuator.

microvolt, *n.* One-millionth of a volt.

microvolts-per-meter, *n.* A measure of the field intensity or field strength of a radio wave. It is the voltage in microvolts between two points one meter apart in space lying on an electric line of force in the plane of the wave front.

microwave, *adj.* Pertaining to radio transmission using very short wave lengths: 30 centimeters or less, corresponding to a frequency of 1000 megahertz or greater.

microwave frequency, *n.* Any of the ultrahigh frequencies suitable for line-of-sight radio communication.

microwave radio. See "radio, microwave."

microwave system. See "system, microwave."

mid-section, *adj. & adv.* Located halfway between two loading points, or at the mid-point of a loading section.

mid-span, *adj. & adv.* Between poles in a pole line, or between manholes in a conduit run.

mil, *n.* (1) One thousandth of an inch. (2) An angle, such that it is subtended by a 1-foot arc at a distance of 1000 feet. One mil equals 0.0575 degree, and 17.4 mils equal one degree.

mil, circular. See "circular mil."

mile, wire, *n.* A single conductor one mile in length.

mileage, *n.* The distance in feet or miles from a subscriber outside the base rate area to the base rate area boundary, used for rate determination. Usually airline distance rather than route distance.

mile of standard cable, *n.* The unit of transmission loss used before the advent of the "decibel" was the "mile of standard cable." It was the volume transmission loss at 800 hertz caused by one mile of a paired conductor having a loop resistance of 88 ohms and a capaci-

tance of 0.054 microfarad, with no series inductance or shunt conductance.

milli-. A prefix meaning "one thousandth part of."

milliammeter, *n.* A meter which measures current in thousandths of an ampere.

milliampere (ma), *n.* One-thousandth of an ampere. A small current.

millihenry (mh), *n.* One-thousandth of a henry. A useful sized unit of inductance. If the current through a one millihenry inductance varies at the rate of one ampere per second there will be one-thousandth of a volt potential across the inductance.

millivoltmeter, *n.* An indicating meter that measures electrical pressure drop in millivolts, used in checking for DC current flow on underground cable sheaths and also, with an "instrument shunt" for measuring much larger currents.

millivolts-per-meter, *n.* A radio wave field intensity equal to one thousand microvolts-per-meter, which see.

milliwatt, *n.* One thousandth of a watt.

minimize, *n. v.* An administrative action to reduce circuit overloads by prohibiting all but the most essential message or telephone traffic. See also "load control, - - -."

minority carrier. See "carrier, minority."

minor relay center, *n.* A tape relay center which does not have alternate route capability.

minor switch, *n.* A 10-point, single-motion stepping switch. The wipers return to the "home" position when released.

mirror, splicer's, *n.* A small sturdy hand mirror, about 3 x 4 inches, used by a splicer to examine the quality of a wiped joint at the back of a splice.

misalignment, *n.* The cumulative departure from the ideal transmission condition where repeater gains equal cable losses in each repeater section of a long circuit.

misalignment, negative, *n.* Condition where cable losses exceed repeater gains in each repeater section of a long circuit. Signal-to-noise ratio is poorer than normal, but modulation distortion and crosstalk are improved.

misalignment, positive, *n.* Condition where repeater gains exceed cable losses in each repeater section of a long circuit. Modulation distortion and crosstalk are higher than normal. Signal-to-noise ratio is improved.

mismatch, impedance, *n.* A difference in the magnitude or phase of two impedances which causes reflections and prevents maximum power transfer. Can be expressed equally as a "reflection coefficient," a "return loss," or a "voltage standing wave ratio."

mitigation, electrolysis, *n.* To arrest or reduce the severity of electrolytic destruction of lead cable sheaths by the application of natural drainage (see "negative return") or forced drainage (see "anode, galvanic").

mixer, *n.* (1) A device for combining two or more audio input signals into a single output signal, with means for adjusting the level of each input separately. (2) In a superheterodyne radio receiver, the stage where the incoming radio signal is mixed with a local oscillator signal to produce an intermediate frequency. Sometimes called a "first detector."

M-L ratio. See "ratio, M-L."

mnemonic, *adj.* Describing a designation which is designed so as to be easy to remember.

mobile base station. See "station, mobile base."

mobile control terminal, *n.* Equipment at the fixed station of a mobile system. When accessed by the mobile operator, it turns on the radio transmitter, sends frequency-shift dial pulses to the transmitter. On incoming calls, it receives the signal from the mobile unit and sends a line lamp signal to the operator.

mobile radiotelephone, *n.* System providing exchange telephone service to a station located in an auto or other mobile vehicle, using radio circuits to a base radio station which is connected to a central office.

mobile telephone service, *n.* (1) Telephone service between a fixed base station and several mobile stations in vehicles, (2) telephone service from mobile stations into the commercial telephone system.

mode, *n.* (1) A method of operation. (2) The most frequent value in a frequency distribution. (3) A pattern in which waves vibrate. (4) One of several configurations in which energy propagates through a waveguide. (5) One of the modes of vibration in a piezoelectric material, either the extensional, flexural, or shear mode.

mode, break-in, *n.* A mode of operation of an echo suppressor which operates to block echoes, but removes the supression if the second customer should attempt to interrupt the talker. See also "mode, suppressor."

mode, dominant waveguide, *n.* The simplest or lowest order mode by which radio waves at a particular frequency can be propagated in a waveguide of particular dimensions. The dominant mode is the preferred mode, because it permits the longest wavelength and the lowest cutoff frequency.

mode I, *n.* A method of operating teletypewriter or data communication systems which provides duplex, synchronous operation. Data is transmitted in line blocks of 80 data characters plus 4 framing units. Reception of each line block is acknowledged, with an OK or error signal.

mode II, *n.* A method of operating teletypewriter or data communication systems which provides duplex, non-synchronous operation, without error detection or correction. All messages are automatically numbered sequentially.

mode III, *n.* A method of operating teletypewriter or data communication systems which provides half-duplex (one way at a time) operation. Otherwise the same as Mode I.

mode IV, *n.* A method of operating teletypewriter or data communication systems which provides half-duplex asynchronous (start-stop) operation. Otherwise the same as Mode II.

mode V, *n.* A method of operating teletypewriter communication systems which provides full-duplex asynchronous (start-stop) operation, with character framing detection and automatic message acknowledgment.

mode, suppressor, *n.* A mode of operation of an echo suppressor in which the talker effectively reduces the long circuit to a one-way path, so that the suppressor blocks transmission from the second customer if he should try to speak at the same time. See also "mode, break-in."

mode, TE, *n.* Transverse electric mode. A mode of radio-frequency wave propagation through a waveguide in which the electric field is always perpendicular to the direction of propagation.

mode, TEM. See "wave, transverse electromagnetic."

mode, TM, *n.* A transverse magnetic mode. A mode of radio-frequency wave propagation through a waveguide in which the magnetic field is always perpendicular to the direction of propagation.

modem, *n.* A single unit of equipment which combines the functions of modulator and demodulator. This is an economical arrangement, since the two circuits can use common elements.

modular, *adj.* Having dimensions which are integral multiples of a unit of length called a module.

modulate, *v.* To vary the amplitude, frequency, or phase of a high-frequency wave, called a "carrier," in step with the amplitude variations of another wave, called the "modulating wave." The carrier is usually a sine wave, but the modulating wave is often a complex voice-frequency wave.

modulating wave. See "wave, modulating."

modulation, *n.* (1) The process whereby the amplitude or frequency or phase of a single-frequency wave (called the carrier wave) is varied in step with the instantaneous value of, or samples of, a complex wave (called the modulating wave). (2) The intelligence which is carried on a modulated carrier wave.

modulation, amplitude, *n.* A process whereby the amplitude of a single-frequency carrier wave is varied in step with the instantaneous value of a complex modulating wave. In amplitude modulation two "sidebands" are created, one consisting of the sum of the carrier and modulating frequencies (upper sideband), and the other consisting of the difference between the carrier frequency and the modulating frequencies.

modulation, angle, *n.* Modulation in which the frequency or phase of a carrier is caused to vary with the modulating signal.

modulation, delta, *n.* A variant of pulse code modulation, in which a code representing the difference between the amplitude of a sample and the amplitude of the previous sample is sent. Operates well in the presence of noise, but requires a wide frequency band.

modulation, double, *n.* A two step modulation in which an intelligence wave modulates a sub-carrier, and then the modulated sub-carrier is used to modulate a higher frequency carrier.

modulation, duobinary, *n.* Modulation of a carrier wave by a three-level pulse coded signal. Twice as much information can be transmitted in a unit bandwidth compared to a two-level signal.

modulation, frequency, *n.* A process whereby the frequency of a previously single-frequency carrier wave is varied in step with the amplitude of a complex modulating wave. Higher order sidebands result from this type of modulation.

modulation, group. See "group modulation."

modulation, high-level, *n.* Modulation produced at a point in a system where the power level approximates that at the output of the system.

modulation, independent sideband. See "independent sideband modulation."

modulation, low-level, *n.* Modulation introduced at a low level point in a system, before amplification.

modulation, multiple, *n.* A two-step modulation process in which the modulated wave from the first step becomes the modulating wave for the next step.

modulation, percentage. See "percentage modulation."

modulation, phase, *n.* Modulation in which the phase angle of the carrier wave is caused to vary by an amount proportional to the instantaneous value of the modulating wave.

modulation, pulse-amplitude, *n.* Modulation in which the modulating wave is caused to amplitude-modulate a pulse carrier.

modulation, pulse-code, *n.* The conversion of an analog (voice) signal to a digital code. The analog signal amplitude is sampled at a rate more than twice the signal frequency, and the amplitude (measured in 32 increments) of each sample is transmitted as 5-bit code. To transmit a 4 kHz voice signal would therefore require the transmission of 5 x 8000 = 40,000 bits per second, as a minimum. Provides undistorted transmission, even in the presence of noise.

modulation, pulse-duration, *n.* Pulse-time modulation in which the value of each instantaneous sample of the modulating wave is caused to modulate the duration of a pulse.

modulation, pulse-frequency, *n.* A form of modulation in which the pulse repetition rate is varied as a function of the instantaneous value of the modulating wave.

modulation, pulse-length, *n.* Pulse-duration modulation.

modulation, pulse-position, *n.* Modulation in which a pulse is delayed from its normal position in time as a function of the modulating wave.

modulation, pulse-time, *n.* Modulation in which the values of instantaneous samples of the modulating wave are caused to modulate the time of occurrence of some characteristic of a pulse carrier.

modulation, pulse-width, *n.* Pulse-duration modulation.

modulation, single-sideband. See "single-sideband modulation."

modulation, spread spectrum, *n.* Modulation in which the information wave modulates a high-frequency pseudo-random noise code generated by a shift register. These pulses are spread over the entire baseband of a radio transmitter, and may be multiplexed with other similar signals by time-division techniques. Spread-spectrum is a highly effective way of combating jamming.

modulation, velocity, *n.* Modulation of an electron stream by alternately accelerating and decelerating the electrons, thus grouping them into bunches.

modulation capability, *n.* Of a transmitter, the maximum percentage modulation that can be obtained without exceeding a specified distortion.

modulation index. See "index, modulation."

modulation plan, *n.* The arrangements by which individual channels or groups of channels are modulated to a final frequency allocation.

modulation rate, *n.* The reciprocal of the unit signal interval measured in seconds. The rate is expressed in bauds.

modulator, *n.* A device for applying the information contained in a complex (modulating) wave to a higher frequency sinusoidal (carrier) wave, so as to enable transmission of the information at the higher carrier frequency.

modulator, balanced, *n.* A "push-pull" type of modulator circuit in which the carrier frequency is applied in phase to the two halves of the circuit, while the modulating signal is applied 180 degrees out of phase. The result is the suppression of the carrier frequency in the output of the modulator.

modulator, FM, *n.* A low-power FM transmitter which will accept an audio input and modulate it on any of the FM broadcast channels in the 88.1 to 107.9 MHz band for transmission over a CATV network.

modulator, product, *n.* A device which combines a baseband signal with a carrier wave.

modulator, ring, *n.* A modulator consisting of four diodes connected in a closed square, or ring.

modulator, SCA, *n.* Subsidiary carrier authorization modulator. A device which will take an audio input and modulate it to a supersonic frequency which can be combined with the regular sonic (50 Hz-15 kHz) input to an FM transmitter, which will thus broadcast two programs simultaneously. The SCA program will not be heard unless the FM receiver is equipped with an SCA demodulator. Used to transmit programs: music, stock reports, etc., for which the subscriber pays.

modulator, television, *n.* A low-power television transmitter which combines two signals: a video signal, and a 4.5 MHz FM sound signal and produces a composite TV sig-

nal which can be fed to a CATV cable network. Used for transmitting video-taped programs, and programs taken from the air with a television demodulator, which see.

modulator, television sound, *n.* A device used at a CATV head end to transmit a music or other audio program to the CATV network for pickup on a specific unused TV channel.

module, *n.* (1) An assembly of electronic circuits or devices performing one or more distinct functions, constructed as an independently-packaged, replaceable unit, as part of a complete equipment. (2) A unit of length used in sizing architectural or other materials. Usually 4 inches or some integral multiple thereof.

modulus of elasticity, *n.* The ratio of unit stress to unit deformation of any structural material which is not stressed beyond its elastic limit, given in pounds per square inch. Typical values are:

Aluminum	— 9,000,000.
Copper	— 17,000,000.
Iron	—25,000,000.
Steel	— 30,000,000.

moisture-repellent, *adj.* Constructed or treated so that moisture will not penetrate.

moisture-resistant, *adj.* Constructed or treated so that exposure to a moist atmosphere will not cause deterioration.

molecule, *n.* The smallest subdivision of a compound which still retains the chemical properties of that compound. In a gas, it is the smallest particle that moves about as a whole.

molybdenum, *n.* A metallic element, similar to tungsten chemically, but softer and more ductile. Used in electron tube filaments and grids.

monaural, *adj.* Describing sound reproduction using only one source of sound, and giving a monophonic effect.

monitor, *v.t.* (1) To listen-in to a voice

communication without disturbing it for the purpose of determining its quality and freedom from interference or trouble. (2) To check on the quality of a teletypewriter circuit by means of a monitoring printer. (3) At a switchboard, to listen-in on a cord circuit to determine whether the circuit is busy. See also "challenge."

monitor, ringing, *n.* A device which is connected to an interrupted ringing supply which it continuously checks. If the ringing signal should fail or become continuous (no interruption) the monitor relays will operate to give an alarm or transfer to standby ringing equipment.

monitor, telegraph distortion, *n.* A device which monitors incoming teletypewriter signals on a circuit, and actuates an alarm if the telegraph distortion exceeds a preset amount.

monitor, tone, *n.* A transistorized device which is connected to busy tone. If the tone should fail or become continuous (no interruption) the monitor relays will operate to give an alarm or transfer to standby tone equipment.

monitoring, *n.* Listening to a communication service without disturbing it to determine its quality or freedom from trouble or interference.

monitoring key. See "key, monitoring."

monocord switchboard. See "switchboard, monocord."

monolithic conduit. See "conduit, monolithic."

monophonic, *adj.* Referring to sound which is transmitted over a single path. The opposite of "stereophonic."

monostable, *adj.* Describing a device or circuit which is stable in only one state. An input pulse causes only a momentary change to the unstable state. The "one-shot multivibrator" is a monostable device.

moon, *n.* The natural satellite of the Earth, at a distance of 238,857

miles and having a mean diameter of 2,160 miles. Has a black body temperature of 140-220 degrees Kelvin. Used as a natural passive reflector to relay radio signals from Wahiawa, Hawaii to Washington, D.C.

Morse code. See "code, Morse."

Morse telegraph, *n.* Telegraphy in which the signals are formed in accordance with the Morse code.

Motion, Laws of. See "Newton's Laws of Motion" in "Appendix B."

motional impedance. See "impedance, motional."

motor, *n.* A machine which converts electricity into power to do work. See also "engine."

motor, induction. See "induction motor."

motor, series, *n.* A motor having the armature and field windings connected in series. A series motor has a high starting torque, but its speed varies with the load.

motor, shunt-wound, *n.* An electric motor whose armature and field windings are connected in parallel. It has a fairly constant speed, but a low starting torque.

motor, stepper, *n.* A device which converts pulsating direct current into rotary mechanical motion. Each DC pulse rotates the stepper a certain fraction of one revolution. The rotor is magnetically held at its last position.

motor, synchronous, *n.* An alternating current motor which operates at a speed determined solely by the frequency of the supply power, and does not slow down as its load increases. Your AC electric clock contains a tiny synchronous motor.

motor, universal. See "universal motor."

motor-boating, *n.* A very low frequency (1-10 Hz) oscillation of an electron tube circuit.

motor effect, *n.* The repulsion force between adjacent conductors which carry currents in opposite directions.

motor-generator, flywheel. See "flywheel motor-generator."

motor-generator set. See "set, motor-generator."

moulding, ground wire, *n.* A half-round wooden moulding of pentachlorophenol treated Douglas Fir, having a milled longitudinal slot so that it has a U-shaped cross-section. Used to protect vertical runs of ground wire on the sides of poles. Available in 8 and 10-foot lengths with ½", ¾", or 1-inch wire grooves. Also available made of polyvinyl chloride.

mounting, *n.* (1) A rack, framework, or steel plate which serves as a support for equipment. (2) The act of fastening equipment to a mounting.

mounting, apparatus, *n.* Framework arranged to hold telephone apparatus in units on mounting plates, printed wiring cards, etc.

mounting, data, *n.* Relay rack (23") mounted housing which integrates a power unit, interrupter, and apparatus mountings to hold printed wiring cards, all cabled to connectors for external connections.

mounting, dial, *n.* A cylindrical fixture used to protect and mount telephone dials on horizontal or vertical faces of switchboards, turrets, etc. Usually requires an auxiliary dial adapter, and often holds the dial face at an angle of 37 degrees from the horizontal for better visibility.

mounting, handset, *n.* The portion of the telephone set which contains the switchhook.

mounting, jack, *n.* Narrow insulating strip arranged to hold a number of similar individual jacks for mounting in a switchboard or relay rack. Commonly for 10 or 20 jacks, but also in 1, 2, 4, 6, 24, 26, 48, or 52 jack sizes.

mounting, key, *n.* Device for holding a multiplicity of keys of similar type, permitting them to be mounted. (a) Narrow insulating strip arranged to mount ten push-button or turn button keys in the same space occupied by a switchboard jack strip. (b) Metal framework arranged to mount multiples of six-button push keys.

mounting, protector (housing), *n.* Housing which encloses and protects a station protector in outdoor installations. Usually a metal base with a slip cover and locking screw.

mounting, protector (mounting), *n.* An insulating base equipped with clips and terminals for mounting protector blocks, fuses, and/or heat coils.

mouth, *n.* The large end of a horn.

mouth, artificial, *n.* A transducer consisting of a loudspeaker providing accurate and reproducible conversion of electrical to sound energy. Used to test the response of telephone transmitters.

moving-coil, *adj.* Describing any device, such as a loudspeaker, meter, microphone, or phonograph pickup, which depends for its action on a coil of wire in a magnetic field which is caused to move by varying currents in the coil.

M regions, *n. pl.* Areas of the solar surface that are responsible for electromagnetic disturbances on the earth.

mu factor. See "factor, amplification."

multiaccess telephone service, *n.* Condition where telephone or PBX has access to several central offices. Provides ultra-reliability.

multi-alternate routing, *n.* Alternate routing with provision for advancing the call to more than one alternate route, tested in sequence.

multiconductor, *adj.* Having more than one conductor within a single cable complex.

multicoupler, receiving, *n.* Device which permits several (2-12) radio receivers to use the same antenna. Typically consists of a broadband input amplifier with several output amplifiers.

multicoupler, transmitting. See "networks, antenna coupling" and "circulator."

multihop, *adj.* Describing a radio propagation path in which there is more than one reflection from the ionosphere.

multi-line telephone, *n.* A telephone set with integral push-button keys used to connect it to any of several lines. Available in 2, 3, 6, 12, 18, and 30 line sizes.

multi-link circuit, *n.* A circuit built up of two or more links.

multimeter, *n.* A meter having multiple scales. Usually means a volt-ohm-milliammeter. See also "analyzer, circuit."

multioffice exchange, *n.* An exchange area which is served by several local central offices.

multiparty line, *n.* A central office subscriber's line which serves more than one customer.

multipath fading, *n.* Variations in the field strength of a radio signal resulting when the signal arrives at the receiving antenna over two or more paths which are not the same length. Some frequencies which traverse longer paths arrive delayed or "out of phase." Out of phase signals cancel each other and thus are very weak. Other frequencies may have normal strength.

multipath transmission, *n.* The transmission of a radio signal which is affected by reflections and refractions so that some portions of the signal follow paths which are longer than others, and therefore delayed and out-of-phase. See also "multipath fading."

multiple, *adj.* Connected in parallel.— *n.* (1) A circuit which is accessible at several points. (2) The aggregate of such points. (3) The parallel connection between corresponding jacks in several switchboard positions, or corresponding pairs in several cable terminals.—*v.* (1) To connect in parallel. (2) To make a circuit accessible at several points.

multiple, bridged. See "bridged multiple."

multiple, junior. See "junior-multiple."

multiple, senior. See "senior-multiple."

multiple, subscriber's, *n.* A bank of jacks in a manual switchboard which give outgoing access to subscriber's lines, and usually have more than one appearance across the face of the switchboard.

multiple, switchboard, *n.* On a large switchboard, the arrangement of lines and trunks to make them accessible to each operator. Each circuit terminates in jacks at frequent intervals (every 3, 4, or 5 panels) along the switchboard. Each such termination is called a "multiple appearance."

multiple, switchboard panel, *n.* The number of panels on a switchboard after which the multiple repeats. On a "three-panel multiple," the appearances are on panels 1-3, 4-6, 7-9, etc. On a "four-panel multiple," the appearances would be on panels 1-4, 5-8, 9-12, etc.

multiple access, satellite, *n.* The ability of a communication satellite to receive signals from several earth terminals simultaneously, and to amplify, translate, and relay these signals back to earth. Several different techniques are used to accomplish this:

    a. Frequency division.
    b. Time division.
    c. Spread spectrum.
    d. Single sideband up, and frequency division down.
    e. Pulse address.

multiple-address, *adj.* (1) Describing a message which is to be delivered to several addressees. (2) Describing a code which specifies the addressees of a multiple-address message.

multiple circuit, *n.* A circuit in which two or more similar elements are connected in parallel.

multiple key telephone set, *n.* A complete key telephone set in a plastic housing with a sloping front panel on which is mounted a dial and either 3 key units (18 buttons) or 5 key units (30 buttons). Requires separate relay units. See also "key telephone set."

multiple marking, *n.* A distinctive marking associated with a jack such as a painted quadrant, underline, circle, signal plug, etc., indicating a condition affecting the line or a station on the line.

multiple twin, *n.* A quadded conductor formed of two pairs twisted together.

multiplex, *n.* Equipment which provides a means of transmitting two or more signals over the same transmission path.

multiplex, DCS standard, *n.* The Defense Communication System has adopted the AN/UCC-4 solid-state universal multiplex as their system standard. This is a 600-channel multiplex capable of data loading on every channel, and is electrically identical with Lenkurt type AN/FCC-17.

multiplex, frequency division, *n.* A multiplex system in which the total transmission bandwidth is divided into narrower bands, each used for a single, separate channel.

multiplex, time division, *n.* Equipment which enables the transmitting of a number of signals over a single common path by transmitting them sequentially at different instants of time.

multiplexing, *n.* The act of combining a number of individual message circuits for transmission over a common transmission path. Two methods are used: (1) frequency division, and (2) time division.

multiplexing, phase, *n.* The process of encoding two (or more) information channels on a single tone.

multiplex operation, *n.* Simultaneous transmission of two or more messages in either or both directions over the same transmission path.

multiplier, frequency, *n.* An electron tube circuit in which the plate circuit is tuned to a frequency which is a multiple of the frequency existing in the grid circuit. See also "doubler, frequency" and "tripler, frequency."

multiplier, instrument, *n.* A precision resistor, placed in series with a voltmeter to enable measurement of a high voltage with a voltmeter having a lower voltage range.

multiplier, voltage. See "multiplier, instrument."

multipling, *n.* The connecting together, point for point, of corresponding jacks on several switchboard positions, or corresponding pairs in several cable terminals.

multipolar, *adj.* Describing a machine or magnetic circuit which has more than one pair of magnetic poles.

multiswitched, *adj.* Describes toll calls or traffic which use three or more intertoll trunks in tandem, interconnected at two or more switching centers.

multitap, *n.* Device used on a system for distributing television signals via cable which will permit connecting several subscriber's coaxial cables to a single coaxial distribution cable. The multitap maintains the proper junction impedances and isolates each subscriber from interaction with the others.

multivibrator, *n.* A form of relaxation oscillator which has two stages coupled so that the input of each is derived from the output of the other. Can act either as a one-shot flip-flop circuit, or as a free-running oscillator.

multivibrator, free-running, *n.* A multivibrator which oscillates without triggering pulses.

multivibrator, one-shot, *n.* A multivibrator which delivers one output pulse, of adjustable width, for each input pulse received.

Murray loop, *n.* A measurement made with a Wheatstone bridge to determine the distance to a ground fault on a wire. The faulty wire and a good wire are looped at the far end of the circuit and this loop is substituted for two arms of the bridge.

MUSA antenna, *n.* Multiple unit steerable antenna. See "antenna, MUSA."

muslin, *n.* (1) A coarse cotton fabric. (2) A 4-inch wide bandage made of muslin, used for wrapping the spliced conductors before a cable splice is closed. (3) A diaper-shaped piece of muslin used for holding desiccant in a splice.

mutilation, pulse, *n.* Gross distortion of pulse signals.

mutual conductance, *n.* Transconductance, which see.

mutual impedance. See "impedance, mutual."

mutual inductance. See "inductance, mutual."

Mylar, *n.* DuPont's trademark for their non-stretching polyester film which is used as a backing for high-grade magnetic tape.

nail, pole dating, *n.* A heavy forged steel nail, hot galvanized, having a rectangular head showing the last two digits of the year. Used for marking poles with the date when set.

nail, station wire, *n.* A #7 wire nail (⅞-inch long) equipped with a steel clip under the head, used for fastening jacketed station wire to a wall.

nail, wiring, *n.* A thin nail, ½ inch or ¾ inch long, having a large flat head with a fiber insulating disk on the under side. Enameled brown or ivory. Used to fasten paired inside wire to walls.

NAND gate, *n.* A multiple-input single-output gate whose output is "one" if any input is "zero," and is "zero" if all inputs are "one."

nano-. A prefix meaning "one-thousandth of a millionth." One billionth.

nanosecond, *n.* One billionth of a second.

Naperian logarithm, *n.* A natural logarithm whose base in 2.718282.

narrowband, *adj.* Describing circuits or equipment capable of handling 2400 bits-per-second signals.

narrow-band facility, *n.* A facility having a bandwidth of 20 kilocycles or less.

n-ary code, *n.* A code in which each code element may take any of n distinct values.

National Electrical Code, *n.* A set of rules published by the National Fire Protection Association, Boston, Mass., covering the installation of electric conductors and equipment in public and private buildings and on their premises. It has the force of law only when enforced by municipalities or states.

National Electrical Safety Code, *n.* A set of safety rules for the installation and maintenance of electric supply and communication lines, published as National Bureau of Standards Handbook #81, and approved by the American Standards Association. It has the force of law only if enforced by municipalities or states.

National Electrical Manufacturer's Association (NEMA), *n.* An industry association which standardizes specifications for wires, cables, and electrical components.

National Yellow Pages Service (NYPS), *n.* Service which permits advertisers to place their telephone directory advertisement in many yellow pages across the nation with only a single contract.

nationwide dialing, *n.* Distance dialing, which see.

NC signal, *n.* No circuit signal. A low tone (480 + 620 Hz) interrupted at 120 IPM (on 0.2 second, off 0.3 second) which indicates that no toll circuit is available.

nearby telephone number, *n.* The telephone number of a subscriber who is located physically near to a person to whom a toll call is directed, but who is not a telephone subscriber. Used in attempts by toll operators to complete emergency telephone calls.

near-end crosstalk. See "crosstalk, near-end."

near-field region, *n.* The region close to a transmitting antenna where the antenna does not appear as a point source of energy, and where power density of the electromagnetic field does not follow the inverse square law.

near-sing, *n.* The condition of a repeatered voice circuit when it is unstable in the 2500-3200 Hz band. See also "hollow circuit."

near zone, antenna. See "zone, near."

needle, cable sewing, *n.* A curved flat metal strip with a hooked end, and metal handle to fit the palm. Used in the lacing of cables. (WECo #287 tool)

needles, dipole. See "West Ford."

needles, test point, *n. pl.* Needle-pointed probes on the end of test cords, used for making test connections to insulated wires without removing the insulation.

negative, *adj.* (1) Said of the pole of a battery or terminal of a circuit which has an excess of the negative charges called "electrons." (2) The opposite of positive. (3) The terminal of a voltage source from which electrons flow, or to which the conventional direct current returns.

negative battery, *n.* The negative side of the central office battery. When the positive side of the central office battery is grounded (as it commonly is) the negative side is called simply "battery."

negative feedback. See "feedback, negative."

negative feeder. See "feeder, negative."

negative impedance. See "impedance, negative."

negative impedance booster. See booster, negative-impedance."

negative impedance converter, *n.* The basic active element of the negative impedance repeater. When a positive impedance is applied at one end of the converter circuit, the negative of that impedance is seen at the other end.

negative resistance, *n.* A property of a circuit in which a reduction in the applied voltage causes an increase in current. The carbon arc, dynatron tube, tunnel diode, and positive feedback amplifier all exhibit negative resistance.

negative return, *n.* In electrolysis mitigation work, a conductor which takes stray earth currents from cable sheaths and returns them to the negative bus of trolley car or trolley bus systems.

negative terminal, *n.* The terminal from which electrons flow, and toward which a conventional current flows in the external circuit.

neon lamp. See "lamp, neon."

neoprene, *n.* A tough synthetic rubber made by the polymerization of 2-chloro-1, 3- butadiene. Very resistant to sunlight, heat, oils, and greases. Widely used as the outer jacket on drop wires. The common chemical name is polychloroprene.

neper, *n.* A unit similar to the decibel, but based on Napierian logarithms. The number of nepers is equal to the natural logarithm of the square root of the ratio of the two voltages, or two currents. One neper is equal to 8.686 decibels.

net, *n.* (1) Net loss. The loss remaining after deducting gain from circuit loss. (2) A network. (3) A group of radio stations which can communicate directly on a common radio frequency.

net loss, *n.* (1) The loss of a toll circuit in its terminal arrangement or simulated terminal arrangement. (2) In a transmission circuit, the sum of all the losses minus the sum of all the gains.

network, *n.* A circuit containing interconnected resistors, capacitors, and/ or inductors, used to simulate the transmission-frequency or delay-frequency characteristics of another circuit.

network, active, *n.* An electrical network which includes a source of energy.

network, annulling, *n.* A series resonant circuit which simulates a missing carrier filter, and annuls the susceptance change in adjacent filters. See also "flanking, filter."

network, balanced, *n.* A network in which the corresponding series impedance elements are identical, and symmetrical with respect to ground.

network, balancing, *n.* A circuit consisting of lumped circuit elements (inductances, capacitances, and resistances) connected so as to simulate the impedance of a uniform two-wire cable or open wire circuit over a band of frequencies. Used with a hybrid coil to convert four-wire circuits to two-wire circuits.

network, bilateral, *n.* A network which passes current and signals equally well in both directions.

network, bridged-T, *n.* A T network having a fourth impedance element bridged across the two series elements, from one input terminal to the corresponding output terminal.

network, C, *n.* A network consisting of three impedance elements. One is bridged across the input or output of the circuit, and the other two equal elements are in series with the two sides of the circuit.

network, carrier line filter balancing, *n.* A network simulating a carrier line filter, to be placed in the line of one side of a phantom group when the other side of the group has a carrier line filter inserted. Serves to maintain phantom group balance.

network, compromise, *n.* A balancing network whose impedance-frequency characteristics are selected to provide a reasonably good balance against any of several line facilities it must simulate. See also "network, balancing" and "network, precision."

network, crossover, *n.* A combined low pass and high pass filter used to divide audio power at a "crossover frequency," sending the low frequencies to a woofer loudspeaker and the higher frequencies to a tweeter speaker. Some crossover networks divide the audio band into three parts: low, mid-range, and high frequency.

network, decoupling, *n.* A filter network placed in leads (such as power supply) which serve several circuits to prevent coupling or interaction between the circuits.

network, de-emphasis, *n.* A network having a transmission characteristic which is the inverse of a pre-emphasis network. It restores the spectrum of the signal to its original condition.

network, dividing. See "network, crossover."

network, equalizing, *n.* A network connected to a line to compensate for and correct its transmission-frequency characteristics. The network has loss-frequency characteristics which are complementary to those of the line, *ie:* the sum of the line loss plus the equalizer loss is a constant at any frequency.

network, equivalent, *n.* One network is equivalent to another if it can replace the other in a system without altering in any way the electrical operation of the system external to the network.

network, hierarchal, *n.* An arrangement of switching centers, such that each center can always trunk directly to the next higher class of switch. The present toll switching system in the United States is such a network, with five ranks of switching centers. These are, in order of ascending rank: end office, toll center, primary center, sectional center, and regional center.

network, hybrid, *n.* A four port network which offers a low impedance path between adjacent ports, but a high loss (isolation) between opposite ports. See also "hybrid coil."

network, L, *n.* A network consisting of two impedance elements, one bridged across the input or output of the circuit, and the other in series with one side of the circuit.

network, ladder, *n.* A ladder-like sequence of similar H, L, Pi, or T networks connected in tandem.

network, lattice, *n.* A network consisting of four elements connected in the form of a square. The input is to one pair of opposite nodes, and the output is from the other pair.

network, linear, *n.* A network having constants and transmission characteristics that do not vary with the magnitude of the voltage impressed or the current flowing through the network.

network, line filter balancing, *n.* A network which simulates the impedance-frequency characteristics of a carrier line filter. Inserted in one side of a phantom group when the other side of the same phantom group contains a carrier line filter.

Required to maintain the phantom group balance.

network, noise weighting. See "noise weighting network."

network, number, *n.* A network of resistors and neon lamps connected to the sleeve terminal of all lines in an ANI central office which, when pulsed, enables an identifier to determine the directory number.

network, paralleling, *n.* A radio-frequency diplexer.

network, passive, *n.* An electrical network which does not include a source of energy.

network, Pi, *n.* A network consisting of three impedance elements. One is bridged across the input, one is bridged across the output, and the third is in series between one input terminal and one output terminal.

network, precision, *n.* Interconnected inductances, capacitances, and resistances which form an artificial line simulating closely the impedance of an actual two-wire line, such as a toll cable circuit of specified gauge and loading. Used with a four-wire terminating set as a balancing network.

network, pre-emphasis. See "pre-emphasis network."

network, R-C. See "R-C network."

network, ringer, *n.* Two capacitors, a resistor, and a diode assembled on a terminal plate and potted in a metal case. Used with a double-wound ringer to provide (a) loud ring, (b) soft ring, or (c) chime operation.

network, shaping, *n.* A network inserted in a telegraph circuit for improving the wave shape of the signals.

network, susceptance annulling. See "network, annulling."

network, switched services, *n.* A network of access lines and trunks linked by common-controlled switching arrangements to switch calls between several served locations of the same customer. The switching equipment may be located in the Telephone Company central office, and be shared with other networks and with conventional telephone users.

network, symmetrical, *n.* A network in which the impedance measured at one pair of terminals with the second pair of terminals open (or shorted) is the same as the impedance at the second pair of terminals with the first pair of terminals open (or shorted).

network, T. See "T network."

network, telephone set, *n.* All of the transmission circuit elements of a telephone set, potted in a metal case with terminals on an insulating cover. Forms a part of the telephone set. Normally contains the induction coil, sidetone balancing network, ringing capacitor, RFI suppression filter, acoustic shock varistor, and sometimes transmission equalization for varying loop lengths.

network, unbalanced, *n.* A network which is not balanced. See "network, balanced."

network, unilateral, *n.* A network which does not pass currents and signals equally well in both directions, such as a network containing a rectifying element.

network, weighting, *n.* A network whose loss varies with frequency in a prescribed manner. See also "noise weighting network."

network, Y, *n.* A star network having three branches, each of which has one terminal connected to a common node.

network inward dialing, *n.* The capability of extending dial signals from a toll network or system into a local network or system.

network out dialing, *n.* The capability of customer dialing from a local network or system to a toll network or system.

networks, antenna coupling, *n. pl.* Networks which permit two radio transmitters to use the same antenna simultaneously. Consists of two pairs of band pass and band rejection filters. One pair passes frequency A and rejects frequency B, the other pair passes frequency B and rejects frequency A. See also "circulator."

Networks, Laws of. See "Kirchoff's Laws" in "Appendix B."

network synthesis. See "synthesis, network."

neutral, *adj.* (1) Neither positive nor negative. (2) Describing a conductor which carries no current during normal operation.

neutral, floating power, *n.* A power neutral whose voltage to ground is free to vary when load conditions change.

neutral conductor, *n.* A conductor of an electric supply system which is connected to a neutral point in the system. In a balanced system it carries no current.

neutral ground, *n.* An intentional ground applied to the neutral point of a circuit, machine, transformer, or system.

neutral operation, *n.* A method of telegraph operation whereby signals are transmitted by opening and closing the loop circuit.

neutral relay, *n.* A relay whose operation depends upon the magnitude of the current through its operating winding, and not upon its direction.

neutral telegraph system, *n.* Type of telegraph where there is only one battery and the loop is opened and closed for signaling. The mark signal is "current" and the space signal is "no current."

neutron, *n.* A neutral (uncharged) elementary atomic particle that together with protons constitutes the nucleous of the atom.

Newton's Laws of Motion. See "Appendix B."

Nichrome, *n.* Trademarked name of a high resistance wire composed of 75% nickel, 12% iron, 11% chro-

mium, and 2% manganese. Use for heating elements and wire-wound resistors.

nickel-cadmium battery. See "cell, nickel-cadmium storage."

nickel-iron battery. See "cell, nickel-iron storage."

Nicopress, *n.* One brand of metal compression sleeves permitting the making of compression splices in open wire line conductors.

Nicotap, *n.* One brand of compression metal sleeve which permits making a tapped connection to an open wire conductor.

night alarm circuit, *n.* An audible alarm circuit which can be turned on during late night hours to warn of incoming calls to a switchboard.

night answer, universal, *n.* Feature of some PABXs which enables any station to answer an incoming trunk call, at night when the switchboard is unattended, by dialing a designated "night answer" digit.

night answering service, *n.* A PBX or PABX service where central office trunks are connected to a predetermined station for answer when the switchboard is not attended.

night service, *n.* Feature of a dial PBX enabling a particular station to receive calls when the PBX is not attended, and to extend these calls to any station on the PBX.

night transfer, *n.* An arrangement whereby manual traffic loads can be concentrated on a few switchboard positions during the light traffic hours after midnight, such as information loads to the toll board.

Nimbus satellites, *n. pl.* One of two series of weather satellites.

nitrogen, *n.* A colorless, odorless, tasteless gas which comprises 78% by weight of the earth's atmosphere. Used to pressurize telephone cables and coaxial transmission lines to prevent entry of moisture at faulty splices or through accidental holes.

Nixie tube, *n.* A gas glow tube having

multiple cathodes which are energized in patterns to form any single digit. Also called a "numerical readout tube."

NNX code, *n.* A central office code. A group of three digits which designates a particular central office. So called because "N" may be any number from 2 to 9, and "X" may be any number from 0 to 9. See also "code, central office."

no-break power unit, *n.* A type of power unit in which voltage and frequency sensing devices control special generating equipment to maintain an uninterrupted supply of power to the load.

no circuit signal. See "NC signal."

node, *n.* (1) One of the several points on a transmission line carrying a standing wave at which the wave (current or voltage) has its minimum amplitude. (2) A terminal of any branch of a network, or a terminal common to two or more branches of a network. Sometimes called a "vertex." (3) A point in a switching network from which many trunks radiate. It may, or may not be a switching center.

node, ascending, *n.* The point where a satellite passes through the plane of the earth's equator, moving from the south.

node, current, *n.* In a transmission system having standing waves, a point at which the current is a minimum.

node, descending, *n.* The point where a satellite passes through the plane of the earth's equator, moving from the north.

node, voltage, *n.* In a transmission system having standing waves, a point at which the voltage is a minimum.

noise, *n.* (1) Any random disturbance in a communication system which tends to obscure the clarity and validity of a signal in relation to its intended end use. (2) Any signal having random fluctuations and frequency components. (3) An un-

wanted signal in a communication system, though if not random it should be called "interference."

noise, ambient, *n.* Noise surrounding a listener which masks sounds to which he listens.

noise, atmospheric, *n.* Noise or static due to natural causes, such as thunder storms.

noise, background, *n.* The system noise when there is no signal present.

noise, battery, *n.* Noise introduced into telephone circuits through the battery supply leads, consisting of a low-frequency noise from the battery charging equipment plus impulse noise from relay contacts. Battery noise is normally held to 56 dbrnC at the battery, and 22 dbrnC at the distributing fuse panel.

noise, carrier, *n.* The noise produced by undesired variations of a carrier level in the absence of any intended modulation.

noise, circuit, *n.* The total electrical noise on a telephone circuit, resulting from power induction, battery noise, contact noise, impulse noise, static noise, and thermal noise.

noise, contact, *n.* Noise resulting from the passage of current through variable resistance contacts. The variable resistance is likely to be caused by mechanical vibration.

noise, cosmic, *n.* Random noise experienced at frequencies between 20 MHz and 100 MHz when a highly directional radio antenna is pointed toward certain regions in the sky, particularly toward the Milky Way.

noise, front-end, *n.* Thermal noise occurring in the first stages of an FM radio receiver, which varies inversely with the RF level at the receiver input. It becomes greater during a "fade," but is not affected by system loading.

noise, galactic, *n.* Radio noise which comes from our own galaxy, the Milky Way, particularly from the direction of the constellation Saggitarius. This noise is equivalent to a temperature of about 100 degrees Kelvin.

noise, granular, *n.* The noise which results when an analog signal having a continuous amplitude is represented by a discrete-time discrete-amplitude digital signal derived by sampling the analog signal.

noise, idle, *n.* Noise which exists in a communication system when no signals are present. See also "noise, intrinsic."

noise, impulse, *n.* Intermittent or spasmodic noise consisting of high-level pulses of short duration, or of other transients with steep wave fronts. Is the result of crosstalk from dial pulses or other switching transients.

noise, induced power, *n.* Noise consisting of harmonics, particularly the third, of the 60 cycle power frequency, transferred by induction from nearby power lines into a telephone circuit.

noise, intermodulation, *n.* In a multichannel transmission system, the spurious frequencies produced by every non-linearity through which the signal passes. These spurious frequencies include the sums and differences of every frequency present in the modulating signal. Because of the extremely large number of frequencies produced, intermodulation noise is very similar to white noise.

noise, intrinsic, *n.* Thermal noise which is normally present in a transmission path or device which is not caused by modulation and which is not affected by input level or system loading.

noise, man-made, *n.* Audio-frequency or radio-frequency noise generated by electrical machines or equipment, such as: commutators, vibrators, relays, auto ignition, etc.

noise, modulation, *n.* Noise in a modulation system which is caused by the signal and varies with signal strength.

noise, pink, *n.* Broadband noise having constant energy per octave.

noise, quantizing, *n.* Noise which is inherent in a pulse code modulation transmission, due to the fact that the coded signal is only an approximation of the original analog signal since an infinite number of amplitudes have been represented by a finite number of steps, usually 128. Quantizing noise can be reduced by increasing the number of amplitude steps.

noise, random, *n.* Noise composed of many uncoordinated and overlapping transient disturbances occurring at random. Known also as "white noise" and "steady-state noise."

noise, reference, *n.* That magnitude of circuit noise which will produce a reading on a circuit noise meter equal to one picowatt of electric power at 1000 hertz.

noise, room, *n.* The ambient noise at the receiving telephone which can reach the user's listening ear via the sidetone path from transmitter to receiver.

noise, shot, *n.* Noise inherent in an electric current, due to the fact that it consists of a stream of finite particles, ie: electrons.

noise, solar, *n.* Random noise which is experienced when a highly directional radio antenna is pointed at the sun. Observed at frequencies above 300 megahertz.

noise, static, *n.* Noise resulting from lightning, aurora, or other atmospheric discharges.

noise, surface, *n.* The noise output from a phonograph record due to dust or scratches on the record.

noise, thermal, *n.* Noise produced by the random motion of free electrons in all electrical conductors. The movement of an electrical charge (electron) through the resistance of the conductor produces a (noise) voltage. Thermal noise is white noise.

noise, white, *n.* A noise whose power per unit of frequency is essentially independent of frequency over a specified frequency range. It is therefore a broadband noise having constant energy per hertz, per 100 hertz, etc. Its amplitude-frequency curve slopes upward at 3 dB per octave.

noise figure, *n*. The ratio of (a) the noise power on the output of a transducer to (b) the portion of that noise which is attributable to thermal noise if the input terminal of the transducer is at the standard noise temperature of 290 degrees Kelvin. It is equal to the input signal-to-noise ratio divided by the output signal-to-noise ratio.

noise filter, *n*. A network of electrical components that inhibits noise signals from passing through or into an electronic circuit.

noise generator, *n*. Any device capable of generating wide-band random noise, such as an electron multiplier tube.

noise killer. See "killer, noise."

noise level. See "level, noise."

noise load ratio (NLR), *n*. Of a radio communication system, the ratio which in decibels is equal to ten times the common logarithm of a quantity consisting of the power in watts of the wideband test signal applied to the baseband, divided by the power in watts of the noise power that then appears in a single channel.

noise-longitudinal, *n*. The 1/1000th part of the total longitudinal circuit noise current, in sigma.

noise-metallic, *n*. The weighted noise current in a metallic circuit at a point where the circuit is terminated in its nominal characteristic impedance.

noise power ratio (NPR), *n*. A measurement made on the baseband signal output of a wideband frequency-division multiplexer which gives the ratio, in dB, of signal power to intermodulation product power plus residual noise power.

noise measurement units. The following units are used to express weighted and unweighted noise power: (a) dba (F1a)—F1a weighted circuit noise power, in db referred to 3.16 picowatts (–85 dbm), which is zero dba. (b) dbrnc—C-message weighted circuit noise power, in db referred to 1.0 picowatt (–90 dbm), which is zero dbrn. (c) dbrn (flat) —Noise power in db referred to 1.0 picowatt (–90 dbm) with no weighting except exclusion of all frequencies except 30-3000 Hz. (d) pwp— Noise power in picowatts, psophometrically weighted.

noise measuring set. See "set, noise measuring."

noise-operated gain-adjusting device, *n*. A circuit which distinguishes between speech and noise, and reduces the circuit gain when speech is not present. Speech detection is based on the fact that the energy content of noise is more constant than that of speech, therefore noise will cause an output from a slow-charge, fast-discharge rectifier circuit.

noise suppression. See "suppression, noise."

noise temperature, *n*. The temperature in degrees Kelvin at which a resistor will develop a particular noise voltage. Used as a measure of the noise generated within a microwave radio receiver when there is no input to the receiver.

noise threshold. See "threshold, noise."

noise-to-ground, *n*. The weighted noise current through a 100,000-ohm noise meter connected between one or more telephone wires and ground.

noise transmission impairment (NTI), *n*. The amount of loss which must be added to a noise-free circuit to produce the same transmission degradation as a specified amount of noise, measured at the receiver.

NTI	Noise
0 db —	17 dba
1 db —	20 dba
2 db —	23 dba
3 db —	25 dba
4 db —	26 dba
5 db —	27 dba

noise unit. See "unit, noise."

noise weighting network, *n.* A frequency selective network which can be used with a noise meter having a flat frequency response to evaluate the interfering effect of a complex noise upon an average listener using a particular class of telephone set.

nominal bandwidth. See "bandwidth, nominal."

nomogram, *n.* A chart having a series of curved or straight-line scales across which a straightedge can be laid to give a graphical solution of an equation involving three variables. Also called a "nomograph."

nomograph, *n.* An alignment chart, which see.

non-blocking, *adj.* Describing a switching network having a sufficient number of paths such that a subscriber originating a call can always reach any other idle subscriber without encountering a busy.

nonbridging, *adj.* Describing switch contacts, such as on an end cell switch, where the switch arm leaves one contact before touching the next contact.

nonconductor, *n.* A substance which does not transmit certain forms of energy, such as sound, heat, and especially electricity.

non-homing switch, *n.* A single-motion rotary stepping switch whose wipers do not return to a normal (home) position when the switch is released, but are disconnected and remain in the bank at the position last occupied.

noninductive, *adj.* Not possessing inductance in any important amount.

non-isochronous, *adj.* Start-stop.

nonlinear, *adj.* Describing any device in which the output is not related to the input by a simple constant. Not proportional.

nonlist, *n.* A listing for a subscriber that appears on the Information Operator's records, but not in the telephone directory.

non-loaded, *adj.* Describing a telephone cable circuit which is not equipped with inductive loading. Do not say "unloaded" if you mean "non-loaded."

non-locking, *adj.* Said of a device which automatically restores to a non-operated condition after being momentarily operated.

nonmagnetic, *adj.* Describing a material which has no effect on a magnetic field, either to attract it or repel it. Such a material has a permeability of 1. See also "diamagnetic," "ferromagnetic," and "paramagnetic."

nonmetallic sheathed cable. See "cable, nonmetallic sheathed."

non-multiple, *adj.* Describing a manual switchboard on which each line or trunk has only a single appearance.

non-numerical switch, *n.* A step-by-step switch which operates automatically and NOT under the control of pulses from a dial.

non-operate current, *n.* The maximum current which can be applied to a relay winding without causing any of the contact springs to make contact.

nonpolar, *adj.* Describing an insulating material whose dielectric constant does not change with a change in frequency.

non-pole pair, *n.* On an open wire line, any of the open wire pairs which are not split by the pole: 1-2, 3-4, etc. See also "pole pair."

non-regulated, *adj.* Not controlled or governed, particularly with respect to voltage, current, or speed.

non-resonant antenna. See "antenna, aperiodic."

non return to zero. See "NRZ signal."

nonsecure mode, *n.* An unencrypted mode of transmission during which classified (confidential, secret, etc.) information may not be discussed.

nonshorting, *adj.* Nonbridging, which see.

nonworking number, *n.* A telephone number which is not in use, but for which there is terminating equipment in the central office. See also "vacant number."

NOR gate, *n.* A multiple-input single-output gate which has a "one" output only when all inputs are "zero."

normal, *n.* (1) The back contacts of a key or relay. (2) The initial or rest position of a switch or relay. (3) A line which is perpendicular to another line or to a surface.

normal contact. See "contact, normal."

normally closed, *adj.* Describing key or relay contacts which are closed when the key or relay is not operated.

normally open, *adj.* Describing contacts of a key or relay which are open when the key or relay is not operated.

normal post springs, *n. pl.* A spring assembly clamped to the normal post at the top of a Strowger step-by-step switch, which is operated by a projection (normal post cam) on the switch shaft. Used to enable restricted service on designated levels of the switch bank.

normals, *n. pl.* The springs of a key or relay which are in contact with the moveable springs when the key or relay is in its normal non-operated position.

north pole, *n.* The pole of a magnet which points toward the north magnetic pole of the Earth. The lines of force internal to a magnet are assumed to leave from its north pole.

Norton's Theorem. See "Appendix B."

no such number signal, *n.* Previously a continuous high tone rising and falling in pitch (woo-woo), indicating that one has dialed an unused office code or a telephone number in an unused series. This is no longer acceptable, and present Distant Dialing practice requires an automatic announcement. See "announcement, vacant number."

notation, binary, *n.* A scheme for representing numbers in which suc-

cessive digits are interpreted as successive powers of the base two.

no-test trunk, *n.* A trunk to the terminating switching equipment in a dial central office which enables a verifying operator to gain access to a line even though it is busy. The preferred term is "verification trunk."

notice, treatment, *n.* A notice to a subscriber whose telephone bill is overdue.

nozzle, *n.* (1) A small projecting vent or pipe. (2) A small projecting pipe through which cable enters a terminal, a ready-access unit, or a loading case. (3) An adapter placed on the end of a cable feeding tube.

nozzle, cable feeder, *n.* A cone-shaped metal reducing adapter placed on the end of a 4-inch cable feeding tube to match it to 3-inch, 3½-inch, or 4-inch conduit.

NRZ signal, *n.* A signal which is continuous through mark and space elements. Examples are multi-level signals and frequency-shift signals. NRZ means "non-return (to) zero."

n th harmonic, *n.* A harmonic whose frequency is n times the frequency of the fundamental.

NTI. See "Noise Transmission Impairment."

n-type semiconductor, *n.* A type of semiconductor material in which there are an excess of electrons (negative charges), and current conduction is therefore by electron carriers. See also "p-type semiconductor."

nuclear power plant, *n.* A power plant in which nuclear energy is converted to heat, and then to electricity. In small sizes are useful as power supplies for mountain-top radio relay stations.

nucleous, *n.* Of an atom, the central part having most of the mass, and a positive charge equal to the total negative charge of the orbital electrons.

null, *n.* (1) A position of zero or minimum reading on a measuring instrument. (2) A position of minimum tone volume when balancing an audio frequency bridge.

null detector circuit, *n.* A circuit which determines when two circuits are in exact electrical balance, having the same voltages or currents.

number, binary, *n.* A number expressed in binary notation.

number, blank, *n.* A telephone number outside of the assigned block of numbers for a particular central office.

number, crossbar channel, *n.* A composite number identifying (a) the line switch horizontal number of the line link, (b) the trunk switch vertical number of the trunk link, and (c) the junctor switch number in a channel.

number, directory, *n.* The full complement of digits required to designate a subscriber in a telephone directory, consisting of a central office code (usually three digits) followed by a four-digit station number. In a few areas a letter suffix is used to control selective ringing, and is also a part of the telephone number.

number, extheo, *n.* An arbitrary designation for the numbers associated with the third of three office codes using the same series of line numbers. The use of three different office codes to access the same 10,000 numbers provides an automatic rate discrimination.

number, non-discriminating, *n.* A line number associated with two central office codes. Such a number is reached regardless of which of the two codes is dialed.

number, nonworking. See "nonworking number."

number, physical, *n.* An arbitrary designation for the telephone numbers associated with the first of three office codes that use the same number series. See also "number, theoretical" and "number, extheo."

number, pin, *n.* The numerical posi-

tion of an insulator pin counting from the left end of a cross-arm as one faces away from the central office. Thus, the pins on the top cross-arm may be numbered 1-10; on the second cross-arm 11-20, etc.

number, special billing telephone. See "special billing telephone number."

number, telephone, *n.* Ideally, a seven-digit telephone address consisting of a three-digit office code followed by a four-digit station number.

number, theoretical, *n.* An arbitrary designation for the numbers associated with the second of three office codes using the same number series. The numbers associated with the first and third office codes are called the physical numbers and extheo numbers, respectively.

number, 2-5, *n.* A seven-digit telephone number consisting of two letters and five numerals. To be superseded by numbers consisting of seven numerals.

number, 2L-5N. See "number, 2-5."

number, unassigned, *n.* A telephone number within the capacity of a particular central office, but not assigned to a customer.

number assignment, paystation, *n.* A distinctive telephone number which indicates to an operator that the telephone is a paystation. The last four digits of the number will be in the 9XXX, 8XXX, or 7XXX series.

Numbering Plan Area (NPA), *n.* Any of the 152 geographical divisions of the United States, Canada, Bermuda, the Caribbean, Northwestern Mexico, Alaska, and Hawaii within which no two telephones will have the same 7-digit telephone number. Each numbering plan area could have the same number of telephones ultimately (less than 8 million), and each has been assigned a distinctive 3-digit "area code." The NPA's will soon (1971) be expanded in number to 215 possible area codes. See also, "code, area."

numbers, aluminum, *n. pl.* Aluminum house numbers (and letters), usually 1½-inch high, used to designate poles with the pole line number and/or the pole number.

number series. See "series, number."

number test trunk. See "verification trunk."

numericals, *n. pl.* The digits which identify a customer in a central office, including a party letter suffix, if used.

numerical switch, *n.* A stepping switch which operates entirely or partially in response to pulses from a dial at the calling telephone.

nut, *n.* A square or hexagonal block of metal having a threaded hole through the center, for screwing onto a bolt.

nut, insulation crushing, *n.* A binding post nut which has an annular ring which crushes the wire when the nut is tightened, and contacts the wire without the necessity of stripping its plastic insulation.

nut, wire, *n.* A conically wound brass spring, usually with a plastic insulating cover, which can be screwed onto a pair of power conductors to connect them without twisting, soldering, or wrapping with tape.

nutdriver, *n.* A hollow-handled socket wrench permitting the placing of nuts over protruding screws. Made to look and operate like a screwdriver.

nylon, *n.* Any of a family of long chain polymeric amides. Makes a strong elastic fiber, silky and insensitive to moisture and mildew. Useful for ropes, coil forms, gears, braid covering on switchboard cords, etc.

Nyquist interval, *n.* The maximum time interval between regularly spaced samples of a wave which will permit complete determination of the waveform of the signal being sampled. Numerically, in seconds, it is equal to the reciprocal of twice the bandwidth of the sampled wave.

NYX code. See "code, area."

oakum, *n.* Loosely twisted hemp or jute fiber impregnated with tar and used for caulking.

objective, design, *n.* Electrical performance characteristics for communication circuits which are based on reasonable engineering estimates of the performance required. A design objective is a projected standard, to serve until such time as a system standard can be established by actual measurement under operating conditions.

observation, service. See "service observation."

occlude, *v.t.* To absorb.

occupancy, *n.* The percentage time that a circuit is in use, expressed as a decimal fraction. Numerically it is equal to the CCS carried by the circuit divided by 36. Also known as a "traffic unit" (TU).

occupancy date, beneficial (BOD), *n.* That date when buildings or other construction will be completed to a point that will permit occupancy by an installation team for the purpose of installing equipment.

ocean block, *n.* A portion of a long submarine cable, consisting of the several sections of cable with their several repeaters which constitute the section between two equalizers. Ocean blocks vary greatly in length, but 200 nautical miles is a typical figure.

octal base, *n.* A universal base for an electron tube which has eight equally spaced pins, oriented by a central key.

octave, *n.* An interval between two frequencies such that one frequency is twice the other.

odd parity, *n.* A form of error-detection used with binary-coded data in which one bit is added to the data for each character such that the total number of ones in the data plus the parity bit is always an odd number.

oersted, *n.* The unit of magnetizing force, or gradient of magnetomotive force in the c.g.s. system. The rate of change of magnetomotive force with distance.

off-hook, *n.* (1) The condition which results when a telephone is lifted from its mounting, allowing the hookswitch to operate. (2) The signal which is sent to the central office (loop closed, current flowing) as a result of the off-hook condition.

off-hook service, *n.* Service which provides for automatically establishing a connection between two specified subscribers as a result of lifting the handset of either.

office, *n.* An indefinite term having one of the following meanings: (1) a switching center, (2) a 10,000 line unit within a switching center, (3) a central office, (4) a building which houses a switching center, (5) a place where business is transacted, (6) a place where records are kept.

office, all-relay central, *n.* An automatic switching center in which the switching is done by all-relay equipment.

office, automatic, *n.* A telephone switching unit where the connections are made without the aid of an operator by automatic switches using called party address information obtained from the calling party's dial.

office, central, *n.* (1) A 10,000-line unit in an automatic switching center. (2) A place where the switching of telephone calls is done, whether automatic or manual.

office, circuit control, *n.* The office (or testboard) which has the authority to direct testing, repair, maintenance, and use of a toll circuit.

office, class of. See "centers, toll switching."

office, common battery central, *n.* A central office which supplies talking and signaling currents to its connected stations and current for the central office equipment from batteries located in the central office.

office, common-control. See "common-control office."

office, community dial (CDO), *n.* A small automatic telephone office designed to serve a small community. Usually unattended, with maintenance supplied from a nearby attended office when required.

office, crossbar central, *n.* An automatic switching center in which the switching equipment uses crossbar switches. Crossbar offices are almost always "common-controlled," which see.

office, dial, *n.* An automatic central office.

office, dial central, *n.* (1) An automatic central office. (2) A 10,000 line unit in an automatic switching center. (3) A switching center where the subscribers initiate their calls by dialing, and where the calls are completed by automatic switching equipment.

office, end. See "end office."

office, local central, *n.* A unit in a telephone switching system which serves primarily as a place for termination of subscriber's lines, accepting originating traffic from those lines and connecting terminating traffic to them. A central office has a maximum capacity of 10,000 numbers.

office, magneto central, *n.* A manual telephone central office which serves magneto telephones.

office, manual central, *n.* A switching center where calls are received and completed manually by operators working at switchboards.

office, master, *n.* A central office which serves a sub-office or a satellite office, and to which all of their trunks are connected.

office, physical-theoretical. See "physical-theoretical office."

office, rotary central, *n.* An automatic switching center which uses rotary selectors instead of the more common step-by-step selectors.

office, satellite, *n.* A telephone central

office which has trunks to only one "master office."

office, single-channel. See "single-channel office."

office, spill. See "spill office."

office, step-by-step central, *n.* An automatic switching center where the switching is done by step-by-step switches.

office, tandem, *n.* A switching center whose principal function is to act as a central switching point on calls between other central offices, thus allowing the consolidation of trunk groups for more efficient operation.

office, 35E97, *n.* Step-by-step central office equipment in which the shelves mount on the front of 5 feet-11 inches wide "universal" trunk boards. Also called "Type 11-A."

office, toll, *n.* (1) A toll center. (2) A toll point.

office, tributary, *n.* An office which has access to the long distance network through a "toll center." A class 5 switching center, or "end office" is a tributary office.

office, unattended dial, *n.* A small automatic central office which is visited only as required for maintenance and routine tests.

office A, *n.* The first of two number series groups in a marker group.

office B, *n.* The second of two number series groups in a marker group.

office of record, *n.* The agency which has the responsibility to reain file copies of orders and record correspondence.

official board, *n.* The PBX used by the Telephone Company for the handling of its own telephone calls. Also: official PBX.

official PBX, *n.* The PBX switchboard used by the Telephone Company for the handling of its own telephone calls.

official PBX operator, *n.* A person handling calls to and from official lines at a Telephone Company PBX.

off-line, *adj.* Describing a communication system in which there is no direct connection between the communication line and the device (teletypewriter, card punch, etc.) which originates the message.

off-line operation, *n.* A method of operation in which encryption and transmission or reception and decryption are performed in separate steps, rather than automatically and simultaneously.

off-net calling, *n.* Telephone calls through a private switching system and transmission network which originate at or are extended to stations in the commercial telephone system.

off-normal, *adj.* (1) Describing the position of a stepping switch which has moved from its normal, at rest position. (2) Describing contact springs which operate when a switch moves from its normal position.

off-premises extension, *n.* An extension telephone (or PBX station) located on property which is not contiguous with that on which the main station (or PBX) is located.

off-scale, *adj.* Said of a meter reading in which the pointer swings hard right and is beyond the calibrated scale.

offset, frequency, *n.* The difference in frequency of a tone injected into the input of a carrier system from that of the tone recovered from the output of the system.

off-the-shelf, *adj.* (1) Said of an item that has been manufactured in quantity, has been proven in use, and does not require further research or development. (2) Said of an item which is available from stock on hand.

ohm, *n.* The unit of electrical resistance. One volt will force one ampere of current through one ohm.

ohm-centimeter, *n.* The unit of resistivity; the reciprocal of conductivity. Numerically, it is the resistance in ohms between opposite faces of a cube of the material which is one centimeter on each side.

ohmic contact, *n.* An electrical contact whose resistance is directly proportional to the current flowing through it.

ohmmeter, *n.* A measuring instrument which indicates directly in ohms the resistance of a circuit to which it is connected. Incorporates a source of measuring potential.

ohm-pound/mile, *n.* A unit which expresses the resistance in ohms of a wire which weighs one pound and is one mile in length.

Ohm's Law for Direct Currents. See "Appendix B."

ohms-per-volt, *n.* A measure of the current drawn by a voltmeter, and therefore of its sensitivity. Obtained by dividing the resistance of the meter in ohms by the full-scale range in volts.

oil, dip of, *n.* The amount of lubricating oil retained in the bristles of a #6 round camel's hair brush after the brush has been dipped ⅜-inch into the oil, and then drawn across the edge of the oil container.

oil, drop of, *n.* The amount of lubricating oil released from the end of a bare tinned #22 AWG copper wire after the wire has been dipped one-half inch into the oil and then quickly withdrawn.

oil, spindle, *n.* A light mineral oil used to lubricate dial central office switching equipment.

oil ring, *n.* A thin metal ring which encircles the shaft of a rotary machine and dips into an oil reservoir, thus bringing oil to the shaft and its bearing.

oil seal, *n.* A device for retaining the lubricant in a shaft bearing.

oil slinger, *n.* A thin ring fixed to a rotating shaft which catches oil creeping along the shaft and throws it out into the bearing housing by centrifugal force.

oil switch, *n.* An electrical switch whose contacts break while immersed in oil. This cools and quenches any arc which may form.

omnidirectional, *adj.* Equally effective in all directions.

on-call circuit, *n.* A permanently designated and identified circuit which is activated only upon the request of the user. Provided when the user cannot anticipate when or for how long he will need the circuit.

one state, *n.* The condition of a binary memory cell when a "one" is stored.

one-way, *adj.* Describing a trunk over which calls pass in only one direction. It may be "one-way incoming" or "one-way outgoing."

on-hook, *n.* (1) The condition which results when a telephone handset is placed on its mounting, which causes the hookswitch to open its contacts. (2) The signal which is sent to the central office (loop open, no current flowing) as a result of the on-hook condition.

on-line, *adj.* Describing a method of operating whereby the transmitting of a teletypewriter message is performed simultaneously with its processing (encryption, etc.).

on-off, *adj.* Describing a signal or method of signaling in which the signal is alternately transmitted and suppressed.

opaque, *adj.* (1) Describing a transmission facility which is unable to pass digital data. (2) Describing the inability of the earth's upper atmosphere to pass radio waves, except through the "atmospheric window." —*n.* A printed announcement or advertisement, a picture, or a sketch which is front illuminated and televised for broadcast over a CATV system.

open, *n.* A break in the continuity of an electrical circuit which prevents current from flowing.

open-circuit voltage, *n.* The voltage at the terminals of a voltage source when no current is being drawn from the source.

open-circuit working, *n.* A method of operating a telegraph circuit in which no current flows in the circuit when the transmitting device is at rest.

open-space cut-out. See "cut-out."

open wire, *adj.* Describing some item of telephone plant which is used with open wire lines.—*n.* Bare line wires, spaced 12 inches, tied to insulators on crossarms bolted near the tops of poles.

operate time, *n.* The interval of time between the application of current to a relay coil and the operation of its contacts.

operation, broadcast, *n.* A type of operation in which a transmitting station sends information which may be received by several stations simultaneously.

operation, call circuit, *n.* A method of manual call passing in which the operator at the originating office depresses a key that connects her telephone set to a "call circuit" leading to an operator in the distant office. The distant operator accepts the order, assigns an idle trunk, and the call is then completed over that trunk.

operation, CLR, *n.* Combined line and recording. A method of handling manual toll calls in which an outward operator answers calls for "long distance," records the toll ticket information, selects an outgoing trunk, and signals the distant operator or dials the called number directly.

operation, conference, *n.* A form of simplex operation in which a group of stations may exchange information over a common network.

operation, diplex. See "diplex operation."

operation, direct dial, *n.* A method of manual call passing in which the originating operator plugs into a dial trunk to the distant office and dials the called number directly.

operation, full-duplex, *n.* A type of operation in which information may be passed simultaneously in both directions over a single circuit.

operation, half-duplex, *n.* Operation in which the circuit can pass information in either direction, but in only one direction at a time.

operation, magneto. See "magneto operation."

operation, multiplex, *n.* Simultaneous transmission of two or more messages in either or both directions over the same transmission path.

operation, neutral, *n.* A method of telegraph operation in which signals are transmitted by opening and closing the loop circuit.

operation, off-line. See "off-line operation."

operation, one-way reversible, *n.* Half-duplex operation.

operation, open-circuit telegraph. See "open-circuit working."

operation, polarential telegraph. See "polarential telegraph operation."

operation, push-to-talk, *n.* A type of operation which permits transmission in either direction alternately.

operation, ringdown, *n.* A method of manual call passing in which the originating operator plugs into an idle trunk to the distant office and operates her ringing key to signal the distant operator. At the conclusion of the call it may again be necessary to ring on the connection to obtain disconnection of the cord circuits.

operation, simplex, *n.* A type of operation which permits transmission in either direction alternately.

operation, single channel, *n.* Permitting customers to reach an operator by dialing "operator" (zero) for both assistance and operator-handled long distance calls.

operation, straightforward, *n.* A method of manual call passing in which an operator plugs into an idle trunk to the desired office, where the call is connected automatically to an idle operator who accepts the order and completes the call over the same circuit.

operation, synchronous. See "synchronous operation."

operation, undirectional, *n.* A type of operation which, due to the limitations of terminal equipments, permits transmission of information in only one direction.

operation, wink. See "wink operation."

operational, *adj.* (1) Able to be used. (2) Ready for use.

operational amplifier. See "amplifier, operational."

operator, *n.* A person whose duties include the operation of a switchboard or comparable equipment.

operator, A, *n.* An operator assigned to an A switchboard. See "switchboard, A."

operator, amateur radio, *n.* A person holding a license issued by the Federal Communications Commission (FCC) authorizing him to operate an amateur radio station.

operator, B, *n.* An operator assigned to a B switchboard. See "switchboard, B."

operator, checking, *n.* An operator who is called in on a subscriber-dialed automatic-ticketed toll call just long enough to obtain the number of the calling telephone and key it into the ticketer.

operator, CLR, *n.* A toll operator whose duties include: (a) answering the call when a customer dials the long distance code, (b) writing the toll ticket, (c) making attempts to reach the called party while holding the calling party on the line, (d) timing the call if a connection is established, and (e) passing the ticket to a TX operator if the initial attempts fail and she dismisses the customer.

operator, DSA, *n.* An operator assigned to a "dial service auxiliary" switchboard in an automatic central office to provide operator assistance to the subscribers served from that office.

operator, long distance, *n.* An operator who works at a toll switchboard and completes toll calls.

operator, ticket. See "ticket operator."

operator, toll, *n.* An operator who works at a toll switchboard to establish, supervise, and time connections between subscribers and toll circuits or between toll circuits.

operator, toll switching, *n.* An operator who completes connections between incoming toll trunks and subscriber's telephone lines.

operator, trouble. See "trouble operator."

operator, TX, *n.* An outward toll operator or team of operators who performs three specialized tasks: (a) Initiating subsequent attempts on toll calls, (b) Completing the call when a person in a distant city calls back on a "leave word" call, (c) Keeping a file of uncompleted and delayed toll tickets, and answering queries regarding their status.

operator codes. See "codes, operator."

operator distance dialing (ODD), *n.* The dialing by an operator at the originating toll center of a long distance call to a subscriber at the terminating toll center, without the assistance of intermediate operators.

operator number identification, *n.* Equipment at a local dial central office used on customer-dialed toll calls which brings in an operator long enough to obtain the calling station number. The operator then keys this number into the CAMA equipment.

operator office, *n.* A central office which serves as the operating center handling assistance traffic for the surrounding community dial offices.

operator recording-completing trunk, *n.* A trunk from a DSA board to a toll board at which the call may be handled on a non hang-up basis.

operator's telephone number, *n.* The following telephone numbers are standard for operators.

Zero operator	— "0"
Inward operator	— NNX-1211
Information operator	— NNX-1311
Conference operator	— NNX-1411
Trouble reporting	— NNX-1611

operator's telephone set. See "set, operator's telephone."

operator trunk, *n.* A trunk over which a customer reaches an operator when he dials "0."

opposition, *n.* The condition of two similar waves of the same frequency when there is a phase difference of 180 degrees between the two waves.

optical path, *n.* (1) A visual path from transmitting antenna to receiving antenna. (2) An above-the-horizon radio path between transmitting and receiving antennas, assuming normal refraction of the radio wave in the earth's atmosphere and first Fresnel zone clearance over the intervening terrain. Note: Definitions #1 and #2 are not equivalent, and definition #2 is the usual meaning for an optical or "line-of-sight path."

optimize, *v.* To adjust for maximum response.

orbit, equatorial, *n.* A path parallel to a plane through the earth's equator which is followed by a communication satellite in its travel around the Earth.

orbit, low altitude satellite. See "orbit, subsynchronous."

orbit, parking. See "orbit, synchronous."

orbit, polar satellite, *n.* A satellite whose orbit is in a plane running north and south through the earth. A satellite in a polar orbit is in a constantly changing position with respect to the earth.

orbit, stationary. See "orbit, synchronous."

orbit, subsynchronous satellite, *n.* A satellite orbit which is at a lower altitude than the 22,300 miles required for a 24-hour synchronous equatorial orbit.

orbit, synchronous, *n.* The path followed by a communication satellite which is at such a distance above the Earth (about 22,300 miles) that the satellite keeps pace with the earth's rotation, and thus hovers above a particular point on the earth.

order, *n.* The information that the originating operator passes over a circuit telling the distant operator what trunk or station line she wishes to be connected to.

order, circuit, *n.* Formal written (sometimes telegraphic) instruction to add, remove, or rearrange toll circuits or service.

order, circuit allocation, *n.* A directive, originating in the engineering or traffic departments, which requires the plant department to provide a new service, alter an existing service, or discontinue a service.

order, commercial, *n.* A formal order originating in the Commercial Department for the installation, augmentation, removal, or rearrangement of a customer's service.

order, delayed, *n.* An order for telephone service which has been accepted from the customer, but which cannot be completed promptly because of lack of facilities.

order, held, *n.* A work order, particularly one for the installation of new telephone service which cannot be completed, possibly because of lack of facilities.

order, keep cost, *n.* A work order which specifies that an exact record be kept of time spent and costs incurred. For the benefit of the accounting department in (a) arranging billing for services provided, or (b) analyzing costs.

order, patch, *n.* An interim circuit order, giving (telegraphic) instructions for the rapid establishment of a new circuit on a patched layout, as distinguished from a permanently wired layout.

order, service, *n.* An order to install, remove, or rearrange a subscriber's communication service.

order, work, *n.* An order with authorization to do work. General term for routine work orders, job orders, keep cost orders, estimated cost

billing orders, actual cost billing orders, etc. See also "estimate."

order tone, *n.* Short spurts of high tone sent back over a trunk to indicate to the originating operator that the order should be passed, and to indicate to the receiving operator that the order is about to be passed.

order wire, *n.* A circuit, voice or teletypewriter, used by maintenance personnel for communications regarding the lineup and maintenance of communication facilities.

ordinary relay contacts, *n.* Those groups of relay contact pairs which make or break last when the relay operates. See also "early" and "preliminary" contacts.

ordinate, *n.* A distance along the vertical or y-axis of a graph.

OR gate, *n.* An OR gate is a multiple input, single output diode device that exhibits an output when one or more of its inputs receives a negative voltage.

orientation, *n.* (1) On a teletypewriter, an adjustment which permits using the central portion of the received pulses to actuate the selecting mechanism. (2) The precise pointing of a directional antenna.

originating office, *n.* The switching center which serves the telephone station originating the call.

originating toll center, *n.* The toll center from which the calling telephone is served.

oscillation, *n.* (1) A periodic variation between maximum and minimum values, as an electric current. (2) A single swing of an oscillating object between the two extremes of its arc.

oscillation, damped. See "damped oscillation."

oscillation, parasitic, *n.* An unwanted oscillation which occurs in a self-resonant portion of a radio-frequency circuit.

oscillator, *n.* A small-power device for generating voice-frequency or radio-frequency alternating current of some specified frequency.

oscillator, audio, *n.* A non-rotating device for producing audio-frequency alternating current. Usually has a low power output (milliwatts) and is capable of varying the frequency.

oscillator, balanced, *n.* An oscillator having the electrical center of its tank circuit at ground potential. The voltages between either end of the tank circuit and its center are equal in magnitude and opposite in phase.

oscillator, Barkhausen, *n.* An oscillator capable of UHF and SHF frequencies, using a triode electron tube with a positive potential on the grid and a negative potential on the plate.

oscillator, beat-frequency, *n.* (1) A generator of test signals or tone whose amplified output is the difference frequency between a fixed frequency and a variable frequency, both produced in the oscillator. (2) A low-power variable-frequency oscillator used in a communication receiver to produce an audible signal when beat against a continuous-wave radio signal.

oscillator, crystal-controlled, *n.* An oscillator whose frequency is determined and controlled by a piezoelectric crystal.

oscillator, feedback, *n.* An oscillator consisting of an amplifier from which a portion of the output is fed back in phase to the input.

oscillator, klystron. See "klystron."

oscillator, local, *n.* In a superheterodyne radio receiver, the oscillator whose signal is mixed with the incoming radio signal to produce the intermediate frequency.

oscillator, magnetostriction, *n.* An amplifier having positive feedback through a magnetostrictive rod. The frequency of oscillation is determined by the mechanical resonance of the magnetostrictive rod.

oscillator, master, *n.* (1) An oscillator

that provides the basic frequency for a number of carrier systems. (2) An oscillator that establishes the carrier frequency of a radio transmitter.

oscillator, negative-resistance, *n.* An oscillator obtained by connecting a resonant circuit to a two-terminal negative-resistance device. Oscillation will be at the resonant frequency.

oscillator, phase-shift, *n.* An oscillator consisting of an amplifier which is caused to oscillate by positive feedback. The positive feedback is provided by connecting the amplifier output to its input through a network which shifts the phase of the signal by 180 degrees.

oscillator, R-C, *n.* An oscillator consisting of an amplifier with controlled positive feedback, in which the frequency of oscillation is determined by the phase of the current fed back as obtained from a variable resistance-capacitance (RC) network.

oscillator, relaxation, *n.* An oscillator whose frequency is determined by the time required to charge a capacitor through a resistor. It produces a sawtooth output.

oscillator, variable-frequency. See "variable-frequency oscillator."

oscillator, Wien bridge, *n.* A type of phase-shift oscillator which uses resistance and capacitance in a bridge circuit to control frequency.

oscillatory circuit. See "circuit, oscillatory."

oscillograph, *n.* An apparatus for producing a graphic record representing the instantaneous values of an electric quantity as a function of time.

oscilloscope, cathode ray (CRO), *n.* A test instrument which uses a cathode-ray tube on whose fluorescent screen are shown the transient and steady-state waveforms of the voltages which are connected for observation.

other line charge, *n.* A charge applied

on a message requiring the use of a line owned by another company, for that company's portion of the revenue.

outage, *n.* A disruption of communications from any cause, whether planned or accidental.

outboard channel, *n.* In single sideband or independent sideband radio transmission, the (translated) voice channel which is farthest in frequency from the carrier frequency. See also "inboard channel."

out-dialing, network, *n.* Telephone dialing which proceeds from a private network into a commercial network, or from a local network into a toll network.

outgoing, *adj.* Describing a trunk which is used only for calls going out to a distant office.

outlet, grounding. See "grounding outlet."

outlet, TV and FM, *n.* A splitter device which permits connecting both a television receiver and an FM radio to the same CATV outlet.

outlet, 75-ohm CATV, *n.* A television outlet in the home which connects through a 75-ohm coaxial cable to a 75 to 300 ohm matching transformer at the television receiver terminals.

outlet, 300-ohm CATV, *n.* A television outlet designed to be connected directly through a short twin-lead cable to the 300-ohm antenna terminals of a television receiver. The outlet contains a transformer to match the 75-ohm drop cable to the 300-ohm receiver.

out-of-band signaling, *n.* Use of narrow band filters to place the voice signal on a carrier channel below about 3400 cps, reserving the 3400-3700 cps band for supervisory signals. Also known as "tone off when idle" signaling.

out-of-order tone, *n.* The tone heard by an operator when she touches the tip of a plug to the sleeve of

a jack held on a plugging-up circuit.

out of phase, *adj.* Describing periodic waves which are of the same frequency, but which do not pass through their maximum and minimum values at the same instant.

outpulse, *v.t.* To send pulses out on a circuit. These pulses may be of direct current or tone.

output, *n.* (1) The current, power, or voltage delivered by a circuit or device. (2) The terminals from which the output energy is delivered.

output, balanced, *n.* An output whose two sides are electrically alike and symmetrical with respect to ground.

output, rated, *n.* The power, or voltage and current, which a device or machine can put out for long periods of time without becoming overheated under specified conditions of ambient temperature and ventilation.

output, unbalanced, *n.* An electrical output having one of the two terminals at ground potential.

outside plant. See "plant, outside."

out-trunk switch, *n.* An electromechanical switch in a dial central office whose function is to concentrate a relatively large number of trunks, as from selector banks, to a smaller number of outgoing trunks. Increases traffic efficiency by providing "full availability."

outward toll. See "toll, outward."

overcoupling, *n.* Coupling between two resonant circuits which is greater than critical coupling. This produces two peaks in the response curve, and provides a wider bandwidth.

overflow, *adj.* Describing switching equipment which operates when the traffic load exceeds the capacity of the regular equipment.—*n.* (1) Traffic which is handled on overflow equipment. (2) Traffic which exceeds the capacity of the switching equipment, and is therefore lost. (3) The carry digit in a digital computer.

overlap, *n.* In teletypewriter practice,

the selecting of a code group while the printing of a previously selected code group is taking place.

overlap, tape, *n.* The amount the trailing edge laps over the leading edge of a spirally wrapped tape.

overload, *n.* (1) An electrical load, such as that on a battery or generator, which is greater than the device is designed to carry. (2) A level of power on a transmission system which is too high, and thereby causes distortion.

overload relay. See "relay, overload."

overmodulation, *n.* Amplitude modulation which is greater than 100%, and therefore causes distortion.

override, *n.* (1) The capability to access a circuit automatically even though it is busy. (2) The capability to feed power to an equipment, even though safety interlocks may have deenergized it.

overshoot, *n.* An excessive response to a sudden change in signal.

over-the-horizon radio. See "scatter propagation."

overtime, *n.* That portion of the conversation time on a toll call that is in excess of the initial period.

overtime period, *n.* On a toll call, the period of time following the initial (minimum charge) time.

overtime rate, *n.* On a toll call which lasts beyond the initial period, the charge for each minute of overtime.

overtone, *n.* A tone which is a harmonic of a fundamental tone.

overvoltage relay, *n.* A moving-coil voltmeter-type relay which is designed to close an alarm contact when the voltage across it increases to a certain pre-set level.

ozone test, *n.* An accelerated test for oxidation by exposing a material to a high concentration of ozone.

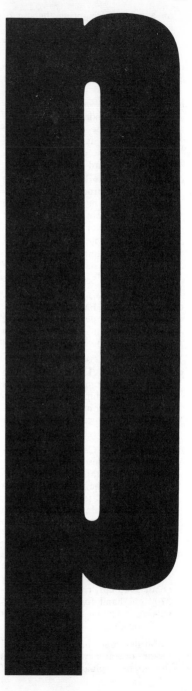

package, telephone. See "Telepak."

pad, *n.* A non-adjustable resistance network used to insert transmission loss into a circuit. It can, if required, be designed to match impedances, *ie:* to work between two circuits having different terminal impedances. Since it contains only resistance, not reactance, it is not frequency discriminating. See also "network, - - -."

pad, climber, *n.* A lined leather pad, about 4 x 4 inches, used under a lineman's climber strap to prevent chafing of the leg.

pad, fixed, *n.* A distortionless attenuation network permanently wired into a trunk termination. Selected in value to reduce the level to that required at an equal-level patch board or at a carrier system input.

pad (mounting), *n.* A six pin electron tube socket with several resistors assembled on the back and wired to the socket terminals. Accepts a plug-in resistance network to form a 600 ohm constant-resistance adjustable pad. Available in either balanced "H" or unbalanced "T" configuration.

pad (network), *n.* The variable portion of a two-piece attenuation network. Commercially known as a "resistor, WECo 89 type," which see.

pad, push-button, *n.* (1) A push-button dial. (2) An operator's keyset.

pad, receiver, *n.* Disposable circular multi-layer pad of absorbent tissue, used between the ear and receivers or head telephone sets to provide a more comfortable fit.

pad (resistance). See "resistance pad."

pad, switching, *n.* Attenuation network in an intertoll trunk. In the circuit when the trunk is used for a terminating call, but switched out when the trunk is used for a through-switched call. Used on low-loss trunks to prevent singing.

pad control, *n.* A method of switching a transmission loss pad into or out of a trunk or toll circuit to permit one circuit being used for both terminating and via traffic. The pad is in on terminating calls, and out on via calls.

padder. See "capacitor, padder."

paging, *n.* To summon a particular person by announcing his name over a public address system, by sounding his unique code on a code call system, or by selectively calling him on a pocket radio receiver which emits an alerting signal.

paging, radio. See "Bellboy."

paid call, *n.* The usual type of toll telephone call, which is billed to the calling telephone number.

paint, asphalt, *n.* A black asphalt base protective paint used for coating wrapped cable joints, battery boxes, and fiber conduit joints. See also "emulsion, asphalt."

pair, *n.* Two wires of a single circuit associated together by twisting, binding, or by an overall braid or cover. May be laid spirally or parallel. The first wire of the pair is designated "tip" and the second "ring," or sometimes "wire" and "mate."

pair, alarm, *n.* Cable pair used to connect a gas pressure contactor to alarm equipment in the central office.

pair, battery, *n.* Paired conductors used for supplying DC power (battery and ground) to equipment remote from the central office.

pair, dead, *n.* A cable pair which is not spliced through to the central office main distributing frame. It may, or may not, be continuous through the remainder of the cable.

pair, extra, *n.* An additional pair in a cable, over and above the nominal number of pairs which are guaranteed to be good by the manufacturer. For instance: pair 51 in a 51 pr cable, pair 101 in a 101 pr cable. Extra pairs are seldom placed in cables manufactured today.

pair, generator, *n.* Paired conductors for supplying (20 Hz) ringing current to equipment. Well insulated conductors, often shielded.

pair, multiple, *n.* A pair which is terminated at several locations, as in several terminals.

pair, non-pole, *n.* On an open wire line, any of the open wire pairs which are not split by the pole, such as 1-2, 3-4, 7-8, 9-10, etc.

pair, pole, *n.* On an open wire line, any of the pairs having one wire on one side of the pole and the second wire on the other side of the pole, such as pairs 5-6, 15-16, 25-26, etc. See also "pair, non-pole."

pair, shielded, *n.* An insulated paired wire covered by an electrostatic shield. The shield may be either a wrapping of foil tape or a braided cover of fine copper wires.

pair, spare, *n.* (1) A pair which is terminated on the main distributing frame, but which is not in use. (2) An extra pair in a cable which is continuous from the central office main distributing frame, and can be picked up and terminated for use when needed.

pair, terminal. See "terminal pair."

pair, tracer. See "tracer pair."

pair, twisted, *n.* A pair of insulated conductors spirally twisted together. Has many uses, such as for jumpers or crossconnections.

pair, universally bad, *n.* A cable pair, sometimes an "extra" pair, which is defective in so many locations that repair would not be economical. This may result from using an extra pair to repair faults in other pairs at several locations.

pair, video, *n.* A pair of #16 AWG solid copper conductors, insulated with foam polyethelene, covered with a helically wrapped polyethelene tape, a parallel fold copper tape, and a helically wrapped copper tape. Provides a low-loss pair for TV pickups, for closed-circuit TV, for telephone carrier circuits, and for wideband circuits to microwave stations. See also "cable, video."

paired cable. See "cable, paired."

pairs, bunched, *n. pl.* (1) A group of pairs tied together at a splice for group identification. (2) A group of pairs having the insulation stripped from the ends of the wires and all ends connected together, or with all ends shorted and grounded. This provides quick identification of the group to a cable splicer who is testing at the other end of the cable.

palladium, *n.* A silvery-white heavy metal similar to platinum in resistivity. Used for relay and key contacts. See also "contacts, dissimilar."

panel, *n.* (1) A metal or insulating plate, on which equipment is assembled and wired for mounting in a cabinet or on a rack. (2) On a switchboard, the space on the face between two adjacent vertical strips called stile strips.

panel, dual pressure gas, *n.* For pressurized cable systems which include both aerial and underground cables, a panel which takes dry air at 150 psig and reduces it to 10 psig for application to underground cables while aerial cables are fed at 7 psig directly from the air dryer unit.

panel, jack, *n.* An area, such as one vertical division of a switchboard or a relay rack, filled with jacks in jack mountings, on which circuits, lines or trunks, appear for interconnection or testing.

panel, patch, *n.* A jack panel which provides jack access to equipment wired into a toll circuit termination. Permits temporary circuit rearrangements and restoration by by-passing, or replacing faulty circuit components.

panel, relay rack, *n.* A metal panel, 3/16 or 1/4-inch thick and 19, 21, 23, or 30 inches wide, which is used to hold equipment on relay racks. The panel height is some multiple of 1-3/4-inches, and it is notched on the edge for mounting screws.

panelboard, *n.* A metal wall cabinet, usually with a door, which houses a group of low-voltage power circuit breakers.

panel dial system, *n.* A common-controlled switching system used in large offices in the Bell System starting about 1920. Now obsolete. The switching is done on large frames on which are mounted hundreds of terminals on vertical banks. Connections are made to these terminals by brushes which move up and down on vertical elevator rods, connected to flexible racks driven from continuously rotating electric motors. The control is by a sender.

Panelescent, *adj.* A registered trademark of Sylvania Electric Products for the electro-luminescent material used in illuminated telephone dials.

paper, electrosensitive, *n.* A paper which turns blue wherever a direct current passes through it. Used with facsimile and highspeed printers.

paper, pressure sensitive, *n.* Paper which can be used to make a copy without the use of carbon paper. The paper is covered with microscopic balls filled with a blue dye. Pressure of a pencil, ball pen, or type bars will crush the balls, release the dye, and leave a permanent mark.

paper tape. See "tape, punched."

parabola, *n.* A conic section formed by cutting a cone with a plane parallel to one side of the cone. It is an open curve with only one focal point. Many antenna reflectors are made in the form of a parabola.

parabolic antenna. See "reflector, parabolic."

parabolic reflector. See "reflector, parabolic."

paraboloid, *n.* A reflecting surface formed by rotating a parabola about one of its axes of symmetry.

paraffin, *n.* A white, waxy solid substance consisting of a mixture of hydrocarbons distilled from petroleum. Melts at 126 degrees F. Used for boiling out paper-insulated cable. Supplied in 11 pound cakes.

parallax, *n.* The apparent change in the position of an object depending on the position from which it is viewed. For instance: the different appearance of a nearby object when viewed only with the left eye, then the right eye.

parallel, *adj.* (1) Said of circuit elements which are connected to the same pair of terminals. (2) Transmitted simultaneously. (3) Said of lines or planes which are the same distance apart at every point.

parallel connection, *n.* Elements in an electrical circuit are said to be connected in parallel when the same voltage appears across each element, and the current divides among the elements in inverse proportion to their resistance or impedance.

parallel resonance, *n.* Condition which exists in a parallel circuit of inductance and capacitance when the inductive reactance is equal in magnitude (but opposite in sign) to the capacitive reactance. The voltage across the parallel circuit, and the current within the parallel circuit, are then at their maximum.

parallel transmission, *n.* The simultaneous transmission over several parallel transmission paths of the several signals which make up one item of information. For instance, the simultaneous transmission of five or seven digital signals to produce one teletypewriter character.

paralleling, rectifier, *n.* The operating of two or more rectifiers in parallel, connected so they will share the load in proportion to their respective current ratings.

paramagnetic, *adj.* Describing a substance which is attracted by a magnetic field, but which has a permeability only slightly greater than 1. See also "ferromagnetic" and "diamagnetic."

parameter, *n.* A quantity which varies with the circumstances of its application, such as "input voltage," "frequency," or "maximum allowable current."

parametric amplifier. See "amplifier, parametric."

paraphrase, *v.* To change the phraseology of a message without changing its meaning.

parasitic, *adj.* (1) Describing unwanted oscillations which occur in portions of radio-frequency circuits which are self-resonant. (2) Describing a passive element in a directional antenna array which acts as a reflector or director in reradiating energy received from the active element.

parasitic element. See "element, parasitic."

parasitically excited, *adj.* Said of an antenna element, such as a "director" or "reflector" which is not connected to a source of radio-frequency energy, but instead is energized through radiation from a near-by element.

parity, *adj.* Describing a self-checking code employing binary digits in which the total number of "ones" or "zeroes" is always even or always odd.—*n.* The state of being equal or equivalent.

parity, block. See "code, geometric parity check."

parity, even, *n.* A type of parity in which the number of "ones" (in a character, or in a word) is always even, made so by the addition of a "parity bit."

parity, lateral, *n.* A parity check, such as that provided by the eighth bit of the ASCII code, for each line of holes across a punched paper tape.

parity, odd, *n.* A type of parity in which the number of "ones" (in a character, or in a word) is always odd, made so by the addition of a "parity bit."

parity bit. See "bit, parity."

parity check. See "check, parity."

parity checking bit, *n.* A bit which is added to the information bits for a particular character so that the total number of bits is always odd (or even). When the bit is received at the far end of the circuit it is checked for odd (or even) parity. If it does not check odd (or even) the character has been received in error.

partial, *n.* A simple tone which is one of the components of a complex sound.

partial dial. See "digits, partial."

party line, *n.* A line on which more than one subscriber receives service.

passband, *n.* A band of frequencies which is passed through a circuit or filter essentially unchanged.

passivation, *n.* Electrolytically treating a metal or semi-conductor to create a chemically bonded oxide layer on the surface which will protect it from corrosion.

passive, *adj.* Describing a device which does not contribute energy to the signal it passes.

passive reflector, *n.* An inert device which receives a microwave radio wave and changes its direction to send it on to the receiving station. They are of two kinds: (a) A mirror-like metal plate on a tower or hill top which acts as a reflector. (b) A pair of parabolic antennas connected by a cable or wave-guide, one receiving the signal and the other sending it on.

passive repeater, *n.* A passive reflector, or a periscope reflector.

paste, burnishing, *n.* A non-corrosive metal polishing paste, usually principally ferric oxide in oil, used for polishing switchboard plugs, and sometimes generator commutators and ringing machine slip-rings.

paster, cable, *n.* Two inch kraft paper tape gummed on one side. Used by the cable splicer to paste around the lead cable sheath and lead sleeve to limit the length of the wiped joint.

patched, *n.* A patched connection.—*v.* To make a temporary connection using a patch cord.

patchboard, *n.* A facility containing patching jacks in a relay-rack mounting which supplements the toll testboard. All items of equipment used on the terminal of a toll circuit (signaling sets, repeating coils, etc.) appear on the patchboard, and can be replaced by patching. Any patches on the primary toll testboard are transferred to the patchboard if they are to remain for more than 1-2 days. See also "testboard, toll."

patchboard, equal-level. See "bay, equal-level patching."

patch cord. See "cord, patching."

patched connection, *n.* A temporary connection between patching jacks made with a patch cord.

patching, *n.* The temporary interconnection of circuits, using a double-ended "patch cord" which is plugged into the jacks on which the circuits are terminated.

path, *n.* (1) The route that a signal follows through a circuit or network. (2) The route that a radio signal follows from transmitter to receiver.

path, line-of-sight. See "line-of-sight path."

path, optical. See "optical path."

path, sidetone. See "sidetone path."

pathfinding, *n.* The process of finding an idle path through a switching network, from entrance port to exit port.

pathfinding, progressive, *n.* Finding an idle path through a multi-stage switching network in which each link is tested from stage to stage (and back if not successful) until the exit port is reached.

pattern, alternate route. See "search pattern."

pattern, antenna. See "pattern, radiation."

pattern, radiation, *n.* A radial graph showing the strength of a radio-frequency field from an antenna as a function of azimuth. See also "lobe, - - -."

pattern, search. See "search pattern."

pause, interdigital. See "interdigital pause."

pawl, *n.* A mechanical device which allows or imparts motion in only one direction.

pawl, holding, *n.* A pawl which holds a mechanism in its operated position until tripped to release. The "double dog" in a step-by-step switch is an example.

pawl, stepping, *n.* Either of two pawls, rotary pawl or vertical pawl, which imparts motion from an electromagnet armature to the shaft of a step-by-step switch.

paystation, *n.* A coin telephone.

paystation, local prepay, *n.* A dial coin telephone which requires deposit of a coin before local calls can be dialed. Toll is handled on a manual postpay basis. Collection and return of coins is automatic, and the operator has no control over it.

paystation, postpay, *n.* A coin telephone served from a manual central office. The operator has no means for refunding coins, for they drop into the coin box when deposited.

paystation, prepay, *n.* A dial coin telephone which requires deposit of a coin before any calls can be dialed. Toll is handled on a manual postpay basis. Collection and return of coins is automatic, but the operator has full control if desired.

paystation, semi-postpay, *n.* A dial coin telephone wihch requires a coin deposit after the called party has answered to enable two-way conversation. Toll calls are handled on a manual postpay basis, but the operator cannot return coins.

paystation, semi-public, *n.* A coin telephone where the usage is not great enough to justify public paystation service, so that the subscriber must guarantee monthly revenue equal to the business telephone rate.

PBX connector, *n.* A trunk-hunting connector.

PBX extension, *n.* A telephone served by a private branch exchange.

PBX tie line. See "line, PBX tie."

PBX trunk, *n.* A trunk from a PBX to a commercial central office. See also "line, PBX tie."

peak, *n.* The maximum instantaneous value of some quantity, such as a voltage or current.

peak amplitude, *n.* The maximum amplitude attained by a wave during a period.

peaking, *n. v.* To tune a circuit for a very sharp response at a particular frequency.

peak inverse voltage, *n.* The maximum value of an "inverse voltage," which see.

peaks, *n. pl.* Momentary bursts of high volume on voice or program circuits. They appear as upward swings on the volume indicator. See also "impulse noise."

peak-to-peak, *adj.* Describing the measurement of an alternating current or voltage, from positive maximum to negative maximum value.

peak value, *n.* Of any quantity, such as current or voltage, which varies with time, the maximum value which occurs during a period of time. If the quantity is a sine wave, the peak value is 1.4142 times the effective value.

peavey, *n.* A heavy wooden lever with a spurred metal tip and a hinged hook near the end. Used for rolling or carrying poles.

pedestal, *n.* A free-standing watertight housing for the above-ground mounting of terminals on buried or underground cables.

peg count, *n.* (1) A count of the number of times an event occurs. (2) A count of the number of calls on a particular group during a specified interval of time. (3) A count of the number of calls handled by an operator during a specified interval of time. Do not confuse with "usage count" or "busy count." See also

"counter, peg-count," and "meter, peg count."

peg-count meter. See "meter, peg-count."

penalty, *n.* A handicap, in dB of transmission loss, imposed on a circuit because of the presence of excessive noise or distortion. See also "impairment, - - -."

penetration, *n.* The depth an alternating current will penetrate below the surface of a conductor. See also "skin effect."

penetration frequency, *n.* The highest radio frequency reflected from an ionospheric layer at vertical incidence. Usually called the "critical frequency."

penny, conduit, *n.* A metal or plastic disc placed in the end of a building conduit during construction to protect it from the entrance of dirt.

pen register, *n.* A electro-magnetic device which makes a dash ink mark on a moving paper tape each time it is energized. Used to monitor dial pulses.

pentachlorophenol, *n.* An organic chemical used as a wood preservative. Desirable because of its cleanliness, pleasing color (gray-green), uniform penetration, and freedom from "bleeding."

Pentaconta switching system, *n.* Trademarked designation of an ITT common-controlled electro-mechanical switching system using relays and crossbar switches.

pentode, *n.* An electron tube having five elements: an anode, a cathode, a control grid, a screen grid, and a suppressor grid.

percentage modulation, *n.* A measure of the degree to which a carrier wave is modulated by a signal wave. Percentage modulation is the ratio of half the difference between the maximum and minimum amplitudes to the average amplitude, expressed in percent.

percent break, *n.* The percentage of the total pulse interval during which the pulsing contacts of dials or relays are open.

percent break, rotary dial, *n.* The pulsing contacts of rotary dials are normally adjusted to be open 61% of the total pulse interval.

percent conductivity. See "conductivity, percent."

percent ripple. See "ripple."

perforated tape. See "tape, punched."

perforator, tape, *n.* A device which records a teletypewriter or data message by punching holes in paper tape, under control of either a local keyboard or an incoming signal.

perigee, *n.* That point in the orbit of a satellite which is closest to the Earth. See also "apogee."

period, *n.* The time required for one complete cycle of a series of events which is repeated regularly and periodically. The reciprocal of the "period" is the "frequency."

period, initial, *n.* On a toll call, the period for which a minimum charge is made, usually 3 minutes.

period, overtime, *n.* On a toll call, the period of time following the initial (minimum charge) period.

period, pulse. See "pulse period."

period, rate. See "rate period."

period, ringing, *n.* Any of the one-second intervals during which ringing current is flowing to the called telephone, interrupted by silent intervals.

period, silent, *n.* The silent interval, usually about four seconds long, between interrupted rings on a telephone station line.

periodic, *adj.* Said of a varying quantity whose values recur at regular intervals of time.

periodic antenna. See "antenna, resonant."

periodic wave. See "wave, periodic."

peripheral equipment, *n.* Equipment which works in conjunction with a communication system or a computer but is not a part of it.

Permalloy, *n.* A magnetic alloy containing 78.5% nickel and 21.5% iron which has a very high (104,-000) permeability and a low hysteresis loss. Used in a powder form to fabricate powdered-metal cores for filters and loading-coils.

permanent, *n.* Condition of a subscriber's line which is shorted or grounded or has the handset off the hookswitch, thus bringing in a "permanent" line signal on the switchboard or tying up the automatic line equipment. Common control equipment considers a line to be permanent if no dial pulses are received within 30 seconds after the off-hook signal is received.

permanent magnet. See "magnet, permanent."

permanent signal cord. See "plugging-up cord."

permanent timing (also "time-out"), *n.* The system for disconnecting any permanent line from the equipment. Any call which has not proceeded to completion after a predetermined number of minutes is automatically released.

permeability, *n.* A measure of the magnetic flux in a magnetic material compared to the flux which would be created in air by an equal magnetizing force. The permeability of air is 1.0.

permeability tuning, *n.* Slug tuning.

permeable, *adj.* Porous so as to permit the passage of ions, gases, or liquids.

permeance, *n.* A measure of the ease with which a magnetic field can be set up in a magnetic circuit. It is the reciprocal of "reluctance," which see.

Permendur, *n.* A magnetic alloy consisting of 50% iron and 50% cobalt which has a high (7900) permeability over a wide range of high flux densities. See also "V-Permendur."

Perminvar, *n.* A magnetic alloy containing 45% nickel, 30% iron, and 25% cobalt which has a low hysteresis loss and a permeability

(2000) which is constant over a wide range of low flux densities.

permissive connection, *n.* A connection between Telephone Company facilities and private communication facilities which is permitted, but on which the Telephone Company cannot guarantee satisfactory transmission.

permittivity, *n.* The property of a material which determines how much electrostatic energy can be stored per unit volume per unit voltage. See also "dielectric constant."

permutation, *n.* Any of the combinations or changes that are possible within a group.

persistence, *n.* The time it takes a cathode ray tube or TV tube phosphor to decline to 10% of its peak intensity after it has been struck by a beam of electrons.

personnel number, *n.* Identifying number assigned to an operator which may be used instead of her name.

person-to-person call, *n.* A call on which the calling party specifies a particular person to be reached, or a particular extension, department, or office to be reached through a PBX attendant.

PERT, *n.* Program Evaluation and Review Technique. A management tool for comparing actual with scheduled program progress.

perturbation, *n.* An irregularity in the motion or orbit of a satellite, caused by some unusual force.

petticoat, *n.* Any of several annular rings on the bottom of a pin insulator which increase the length of the leakage path to the pin. See also "skirt."

phantom, *n.* A third voice circuit superimposed on two 2-wire voice circuits, all three circuits being suitable for transmitting voice-frequency signals without mutual interference.

phantom coil, *n.* (1) One of the two repeating coils installed in two side circuits to derive a phantom circuit. (2) A repeating coil installed in the phantom legs for impedance matching or longitudinal noise isolation.

phantom group. See "group, phantom."

phase, *n.* (1) The time displacement between two currents or two voltages or between a current and a voltage measured in electrical degrees, where an electrical degree is 1/360 part of a complete cycle. (2) The number of separate voltage waves in a commercial alternating current, designated as "single phase," "three phase," etc. Abbreviated as the Greek letter Phi (Φ).

phase angle, dielectric. See "dielectric phase angle."

phase constant, *n.* A measure of the phase shift of a signal as it traverses a transmission line, equal to the phase shift in radians over a one mile section of line at a particular frequency. It is the imaginary part of the "propagation constant," which see.

phased-array, *n.* An antenna consisting of a plurality of individual antennas, called elements, which are arrayed in a grid and interconnected so that a specific phase relationship exists between them, forming a narrow beam.

phase distortion, *n.* Delay distortion, which see.

phase equalizer. See "equalizer, delay."

phase inverter, *n.* A stage in an amplifier which changes the phase of a signal by 180 degrees, so that it can be used to feed one side of a push-pull amplifier.

phase-locked, *adj.* Said of two alternating currents whose frequencies are locked together so that their phase is at all times identical.

phase modulation. See "modulation, phase."

phase quadrature. See "quadrature."

phase sequence, *n.* The sequence in which the phases of a polyphase electric power circuit reach their maximum positive voltage.

phase shift, *n.* (1) The continuing

change in phase as a wave proceeds, in space or along a transmission line. (2) A change in the phase relationship between two waves.

phase-shift keying. See "keying, phase-shift."

phase splitter, *n.* A device which produces, from a single input wave, two or more output waves which differ in phase from one another.

phase velocity. See "velocity, phase."

phenolic, *n.* A phenolic resin. See "resin, phenolic."

phon, *n.* A subjective unit defining the loudness of a sound. It is that level of a complex sound which is judged to be equal to 0.0002 microbar of a 1000 Hz sine wave.

phone, *n.* (1) Telephone. (2) Earphone. (3) Head phone.

phone, panel, *n.* A flush-mounted wall phone on which only the dial, switchhook, and handset appear on the front panel.

phoneme, *n.* A class of speech sounds which are alike, except as they are modified by the sound of adjacent letters.

phonetic alphabet. See "alphabet, phonetic."

phosphor, *n.* A chemical substance which will give a luminous glow when bombarded by photons or electrons.

photocathode, *n.* An electron tube electrode which will emit electrons when struck by photons.

photocell, *n.* Either (1) a photo-conductive cell, (2) a photovoltaic cell, or (3) a phototransistor. See "cell, photo-" or "phototransistor."

photodiode, *n.* A semiconductor diode whose conductivity to an electric current varies with the light that falls on its junction. Useful for the photoelectric sensing of information on punched cards or punched paper tape.

photoelectric, *adj.* Pertaining to the effect in which photons (light) impinging on certain metals will release bound electrons and thus cause a flow of current. Photoelectric effect does NOT include "photoconductivity" or "photovoltaic effect."

photon, *n.* (1) An elementary particle of light. (2) a quantum of electromagnetic radiation.

phototransistor, *n.* A junction transistor device in which light collected by a tiny lens impinges on the base. The transistor collector current increases with increased light intensity.

phototube, *n.* An electron tube whose current output depends upon the number of photons which strike its photocathode.

photovoltaic, *adj.* Pertaining to the electron flow which can be caused by exposing the junction between a metal and a semiconductor to radiation. Photographic exposure meters use this principle, as do the devices which turn on the lights in outdoor paystation booths at night.

physical, *adj.* Real; tangible.

physical circuit, *n.* A metallic two-wire circuit, not equipped with repeating coils for deriving a phantom circuit. See also "side circuit."

physical number. See "number, physical."

physical-theoretical office, *n.* Division of the maximum of 20,000 directory numbers in one marker group into two (physical, theoretical) or three (physical, theoretical, extra-theoretical) central offices using several central office codes to permit rate discriminations or to minimize directory number changes. (#5 X Bar).

pi, *n.* The ratio of the circumference of a circle to its diameter, equal to 3.1415927.

pick, *n.* The distance, in picks per inch, between two adjacent cross-over points of braid filaments.

pick, test, *n.* A test prod having a multiple point consisting of a group of fine sewing needles. Can make a test connection through insulation without damaging it.

pick-up, pickup, *v*. To originate a broadcast program.—*n*. (1) The act of placing a microphone and amplifier at a remote pick-up point and feeding the resulting program over an equalized line back to the broadcasting station. (2) Interference from a nearby circuit. (3) The minimum value of current at which a relay starts to operate. (4) A phonograph pickup.

pickup, stereo, *n*. A phonograph pickup used with stereo records, in which a single stylus actuates two elements, one of which reproduces the left channel and the other the right channel. See also "recording, stereo."

pico-. A prefix denoting one millionth of a millionth. Pronounced "pie-ko."

picofarad (pf), *n*. A very small unit of capacitance, equal to one millionth of a microfarad. Previously called a micromicrofarad (mmf).

Picturephone, *n*. Bell System name for its "see while you talk" telephone set. It consists of three units: (a) a standard telephone with a TTMF dial, (b) a combined camera, loud speaker, and TV screen unit, and (c) a control unit with an integral microphone.

Picturephone control unit, *n*. A desktop unit containing a microphone, push buttons to disable the camera and turn off the picture tube, and controls for volume of sound, contrast and size of the picture, and height of the camera field. Together with the display unit, service unit, and touch-tone telephone, it is used to provide simultaneous oral and visual telephone communication.

Picturephone display unit, *n*. A desktop unit containing a picture tube, a camera tube, and a loudspeaker. One of the four units used to provide simultaneous oral and visual telephone communication.

Picturephone service unit, *n*. A wallmounted equipment cabinet containing a low-voltage power supply, control circuits, and a station set equalizer used with Picturephone service. May be placed 85 feet away from the associated control and display units.

Picturephone trunk, *n*. A six-wire trunk which combines a two-wire trunk for signaling and talking and a four-wire equalized trunk for the video signal, used to provide Picturephone service.

piezoelectric effect, *n*. Property of some crystals, when compressed in certain directions, of showing electric charges of opposite polarity on pairs of the crystal face. These charges are proportional to the pressure, and disappear when the pressure is removed. From the Greek word "piezo" $=$ "to press." Observed in crystals such as quartz, tourmaline, and Rochelle salt.

pigtail, *n*. (1) A short, very flexible braided or stranded wire used to carry current from a moveable member, such as a generator brush. (2) The splice made by twisting together the bared ends of two conductors laid side by side.

pike, *n*. (1) A sharply pointed steel prod, usually fixed on the end of a spear-like pole. (2) A pike pole. See also "pole, pike."

pileup, spring, *n*. The assembly of contact springs together with their separating insulators, held together as a unit, which is the essential part of a relay, key, or jack.

pilot, *n*. (1) A pilot lamp. (2) A pilot channel. (3) A pilot regulator. (4) A pilot tone.

pilot alarm. See "alarm, pilot."

pilot cell, *n*. One cell of the 26-cell central office storage battery chosen as the one on which daily readings of specific gravity will be made. All cells are read once a week.

pilot channel. See "channel, pilot."

pilot frequency, *n*. The tone which is transmitted with the intelligence signals on each group of channels on a broadband transmission system. The standard pilot is 96 kHz at a zero transmission level point level of –20 dBm.

pilot lamp. See "lamp, pilot."

pilot regulator, *n.* A device which monitors a pilot tone and then adjusts the gain of associated amplifiers so as to keep the overall system transmission loss constant.

pilot tone, *n.* In a transmission system, a single-frequency unmodulated wave transmitted over the system to indicate or control its characteristics, particularly its overall transmission loss.

pilot wire. See "channel, pilot."

pilot-wire regulator. See "regulator, pilot-wire."

pin, *n.* (1) An electrical terminal in a connector or on an electron tube base. Pushes into a socket to make a connection. (2) An insulator pin.

pin, base, *n.* One of the metal prongs on the base of an electron tube which makes contact with springs in a tube socket.

pin, conduit dowel, *n.* A 3-inch long metal pin, placed in the alignment holes between two sections of multiple tile conduit to maintain them in alignment.

pin, connecting, *n.* A headed steel pin, usually about ¾-inch diameter, having a quick-locking latch on the end opposite the head. Used to facilitate rapid assembly and disassembly of construction equipment, such as pole derricks.

pin, residual. See "residual pin."

pin, steel insulator, *n.* An insulator pin made of steel and having a ⅝ bolt shank. Fitted with a plastic or wooden cob on which an insulator may be screwed. Used in long-span construction and river crossings where wooden pins do not have sufficient strength.

pin, transposition, *n.* An insulator pin mounted on a steel bracket. Designed to be bolted to a crossarm to support a transposition insulator.

pin, wooden insulator, *n.* A locust wood peg, 1¼" D x 8" long, having a coarse square thread cut on the upper end. Used to mount glass insulators on a cross-arm.

Pi network. See "network, Pi."

pink noise, *n.* Random electrical noise which has constant energy per octave. Pink noise is made from white noise by putting it through a filter which has a slope of –3 db per octave.

pin position. See "position, pin" and "number, pin."

pipe alarm meter. See "meter, pipe alarm."

pipeline, gas, *n.* A dry air feeder pipe, commonly an aluminum foil lined polyethylene pipe of ¾" ID, which is placed in a main duct run and carries dry air at 10 psig from the central office pipe alarm meter panel to manifolds at 6000 foot intervals along the cable route, from which it is distributed to the pressurized cables in that manhole. The pipeline has a low pneumatic resistance so a drop in pressure at an outlying point is very quickly detected at the pipe alarm meter panel.

pitch, *n.* The subjective property of a sound which determines its position on a musical scale, depending principally on its frequency and, to a much lesser degree, upon its loudness and waveform.

pitch, standard acoustical, *n.* The standard pitch to which musical instruments are normally tuned is based on the "A" above "middle C" having a frequency of 440 hertz.

plaintext, *adj.* Not coded or encrypted.

plan, benefit, *n.* Commitment of a telephone company to its employees covering payments for illness, disability, pensions, and death.

plane-polarized, *adj.* Describing electromagnetic waves, such as radio or light, which vibrate in only one dimension. See also "polarization, - - -."

plant, *n.* A general term applied to any of the physical property of a telephone company which contributes to the furnishing of communication services. See also "outside plant" and "inside plant."

plant, distribution, *n.* All of the cable and wire system to which telephone users may be directly connected. See also: "plant, feeder."

plant, exchange, *n.* All of the inside and outside plant used to provide local exchange service to subscribers, as distinguished from plant used for toll service.

plant, feeder, *n.* The large underground or aerial cables containing subscriber's loops which run from the central office to points where they connect to distribution cables. No subscribers are connected directly to feeder cables.

plant, inside, *n.* (1) Literally, all telephone plant which is inside of buildings. (2) Central office equipment.

plant, outside, *n.* That telephone plant, such as poles, conduits, cables, and wires, which is out-of-doors, not in buildings.

plant, toll, *n.* That portion of the telephone company plant, inside and outside, which is used to furnish toll or long-distance telephone service, as separate from exchange service.

Planté plate, *n.* A storage battery plate consisting of a thick lead plate which is cut with deep grooves. Upon charging, the material in the grooves is changed to lead peroxide.

plant unit. See "unit of property."

plasma, *n.* A gas at an extremely high (20,000 degrees Kelvin) temperature and completely ionized, which is therefore conductive and affected by magnetic fields.

plate, *n.* (1) One of the electrodes in a storage cell. (2) One of the metal surfaces in a capacitor. (3) The anode in an electron tube.

plate, adhesive mounting, *n.* Flat fiber mounting plate used to mount connecting blocks and terminals to smooth, dry walls. Is backed by a rubberized adhesive to adhere it

to the walls without the use of screws.

plate, angle mounting, *n.* Short strap mounting plate which is bent at a right angle. Long leg of angle mounts equipment; short leg fastens to wall or other flat surface.

plate, lift, *n.* A rectangular steel reinforcing plate used under an angled thimbleye bolt which allows the vertical component of the stress to be taken by a pair of ½-inch lag screws driven into the pole.

plate, mounting, *n.* Long flat metal strip or angle drilled to mount a quantity of a particular item of equipment, such as relays, resistors, capacitors, etc. The length is usually such as to permit mounting directly on a relay rack.

plate, number, *n.* (1) The annular plate under the finger wheel of a rotary dial, which bears the numbers 1 through 0. (2) The small aluminum plate on a stile strip of a switchboard bearing numbers giving the hundred group designation of the line jacks to the right of the number plate.

plates, face, *n.* Flat plates, usually plastic, used to surround keys, dials, etc. on equipment. They provide protection, preclude entry of dirt, hold designations, and improve appearance.

platform, cableman's, *n.* A wooden platform with moulding edge, usually 46x46 inches but sometimes 38x54 inches. Fitted with ⅝-inch support ropes fastened to eye bolts in each corner. Provides a work platform for cable splicers while working on aerial splices.

platform, ladder, *n.* A detachable enlarged step which can be hung on a ladder to provide a larger area on which to stand and work.

plating, *n.* The application of one metal over another by electrolysis.

pliers, *n.* A small pair of pincers: an instrument having two short handles extended into pivoted jaws suitable for grasping or cutting.

pliers, cable sheath, *n.* A pliers-like tool for opening and closing split openings in cable sheaths.

pliers, combination, *n.* A small pair of pincers with jaws for holding round or flat objects. Jaws can be set to open normal or wide.

pliers, diagonal, *n.* Pliers with cutting jaws at an angle to the handles to permit cutting off wires close to terminals.

pliers, duck-bill, *n.* Pliers with wide flat jaws, suitable for straightening or bending flat springs.

pliers, gas, *n.* Same as "combination pliers."

pliers, heat coil, *n. pl.* Small pincers having the jaws shaped to hold a ⅜-inch diameter cylinder, thus fitting them to remove and replace heat coils.

pliers, lamp-cap, *n.* Pliers with hook-shaped jaws which can be used to grip and extract lamp caps from the lamp jack.

pliers, lineman's, *n.* Heavy, 8-inch long pliers with both holding and side-cutting jaws.

pliers, long-nose, *n.* Pliers with long, narrow holding jaws suitable for wrapping wire around closely-spaced terminals.

pliers, side-cutting, *n. pl.* A pincers having holding jaws which also have a set of cutting blades on the sides of the jaws, placed close to the hinge for maximum leverage.

plow, cable laying, *n.* Machine which pulls a narrow plow blade through the earth to a fixed pre-set depth, and feeds a cable or wire to the bottom of the earth slot via a tube on the trailing edge of the plow blade.

plow, sabre, *n.* A buried cable-laying plow whose cutting edge is vibrated to give a vertical sawing action, thus greatly (80%) reducing the power required to pull it through the ground. The vibration of the wheels behind the blade closes the slit in the earth.

plow, vibratory. See "plow, sabre."

plug, *n.* A contact member on the end of an electrical cord which terminates the cord conductors. It can be inserted into a fixed jack, connector, or receptacle to make temporary connections with the conductors they terminate. It may make one or many contacts. The familiar switchboard plug has three contacts, called "tip," "ring," and "sleeve."

plug, attachment, *n.* A cap-shaped device having metal blades which, when inserted in a receptacle, make contact with flat metal springs in the receptacle and thus establish connection between the receptacle circuit and the conductors of the flexible cord connected to the attachment plug. Also called a "plug cap."

plug, cable, *n.* Plug consisting of a rectangular block of insulating material containing 14 to 50 strip contacts, the whole protected by a shell with a cable clamp. Mates with a "cable connector."

plug, coaxial, *n.* A plug placed on the end of a 75-ohm coaxial cable to permit its quick connection to a coaxial jack.

plug, conduit, *n.* A plug of soft rubber, round or square, which can be inserted in the end of a duct at a manhole or vault and then expanded to provide a gas and water-tight seal.

plug, drift. See "drift plug."

plug, dummy, *n.* (1) A plug which makes no electrical connection, but which holds the jack springs in their operated position. Usually made of plastic. (2) A small spring cap which closes the hole in a jack sleeve and blocks the jack from inadvertent use.

plug, gas pressure, *n.* An intentional stoppage or dam inside a cable sheath which prevents the flow of dry air or nitrogen used to pressurize the cable. Installed in branch cables or cable terminal stubs to prevent the flow of gas from a main cable.

plug, open, *n.* A plug which can be inserted into a jack to hold the jack springs in their open "off-normal" position. The plug is not connected to anything.

plug, out-of-service, *n.* A plug which, when inserted in a jack, makes that circuit inoperative or makes it appear busy.

plug, phone, *n.* A standard single plug having a ¼-inch diameter sleeve, and only tip and sleeve connections.

plug, phono, *n.* A phonograph plug. See "plug, pin."

plug, pin, *n.* A small single-contact plug (sometimes 2 contacts, including the shield) used to make temporary circuit connections with a pin jack. The pin is only ⅛" in diameter. Not used for switchboards.

plug, polarized, *n.* A multi-conductor plug constructed so that it can be inserted into a jack or receptacle in only one position.

plug, resistance, *n.* A plug with a self-contained resistance, which can be inserted into a jack to place a resistance across the circuit. Resistances of 600 ohms and 300 ohms are most common.

plug, reversing, *n.* A plug in which the tip side of the cable pair is connected to the ring side of the equipment, and vice versa. Used in reversing a line or trunk at the main distributing frame.

plug, short & ground, *n.* A solid metal finger plug with insulated handle. Shorts the tip, ring, and sleeve of the jack. The plug has a terminal which can be grounded.

plug, shorting, *n.* A plug which, when used, connects the tip and ring springs of the jack together, thus shorting the circuit.

plug, switchboard, *n.* A plug having tip, ring, and sleeve conductors used on switchboard cords to make temporary connections to jacks. Of many varieties, but two standard

sizes, the most common having a sleeve diameter of .250 inch, and the other a diameter of .221 inch.

plug, three-conductor, *n.* Switchboard plug which carries three conductors: tip, ring, and sleeve.

plug, test, *n.* Device consisting of two shaped springs, insulated from each other and connected to a test cord. Intended to be slipped in place of the heat coil on a central office protector frame to provide a connection both to the outside cable pair and the inside equipment. Used in pairs marked "T" (tip) and "R" (ring).

plug, twin, *n.* Two telephone plugs held in a common frame or shell which holds the plugs spaced ⅝-inch between centers.

plug, two-conductor, *n.* Switchboard plug which carries two conductors: tip and sleeve. Sleeve is normally ¼" diameter.

plug-ended, *adj.* Said of a one-way trunk which terminates at a "B" switchboard on a single cord with plug (and associated lamps and talk key). This trunk cord and plug can be plugged directly into the jack multiple to extend the call to the called line.

plug-in, *adj.* Describing any device having terminals so it can be connected by simply pushing it into a suitable socket or connector.

plugging-up circuit, *n.* Supervisory circuit associated with a plugging-up cord.

plugging-up circuit, telegraph, *n.* This circuit provides a temporary termination at the service board for a spare or released telegraph line or loop leg. When patched to a line or leg it provides visual and audible indication of a change, either from mark to space or space to mark.

plugging-up cord, *n.* A cord on a trouble supervisory position, used to extinguish permanent line signals. If the line should come clear, the supervisory lamp and alarm on the plugging-up cord will alert the supervisor to take the cord down and thus free the line for use.

plugmold, *n.* A section of rectangular metal surface conduit fitted with 15 ampere, 125 volt power outlets every 6, 12, 18, 30, or 60 inches.

plug shelf, *n.* The fixed back portion of the lower horizontal part of a switchboard, through which the plugs protrude.

plug-supervision trunk (DCS), *n.* A trunk arranged so that plugging into it automatically operates the line signal at the far end. The proper term is "automatic signal trunk." Its operation is essentially ringdown, for there is no through supervision at intermediate switchboards.

plumbing, *n.* A waveguide system. The waveguide and its fittings.

plunger, *n.* A moveable rod or piston inserted in a resonant cavity or waveguide to tune it or to introduce variable attenuation.

plunger lineswitch. See "lineswitch, plunger."

p-n device. See "diode, junction."

pocket, tool, *n.* A small tool case of plastic or leather made to fit a hip or shirt pocket, which can hold small tools and protect the clothing from wear.

pocketing, call, *n.* The directing of a call to a trunk group in which all trunks are busy, at the same time that trunks are idle in an alternate trunk group. Can occur in a trunk group which does not have "full availability," or when a call is delayed in entering a heavily-loaded trunk group.

point, access, *n.* The lower class of junction point in a dedicated outside plant. A semi-permanent splice point at a junction between a branch feeder cable and distribution cables. Used to allocate pairs to subscribers.

point, code, *n.* A terminal punching located in a cross-connection field of a marker, and energized by registration of a 1-, 2-, or 3-digit code.

point, control, *n.* The higher class of

junction point in a dedicated outside plant. A semi-permanent splice point at the junction between main feeder cables or branch feeder cables, or between several branch feeder cables. Used to allocate groups of pairs to branch feeder cables.

point, load, *n.* A point at which loading coils are inserted in cable circuits to improve their transmission characteristics. See also "spacing, load coil."

point, pick-up, *n.* The location where a remote broadcast originates.

point, singing, *n.* (1) The condition where singing just starts. (2) The total gain of a two-wire repeater, E-W plus W-E, as the repeater just starts to sing when connected to working lines East and West which are terminated at the far end.

point, toll. See "toll point."

point, transmission level (TLP), *n.* Any point in a transmission system where a power level measurement is made.

point, vacant code, *n.* A code point which is not assigned. If a call is directed to a vacant code point, it is routed to an operator or a vacant code trunk.

point, zero transmission level. *n.* The reference, from which other transmission levels are measured, or to which other transmission levels are referred. In toll systems, usually the transmitting toll switchboard.

pointer, *n.* The indicating needle that moves over the scale of a meter.

point-to-point, *adj.* Describing communication between two fixed stations.

point transposition. See "transposition, point."

poisoning, cathode, *n.* The reduction of electron emission from the cathode of an electron tube due to gases released from the metal elements in the tube.

poison ivy wash, *n.* A 10% solution of ferric chloride used to treat dermatitis from poison plants. Packed in 4-cc vials for first-aid kits.

Poisson distribution, *n.* A mathematical formula or a graph of a curve whose mean and variance are equal, and which expresses the probability that an event will occur with greater or lesser frequency than the mean of all events.

poking tape, *n.* The act of preparing a perforated teletypewriter tape for automatic transmission, by typing the message into a tape perforator.

polar, *adj.* (1) Polarized. (2) Having a dielectric constant which decreases with increasing frequency.

polarential telegraph operation, *n.* A method of operating a telegraph loop in which the central office end of the loop sends polar signals, while the subscriber end sends differential signals.

polarity, *n.* (1) The property of a magnet, whose poles are either north-seeking or south-seeking. (2) The property of a terminal of a battery or circuit which has either (a) an excess of electrons (negative) or (b) a deficiency of electrons (positive).

polarization, *n.* (1) The formation of chemical products near the electrodes of an electric cell (such as a dry cell) which inhibits further flow of current through the cell. (2) The restriction of the vibration of an electromagnetic wave to a single plane.

polarization, circular, *n.* Of an electromagnetic wave, the rotation of the plane of polarization through 360 degrees as the wave propagates forward. Created by combining equal magnitudes of vertically and horizontally plane polarized waves, with the phase of one exactly 90 degrees ahead of or behind the other. Depending on the sequence, this creates right-hand or left-hand rotation.

polarization, elliptical, *n.* Of an electromagnetic wave, the rotation of the plane of polarization through

360 degrees as the wave propagates forward. Created by combining vertical and horizontal plane polarized waves whose amplitudes are not equal, or if equal whose vertical and horizontal components are not separated by exactly 90 degrees in phase. See also "polarization, circular."

polarization, horizontal, *n.* Polarization of an electromagnetic wave in which the electric field lies in a plane parallel to the earth's surface.

polarization, left-hand, *n.* Polarization of a circularly or elliptically polarized electromagnetic wave in which the rotation of the electric field vector is counterclockwise, looking in the direction of wave propagation.

polarization, plane, *n.* The restriction of the vibration of an electromagnetic wave to a single plane. The electric field of the wave may be horizontal, vertical, or at any intermediate angle.

polarization, right-hand, *n.* Polarization of a circularly or elliptically polarized electromagnetic wave such that the rotation of the electric field vector is clockwise, looking in the direction of wave propagation.

polarization, vertical, *n.* Polarization of an electromagnetic wave in which the electric field lies in a plane perpendicular to the earth's surface.

polarization loss. See "loss, polarization."

polarized, *adj.* (1) Flowing in one direction. (2) Sensitive to the direction of current flow. (3) Vibrating in a particular direction or manner. (4) In a dry cell, restricted in current flow by the formation of electrolysis products around the electrodes.

polar relay, *n.* A relay whose operation depends upon the direction of the current through its operating winding.

polar telegraph. See "telegraph, polar."

pole, *n.* (1) A long, round, slender,

slightly tapering column of wood, concrete, or steel used to support overhead cables and wires. (2) One of the two poles of a magnet, north or south. (3) One of two terminals of a battery or circuit, negative or positive. (4) One of the terminals of a switch.

pole, butt treated, *n.* An older treated pole on which only the portion to be set in the ground was treated (often by dipping) with a preservative chemical.

pole, commutating. See "interpole."

pole, dead-end, *n.* Either the first or last pole of a pole line, on which cable(s) or open-wire ends.

pole, gin, *n.* A pole set in a very shallow hole and guyed temporarily, used as a point of attachment for a block and tackle to be used to lift and permanently set a longer pole. Gin poles are used only when the pole to be set is too long to be lifted and held upright by the derrick on the construction truck.

pole, joint, *n.* A pole whose use is shared by two or more utility companies.

pole, junction, *n.* (1) A pole at a junction between cable and open wire. (2) A pole at a junction between two open-wire lines. (3) A pole at a junction between two open-wire transposition sections.

pole, magnetic. See "magnetic pole."

pole, north. See "north pole."

pole, pike, *n.* A strong wooden rod, 2 inches in diameter and 10 to 20 feet long, fitted with a ¾″ D sharp steel point at one end. Used for pushing, raising, and supporting poles while they are being set in the ground, or being straightened.

pole, pressure-treated, *n.* A pole which has been placed in a sealed tank and impregnated under pressure to a considerable depth with a preservative chemical, such as creosote or pentachlorophenol.

pole, sky-grey, *n.* Pole treated with pentachlorophenol in polypropylene glycol colored blue-grey. Coloring tends to blend with the sky, thus improving the appearance of the pole.

pole, south. See "south pole."

pole, terminal, *n.* (1) Any pole which carries a cable terminal. (2) The pole at the end of a cable, particularly one at which an open wire line is connected to the cable.

pole, treated, *n.* A pole which has been treated with a chemical for its entire length to prevent damage from rot or insects. The two most common chemicals used are creosote and pentachlorophenol.

pole class. See "class of pole."

pole face, *n.* The end of a relay core next to the armature.

pole fixture. See "fixture."

pole house. See "house, pole."

pole key. See "key, pole."

pole line, *n.* A series of poles in a line, used to support cables or wires.

pole pair, *n.* On an open wire line, any of the open wire pairs in which one wire is on one side of the pole and the second wire is on the other side of the pole. For instance, pairs 5-6, 15-16, 25-26, etc. See also "non-pole pair."

pole-piece, *n.* Either extremity of a magnet or of the core of a relay, at which the magnetic flux is concentrated.

pole-to-pole guy. See "guy, pole-to-pole."

pole-to-stub guy. See "guy, pole-to-stub."

poling, *n.* The adjustment of polarity. Specifically, in wire line practice, the use of transpositions between transposition sections of open wire or between lengths of cable to cause the residual crosstalk couplings in individual sections or lengths to neutralize one another.

polisher, plug, *n.* A quick-opening cylindrical vise used to hold a switchboard plug. The polisher is a length of cotton rope impregnated with jeweler's rouge, which is wrapped once around the plug and then pulled back and forth.

polite search, *n.* In the automatic alternate routing of precedence calls, the act of searching in sequence all ten available trunk groups (direct, direct triple, and alternate triples) for an idle circuit. If no idle circuit is found, an NC (no circuit) 120 IPM tone is returned, but pre-emption is not exercised.

polychloroprene, *n.* Neoprene.

polyester, *n.* A plastic resin formed by the reaction between a dibasic acid and a dihydroxy-alcohol.

polyethylene, *n.* A thermoplastic material composed of polymers of ethylene. A tough, white insulator having a waxy appearance, very low moisture absorption, and low dielectric losses even at radio frequencies. Resists sunlight if colored black.

polygrid network, *n.* A highly survivable toll switching network in which all switching centers are of the same rank, and in which each center is interconnected with a multiplicity of other centers over separate trunking paths.

polygrid routing plan, *n.* Plan for a toll switching network consisting of adjacent interconnected hexagonal "home grids," the whole served by superimposed "long-haul" trunks as required.

polymer, *n.* A long chain molecule which is formed by the linking (polymerization) of many molecules of normal sizes. Polymers are good insulators, and do not absorb water.

polymerization, *n.* A chemical reaction in which several small molecules combine to form a much larger molecule. The reaction by which polyethelene, neoprene, and thermosetting adhesives are made.

polyphase, *adj.* Describing an electrical circuit or electrical equipment which uses two or more phases. Polyphase circuits having two, three, and six phases are common.

polyphase circuit, *n.* A symmetrical power circuit of more than one phase.

polystyrene, *n.* A crystal-clear plastic having excellent insulation resistance, and a dielectric constant which is independent of frequency. Excellent for use as an insulator, and as the dielectric in a capacitor.

polyurethane, *n.* Any of several rubber polymers produced by the polymerization of a hydroxyl (OH) radical with several NCO groups.

polyurethane gel, *n.* A material used to construct gas plugs in cables. Consists of a liquid polyurethane loaded with fiberglass, and a liquid hardener. It hardens within one hour after mixing, and will resist gas pressure after two hours.

polyvinyl, *n.* Polyvinyl chloride.

polyvinyl chloride (PVC), *n.* A thermoplastic material composed of polymers of vinyl chloride. A tough, non-flammable, water resistant insulator much used for wire insulation. It has higher dielectric losses than polyethelene.

pony circuit, *n.* A very short telegraph or teletypewriter circuit, usually within the same room or building, used to change the termination of an incoming circuit from one point to another.

pony insulator. See "insulator, pony."

porcelain, *n.* A fine, white, hard ceramic, usually with a dense transparent glaze, much used for insulators because of its low moisture absorption.

port, *n.* (1) Entrance or exit (input or output) of a multiterminal radio-frequency device, such as a circulator. (2) Any of several terminals of a multiterminal voice-frequency transmission network. A port may be 2-wire or 4-wire, and one-way in, one-way out, or two-way.

Porta-a-Punch. See "card, Porta-a-Punch."

position, *n.* That portion of a switchboard or testboard designed for operation by one person.

position, inward toll, *n.* A toll switchboard position used to receive calls over intertoll trunks, and to establish inward connections to local customers.

position, inward and through toll, *n.* A toll switchboard position used to handle both inward and through traffic.

position, outward toll, *n.* A toll switchboard position used to receive toll calls from customers and to complete, time, and ticket such calls. Outward positions may also handle DSA traffic.

position, through toll, *n.* A toll switchboard position used to establish connections between intertoll trunks.

position, pin, *n.* The numerical position of an insulator pin counting from the left end of a crossarm as one faces away from the central office. Thus the pins on the top crossarm may be numbered 1-10; the pins on the second crossarm may be numbered 11-20, etc.

position, ticket. See "ticket position."

position, ticket filing. See "ticket filing position."

position, toll switching. See "toll switching position."

position, traffic service (TSP), *n.* A pushbutton console switchboard whose operator is automatically called in on the connection just long enough to give some particular personal assistance, such as that required by person-to-person, credit-card, and charge-to-third-number calls.

positive, *adj.* (1) Having the type of charge which is generated on a glass rod when it is rubbed with a piece of silk. (2) Having the capability to attract negative charges, or electrons. (3) The opposite of negative.

positive feedback. See "feedback, positive."

positive-negative signaling. *n.* An outmoded signaling scheme which uses a simplex signaling path derived from the talking pair. It gave a greater range than loop signaling, but was susceptible to earth potentials, and noise due to longitudinal unbalance. Also called "battery and ground signaling."

positive terminal, *n.* The terminal toward which electrons flow, and from which a conventional current flows in the external circuit.

positron, *n.* A positive electron. An elementary particle having the same mass as an electron, but with a positive charge.

post, binding, *n.* A threaded stud equipped with binding nuts under which wires can be clamped to make an electrical connection. Part of a terminal. The stud commonly used has #8 or #10 fine-pitch screw threads.

posted delay, *n.* The anticipated delay in minutes to complete a toll call through a congested trunk group. Notice of the delay may be posted on a bulletin board above the switchboard, or given in a recorded message.

postpay coin telephone, *n.* A manual telephone for paystation use. Upon lifting the handset, the user is connected to an operator who requires deposit of the appropriate coins before completing the call. Coins deposited by the customer cannot be returned.

pot, *n.* (1) A solder pot. (2) A paraffin pot. (3) A potentiometer (slang).

pot, paraffin, *n.* A tinned, 9-quart steel kettle with lid, used by a cable splicer's helper to heat paraffin for the drying of splices in paper insulated cables.

pot, solder, *n.* A heavy cast-steel pot with steel bail handle, used on a gasoline furnace by a splicer's helper to melt solder for the wiping of lead cable sleeves.

potential, *n.* The relative voltage or amount of electric charge existing at a point in a circuit as referred to another point in the circuit, usually ground.

potential, ground, *n.* Having the same (zero) potential as the earth.

potential difference, *n.* The difference in voltage existing between two points in a circuit.

potentiometer, *n.* A three-terminal device consisting of a resistor having an adjustable tap, which can be used for a voltage divider.

potentiometer, telegraph hub, *n.* The pair of resistors connected to the receive hub which supply battery potential to the hub. One 5300 ohm resistor connects to +130 volt battery, while the other 4400 ohm resistor connects through a diode to ground.

potentiometer, telegraph loop, *n.* An adjustable resistance used to build out all telegraph loops to a uniform resistance of 2880 ohms.

pot-head, *n.* (1) A device insulating the end of a power cable and permitting connection of open power conductors. (2) A telephone cable terminal. (obsolete)

potting, *n.* The sealing of electrical components or a cable end with a liquid which thermosets into an elastomer and excludes moisture.

pouch, tool, *n.* A divided leather pocket arranged to hang from a belt and to hold pliers, screwdrivers, and other small tools.

powdered-metal, *n.* Material for magnetic cores composed of finely powdered iron or permalloy whose particles are insulated with varnish before being compressed in molding dies, then heat-treated. In a powdered-metal core the eddy currents are very restricted, and therefore iron losses are low.

powder-powered, *adj.* Describing the gun or the hardened fastening devices which it shoots into masonry or steel by the use of gun powder in blank cartridges.

power, *n.* The time rate at which work is done. Power in watts equals the amount of work in joules divided by the time during which the work was done in seconds.

power (alternating current), *n.* Power in an alternating current circuit is obtained by multiplying three factors: (a) the effective voltage, (b) the effective current, and (c) the cosine of the phase angle between the current and the voltage: $P = EI \cos \theta$. The Greek letter theta is: θ

power (direct current), *n.* The power in a direct current circuit, assuming $P =$ watts, $E =$ volts, $I =$ amperes, and $R =$ ohms, can be obtained in any of these ways:

    (a) $P = EI$
    (b) $P = I^2 R$
    (c) $P = E^2 / R$

power, apparent, *n.* The value of power in an alternating current circuit, obtained by multiplying the voltage by the current. The real power is obtained by multiplying the apparent power by the power factor. See also "power factor."

power, auxiliary, *n.* Power used at a communication facility which is not required to maintain uninterrupted communications, such as power for air conditioning and some lights.

power, available, *n.* The power which a linear source of energy is capable of delivering into its conjugate impedance.

power, average speech, *n.* The total speech energy radiated over a period of a time, divided by the length of the period. The average power for American speech, including silent intervals, is about 10 microwatts.

power, Class B auxiliary, *n.* A standby power plant to cover extended outages (days) of primary power.

power, Class C auxiliary, *n.* A quick-start (10-60 seconds) standby power plant to cover short-term outages (hours) of primary power.

power, Class D auxiliary, *n.* An uninterruptible (no-break) power unit using stored energy to provide continuous power within specified voltage and frequency tolerances.

power, effective radiated, *n.* The radio

frequency power, in watts, supplied to an antenna multiplied by the gain of the antenna in the direction of transmission.

power, no-break. See "no-break power unit."

power, reactive. See "reactive power."

power, real, *n.* The power in an alternating current circuit which is used in doing work. It is measured in watts, and is equal to the product of voltage times current times power factor. See also "power, apparent" and "power factor."

power, ringing, *n.* Power used to ring telephone bells or to signal on circuits. Commonly 20 Hz at 100 volts RMS.

power, signal, *n.* Power used to operate buzzers or signal lamps, commonly 10 or 18 volts, 60 Hz alternating current.

power, wattless. See "reactive power."

power amplifier, *n.* An amplifier designed to deliver high output power to its load, rather than a high voltage.

power board. See "board, power."

power circuit, primary. See "primary power circuit."

power control unit (PCU), *n.* The portion of the central office power equipment which has the following functions:

  (a) Controlling charger operation.
  (b) Sensing and regulating battery voltage.
  (c) Fusing and metering charge and discharge circuits.
  (d) Switching from 23-cell to 26-cell operation.
  (e) Trickle charging the end cells.

power density, *n.* Power in watts per hertz, or the total power in a band of frequencies divided by the bandwidth in hertz.

power equipment, unitized. See "equipment, unitized power."

power factor, *n.* The power factor of an alternating current circuit is the ratio of the true power in watts, as measured by a wattmeter, to the apparent power obtained by multiplying the current and the potential, in amperes and volts. The power factor is usually less than unity because the current and potential are seldom in phase. If the current and voltage waveforms are sinusoidal, the power factor is equal to the cosine of the phase angle between current and potential.

power factor, unity. See "unity power factor."

power level, *n.* The amount of power at a point in a circuit compared with some reference power.

power plant, *n.* (1) A station which generates power from fuel. (2) An assembly of storage battery and charger, sometimes also supplying ringing power and/or signal lamp power.

power plant, nuclear. See "nuclear power plant."

power supply, emergency, *n.* A source of alternating current power, usually a motor-generator set, which is automatically switched on when the commercial AC power fails. See also "power, - - - auxiliary."

practices, *n. pl.* A set of published instructions for doing work in a uniform, standard manner. They list objectives, and describe the tools, materials, and methods to be used to accomplish them.

preamble, *n.* The first portion of a telegraphic message, which gives a message number, date-time group, address, etc.

preamble, message. See "header, message."

preamplifier, *n.* A low noise amplifier designed to take a very low level signal, such as that from an antenna or microphone, and boost it to a level which can be accepted by a receiver or standard amplifier.

precedence, *n.* A rank assigned to indicate the degree of preference or priority to be given in processing an offered call or in protecting a call in progress.

FO   Flash Override   0
F   Flash   1
I   Immediate   2
P   Priority   3
     Routine   4

precedence (level), *n.* A relative priority rating assigned to a telephone user which permits him to preempt a trunk circuit already in use by a lower priority subscriber. See also "level, precedence."

precision, *n.* The quality of being stated with exactness.

precision balance, *n.* The degree of balance between line and network at a hybrid coil obtained by using a balancing network designed to match the line facility exactly, and also adjusting the net building-out capacitor for the exact line end section capacitance. Usually implies a return loss of 20 dB, or greater.

precision network. See "network, precision."

prediction chart, radio, *n.* Chart, based on predicted sunspot numbers, enabling estimation of the maximum useful frequency (MUF) for high-frequency radio communication.

pre-emphasis, *n.* Deliberately distorting a signal by increasing the power in the higher frequencies at the transmitting end of a communication system, followed by a complementary de-emphasis at the receiver. The customary emphasis is 6 db per octave. Its purpose is to improve the signal-to-noise ratio.

pre-emphasis network, *n.* An equalizer which causes greater loss to the lower frequencies, thus emphasizing the higher frequencies so that they will have sufficient power to override noise on the transmission path. See also "pre-emphasis."

preempt, *v.* To disconnect an established telephone connection in order to obtain a trunk over which to establish a connection for a subscriber having a higher precedence.

preemption, *n.* The procedure, manual or automatic, by which a telephone user having a high precedence seizes an active trunk circuit already in use by a lower precedence user.

preemption, reverse. See "reverse preemption."

preemption, ruthless, *n.* The act of seizing a busy voice circuit without prior warning to the parties who are using the circuit.

preempt search, *n.* In the automatic alternate routing of precedence calls, the act of searching in sequence all available trunk groups (direct, direct triples, and alternate triples) for an idle circuit. If no idle circuit is found, the most direct circuit with the lowest precedence call will be pre-empted.

preempt tone, *n.* A 480 Hz tone which indicates to the telephone users who are talking that their trunk has been pre-empted by a higher precedence call, and that they should hang up before placing their call again.

pre-equalization, *n.* The introduction of planned distortion into the input of an electrical circuit which will compensate for (is opposite in sign from) distortion which the signal will suffer in traversing the circuit.

preferential answering, *n.* The giving of higher priority or preference to answering a particular class of calls (such as a toll call) even though a call of another class (such as a local or DSA call) may have been waiting longer.

preferential hunting, *n.* A system to reduce hunting time and switch wear on step-by-step linefinders. The lines are divided into two groups, A and B. Group B lines are connected to the banks reversed, top to bottom, so that a linefinder normally never searches above the fifth bank level.

preferential jack, *n.* A jack in a line or trunk group marked to indicate to the operator that she should begin with that jack when testing for an idle line or trunk.

prefix 1, *n.* A prefix used on customer-dialed direct-distance-dialed station-to-station calls outside of the local area.

prefix 112, *n.* A prefix used on customer-dialed direct-distance-dialed station-to-station calls outside of the local area, in those step-by-step central offices which have not yet been converted for "prefix 1" calling.

prefix 0, *n.* A prefix used for special direct-distance-dialed toll calls, such as person-to-person and collect calls, which require operator assistance.

prefixing, digit, *n.* The action of a register-sender, under control of a translator, of adding sufficient digits to route the call through the proper switch train, such as adding a foreign area code to the seven-digit number.

pregroup, carrier, *n.* In carrier systems using more than one stage of modulation, a pregroup consists of four channels individually modulated to occupy the frequency range from 8 to 24 kilohertz.

prelash, *v.* To fasten (lash) an aerial cable to its suspension strand before installing it on the pole.

preliminary pulse, *n.* A pulse caused by accidentally bumping the hookswitch after or while lifting the handset. Causes the same reaction as if a digit "1" had been dialed.

preliminary relay contacts, *n.* Those groups of relay contact pairs which make or break before the early contacts when the relay operates. See also "early" and "ordinary" contacts.

prepay coin telephone, *n.* A dial, wall telephone for paystation use. The user must deposit a coin before receiving dial tone. Requires a special trunk circuit at the central office, and sometimes a special ringer box. Coins can be collected or returned by the operator.

prepostpay coin telephone, *n.* A coin telephone which operates as prepay on calls dialed directly to local

numbers but which operates as postpay when "Operator" is dialed.

presbycusis, *n.* That portion of hearing loss which can be specifically ascribed to the effects of aging.

preselecting, *adj.* Describing a selecting switch which keeps its wipers standing on idle trunk contacts so that it can operate rapidly to extend the connection, without having first to hunt for idle terminals. Used for switches which must operate during the interdigital time.

preselector, *n.* A device placed ahead of a frequency converter or like device, which passes signals of desired frequencies and attenuates others.

present worth, *n.* The amount of money it would be necessary to set aside now at a specified rate of interest so that a certain sum would be available at a specified time in the future.

presser, connector, *n.* A plier-like device used to press or crimp wire connectors when splicing cable.

press-to-talk, *adj.* Describing a telephone handset in which the transmitter is disconnected until a push-button in the handle is depressed. Used where the ambient noise is high level.

pressure, gas. See "system, gas pressure."

pressure guard. See "contactor, gas pressure."

pressure-sensitive, *adj.* Describing an adhesive made to adhere to a surface after a brief application of pressure. Permits easy removal if done before the adhesive dries.

pressure tap, CATV. See "tap, CATV pressure."

pressurization, *n.* The use of dry air or dry nitrogen, at a pressure 2-6 pounds above atmospheric pressure, inside of telephone cable sheaths or coaxial cable lines to prevent the entry of moisture at faulty splices or accidental holes.

pretranslation, *n.* The process of determining from the first one, two, or three dialed digits how many more digits the register should expect to receive on that particular call.

pretranslator, crossbar, *n.* Device provided in dial offices where some calls require the dialing of more digits than others. It analyzes the first few digits dialed and notifies the register how many total digits should be received before seizing a marker. (#5 X Bar)

pre-wiring, *n.* The practice of concealing station wire or cable in the walls of buildings while they are being constructed. It is cheaper for the Telephone Company, and more satisfactory for the occupant.

primary, *adj.* First. Fundamental. Principal.—*n.* (1) A primary winding. (2) A primary power circuit. (3) A primary cell.

primary cell, *n.* A cell whose electrical energy is derived from an irreversible electrochemical reaction, and is therefore incapable of being charged by an electric current.

Primary Center, *n.* Any of the third rank toll switching points in the distance dialing network. It may home on Sectional Centers or Regional Centers, or both. Also known as a Class 3 toll office.

primary distribution system, *n.* An electrical distribution system in which high voltage AC "primary" circuits supply the primary windings of "distribution" transformers whose secondary windings supply power to "distribution" circuits at the utilization voltage.

primary power, *n.* A reliable source of power which normally serves the load.

primary power circuit, *n.* Any of the power circuits that carry electricity at voltages higher than distribution voltage. Primary voltages range from 2400 volts to over 200,000 volts.

primary relay station, *n.* A major relay station which has been assigned net control responsibilities for its geographical area.

primary service area. See "area, primary service."

primary trunk, *n.* The intra-office trunk between a linefinder or line-switch and a local first selector.

primary winding, *n.* The transformer winding which receives energy from a supply source.

Princess phone, *n.* The Bell System's designation for a small desk telephone set. Features an illuminated dial.

Principal Outlet, *n.* An older class of toll switching center, now called a "Primary Center." See also "centers, toll switching."

printed circuit, *n.* A copper foil circuit formed on one or both faces of an insulating board, to which circuit components are soldered. The copper foil pattern serves as connections between components, and is produced either by etching or plating.

printer, *n.* (1) A printing telegraph. (2) A teletypewriter.

printer, page, *n.* A teletypewriter which produces typed copy on a roll or fanfold of paper which is page width: 8 or 8½ inches.

printer, tape, *n.* A teletypewriter which produces typed copy lengthwise on a narrow paper tape.

printer, toll ticketing, *n.* A machine which prints toll tickets with alphanumeric characters under the control of automatic message accounting punched tapes.

printer, traffic, *n.* The printing portion of a telephone traffic recorder.

printing telegraphy. See "telegraphy, printing."

printroller, *n.* A device which functions as an interface between an automatic equipment routiner and a printer. It provides the necessary controls to print out on tape a record of all faulty conditions detected by the routiner. A printer-controller.

print-through, *n.* The transfer of magnetic signals between adjacent layers of magnetic tape when stored on the reel for long periods of time.

Priority (P), *n.* The fourth highest ranking message precedence. See "precedence."

privacy, *n.* Equipment at a terminal of a radiotelephone circuit which so "scrambles" the voice frequencies that they would be unintelligible to a listener. At the far terminal they are "unscrambled" and made intelligible again.

privacy equipment. See "scrambler, speech."

private automatic branch exchange (PABX), *n.* A small, private, dial central office having an attendant's cabinet.

private automatic exchange (PAX), *n.* A small unattended automatic central office located on a subscriber's premises and serving only his stations with local and trunked service. When equipped with an attendant's switchboard or turret it becomes a PABX.

private branch exchange (PBX), *n.* (1) A private telephone switchboard. (2) A small, private, manual central office. (3) A small, private central office, either manual or dial. (This meaning is i n e x a c t. PBX should not be used to mean a dial office. See also PAX, and PABX.)

Private Line Teletypewriter Service (PLTTY), *n.* Leased line teletypewriter service, not a part of the dial teletypewriter exchange service (DTWX) switched network.

privates, *n. pl.* In an automatic switching system, the third and fourth wires which c o r r e s p o n d to the "sleeve" and "lamp" wires of a manual switching system. Usually called the "control" (C) and "extra control" (EC) wires.

probability traffic table, *n.* Any of the telephone traffic tables designated P-1, P-2, P-3, etc. used for automatically switched traffic, and based on the probability that a designated percentage of offered calls will find "all trunks busy" during the busy hour. (P-1 indicates that 1% will find ATB, etc.) Each table relates two factors for a particular grade of service (probability of busy) (a) Traffic load, in CCS, (b) trunks per group. If either is known, the other can be found from the table. Modern probability tables are designated with probability ($P=0.01$ or $GS=1$ in 100) rather than with percentage busy (P-1).

probe, *n.* (1) A test prod, sometimes with circuit components like an RF detector in its handle. (2) A wire loop inserted into a resonant cavity or waveguide, used to couple an external circuit.

processing, data, *n.* Mechanical or electrical handling of data: sorting, collating, performing mathematical steps, storing, erasing, or printing.

processor, signal, *n.* In an electronic switching system, a digital logic unit that is subordinate to the central control and assists it by performing the simpler, more repetitive tasks, such as scanning the lines for off-hook conditions, providing dial tone, etc.

prod, pole, *n.* Steel rod tool used for poking in the butt of a pole to determine the existence and extent of rotten wood.

prod, test, *n.* A needle point with an insulating handle, connected to a test lead and used to make temporary test connections in restricted places.

product modulator. See "modulator, product."

profile chart, *n.* A chart showing the vertical elevation of all terrain and obstacles between two points. Profile charts are widely used in radio system planning.

program, *n.* (1) The instructions which are placed in the memory of a common-controlled switching system. (2) A radio or television program.—*v.* To prepare a set of instructions in the form of a program.

program, emergency action, *n.* Automatic routine in an electronic switching system (ESS) which is called into action when the switch does not complete calls properly.

program, generic, *n.* A specific program designed to fit all common-controlled switching systems of a general type. It programs the control of all functions which are common to all of these offices. Individual variations are then handled by variations in translations.

program, stored, *n.* The instructions which are placed in the memory of a common-controlled switching unit and to which it refers while processing a call for instructions regarding class marks, code conversions, routing, as well as for trouble analysis. Stored programs commonly use alterable magnetic marks to record the program instructions. See also "program, wired."

program, wired, *n.* A program utilizing logic devices which are interconnected by hard wiring. Any change in the program requires that the logic devices be rewired.

program circuit, *n.* A telephone circuit which has been equalized so that it is suitable for transmitting radio boadcast program material. Circuits are available having an upper cutoff of 3700, 5000, or 8000 hertz.

programming, *vt.* (1) Defining objectives and making schedules for achieving them, segregating activities sharing the same objective into programs, and estimating resource requirements. (2) To work out a sequence of operations to be performed by a computer.

project, *n.* A formal plan, including an estimate of cost, for adding a sizeable amount of telephone plant. See also "estimate."

propagation, *n.* The traveling of an electrical wave along a transmis-

sion line, or of an electromagnetic wave through space.

propagation, anomalous, *n.* Abnormal radio propagation in which radio signals are detected, sometimes for a period of several hours, at distances over which radio transmission should be impossible. Caused when radio waves become trapped in a "duct" or ionized layer and follow it for long distances.

propagation, forward scatter. See "scatter propagation."

propagation, radio, *n.* The transfer of energy through space by electromagnetic radiation at radio frequencies.

propagation, sporadic. See "sporadic propagation."

propagation, velocity of, *n.* The speed with which a signal wave travels through a particular transmission medium. It varies greatly, as follows:

Medium	Speed, Miles per Second
Light through space	186,284
Radio through air	142,000
Coaxial cable	133,000
Open wire carrier	117,500
Cable carrier	105,000
Cable, 19 ga NL	46,930
Cable, 16 ga B22	20,010
Cable, 19 ga H44	19,787
Cable, 19 ga H174	10,220

propagation constant, *n.* An algebraic expression which states what changes an electrical wave will experience in traveling through a transmission medium. It is a complex quantity whose real part is the "attenuation constant" (in nepers per unit length) and whose imaginary part is the "phase constant" (in radians per unit length).

propagation time delay, *n.* The time required for a wave to travel between two points on a transmission path.

property, expendable, *n.* Property that is consumed or which loses its identity in use and which therefore may be dropped from stock record accounts when it is issued or used.

property unit. See "unit of property."

prorate, *v.t.* To divide, distribute, or assess proportionately.

protect, *v.t.* (1) To shield from injury or destruction. (2) To equip with devices for safeguarding from excessive voltages or currents. (3) To encrypt before transmission.

protection, conduit, *n.* A shield against injury to underground conduit by inadvertent digging, settling, or landslides. Usually a slab of concrete (top, or top and bottom) or complete encasement in concrete.

protection, overload, *n.* Protection, such as a circuit breaker, which opens when the current through a circuit or device is greater than it was designed to carry.

protector, *n.* (1) A device which is applied to a telephone line to protect the connected equipment from over-voltage and/or over-current. Excessive voltages and currents are shunted to ground. (2) A base of insulating material equipped with protector units, or carbon protector blocks, and sometimes fuses. Provides protection against over-voltage and over-current. When installed out of doors, it may require a "protector mounting."

protector, cable. See "shield, cable duct."

protector, central office, *n.* An assemblage of protector elements mounted on the vertical side of the main distributing frame, on which all outside plant cables terminate when they enter a central office. Provides over-voltage and over-current protection, plus a convenient place to open the cable pair for testing. See also "connector, 300-type."

protector, crossarm. See "protector, open wire."

protector, drawing-in, *n.* A cylindrical aluminum shield with belled entrance, for placing in conduit at a manhole to provide a smooth lip which will not damage the cable as it is being pulled in.

protector, fused station, *n.* A device to protect a telephone station from excessive voltages and currents coming from the outside plant. Consists of a pair of 7-ampere fuses in series with the line, plus a pair of carbon blocks which discharge high voltages (over 350V) to ground.

protector, fuseless station, *n.* A station protector which has no line fuses, but has heavy-duty grounding-type protectors that provide metallic grounding when subjected to a high current flow.

protector, gas tube, *n.* A protector whose voltage limiting element is a vacuum tube having three electrodes in an easily ionized gas, such as neon or argon. When the voltage across the electrodes reaches a limit depending on their spacing, the gas ionizes and the high voltage is drained to ground.

protector, guy wire, *n.* A half-round cylinder of galvanized steel, 7 or 8 feet long, which can be bolted over an anchor guy wire just above the ground. It makes the guy wire more visible to pedestrians and lessens the chance of injury if they should run into the guy.

protector, MDF. See "protector, central office" and "connector, 300-type."

protector, open wire, *n.* Pairs of carbon blocks on a porcelain base with weatherproof cover. Mount on crossarms or poles, and are used to drain lightning and static voltages from open wire circuits. Available in one-pair and five-pair types.

protector, power contact, *n.* An open-space cutout used to protect open wire lines from over-voltage caused by lightning or contact with power lines. Consists of three cylindrical carbon blocks spaced 0.02 inch, mounted on a heavy porcelain base with metal cover. Two electrodes are connected to the line and the third to ground. Available in 2000 and 3000 volts breakdown ratings.

protector, power cross. See "protector, power contact."

protector, station, *n.* A device to protect a telephone station from excessive voltage coming from the outside plant. See also "protector, fused station" and "protector, fuseless station."

protector color code, *n.* Protector discharge blocks are often color-coded to indicate the air gap, and resultant breakover voltage.

Color	Voltage	Air Gap
White	350V	.003″
Blue	700V	.006″
Yellow	1100V	.010″
Red	2500V	.022″

protector mounting, *n.* (1) A housing with a cover or door which encloses a protector when used out-of-doors. (2) The portion of the protector which holds the protector units or fuses, usually an insulating base with contacts and terminals.

protector unit, *n.* A small device which screws into a protector to provide over-voltage protection. Consists of a pair of spaced carbon blocks as discharge electrodes, plus a lead alloy spacer pellet which melts during a sustained current flow and provides metallic grounding.

proton, *n.* A positively-charged elementary particle which is part of the nucleous of the atom. Its mass is 1837 times greater than that of an electron.

prototype filter, *n.* A basic filter, of constant-k design.

proximity effect, *n.* The tendency for high-frequency currents flowing in the same direction on parallel conductors to flow in that portion of the conductor which is farthest from the other conductor.

pseudo-random, *adj.* Said of a signal which seems to lack any definite pattern, but actually is a logical sequence of pulses which repeats after a very long (months) time interval.

psophometer, *n.* A type of noise measuring set used in Europe. Consists of a vacuum-tube voltmeter which includes a psophometric weighting network. Psophometric weighting is very similar to FIA weighting. The psophometer is calibrated so that an 800 Hz tone at zero dBm into a 600 ohm resistance will produce a meter reading of 0.775 volt, psophometrically weighted.

psophometric weighting, *n.* A noise weighting used in Europe with a noise meter called a "psophometer." Similar to FIA weighting, but is calibrated at 800 Hz instead of 1000 Hz. An 800 Hz tone of one milliwatt into 600 ohms produces a psophometer reading of 0.775 volt.

p-type semiconductor, *n.* A type of semiconductor in which there is a deficiency of electrons. These spaces where there are no electrons (holes) are the equivalent of a positive charge. In p-type material it is the holes which carry the current. See also "n-type semiconductor."

public-address system. See "system, public-address."

public music channel (CATV). See "channel, public music."

pull, *n.* (1) The unbalanced stress on a pole caused by a change in the direction of the pole line. (2) A measure of the deviation angle at the corner in the pole line, expressed by the number of feet of offset at a point fifty feet from the pole.—*v.t.* To set up a connection through a link, junctor, or matrix by applying opposite markings to "pull leads" at the two ends of the connection.

pull-box, *n.* A box with cover inserted in a long conduit run, especially at a corner, to facilitate pulling wire or cable into the conduits. If in a building, the box is of sheet steel and 4″x4″x2″ or larger. If in the earth, the box and cover are of concrete, and 12″x12″x18″ or larger.

puller, fish tape, *n.* An aluminum handle having a slot into which a fish tape can be dropped, and in which a wedge tightens when the tape is pulled. Provides a hand grip on the tape, allowing it to be pulled without being bent.

puller, slack. See "slack puller."

puller, strand, *n.* Device which grips steel strand, allowing attachment of a Coffing hoist or winch line for tightening the strand.

pull finder. See "finder, pull."

pulling. frequency, *n.* A change in the output frequency of an oscillator caused by a change in its load impedance.

pulling eye. See "eye, pulling."

pulling-in iron. See "iron, pulling-in."

pull lead, *n.* Lead on which a momentary current operates a relay which is then held operated by other means, such as a hold winding or a permanent magnet.

pull-through, *adj.* Describing a manhole through which cable is pulled and racked without making a cable splice.—*n.* In pulling underground cable, the practice in which a single length of cable is pulled into two adjoining underground sections, and the cable in the intermediate or pull-through manhole is racked without making a cable splice.

pulsating current, *n.* A current which changes in amplitude but does not reverse its direction.

pulse, *n.* (1) A signal of short duration used for the transmission of information. Implies a steep wavefront. (2) A short signal of either positive or negative direct current. (3) A short burst of audio or radio-frequency alternating current.—*v.t.* To transmit a sequence of momentary spurts of direct current or tone, coded so as to provide telephone address or control information to a switching center.

pulse, dial, *n.* A momentary interruption in the direct current flowing in the loop of a calling telephone, produced by the opening and clos-ing of pulse springs on the calling telephone's dial. The pulsing contacts are open 61% of the total pulse interval.

pulse, enabling, *n.* A pulse which opens a normally closed electrical gate, or that prepares a circuit for some subsequent action.

pulse, inhibit, *n.* A current pulse applied to an inhibit winding on a magnetic memory core which prevents the core from being affected by a "write" pulse.

pulse, matched. See "matched pulse."

pulse, preliminary. See "preliminary pulse."

pulse, read, *n.* A pulse which causes information to be read out of a memory cell.

pulse, synchronizing, *n.* A sharp pulse which causes two or more circuits to start operating at the same instant, or which keeps them in synchronism after they are operating.

pulse, write, *n.* A pulse which causes information to be stored in a memory cell.

pulse address, *n.* A method of addressing any station which receives a wideband signal, in which each user station is assigned an unique combination of time and frequency slots.

pulse checking, *n.* The provision of ringing current of the proper frequency to a terminal-per-station party-line subscriber, controlled at the connector by a timed ground pulse received over the EC lead which is bridged on a frequency bunching block.

pulse code modulation. See "modulation, pulse code."

pulse correction, *n.* (1) The action in a dial pulse repeater by an R-C network-controlled pulsing relay to transmit pulses of correct amplitude, length, and shape, even though the received pulses were distorted. It does not correct pulse repetition rate (speed) or pulse spacing. (2) The re-shaping or re-constitution of signaling pulses which have become distorted by transmission over circuits or through equipment. See also "regeneration, pulse."

pulse-frequency modulation. See "modulation, pulse-frequency."

pulse interval, *n.* The time from the start of a pulse until the start of the next pulse in the train.

pulse jitter. See "jitter, pulse."

pulse length. See "duration, pulse."

pulse link, auxiliary, *n.* A device used to repeat signals from one signaling section to another signaling section in tandem, when both sections use the same type of signals.

pulse-link repeater. See "repeater, pulse-link."

pulse modulation. See "modulation, pulse - - -."

pulse period, *n.* The total length of time in seconds used to open and close the pulsing springs, of a dial or relay, once.

pulse-position modulation. See "modulation, pulse-position."

pulser, *n.* A pulse generator.

pulse ratio, *n.* Percent make. The percentage of the total pulse interval during which the pulsing contacts are closed.

pulse regeneration, *n.* The property of a circuit which will accept a train of distorted pulses (teletypewriter, dial, etc.) and will retransmit at the correct speed a train of correctly spaced pulses of correct wave shape, amplitude, and make-to-break ratio.

pulse repeater. See "repeater, pulse."

pulse repetition frequency (PRF), *n.* The number of times per second a pulse is transmitted.

pulse shaping. See "shaping, pulse."

pulse train. *n.* A succession of pulses which follow each other, usually at equal intervals.

pulse width. See "duration, pulse."

pulsing, *n.* The act of transmitting address information by digital pulses over a circuit to a switching unit for the purpose of reaching a called subscriber or an operator. Pulsing may be: (a) dial, (b) multifrequency, (c) panel call indicator, or (d) revertive.

pulsing, dial, *n.* The transmitting of telephone address signals by momentarily opening a DC circuit a number of times corresponding to the decimal digit which is dialed. Frequently accomplished by hand operation of a wheel having holes labeled "1" through "0" which controls a spring-driven interrupter operating at ten pulses per second.

pulsing, dual tone multifrequency (DTMF), *n.* A method of sending numerical information from a telephone or PBX switchboard by sending specific pairs of voice frequencies, one from a group of four low frequencies; the other from a group of four high frequencies, to indicate the ten digits and four precedences, etc., as follows:

1	697 + 1209 Hz
2	697 + 1336 Hz
3	697 + 1477 Hz
4	770 + 1209 Hz
5	770 + 1336 Hz
6	770 + 1477 Hz
7	852 + 1209 Hz
8	852 + 1336 Hz
9	852 + 1477 Hz
ø	941 + 1336 Hz
FO	697 + 1633 Hz
F	770 + 1633 Hz
I	852 + 1633 Hz
P	941 + 1633 Hz
STart	941 + 1477 Hz

pulsing, frequency-shift, *n.* A method of rapid signaling using frequency shift between frequencies 1070 Hz and 1270 Hz. Used with narrowband line facilities, such as in the teletypewriter switching network.

pulsing, key, *n.* The transmitting of telephone address signals by successively punching any of ten keys labeled "1" through "0" on a keyset which resembles a ten-key adding machine keyboard. See also "pulsing, multifrequency."

pulsing, loop, *n.* In telephone practice, signaling accomplished by repeatedly opening the loop at the sending end of the circuit, thereby interrupting the loop current. The ordinary rotary telephone dial is a loop pulsing device.

pulsing, multifrequency, *n.* A method of transmitting address signals at voice frequency in which the identity of the ten digits, "0" through "9," are each determined by various combinations of two each of six frequencies. The two frequencies representing each digit are transmitted simultaneously over the trunk.

MF PULSING FREQUENCIES

DIGIT	FREQUENCIES	DIGIT	FREQUENCIES
1	700 + 900 Hz	6	1100 + 1300 Hz
2	700 + 1100 Hz	7	700 + 1500 Hz
3	900 + 1100 Hz	8	900 + 1500 Hz
4	700 + 1300 Hz	9	1100 + 1500 Hz
5	900 + 1300 Hz	0	1300 + 1500 Hz

SIGNAL	
KP*	1100 + 1700 Hz
ST**	1500 + 1700 Hz
CC***	700 + 1100 Hz
CR****	1100 + 1700 Hz

*	Prepare for digits.	***	Coin collect.
**	End of pulsing.	****	Coin return.

pulsing, panel call indicator, *n.* A system of DC pulsing in which each digit is transmitted as a series of four marginal and polarized pulses.

pulsing, revertive, *n.* Pulsing over a trunk from the terminating office rather than from the originating office. When seized, the incoming office trunk sends open or ground pulses over the trunk to the originating office which counts the pulses and opens the trunk when the correct number have been received.

pulsing, sequential. See "sequential pulsing."

pump, *v.t.* To add outside energy to the orbiting electrons in a laser or maser, thereby exciting them to a higher level of energy.

pump, manhole, *n.* A self-priming centrifugal pump, usually driven by a single-cylinder air-cooled gasoline engine, used to pump water from flooded manholes. Pumps 7000-10,000 gallons of water per hour.

punch, card, *n.* A machine having a typewriter keyboard used to punch information into data cards. Also called a "keypunch."

punch, tape, *n.* Electromechanical device which punches holes in a paper tape corresponding to the electrical signals of a teletypewriter or data code.

punched card. See "card, data."

punched tape. See "tape, punched."

punched tape reader. See "reader, paper tape."

punching, *n.* A notched, flat metal stamping, tinned, forming a terminal to which wires can be soldered. Part of a terminal block.

puncture, *n.* A breakdown of a solid dielectric or insulation resulting in a hole.

pure tone. See "tone, pure."

push-back, *adj.* Describing a braid or shield on a wire which can be pushed back easily to expose the conductor.

pushbutton, *n.* A normally open, non-locking two-pole switch which can be operated by the pressure of a finger on a button.

pushbutton station, *n.* An assembly of one or several pushbuttons in a common mounting, sometimes including indicator lamps.

pusher, pipe. See "jack, pipe pushing."

push-pull amplifier, *n.* A balanced amplifier using two identical vacuum tubes operating 180 degrees out of phase to feed a center-tapped output transformer. Distortion produced by one tube is cancelled by the other tube.

push-to-talk, *n.* Method of operation of a telephone in which the telephone transmitter is not connected into the circuit until a push-button in the handle of the handset is depressed. Avoids poor transmission due to excessive room noise or improper VODAS operation.

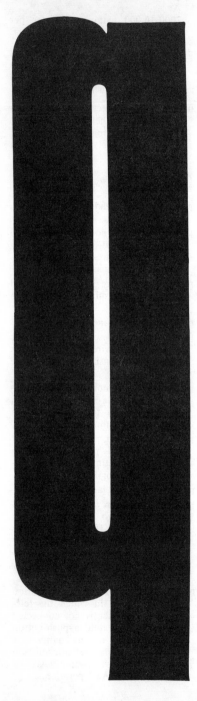

Q-factor, *n.* A measure of the excellence, or lack of resistance losses, of a coil. It is equal to the coil reactance divided by the coil resistance, both in ohms.

Q signal, *n.* Any of the forty, three-letter codes starting with the letter Q, used in radiotelegraphy to represent entire sentences. Examples are:

QRM — I am being interfered with.
QRN — I am troubled by static.
QRU — Have you anything for me?
QRV — Are you ready?
QSL — Please acknowledge receipt.

quad, *n.* (1) Four wires. (2) A group of four wires composed of two pairs twisted together. The quad twist is of a shorter length than the pair twist.

quad, spiral four, *n.* A group of four conductors, twisted into a spiral with all wires parallel. It is not a true quad, and both side-to-side and side-to-phantom crosstalk are high. Opposite wires make the best pairs.

quad, tracer. See "tracer quad."

quadded, *adj.* Formed into four-wire, two-pair units called "quads."

quadrature, *adj.* Said of two waves, voltages or currents, which are separated in phase by 90 degrees, or one-quarter of a cycle.

quadrature component, *n.* That component of a voltage or current which is entirely due to inductive or capacitive reactance in the circuit.

quadruple diversity, *n.* Diversity radio reception in which four signals are combined to produce one improved signal. Usually a combination of frequency and space diversity.

quadruplex circuit, *n.* A telegraph circuit which can carry two messages in each direction simultaneously.

quality, *n.* The inherent capacity to transmit sounds or signals without objectionable distortion.

quantity of electricity, *n.* The quantity of electricity is measured in "coulombs." A coulomb is the quantity of electricity which passes a point in a circuit during one second when a current of one ampere is flowing.

quantize, *n.* (1) To periodically sample the amplitudes of a complex wave, and to represent each amplitude thus sampled by one of a finite number (usually 128) of amplitudes. (2) To restrict a variable to a discrete number of possible values.

quantizing, *n.* Process used in pulse code modulation, whereby all of the possible signal amplitudes are represented by one of about 128 finite steps.

quantizing noise, *n.* Noise arising in the pulse code modulation process because the code-derived facsimile does not exactly match the original message waveform.

quarter-wave, *adj.* Having an electrical length of one-quarter wavelength.

quarter-wave transformer. See "transformer, quarter-wave."

quartz, *n.* Crystal consisting of pure silicon dioxide. The original piezoelectric material, still widely used to control the frequency of oscillators. See also "ceramic, polycrystalline."

quasar, *n.* Quasi-stellar radio source. Sources of intense radio-frequency radiation which visually appear as very distant stars.

quench, *v.t.* (1) To stop an oscillation abruptly. (2) To cool a very hot object suddenly.

queue, *n.* (1) A series of calls waiting for service. (2) A series of messages waiting for outgoing transmission paths.

queue indicator, *n.* A device in a high rank toll switching center which indicates the number of incoming trunks waiting for senders, and when that number exceeds a preselected maximum signals the lower rank offices to cancel some of the calls which normally would be forwarded.

queuing, *v.t.* (1) To arrange in a line in the order of arrival. (2) To hold calls for an operator, and then to present them to the operator sequentially in the order received.

quick-acting relay, *n.* A relay which operates immediately after its operating circuit is closed and restores immediately after its operating circuit is opened, without any time delay.

quick-break fuse, *n.* A fuse in which the fusible link or wire is under spring tension so that the circuit is broken quickly. One example is the grasshopper fuse.

quick-break switch, *n.* A knife switch used on older telephone power boards for interrupting battery. Has a secondary spring-loaded blade which breaks last and very rapidly.

quick-connect, *adj.* Describing a terminal or terminal block on which insulated conductors can be terminated quickly by placing them on a notch in a split terminal lug, and pushing them in place with a tool.

quick-connect terminal. See "terminal, quick-connect."

quiescent, *adj.* (1) Inactive. (2) Without an input signal.

quiet battery, *n.* Talking battery, which see.

quieting, *n.* Reduction of system noise, particularly during "quiet" interspeech intervals.

raceway, *n.* A metal or insulating, closed or covered channel through which wires are run in interior wiring.

rack, battery, *n.* A structural steel framework having rails on which a multi-cell storage battery can be mounted. Available in one or two-tier and two or three-step models. Earthquake protection, which prevents the cells from being shaken off the rack, is often specified.

rack, cable, *n.* A ladder-like steel structure, hung horizontally below the ceiling in equipment buildings to form a support for the switchboard cable which interconnects the equipment.

rack, plastic tubing, *n.* A strip of moulded plastic containing ten grooves to position and hold plastic or copper gas tubing. Used on pressurized cable systems.

rack, power, *n.* A heavy, 23-inch relay rack used to mount power equipment in smaller central offices. Can be used to mount rectifiers, ringing generators, tone generators, interrupters, transfer switches, meters, and fuse panels.

rack, relay, *n.* A floor-supported steel framework to hold telephone relay equipment on mounting plates. Consists of parallel pairs of steel channel verticals, spaced 19, 23, or 30 inches and drilled for mounting screws, plus a floor angle and top angle.

rack, station signaling. See "station signaling rack."

rack, underground cable, *n.* A strip of galvanized channel steel, 1½ inches wide, in which there are T-slots in which cable hooks can be placed and used to support cables on the walls of manholes or cable vaults. Available with 8, 14, or 18 T-slots, and 15, 24, or 30 inches long, respectively.

rack, wall relay, *n.* Relay rack for mounting against the wall, having two relay gates (each approx. 24″ wide x 34″ high) arranged for mounting 19″ or 23″ mounting plates. Requires separate push-on cover.

radar, *n.* RAdio Detection And Ranging. The determination of distance through space by measurement of the time required for a radio signal to travel to the target and back again.

radian, *n.* The angle at the center of a circle formed between two radii which cut off an arc of the circle whose length is equal to the radius. One radian is equal to 57.2958 degrees.

radiant energy, *n.* (1) Any energy which radiates in the form of radio waves, infra-red (heat) waves, light waves, x-rays, etc. (2) Electromagnetic radiation.

radiate, *n.* (1) The spreading out of radiant energy, as from a center. (2) To transmit energy in waves which are sharply directional.

radiation, *n.* (1) The emission of energy in electromagnetic waves. (2) The energy which is thus radiated.

radiation, electromagnetic, *n.* A wave, such as radio or light, propagated at the speed of light, and consisting of a magnetic field and an electric field, at right angles to each other and to the direction of propagation.

Radiation, Law of. See "Stefan-Boltzmann Law of Radiation" in "Appendix B."

radiation, spurious, *n.* Any emission from a radio transmitter at frequencies outside of its authorized frequency band.

radiation efficiency. See "efficiency, radiation."

radiation pattern. See "pattern, radiation" and "lobe, - - -."

radiation resistance. See "resistance, radiation."

radiator, *n.* Any of the parts of an antenna which radiate electromagnetic waves, either directly into space or against a reflector. See also "element, radiating."

radiator, tower, *n.* A tall metal structure which of itself constitutes a radio transmitting antenna.

radio, *n.* (1) The science of communicating over a distance by converting sounds or signals to electromagnetic waves and radiating these through space. (2) A radio receiver. (3) A message sent by radio; a radiogram.

radio, microwave, *n.* Radio using frequencies between 1,000 MHz and 100,000 MHz.

radio, mobile, *n.* (1) Transportable radio set. (2) A radiotelephone station in a vehicle.

radio beam, *n.* A radiation of radio waves which is very sharply directional.

radio broadcast. See "band, broadcast."

radio broadcasting, *n.* Radio transmission of program material intended for general reception by the public.

radio channel, *n.* A band of frequencies wide enough, and of the proper frequency for radio communication. The band width required depends on the type of signal, the frequency, and the type of modulation used.

radio circuit, *n.* A communication circuit between two points via radio. One circuit may be comprised of many channels, which may be used for voice, teletypewriter, or data communication.

radio frequency, *n.* Any frequency at which electromagnetic energy can be radiated through space. Overlaps audio frequencies on the lower end and light frequencies on the upper end of the band. From 6,000 Hz to over 300,000 MHz.

radio-frequency interference (RFI), *n.* Interference to radio reception, due to equipment which generates sparks in portions of circuits which may be resonant at radio frequencies.

radiogram, *n.* A message transmitted via radio, especially by radioteletypewriter.

radio horizon, *n.* The line at which a

radio sky wave from a transmitting antenna is tangent to the earth. Its distance from the transmitter is dependent on the height of the transmitting antenna, on topography, and on atmospheric refraction.

radio link, *n.* A radio system used to provide communication between two specific points.

radio relay message unit (MUR). See "unit, radio relay message."

radio relay system. See "system, radio relay."

radiosonde, *n.* The technique of detecting, transmitting, and recording atmospheric conditions of the upper atmosphere, particularly temperature and humidity, by means of airborne (weather balloon) instrumentation.

radio telegraph, *adj. n.* The use of radio for telegraphy.

radiotelegraphy, continuous wave. See "continuous wave radiotelegraphy."

radiotelephone, *adj.* Pertaining to the use of radio for telephony.—*n.* A transceiver, or radio receiver and transmitter, used for telephone communication via radio waves.

radius, effective Earth's, *n.* In the calculation of radio propagation loss, a value for the Earth's radius used in place of the actual Earth's radius so as to correct for atmospheric refraction when the index of refraction decreases linearly with height. Under the conditions of standard refraction the effective radius is 4/3 times the geometric radius.

radix, *n.* A base of a number system.

radome, *n.* A dome-shaped cover for a parabolic antenna which protects it from wind damage and from the attenuating effects of rain, snow, and ice. Made of a material which is transparent to the radio energy, such as fiber-glass, nylon, etc.

rail, guard, *n.* Angle (1½″x1½″) iron frame with the top 6 inches above the floor which surrounds all equipment frames and racks, intended to prevent damage to the equipment

from ladders or other floor-supported objects.

rail, manhole guard. See "guard, manhole."

rail, piling, *n.* The wooden or plastic block at the bottom of a switchboard panel on which the jack strips are laid, or piled.

rain-barrel effect, *n.* Echo.

raintight, *adj.* So constructed that exposure to a driven rain will not result in the entrance of water.

rake, *v.i.* To incline a pole from the vertical by moving the top of the pole away from the direction of pull; done to reduce the force on the pole. (Reduces the bending moment at the ground line, which is the point of greatest stress.)

random-access discrete-address (RADA), *n.* The radio communication system of the future, in which many channels are pulse modulated on a broadband carrier, and each addressee picks off the message assigned to his particular frequency and time slot.

random noise. See "noise, random."

random wound, *adj.* Describing a coil which is wound without care to ensure that the wire is in layers. Random wound coils have fewer turns for a given volume.

range, dynamic, *n.* Of a transmission system, the difference in decibels between the noise level of the system and its overload level.

range adjustment, teletypewriter, *n.* An orientation device which enables one to move the cam followers with respect to the cams on a teletypewriter distributor. Allows compensation for signal distortion by enabling the teletypewriter to use any part of the received pulse, from start to end. The range adjustment has a scale of 120 points; 100 points being equal to the width of one pulse. If the teletypewriter will operate over a range of 70 points (15-85) it indicates a good circuit.

range extender. See "extender, range".

rank, switching center, *n.* In the Nationwide Toll Switching Plan, there are five ranks and six classes of switching centers, listed here in order of their rank:

Class 1 — Regional Center
Class 2 — Sectional Center
Class 3 — Primary Center
Class 4C — Toll Center
Class 4P — Toll Point
Class 5 — End Office

raster, *n.* (1) The pattern of lines followed by the scanning beam in a television camera tube. (2) The area which is scanned.

rate, *n.* The price for the initial period of a toll call. It is determined by (1) the distance from the originating to the terminating toll center, (2) whether the call is station-to-station or person-to-person, (3) the rate period (day, night, Sunday), and (4) the rate schedule.

rate, baud. See "baud rate".

rate, bit, *n.* The speed at which digital information is transmitted, usually expressed in bits per second.

rate, charging, *n.* Of a storage battery, the current in amperes at which the battery is charged.

rate, data. See "data rate, - - -."

rate, error, *n.* The frequency of occurrence of errors in a received telegraph, teletypewriter, or data signal. A good commercial circuit would not have an error rate greater than the following:

Signal	One Error Per
Telegraph	10,000
Teletypewriter	10,000
Data	100,000

rate, modulation, *n.* The reciprocal of the unit signal interval in seconds, expressed in bauds.

rate, overtime, *n.* On a toll call which lasts longer than the initial period, the charge for each minute of overtime.

rate, time, *n.* Of a storage battery, the current in amperes which will discharge the battery to a specified final voltage during a specified time.

rate period, *n.* The time-of-day and day-of-the-week, as it affects charges for toll calls, *ie:* daytime, evening, night, Sunday.

rate treatment number, *n.* A single multi-digit number which designates the set of rates which applies to a particular telephone call. Used by a "charge computer" to determine charges on a toll call.

rater, *n.* An automatic device which examines the calling and called numbers on a toll call, consults a calendar and clock, asks whether the call is station-to-station or person-to-person, then assigns a "rate treatment number" which specifies the rate table to be used.

rating, *n.* (1) The number of watts that a circuit component can dissipate without becoming overheated. (2) The rated output, which see. (3) The voltage which may be safely applied to a circuit or device.

ratio, *n.* The relative size of two quantities, indicated by the quotient obtained by dividing one quantity by the other.

ratio, bandwidth, *n.* In a carrier, the width of the baseband divided by the width of a single channel, both in hertz.

ratio, carrier-to-noise, *n.* The ratio of the magnitude of the carrier to that of the noise, after selection but before any non-linear process such as limiting or detection. Usually stated in terms of RMS values.

ratio, deviation. See "deviation ratio."

ratio, front-to-back, *n.* (1) The ratio of forward resistance to back resistance of a diode. (2) The ratio of field strength in the front lobe of a transmitting antenna to that in the back lobe. (3) The ratio of the forward sensitivity of a receiving antenna to its backward sensitivity.

ratio, image. See "image ratio."

ratio, LC, *n.* The ratio of inductance to capacitance, equal to the inductance in henrys divided by the capacitance in farads.

ratio, M-L, *n.* In a section of exposed telephone line, the ratio of metallic circuit noise to longitudinal circuit noise in sigma.

ratio, notch-to-no-notch, *n.* Noise power ratio, which see.

ratio, pulse. See "pulse ratio."

ratio, signal-plus-noise-to-noise, *n.* The ratio between signal and noise as it is actually measured. If expressed in decibels, to convert to signal-to-noise ratio it is necessary to convert the dB to a power ratio, subtract N from (S+N), then convert S/N back to decibels.

ratio, signal-to-noise, *n.* The ratio, in decibels, of signal power to total noise power in a channel. It is numerically equal to the "noise power ratio" plus the "bandwidth ratio" minus the "noise load ratio."

ratio, standing wave (SWR), *n.* At a given frequency in a uniform waveguide, the ratio of the maximum to the minimum amplitudes of corresponding voltages or currents along the waveguide in the direction of propagation.

ratio, turns. See "turns ratio."

rating, storage battery, *n.* The number of ampere-hours which a storage battery will deliver when discharged to a specified final voltage (usually 1.85 volts) over a specified period of time (usually 8 hours).

Rayleigh distribution, *n.* A mathematical statement of the frequency distribution of random variables, for the case where the variables have the same variance and are not correlated.

Rayleigh fading, *n.* Radio fading due to multipath which follows the Rayleigh probability curve stating the natural distribution of random variables.

Rayleigh scattering, *n.* Attenuation of a radio wave due to scattering from a gaseous atmosphere, in which the scattering is proportional to the inverse fourth power of its wavelength.

RC constant, *n.* The "time constant" of a resistor-capacitor circuit, equal to the resistance in ohms times the capacitance in farads, expressed in seconds. It is the time required for current in an R-C circuit to rise to 63% of its final steady-state value, or to fall to 37% of its initial steady-state value.

RC digit. See "route control digit."

R-C network, *n.* A simple network consisting only of resistance and capacitance, with no inductance elements. Usually a resistor in series with a capacitor.

reactance, *n.* (1) That portion of the impedance of an electrical circuit which is due only to inductance or capacitance, not to resistance. Its value in ohms is dependent upon the frequency. (2) A circuit component, such as a coil of wire or winding, which has inductive reactance.

reactance, capacitive, *n.* Reactance which is due to capacitance in a circuit. In a circuit having net capacitive reactance, the current wave leads (precedes) the voltage wave.

reactance, inductive, *n.* Reactance which is due to inductance (possibly from a coil of wire) in a circuit. In a circuit having net inductive reactance, the current wave lags behind the voltage wave.

reactance, leakage, *n.* That portion of the reactance of a transformer primary which is due only to leakage flux.

reactive, *adj.* Possessing reactance, either capacitive or inductive.

reactive power, *n.* The power in an alternating current circuit obtained by multiplying voltage, current, and the sine of the phase angle between voltage and current. Reactive power is delivered to the circuit during part of the cycle, but returned to the source during another part of the cycle when the polarity of voltage or current is reversed. Sometimes also called "circulating power" or "wattless power."

reactive volt-amperes (VAR), *n. pl.* The reactive power in a circuit carrying an alternating current of one ampere in quadrature with a potential of one volt.

reactor, *n.* (1) A device which provides either capacitance or inductance to a circuit. (2) In practice, the term "reactor" is used almost exclusively to mean a circuit component having inductive reactance.

reactor, saturable, *n.* An iron-core reactor having a second control winding carrying a direct current whose value is changed to vary the saturation of the iron core and thereby vary the reactance of the first winding which carries alternating current. With no direct current flow the reactance is a maximum, and decreases with increasing direct current flow.

read, *v.* To obtain information from a storage device.

reader, card, *n.* A machine that senses the information on punched data cards, using photoelectric sensors or metal brushes.

reader, dial card. See "dial, card reader."

reader, magnetic tape, *n.* A data-processing device which can read at high speed the signals recorded on magnetic tape, and deliver these signals to a computer or other data-processing equipment.

reader, optical character (OCR), *n.* A photoelectric device which scans printed or typed copy and produces electrical signals that can be fed directly to a tape punch or to a telegraph line facility. Obviates the need for manual tape punching, but requires copy using special machine readable characters, such as those on the lower left hand edge of your bank checks.

reader, paper tape, *n.* An input device into which one can feed paper tape which has been punched with ASCII or ITA #2 code, and have it machine converted to a parallel (or serial) digital electrical output. Available to handle 8 track 1-inch tape, or 5 track 11/16, ⅞ or 1-inch tape at speeds of 150, 300, 600, or 1200 bauds.

readout, *n.* The visual display of the output of a measuring instrument, or of a memory, or of a computer.

readout, destructive, *n.* The reading of a memory cell, such as a toroidal ferrite core, where the contents of the memory cell are destroyed when it is interrogated by a "read" pulse. A "write" pulse is then required to re-insert the bit in memory.

readout, non-destructive, *n.* The reading of a memory cell, such as a twistor, which can be interrogated by a "read" pulse without affecting the bit which is in storage.

ready-access closure. See "closure, splice."

real-time, *adj.* Without delay.

real-time system, *n.* An information system whose input or output rate cannot be controlled by the system, but depends on external factors.

real-time transmission, *n.* An inexact military term implying instantaneous transmission, but meaning transmission by means in which there is no avoidable delay, such as "record and retransmit," "store-and-forward," or "off-line" operation. Applies equally to radio transmission at 142,000 miles per second, heavily-loaded cables at 9,800 miles per second, or earth-to-satellite-to-earth transmission taking 3/10ths of a second.

recall, *v.* To signal on a circuit to bring in the distant operator.

recall, attendant, *n.* A feature of some PABX's which enables a station engaged in a trunk call to bring in the attendant by flashing the hookswitch and dialing "O." When the attendant answers, a three-way conference connection exists.

recall signal, *n.* Any cord lamp signal requiring an answer or challenge.

receiver, *n.* (1) A telephone receiver or earphone. (2) A device for receiving and demodulating radio signals. (3) A device for converting television signals into pictures and associated sound.

receiver, double-detection, *n.* A superheterodyne radio receiver.

receiver, hand, *n.* (1) Small telephone receiver in a holder designed to be cupped in the hand when held. (2) Small telephone receiver with a handle. (3) Complete telephone receiver, consisting of (a) a receiver unit, housed (b) in a receiver holder.

receiver, paging, *n.* Small (4½"x2"x ¾") lightweight (4 oz) FM radio receiver to be carried in a coat pocket by persons who need to be paged when they are away from their phone. Tuned reeds decode the paging signal and produce repeated "beeps" in the paged receiver. The paged person then goes to the nearest phone to call his office.

receiver, radio, *n.* The equipment which receives radio signals and amplifies and demodulates them to produce an output bearing the original intelligence.

receiver, superheterodyne radio, *n.* A radio receiver in which the input signal is converted to an intermediate frequency, then amplified, then detected to an audio frequency, and finally amplified at audio frequency.

receiver, telephone, *n.* The portion of the telephone instrument held closely to the human ear which converts the analog electrical speech signal into sound waves. It consists of a case containing an electromagnet, a biasing permanent magnet, and a moveable diaphragm. The electromagnet moves the diaphragm in step with the electrical speech signal, and the permanent magnet prevents frequency doubling. Do not use the ambiguous term "receiver." Always specify either "telephone receiver" or "earphone."

receiver, tone, *n.* An electronic detector device which listens on an incoming line or trunk, decides whether DTMF or MF address signals are present and, if so, delivers direct current marks indicating the value of the digits received to a register-sender.

receiver, touch calling, *n.* An electronic detector circuit which listens on an incoming call, decides when DTMF address signals are present and, when they are, delivers direct current marks to a register-sender to indicate the values of the digits received.

receiver, tuned radio-frequency, *n.* A radio receiver in which the signal from the antenna is amplified at radio frequency, then detected (demodulated to audio frequency), then amplified at audio frequency.

receiver, watch case, *n.* Any telephone receiver housed in a cylindrical case about 1½"Dx1" thick. To be hand-held, or used with a head band.

receptacle, *n.* An electrical outlet.

receptacle, coin, *n.* A metal box which can be sealed and inserted in a coin telephone to receive coins as they are collected. In some types the coin opening closes and locks automatically as the receptacle is withdrawn from the telephone.

reception, *n.* (1) Listening to, copying, recording, or viewing any information-bearing signals. (2) A manner in which these signals are received.

reception, diversity. See "diversity,---."

Reciprocity Theorem. See "Appendix B."

recloser, automatic circuit, *n.* A power circuit breaker which will act to automatically reclose a circuit a short time after having interrupted it. Usually after several unsuccessful attempts to reclose, the breaker will lock in the open position.

record, circuit layout, *n.* A description and representation of a circuit layout in sketch or tabular form. It should show routing, facilities, intermediate and terminal locations, makeup, transmission loss, levels, and cross-connectable equipments.

record, line card, *n.* A card, kept in the repair service center, which shows the subscriber's name and address, lists the station equipment he has, and lists the cables and pairs used for the subscriber's loop. The card also has spaces to list troubles reported, troubles found, and the dates reported and cleared.

record communications, *n. pl.* Any type of communications which produces a printed, punched, or written record. Examples are: teletypewriter, data card, or facsimile transmission.

recorder, *n.* A device which makes a record of changes in varying electrical quantities or signals. Examples: A recording millivoltmeter, and a tape recorder.

recorder, AMA, *n.* Device which controls the perforator which punches automatic message accounting data in paper AMA tape. One recorder and associated perforator serve up to 100 AMA trunks. (#5 X Bar).

recorder, answering time, *n.* A portable measuring device which can be connected to a group of trunks to determine how many incoming calls are not answered within a specified time period. The incoming calls are measured against a value of time which can be preset to 2, 3, 4, 5, 6, 8, 10, 15, 20, or 30 seconds, and all calls which are not answered within that time are tallied on a counter.

recorder, dial tone delay, *n.* A portable measuring device which measures what percent of the test calls it initiates do not receive dial tone within the standard interval of three seconds. Some varieties of recorder will provide a peg count of the following conditions:
a. Dial tone in 1 second

b. Dial tone in 2 seconds
c. Dial tone in 3 seconds
d. No tone in 3 seconds
e. Total calls attempted.

recorder, integrated telephone, *n.* A hand telephone set having a voice recorder as an integral component. Uses a dial-in-handset.

recorder, magnetic tape, *n.* A device which can record audio-frequency signals on a ¼-inch wide plastic tape coated with magnetizable iron oxide particles. Consists of a tape transport, a recording head, a playback head, an erase head, and an amplifier.

recorder, traffic, *n.* A device for measuring the amount of telephone traffic carried by a group or several groups of switches or trunks, and for periodically printing a record of that traffic. Consists of rotary stepping switches which every 100 seconds scan the "C leads" of each group of switches or trunks and register the number of busies encountered, then each 15, 30, or 60 seconds print out the busy count. Since the scanning period is 100 seconds, the registers read directly in CCS.

recorder, video tape, *n.* A tape recorder capable of recording a video (television) signal having a bandwidth of 4 megahertz. Uses a revolving recording head which laterally scans across a moving one-inch magnetic tape.

recorder-announcer, intercept, *n.* A tape recorder which can provide a short (usually 12-seconds) announcement, such as required for the interception of calls to disconnected lines, vacant levels, etc. See also "announcements - - -"

recorder-connector, *n.* A control unit which connects and impedance matches a subscriber's tape recorder to his telephone line, and places a 1400 Hz, 1/5-second warning "beep" tone on the line at 15-second intervals.

recording, stereo, *n.* A phonograph

record having a single spiral groove on which a stereophonic signal has been recorded. The groove is V-shaped with walls inclined 45 degrees from the vertical, thus at 90 degrees from each other. The left stereo channel is recorded in fluctuations of one groove wall, and the right stereo channel is recorded on the opposite wall.

recording-completing trunk, *n.* A trunk outgoing from a local office to a toll office over which ticket information is passed (recording) and over which the toll call is completed on a no-hang-up basis.

recording trunk, *n.* A trunk outgoing from a local office to a toll office over which ticket information is passed, but which is not arranged for completing toll connections.

records, assignment, *n.* Charts or books listing all cable pairs, terminals and terminal pairs, and equipment, together with the interconnections which have been made between them.

records, plant assignment, *n. pl.* The records which show what cables, cable pairs, and wires are used for each subscribers loop, and in what terminals and on what terminal pair the loop is cross-connected or terminated.

record traffic, *n.* Message traffic by some means, such as teletypewriter, which provides a printed record of the messages.

recovery time, *n.* The length of time that a condition remains in effect after the control signal which initiated the effect has disappeared. See also "delay, hangover."

rectification, *n.* The process of converting alternating current into a current which flows in only one direction. Unidirectional current is not necessarily a constant-voltage noise-free direct current.

rectifier, *n.* An electrical device for converting alternating current to direct current. Implies an output which is not pulsating, and is rea-

sonably free from noise components. The term rectifier does not apply to a rotary machine, such as a rotary converter.

rectifier, bridge, *n.* A full-wave rectifier having four rectifying elements connected in a "bridge circuit" (which see). When an alternating voltage is applied to a pair of opposite nodes, a direct voltage appears on the other pair of nodes.

rectifier, controlled, *n.* A rectifier using a "silicon controlled rectifier" (SCR) as the rectifying element. The SCR can be triggered at any point in the alternating current cycle to control the current. Will operate on either 60 Hz or 50 Hz power supply.

rectifier, crystal. See "diode, crystal."

rectifier, constant-voltage. See "charger, constant-voltage."

rectifier, cuprous oxide, *n.* A dry-disc rectifier in which rectification occurs at a layer of cuprous oxide on a copper plate. Current will flow from the cuprous oxide to the copper, but not in the reverse direction. The efficiency is in the range 60-70%.

rectifier, diode, *n.* A half-wave rectifier of two elements, between which current flows in only one direction. It may be (a) an electron-tube diode in which current flows only from cathode to anode, (b) a point contact semiconductor diode, or (c) a semiconductor junction diode.

rectifier, dry disc, *n.* A rectifier using metal discs as rectifying elements. See "rectifier, cuprous oxide" and "rectifier, selenium."

rectifier, full-wave, *n.* A rectifier which uses both positive and negative half-cycles of the alternating current supply to produce direct current.

rectifier, half-wave, *n.* A rectifier which uses only either the positive half-cycle or the negative half-cycle of the alternating current supply to produce direct current.

rectifier, mercury arc, *n.* A rectifier

which uses an electron tube having an electron-emitting cathode and one or more anodes in an envelope containing mercury vapor.

rectifier, selenium, *n.* A dry-disc rectifier at which rectification takes place between a thin coating of selenium and the iron disk on which it is coated. Current flows from the iron to the selenium, but not in the reverse direction. Efficiency is 60-70%.

rectifier, silicon-controlled, *n.* A type of central office battery charger using three-terminal p-n-p-n silicon transistors instead of diodes. The output of the transistors can be very closely controlled by adjusting their firing time. This type of rectifier will operate on either 60 Hz or 50 Hz, and thus is useful in those parts of the world where AC power frequencies are non-standard or variable.

rectifier, silicon power, *n.* A rectifier in which a silicon diode is used as the rectifying element.

rectifier, thyristor, *n.* A power rectifier which uses a thyristor as the rectifier and voltage controlling element.

rectifier, Tungar. See "tungar tube."

rectifier, vibrating. See "vibrating rectifier."

rectifier enclosure unit (REU), *n.* Cabinet enclosure which mounts two central office battery charging units. Includes two voltmeters, two ammeters, and alarm lamps for the rectifier fuses.

rectify, *v.* To convert an alternating current into a direct current.

recycle, *n.* In a crossbar office, the action which releases an initially selected trunk, and permits an attempt to establish the connection to another trunk of the same route, but using a different group of junctors and trunk links.

recycling, circuit breaker, *n.* The property of some power circuit breakers which, when tripped by a fault, will reset one or more times

automatically before tripping out completely.

red, *adj.* Refers to a type of transmission facility or area approved for containing clear text classified information.

red area, *n.* An area where classified communications are in a clear, unencrypted form.

red/black criteria, *n.* Criteria which specifies the electrical and physical isolation required between unencrypted (red) and encrypted (black) communication circuits.

red circuit, *n.* A circuit which carries sensitive information in an unencrypted form. Such circuits must be confined to protected areas.

reducer, acoustic shock, *n.* A device, usually a varistor, bridged across a telephone receiver to limit the voltage and thereby prevent acoustic shock from a too large input to the receiver. See also "varistor."

reducer, click. See "reducer, acoustic shock" and "varistor."

reducer, frequency. See "generator, sub-harmonic."

reducer, noise, *n.* A voice-activated expandor which reduces noticeable noise and interference by reducing the gain during the intervals between speech syllables.

reducer, voltage. See "tap, battery."

reduction, data, *n.* (1) The transformation of raw data into a more useful form. (2) The drawing of a smooth curve through plotted positions of empirical data.

redundancy, *n.* (1) Any excess of signal elements over those required to carry the message. Speech is a highly redundant form of message coding. Certain data signals have no redundancy in themselves, and must use an extra redundant data bit for error checking. (2) The fraction of the total information content of a message which can be eliminated without loss of meaning.

redundant, *adj.* (1) Exceeding what is necessary or normal. (2) Containing more information than is needed for intelligibility. About 75% of the information content of normal speech is redundant. (3) Said of the elements of equipment which exists in duplicate so that if one fails the second continues operation without interruption.

redundant code, *n.* A code which uses more signal elements than are necessary to represent the intrinsic information.

reedcapsule, *n.* The contact element of a correed relay. Consists of an hermetically sealed glass tube enclosing two flat ferromagnetic metal reeds supported at their ends and forming contacts where they overlap at the center of the tube. The overlap contact region is usually gold plated to ensure a low contact resistance. See also "correed."

reed relay. See "relay, reed."

reel, cable, *n.* Large steel or wooden spool on which cable is wound for shipping, storage, and dispensing. Hold 1000 feet of the larger cables to 5000 feet of the smaller cables. The larger reels are returnable to the manufacturer for credit.

reel, pay-out, *n.* A horizontally mounted reel having a friction-controlled disk brake, which will hold a full roll of open wire and allow it to be pulled from the reel.

reel, take-up, *n.* A heavy reel on the side of a telephone construction truck, power driven from the engine, and used to reel up salvaged wire and strand. The outer side of the reel is removable to allow removal of the wire coil.

reference circuit, voltage, *n.* A circuit which holds the DC voltage across it very constant, so that it can be used as a reference to regulate the voltage of another circuit. The voltage stable element is often a cold-cathode discharge tube.

reference level, *n.* The amount of power in a circuit at a reference point, usually zero dbm of 1000 Hz.

reference noise, *n.* The amount of noise which is meant when specifying a noise power in "decibels above reference noise" (dbrn). This reference noise power is one picowatt (-90 dbm) at 1000 Hz.

reference voltage, *n.* A voltage used for comparison and control or correction. For example: a DC voltage used to control the output voltage of a rectifier, or an AC voltage used to control the voltage and phase of an oscillator.

reflected impedance, *n.* The impedance connected to the secondary of a transformer as measured looking into the primary winding.

reflection, *n.* (1) The deflection or bouncing back of sound, radio, or light waves when striking a plane and relatively smooth surface. (2) The return or change of direction which occurs when electromagnetic or radio waves strike a surface or travel from one medium to another. Reflection of electromagnetic waves can occur at an impedance mismatch in a transmission facility.

reflection, diffuse, *n.* Reflection from a rough surface where the reflected rays are distributed in all directions in accordance with the cosine law.

reflection, radio wave, *n.* Incorrect term sometimes used when "refraction" is meant.

reflection, specular, *n.* Reflection from a flat, mirror-like surface in which the angle of incidence is equal to the angle of reflection.

reflection coefficient. See "coefficient, reflection."

reflection factor. See "coefficient, reflection."

reflection loss. See "loss, reflection."

reflectometer, *n.* A device which can be coupled to a waveguide so as to measure the energy traveling in each direction through the waveguide, and thus determine the standing wave ratio.

reflector, *n.* A metal plate, metal screen, or any of a group of spaced tuned rods which are placed back of the active element of an antenna to make it directive. See also "element, parasitic."

reflector, corner. See "antenna, corner reflector."

reflector, parabolic, *n.* A symmetrical metal, or metal mesh, antenna reflector whose cross-section is a parabola. Makes a highly directional antenna, for a radio wave originating at the focal point of the parabola is reflected in a parallel beam.

reflector, passive. See "repeater, passive."

reflector, periscope, *n.* A type of passive reflector used where the angle between the two radio paths is small. Consists of two plane reflectors face to face which provide a double reflection.

reflector electrode, *n.* A negative electrode in a reflex klystron which reflects the electron stream back through the resonator grids, thus providing positive feedback and sustained oscillations.

reflex klystron. See "klystron, reflex."

refraction, *n.* The bending of a sound, radio, or light wave as it passes obliquely from a medium of one density to a medium of another density in which its speed its different.

refrangible, *adj.* That which can be refracted, as radio waves and light waves.

refund key, *n.* The key with which an operator returns the deposit at a prepay coin telephone.

regenerate, *v.* (1) To restore pulses to their original wave shape, amplitude, and make-to-break ratio. (2) To restore information in a memory to its original state.

regeneration, *n.* (1) The process of receiving distorted signal pulses and from them recreating new pulses at the correct repetition rate, correct pulse amplitude, and correct pulse width. See also "pulse correction." (2) The increase of signal power in a circuit by the use of positive feedback.

regeneration, memory, *n.* The process of restoring a memory device to its previous state.

regeneration, pulse, *n.* The action of a circuit which receives a train of distorted pulses (dial, data, or teletypewriter) and retransmits at the correct speed a train of correctly spaced pulses of correct wave shape, amplitude, and make-to-break ratio.

regenerative repeater, *n.* A device which receives distorted digital signals, then reshapes and retimes the signals before retransmitting them.

regenerator, pulse, *n.* Device which receives distorted pulses sent at various speeds, stores, then resends them at a standard speed and break-make ratio.

region, E. See "E layer."

region, F. See "F layer."

region, far-field. See "far-field region."

region, ionospheric. See "D layer," "E layer," and "F layers."

region, near-field. See "near-field region."

region, scattering. See "scattering region."

Regional Center, *n.* Any of the twelve highest rank (Class 1) switching centers in the Nationwide Distance Dialing Plan. These are:
White Plains (N.Y. City)—N.Y.
Wayne (Philadelphia)—Pa.
Rockdale (Atlanta)—Ga.
Norway (Chicago)—Ill.
St. Louis—Missouri
Dallas—Texas
Denver—Colorado
Sacramento—Calif.
San Bernardino—Calif.
Pittsburgh—Pa.
Regina, Saskatchewan—Canada
Montreal, Quebec—Canada

register, *n.* (1) A device which can store digital information. Formerly a counting relay circuit; today usually a magnetic core device. (2) The first unit of common-control equipment in a dial office. It receives address information, either as dial pulses or as DTMF signals, and stores it for possible conversion or translation. The register is frequently combined with a sender. (3) A message register.

register, incoming, *n.* A register which receives pulsing (dial, multifrequency, or revertive) from an incoming trunk, and transmits it to a marker via an incoming register marker connector.

register, message, *n.* An electromechanical device which counts the number of times it receives a direct current pulse. It consists of a relaylike coil and armature whose movement steps a decimal dial odometer. Used for the "peg count" of messages, and for the registration of busy and overflow conditions.

register, originating, *n.* Device which furnishes dial tone to subscribers and records the digits which are dialed. It can also test to determine whether the call is made by the tip party or the ring party. (#5 X Bar)

register, pen, *n.* An electo-magnet actuated pen which makes a dash mark on a moving paper tape each time, and for the length of time, it is energized. Used to monitor dial pulses at a service observing board.

register, shift, *n.* A register that shifts every bit stored in it one place to the left upon the application of a shift pulse. Used (a) to perform multiplication, (b) to convert serial data to parallel data (and vice versa), and to generate pseudorandom signals.

register circuit, *n.* A circuit which records and holds information until it is needed by another functional circuit.

register key, *n.* A key by which the operator tallies a call on the calling telephone's message register. When coin keys are provided, the collect key functions as a register key.

register-sender, *n.* A unit of common

control equipment in a dial central office which combines the functions of a "register" and a "sender," which see.

registration, zone. See "zone registration."

regrade, *v.* To restrap a selector distributing terminal assembly, thereby increasing or reducing the number of trunks outgoing from the selector levels.

regulated, *adj.* Controlled for improved uniformity. See also "voltage-regulated," "current-regulated," "attenuation-regulated."

regulation, *n.* (1) The stabilization of route transmission losses by the use of a pilot-wire regulator. (2) Voltage regulation.

regulation, baseband, *n.* Controlling the level of the baseband output from a multi-link or marginal radio system so that it remains constant, even with a $\pm$ 3 db variation in receiver output.

regulation, transient. See "transient regulation."

regulation, voltage, *n.* (1) The capability of a generator or transformer to maintain a constant output voltage while the load changes from zero to full load. Dividing the voltage change by the rated full-load voltage times 100 gives the regulation in percent. (2) The output voltage change that occurs between no-load and full load.

regulator, exchange voltage, *n.* A low-voltage, voltage-regulated rectifier placed in series with a central office battery and its load. As the battery voltage varies with a changing load, the regulator supplies the exact voltage needed to provide a constant standard voltage to the load.

regulator, feedback controlled, *n.* Regulator in which the level of a pilot signal is compared to a reference level. The difference or "error" is used to control the gain of the repeater so as to reduce the error.

regulator, feedback transmission. *n.* A transmission regulator in which the pilot signal level is continuously compared with a reference level, and the error is used to adjust a gain control which corrects the error.

regulator, gas pressure, *n.* A mechanism which receives dry nitrogen or dry air directly from a high pressure 1900 psi gas tank and reduces its pressure to about 8-10 psi for introduction into a pressurized cable.

regulator, induction voltage, *n.* A variable transformer used for regulating the voltage supplied to a power load. Its primary is connected across the power circuit, and a low-voltage secondary is connected in series with the power circuit. The secondary windings are automatically rotated so that their voltage varies and can either buck or aid the line voltage, as required to keep the output voltage constant.

regulator, pilot-wire, *n.* A bank of variable-gain voice repeaters controlled by the resistance of pilot-wires in a toll cable. As the temperature of the cable rises, the repeater gains are automatically increased to keep the transmission loss constant over the regulator section.

regulator, voltage, *n.* An electrical device, frequently a variable ratio transformer, which maintains its output voltage at a substantially constant pre-determined level.

regulator section. See "section, regulator."

rejection, image, *n.* The action of a superheterodyne receiver in suppressing signals at the image frequency.

rel, *n.* The unit of magnetic reluctance, equal to one ampere-turn per magnetic line of force.

relative humidity. See "humidity, relative."

relaxation oscillator. See "oscillator, relaxation."

relay, *n.* (1) An electro-magnetic device in which current through a coil moves an armature to operate spring contacts which open and close circuits. (2) An intermediate station on a multi-link radio system.

relay, alarm, *n.* A relay whose function is to actuate an alarm signal.

relay, automatic tape, *n.* A message relay in which the tape messages are electrically routed based on routing information in the message header.

relay, battery isolation, *n.* A relay used in an automatic or tape relay center to isolate the high-current neutral teletypewriter loop circuits from the low-current polar circuits within the relay center.

relay, biased, *n.* A polarized relay with two similar windings. Steady current through the biasing winding returns the armature to the non-operated position when no current flows in the operating winding. Double current in the operating winding operates the relay. This method of construction permits the use of a very light weight armature and contact system, thus enabling very high speed operation.

relay, bridge cut-off, *n.* In a subscriber's line circuit, the relay which operates on an incoming call to disconnect the equipment used for making outgoing calls.

relay, B-type, *n.* Small, sensitive, reliable flat-type relay, having front access to micrometer adjustment screws permitting extremely accurate adjustments. Has one set of contact springs.

relay, codel, *n.* A relay which is operated, and released, by pulses and does not require a holding current. See also "codelreed."

relay, coin, *n.* In a coin telephone, the polarized relay which controls the collection or refund of coins deposited by the user, under control of a 110 volt positive or negative DC signal originated by the operator or the central office coin trunk. Deposited coins rest on a trap door until the coin relay tilts the trap door to send them either to the coin receptacle or to the coin refund chute.

relay, combined line and cut-off, *n.* A multi-winding two-step relay in a subscriber's line circuit which combines both line relay and cut off relay functions. See also "relay, line" and "relay, cut-off."

relay, cut-off, *n.* In a central office line equipment, the relay which disconnects the line relay from the line when there is an incoming call to that line, or when an outgoing call is completed.

relay, dash-pot, *n.* A relay which operates very slowly (seconds or minutes after current is applied to the winding). Current is applied to a solenoid which pulls on a piston in an oil filled cylinder. Slow release of the oil through a small orifice provides the time delay. At the end of the piston travel relay contacts are made. Used to provide delayed alarms.

relay, differential, *n.* A relay with two windings, one of which can override the other in determining the operation of the relay. See also "relay, biased."

relay, EA-type, *n.* A relay similar to an E-type, except the relay coil is insulated by filling with cellulose acetate, thus making it thinner. May be mounted on 1-inch horizontal centers.

relay, E-type, *n.* Heavy-duty all-purpose flat-type telephone relay. Has two sets of contact springs. Adjustment must be accomplished by bending springs and adjusting armature gap.

relay, flat-type, *n.* Small, sensitive telephone relay whose core is a flat iron bar. Typically 1¼″ wide x 1¾″ high x 3½″ long as installed on a mounting plate.

relay, F-type, *n.* Heavy-duty flat-type telephone relay with two sets of contact springs. They are slow-releasing due to a winding of bare copper wire over the core, and have an adjustable armature stop pin to regulate the time of release.

relay, G-type, *n.* Small, sensitive, flat-type telephone relay having one set of contact springs, and housed in a crosstalk-proof shell. Has a high impedance at voice frequencies due to laminated construction of the core.

relay, H-type, *n.* Heavy-duty all-purpose flat-type telephone relay with two sets of contact springs, and having a high impedance at voice frequencies due to a laminated core.

relay, J-type, *n.* A small flat-type telephone relay having one set of contact springs, and made for use with 16-20 Hz operating current.

relay, latching, *n.* A relay which latches automatically when operated, and is held mechanically in the operated position until unlatched by energizing a release winding.

relay, line, *n.* (1) The relay in a subscriber's line equipment in a telephone central office which operates when he lifts his handset to make a call. (2) The relay in series with a telegraph line and operated by the telegraph signals which controls operation of a local telegraph sounder.

relay, locking, *n.* A relay which in operating closes contacts to provide current to a holding winding which holds the relay operated until the holding circuit is opened.

relay, main-line telegraph, *n.* A telegraph relay whose 150-ohm coil is placed in series with a neutral telegraph circuit, and whose make contact operates a local sounder from which the coded signals are read aurally.

relay, marginal. See "marginal relay."

relay, mercury, *n.* A relay which makes contacts by tilting a mercury switch, an evacuated glass tube with sealed-in contacts and a pool of mercury which bridges the contacts when the tube is tilted.

relay, mercury-wetted, *n.* A relay which has sealed contacts which are constantly wetted by mercury. Ensures an excellent resistance-free contact.

relay, multi-contact, *n.* A relay designed to close a large number of contacts (24 or more) simultaneously.

relay, neutral, *n.* A relay whose operation depends only upon the magnitude of the current through its operating winding, and not upon its direction.

relay, non-adjustable, *n.* A relay housed in a sealed case so that it cannot be adjusted or cleaned. For reliability, usually uses dual mercury-wetted contacts enclosed in a hydrogen atmosphere.

relay, overload, *n.* A relay that operates when the current flow in a circuit exceeds the normal or some predetermined value for that circuit.

relay, overvoltage. See "overvoltage relay."

relay, pad control, *n.* A relay which controls the 2 dB switching pad on a combination toll circuit, taking it out when on a "via" connection and leaving it in on a "terminal connection." This relay can be controlled by the potential on the sleeve of the toll circuit jack.

relay, polar, *n.* A relay whose operation depends upon the direction of the current through its operating winding.

relay, polarized, *n.* A relay which has a permanent magnet field, and whose armature is not biased by a spring. Its operation thus depends on both the direction and magnitude of the net operating flux. It often has two windings: a line winding and a biasing winding. See also "relay, biased."

relay, quick-acting. See "quick-acting relay."

relay, rare gas, *n.* A gas discharge tube used to drain high voltage induced charges from rural telephone lines. Consists of line and ground electrodes in a tube filled with argon gas.

relay, reed, *n.* A relay composed of reed units consisting of contacts on moveable magnetized reeds sealed into small glass tubes. Coils around the glass tubes are pulsed with a current to operate the reed.

relay, resonant-reed, *n.* A relay whose resonant reed vibrates sufficiently to close a contact only when energized by current of a particular frequency. Used in 135 cycle ringing, and to provide selective ringing for mobile radiotelephone stations.

relay, R-type, *n.* A flat-type telephone relay, similar to the E-type except that the core is of elliptical cross-section, thus giving a larger winding space and shorter length of turn than on the E-type.

relay, sealed. See "hermetically sealed relay."

relay, sensitive, *n.* A relay, usually having a d'Arsonval movement, which will operate on currents of 10 milliamperes or less.

relay, slow operate, *n.* A relay which has a heavy copper slug over its core on the armature end which delays build-up of the magnetic flux, and thus makes the relay slow to operate.

relay, slow release, *n.* A relay which has a heavy copper slug over the heel end of its core which delays decay of the magnetic flux and thus makes the relay slow to release. Some slow release relays have instead a copper sleeve over the entire length of the core, under the winding.

relay, slow to operate and release, *n.* A relay in which the buildup and decay of magnetic flux in the core is delayed after the operating winding is energized or deenergized. This delay is caused by a copper collar on the armature end of the core which makes the relay slow to operate, plus a copper sleeve over the core which makes it slow to release.

relay, supervisory, *n.* A relay in series with the direct current supply to a talking circuit which releases when the subscriber hangs up and, in doing so, operates a supervisory lamp or signal.

relay, tape, *n.* A station at which incoming teletypewriter messages are received in the form of perforated tape, then torn off and fed into an automatic transmitter on the proper outgoing channel. See also "tape relay, - - -."

relay, thermal, *n.* A slow operate relay actuated by the effect of a heating coil on a bimetallic strip.

relay, time-delay. See "relay, dashpot," "relay, slow operate," "relay, slow release," and "relay, slow operate and release."

relay, torn-tape. See "torn-tape relay."

relay, transfer, *n.* A relay which acts to substitute a stand-by unit of equipment when the primary unit fails.

relay, tuned. See "tuned relay."

relay, two-step, *n.* A relay in which only a part of the make springs operate on a first step, and additional springs operate later when the core flux is increased, either because the current through the winding has increased or because a second winding has been energized.

relay, undercurrent, *n.* A relay designed to operate when the current it is monitoring drops below a preset value.

relay, undervoltage, *n.* A moving coil voltmeter-type relay which is designed to close an alarm contact when the voltage it is monitoring drops to a preset level.

relay, U-type, *n.* Round core, flat-type general purpose telephone relay with two sets of contact springs. Capable of operating large spring combinations.

relay, vacuum. See "vacuum relay."

relay, voltage alarm, *n.* A relay constructed like a d'Arsonval voltmeter, but with high-voltage and low voltage alarm contacts which close whenever the battery supply voltage in a dial office is higher or lower than acceptable pre-set limits.

relay, voltmeter, *n.* A single-pole, double-throw relay constructed like a D'Arsonval voltmeter with one contact on the pointer and two adjustable contacts on the scale. Used to provide low-voltage and high-voltage alarms.

relay, wire-spring, *n.* General purpose telephone relays useful when many springs are required. Has two or three parallel rows of wire contact springs, each row moulded into an individual base. The springs are tensioned during manufacture, and are positioned by a fixed card attached to the relay frame and a moving card actuated by the armature. Moving contact springs are in pairs to provide twin contacts, each moving wire having bar contacts with a gold overlay.

relay, Y-type, *n.* A relay which is the same as the U-type, except that it is designed for slow-release.

relay center. See "center, tape relay," "major relay center," and "minor relay center."

relay rack. See "rack, relay."

relays, Codel, *n. pl.* A group of four, sometimes five, relays used for the temporary storage of digital information in switching equipment. See also "code, Codel" and "code, two-out-of-five."

relay station. See "station, radio relay."

relay station, primary, *n.* A major relay station which has been assigned net control responsibilities for its geographical area.

release, *adj.* Describing any of several mechanisms which operate to return automatic switching equipment to its idle condition when the subscriber hangs up his telephone handset.

release, timed, *n.* Release of a circuit which has mal-functioned, after a delay interval. The amount of delay is usually regulated by a dash-pot relay.

release alarm, *n.* An alarm in a dial central office which indicates failure of selectors or connector to release because one party has not hung up, or linefinders failing to start after being seized. This minor alarm is delayed until 10-20 seconds after the non-standard release condition occurs.

release current, *n.* That value of current at which a relay will just release after having been operated for an appreciable time.

release time, *n.* (1) The time, in seconds, from the hang-up of the calling subscriber until the switching system has restored to normal. (2) In a step-by-step switch the time from the opening of the holding bridge until the switch has restored to normal.

reliability, circuit, *n.* The percentage time a circuit was available to the user during a specified period of time.

reluctance, *n.* The property of a magnetic circuit which determines the total magnetic flux (lines of force) which will result when a given magnetomotive force is applied. Reluctance is to a magnetic circuit what resistance is to a direct current circuit.

remanence, *n.* The magnetic flux which remains in a magnetic circuit after the magnetomotive force is removed.

Remendur, *n.* A ductile magnetic alloy developed at the Bell Laboratories which has the highest known remanence, or residual magnetic induction. An alloy of cobalt-iron-vanadium. Has capability of a remanence as high as 21,500 gauss, a square hysteresis loop, a high elastic modulus, and a high curie temperature. Ideally suited for the magnet of ferreed switches.

remote (broadcast), *n.* A point at a distance from the broadcasting studio where a broadcast originates. The "pick-up" point.

remote control, *adj. n.* A system for turning on and off, adjusting, and tuning of devices from a distance, usually over communication circuits.

reorder signal, *n.* An audible, flashing, or audible and flashing signal at the rate of 120 pulses per minute, to indicate that the trunk or circuit should be released and a new attempt originated.

reorder tone. See "tone, reorder."

repair card. See "card, repair."

repair clerk, *n.* A workman at a repair desk who receives reports of trouble from the subscribers, annotates them on the subscriber's line card, and passes the line card to the local testdeskman.

repairman, *n.* A workman who investigates troubles in subscriber's station equipment, guided by the local testdeskman, and who repairs or replaces that equipment and its serving drop wire.

repair time. See "time, repair."

repeater, *n.* (1) A device which serves as an interface between two circuits, receiving signals from one circuit and transmitting them to the other circuit. (2) A device which serves to amplify signals which have become too weak.

repeater, AT2, *n.* Automatic Electric series-connected negative impedance voice repeater.

repeater, AT6, *n.* Automatic Electric series-shunt connected negative impedance voice repeater.

repeater, baseband, *n.* In a microwave radio relay system, a combination of receiver and transmitter which receives an attenuated radio signal, demodulates it to baseband, amplifies the baseband signal, and modulates the transmitter which sends the signal to the next station. The availability of the baseband makes it possible to drop or insert carrier channels or carrier groups as required.

repeater, battery and ground. *n.* A dial pulse repeater which uses battery and ground signaling, which see.

repeater, carrier, *n.* An amplifier for insertion at intermediate points in a cable carrying carrier circuits. Used to amplify the carrier signals so that they will arrive at the far terminal with an adequate signal-to-noise ratio.

repeater, digit-sending, *n.* A dial pulse repeater which, when accessed, automatically sends one or more digits over the trunk.

repeater, duplex, *n.* A dial pulse repeater which uses duplex signaling, which see.

repeater, duplex telegraph, *n.* A telegraph repeater having separate paths for the two directions of transmission.

repeater, E&M, *n.* A dial pulse repeater which uses E&M signaling, which see.

repeater, E&M lead signal, *n.* An E&M signal lead extension circuit, which allows E&M leads over 25 ohms long.

repeater, E2, *n.* Western Electric series connected negative impedance voice repeater.

repeater, E3, *n.* Western Electric shunt-connected negative impedance voice repeater.

repeater, E6, *n.* A two-wire, voice-frequency transistorized repeater designed to reduce the transmission loss on exchange trunks. Consists of a series-connected and a shunt-connected negative impedance repeater.

repeater, E7, *n.* A 48-volt, transistorized negative-impedance voice repeater used on non-loaded loops for TWX and DATA-PHONE services. Acts as a series repeater at low frequencies, and as a shunt repeater at high voice frequencies.

repeater, E23, *n.* Western Electric series-shunt connected negative impedance voice repeater.

repeater, extra-pulse, *n.* A dial pulse repeater which, when it is accessed, automatically sends one pulse over

the trunk to step the incoming selector to the first level.

repeater, flexible submarine, *n.* A one-way carrier repeater for use on twin submarine cables which was constructed in a long flexible case which would pass over the sheave on the cable laying ship.

repeater, four-wire, *n.* A telephone voice repeater for amplifying the voice signals in a four-wire telephone circuit. It has two separate amplifying units; one amplifying in the east-to-west direction, and the other in the west-to-east direction. No hybrid coils or balancing networks are required.

repeater, frogging, *n.* A carrier repeater which will change carrier frequencies from high-group on the input to low-group on the output for one direction of transmission, and from low-group to high-group in the other direction of transmission.

repeater, half-duplex telegraph, *n.* A duplex telegraph repeater provided with an interlock which restricts the transmission of signals to one direction at a time.

repeater, heterodyne, *n.* A radio relay repeater in which the entire received radio signal is heterodyned (shifted in frequency as a block) to another frequency band, amplified, and retransmitted. The signal is not demodulated in the process. See also "repeater, IF heterodyne."

repeater, high-low. See "high-low repeater."

repeater, IF heterodyne, *n.* A type of radio heterodyne repeater (which see) in which the incoming signal is shifted to a low intermediate (IF) frequency for amplification then shifted up again to the desired channel for retransmission.

repeater, impulse. See "repeater, pulse."

repeater, intermediate, *n.* A repeater, or one of several repeaters, which may be spaced along a long voice or carrier circuit to maintain the proper transmission level, and therefore an adequate signal-to-noise ratio.

repeater, knuckle-joint submarine, *n.* The newest type of bidirectional carrier repeater developed for use on single-tube coaxial submarine cables by the U.S. Underseas Cable Corporation. Has a short pressure-tight repeater housing with knuckle joint cable entrances which go over an 87 inch diameter sheave on the cable laying ship.

repeater, low-high. See "low-high repeater."

repeater, microwave, *n.* A repeater station in a microwave radio relay system. Spaced 20-35 miles apart in a typical microwave system. See also "system, microwave relay."

repeater, negative-impedance, *n.* A voice repeater which operates by inserting negative resistance (or reactance) into the circuit, thus reducing the overall impedance and increasing the current in the circuit. This is the equivalent of introducing a transmission gain. The negative impedance repeater does not interrupt the D.C. continuity of a circuit, it is bilateral (two-way), and it is inexpensive. There are two types: series connected, and shunt connected. They are frequently used together.

repeater, passive, *n.* A radio-frequency device used to change the direction of a radio beam without amplification. (a) The common type is a large, flat metal or metal screen surface which acts as a simple radio-frequency mirror. Typical sizes range from 6x8 feet to 24x30 feet. (b) Less common is the repeater consisting of two parabolic antennas connected back-to-back through a short section of waveguide. The plane reflector type is preferred because of its lower losses.

repeater, pulse, *n.* In automatic switching of telephone calls, a device which receives dial pulses from one circuit and repeats them to another circuit. It is a point of interface between the three-wire central office trunk and the two-wire outside plant trunk. Available with many types of signaling.

repeater, pulse correcting, *n.* A dial pulse repeater which receives distorted dial pulses and retransmits them with correct pulse amplitude, pulse length, and pulse shape, but which can do nothing to correct incorrect pulse repetition rate (speed) or pulse spacing.

repeater, pulse-link, *n.* A repeater used when it is desired to connect one E&M signaling circuit directly to another of the same type. It will convert E lead signals (open-ground) to M lead signals (ground-battery) and vice versa.

repeater, radio, *n.* An intermediate radio station on a radio relay system. See "system, radio relay."

repeater, regenerative, *n.* A repeater which accepts distorted digital signals (data, teletypewriter, or digitalized voice) and recreates the signal with pulses of correct repetition rate, pulse amplitude, and pulse width.

repeater, regenerative telegraph, *n.* An electronic device which will repeat any incoming teletypewriter signal with the elements composing each character retimed, reformed, and delayed by one-half of a signal element. The timing is by a square wave oscillator which starts on receiving a start pulse and continues for eight signal elements, then stops until it receives the start pulse of the next character.

repeater, RF heterodyne, *n.* In a microwave radio relay system, a radio repeater which receives an attenuated radio signal, heterodynes the signal down to an intermediate (IF) frequency (usually 70 MHz), amplifies the IF signal, then heterodynes it back up to the microwave frequency and feeds it to a microwave power amplifier for transmission to the next radio station in the system. Permits a high power output and an excellent signal-to-noise performance.

repeater, rigid submarine, *n.* A bidirectional carrier repeater contained in a rigid case for application to single-tube submarine cables. Necessitates use of a cable laying machine having flexible tractor-like articulated treads, instead of the older sheave.

repeater, series-shunt negative-impedance, *n.* A negative-impedance repeater which combines the series-connected and shunt-connected types, thus obtaining a greater gain and improved stability.

repeater, series-type negative-impedance, *n.* A negative-impedance repeater which is connected in series with the circuit and which permits direct current to flow over the circuit. It is stable (does not sing) when the far end of the circuit is open.

repeater, shunt-type negative-impedance, *n.* A negative-impedance repeater which is connected across (in shunt with) the circuit. Frequently combined with a series-connected repeater. It is stable (does not sing) when the far end of the circuit is closed or shorted. See also "repeater, series-shunt negative-impedance."

repeater, single-line telegraph, *n.* A telegraph repeater for simplex working (one direction at a time) designed to repeat telegraph signal from one single wire telegraph circuit to another. Consists of an east relay, a west relay, and a holding circuit.

repeater, telegraph, *n.* An electromagnetic relay device which receives attenuated telegraph signals from one line and retransmits them with renewed energy to another line. See also "repeater, duplex."

repeater, telegraph loop, *n.* A pulse repeating device which serves to interconnect a 62 milliampere neutral telegraph loop to an electronic hub circuit operating at $+60$ volts for mark and -30 volts for space.

repeater, telephone, *n.* An amplifying device using transistors or vacuum tubes which receives attenuated voice signals from a telephone circuit, amplifies them without adding distortion, and sends them on with renewed energy.

repeater, terminal, *n.* A voice or carrier repeater at the end of a circuit, which may require auxiliary signaling, balancing, or 2 wire-to-4 wire conversion equipment which would not be needed at an intermediate repeater.

repeater, two-wire, *n.* A voice frequency repeater which amplifies transmission in both directions on a two-way voice circuit by separating the east-to-west and west-to-east transmissions with hybrid coils, and amplifying them separately. Consists of east and west hybrid coils with their associated balancing networks, an east-to-west amplifier, and a west-to-east amplifier.

repeater, V4, *n.* A small transistorized amplifier suitable for voice or data transmission over four-wire facilities. The designation applies to either of two units: The 24V4 terminal repeater which provides two to four-wire conversion, and the 44V4 intermediate repeater which provides only gain and equalization.

repeater, V-type, *n.* An all-purpose voice repeater, each consisting of an amplifying element having negative feedback and gain control. Hybrid coils, etc., when required, are mounted separately.

repeater, 22-type, *n.* A voice repeater for two-wire circuits having two amplifying elements. One amplifier is for the east-to-west path, the other for west-to-east. Two hybrid coils connect to the two-wire lines East and West, and require two balancing networks.

repeater, 44-type, *n.* A voice repeater for four-wire lines having four amplifying elements (two 2-stage amplifiers). The east-to-west path and the west-to-east path are completely separate, each with its own amplifier.

repeater section, *n.* The section of cable, or other facility, between two repeater points plus one repeater is termed a "repeater section."

repeater station. See "station, repeater."

repeating coil. See "coil, repeating."

repeller. *n.* An electrode in a reflex klystron tube whose function is to reverse the direction of electron flow so that the electrons will traverse the resonant cavity for the second time in a reverse direction.

reperforator, *n.* A machine which punches Baudot code into paper tape from incoming teletypewriter signals.

repertory dialer. See "dialer, repertory."

repertory dialing, *n.* Dialing of a complete telephone number, or area code plus number, by pressing a single button key. The telephone set, or accessory dialer, has a number of buttons each of which can be programmed to produce an individual telephone number.

repetition rate, *n.* The rate at which regular recurring pulses are repeated.

repulsion, *n.* The mechanical force which tends to push apart adjacent conductors carrying currents in opposite directions, or tends to separate bodies having like electric charges or magnetic poles of like polarity.

requisition, *n.* A written authoritative request for supplies, services, or personnel, already authorized but not made available without a specific request.—*v.* To make such a request.

rering, *n.* A signal used by an operator at the calling end to recall an operator at the called end of an established connection. Produces a recall signal on the distant operator's answering cord.—*v.* To ring on the front cord of an established connection in an attempt to recall the distant operator.

reroute, *n.* An alternate similar transmission path, over which a circuit is routed when the original path fails.—*v.* To divert a communication circuit to another similar transmission path, because of or in anticipation of failure of the original path.

reserve, battery busy-hour, *n.* Busy hour reserve is the number of hours a battery can be discharged, at the busy-hour drain rate and with all chargers off, until the voltage at the battery terminals is one volt higher than the minimum voltage required at the equipment.

reset, *v.* (1) To place a binary cell in its initial or zero state. (2) To restore to the original state or starting position.

residual charge, *n.* A small charge remaining in the dielectric of a capacitor after a single quick discharge.

residual current, *n.* In an unbalanced polyphase power circuit, the vector sum of the currents in the several phase wires.

residual flux, *n.* The magnetic flux which remains in a magnetic circuit after the magnetomotive force is removed.

residual gap, *n.* In a relay, the length of the gap between the center of the pole face and the armature when the armature is in its operated position.

residual magnetism, *n.* The magnetism which remains in an electromagnet or relay core after its energizing circuit is opened.

residual pin, *n.* A non-adjustable non-magnetic pin or button on a relay armature or core which maintains a minimum residual gap.

residual screw, *n.* A non-magnetic screw through the center of a relay armature which strikes on the pole piece when the relay is operated. It permits adjustment of the residual gap.

residual stud, *n.* A permanently-set non-adjustable non-magnetic spacer fastened either to the armature or the pole piece of a relay, thus providing a permanent residual gap.

residual voltage, *n.* In an unbalanced polyphase power circuit, the vector sum of the voltages of the several phases.

resin, epoxy, *n.* A two-part liquid epoxy resin used for sealing, repairing, or splicing rubber or plastic insulated cable. Supplied in a two-part plastic bag in which the two liquids can be mixed by kneading. See also "epoxy."

resin, phenolic, *n.* A large class of insulating materials having as their base the synthetic resin formed by the condensation of phenol with formaldehyde.

resistance, *n.* (1) The property of a conductive material that determines the current which will be produced by a given difference of potential. The practical unit of resistance is the ohm. (2) A circuit element having resistance. See also "resistor."

resistance, antenna, *n.* The quotient obtained by dividing the power in watts supplied to an antenna by the square of the effective antenna current.

resistance, contact, *n.* The electrical resistance measured across relay or switch contacts with normal current flowing. A good contact would have a resistance of about one milliohm (one-thousandth of an ohm.)

resistance, effective, *n.* (1) The ohmic resistance of a conductor at high frequencies, greater than the DC resistance because of "skin effect." (2) The total resistance in an alternating current circuit, including DC resistance and the resistance due to eddy currents, hysteresis, and dielectric losses.

resistance, insulation, *n.* The resistance offered by insulation to the flow of a direct current through it.

resistance, internal. See "internal resistance."

resistance, leakage, *n.* The resistance of a path over which a leakage current flows. Normally of a high value, measured in megohms.

resistance, loop. See "loop resistance."

resistance, negative, *n.* A property of some circuits containing no reactance in which the current increases as the voltage is decreased.

resistance, pneumatic, *n.* Resistance to the flow of gas in a pipe or in a cable, caused by friction. This pneumatic resistance reduces the rate of flow, and also produces a pressure drop analogous to the voltage drop through an electrical resistance.

resistance, protective, *n.* A resistance placed in series with the power supply to a circuit, which will limit the current to a safe value in case the circuit is shorted.

resistance, radiation, *n.* The effective resistance of an antenna, equal to the power it radiates divided by the square of the effective antenna current.

resistance, subscriber's loop, *n.* The total effective resistance of the loop from the central office to and including the subscriber's instrument. Usually assumed to be the resistance of the outside plant at 68 degrees F, plus 200 ohms for the subscriber's telephone plus 100 ohms for inside wire, heat coils, temperature variation, etc.

resistance battery, *n.* A negative battery potential as seen through a current-limiting resistor.

resistance box, *n.* A box containing a number of precision resistors which can be connected into an external circuit by operating decade dial switches. It is for test purposes only, for the allowable current through such a box is low.

resistance bridge. See "bridge, Wheatstone."

resistance coupling, *n.* The method of connection between stages of an amplifier in which a coupling capacitor connects the plate of one stage to the grid of the following stage, while resistors provide the output and input impedances of the two stages.

resistance design of loops, *n.* The selection of wire gauges for subscriber's loops based solely on signaling criteria. Loading is then applied on loops over 18,000 feet long for transmission improvement.

resistance drop, *n.* The drop in voltage which occurs between two points in a circuit due to current flowing through the resistance of the circuit. Multiplying the current in amperes times the resistance in ohms gives the voltage drop in volts, which is the reason it is sometimes called "IR drop."

resistance-grounded, *adj.* Grounded through a resistance which will limit the current flow to ground in case of a ground fault.

resistance lamp. See "lamp, resistance."

resistance pad, *n.* Any of the several assemblies of resistors potted in a six-pin tube base. Used with a pad (mounting) to form balanced or unbalanced, constant-resistance attenuation networks having losses from 0.5 db to 35.0 db.

resistivity, *n.* A measure of the ability of a material to resist passage of a current, either through it or on its surface.

resistivity, surface, *n.* The surface resistance between electrodes forming opposite sides of a square, the size of the square being immaterial.

resistivity, temperature coefficient of, *n.* The amount that the resistance of a conductor will increase for each one degree Centigrade increase in temperature. Typical values are:

Aluminum — 1.0034
Copper — 1.0038
Iron — 1.0052
Nickel — 1.0060
Silver — 1.0038
Zinc — 1.0037

resistor, *n.* A circuit component which provides a certain pre-determined amount of resistance.

resistor, bias, *n.* A small resistance inserted in the cathode circuit of a vacuum tube to provide its grid bias through the voltage drop caused by the cathode current.

resistor, carbon, *n.* Small rod of carbon composition having axial leads and overall moulded insulation. Obtainable in graded resistance values from 10 ohms to 22 megohms, and in 5%, 10% and 20% accuracy tolerance.

resistor, cathode, *n.* A bias resistor, which see.

resistor, current-limiting, *n.* A resistor inserted in a circuit to limit the flow of current to a safe value in the event of a fault or short circuit.

resistor, dropping, *n.* A resistor placed in series between a voltage source and a load for the purpose of reducing the voltage supplied to the load.

resistor, flat-type, *n.* A resistor made by winding resistance wire on a flat non-magnetic metal core (approx. 1½ x 3½ inches) with overall insulation. Mounted by its terminals which extend through the mounting plate. Has one or two windings (2 or 3 terminals). Has very low inductance and good heat dissipation.

resistor, noninductive, *n.* A resistor constructed in such a manner that its inductance is negligible.

resistor, tapped. See "tapped resistor."

resistor, WECo 89-type, *n.* A resistance network potted in a 6-prong tube base, which makes an attenuation network when plugged into a tube socket on which fixed resistors are wired. Available with attenuation losses starting at 0.50 db and increasing in 0.25 db steps to 22.0 db, then 0.50 db steps to 30.0 db. Used to adjust toll trunks to a precise value of transmission loss overall.

resistor, wire, *n.* Resistor in which the resistance element is wire wound on a core, with overall insulation.

resistor, wirewound, *n.* A small insulating rod with resistance wire winding having axial leads and overall moulded insulation. Available in graded resistance values from 0.24 ohms to 1800 ohms, and in 5%, 10% and 20% accuracy tolerance.

resolution, *n.* Of a measuring instrument, the minimum scale value which can be read. Not the lowest scale value, but to how many significant figures. See also "accuracy."

resonance, *n.* (1) The condition of a series electrical circuit when the capacitive reactance and the inductive reactance are equal. (2) The condition most conducive to continued vibration or oscillation. (3) The condition of being in tune.

resonance, parallel, *n.* The condition which exists in a circuit comprising capacitance and inductance in parallel, when the current entering the parallel circuit from outside is in phase with the voltage across the parallel circuit. The impedance of a parallel circuit is a pure resistance. Also called "anti-resonance." In a parallel resonant circuit, the capacitive susceptance is equal to the inductive susceptance.

resonance, series, *n.* The condition which exists in a circuit comprising capacitance and inductance in series, when the current through the circuit is in phase with the voltage across the circuit. When this occurs, the impedance of the circuit is equal to its resistance. In a series resonant circuit the capacitive reactance and the inductive reactance are equal in magnitude.

resonant, *adj.* In a condition of resonance.

resonant cavity. See "cavity, resonant."

resonant frequency, *n.* The frequency at which the inductive reactance and capacitive reactance of a series circuit are equal. It is numerically

equal to $\frac{1}{2} \pi$ LC in hertz, where L is in henrys and C is in farads.

resonator, *n.* A resonant cavity. See "cavity, resonant."

response, *n.* (1) The fidelity with which the output waveform of a device corresponds to the input waveform. (2) A tabulation of the deviations from perfect fidelity.

response, audio, *n.* (1) The fidelity with which audio frequency equipment reproduces its input signal. (2) A system for generating an audible, verbal response from a machine, such as a time announcing machine.

response, frequency, *n.* The transmission gain or loss of a system, measured over the useful bandwidth, compared to the gain or loss at some reference frequency.

response, image. See "image response."

response, spurious, *n.* Response of a frequency-selective system, such as a radio receiver, to an undesired frequency.

response, transient, *n.* The response of an amplifier or circuit to high-frequency components of a signal. Evaluated by the response to a square-wave test signal.

restoration, circuit, *n.* The reestablishment of a communication service which had been disrupted or degraded, by the use of spare facilities, preemption of other facilities, or by maintenance actions.

restoration, DC. See "clamping."

restore, *vi.* To return a relay or automatic switch to its non-operated position.—*vt.* (1) To place a memory cell in its original state. (2) To take action to reactivate a disrupted transmission path, by reroute or by repair.

restorer, direct current, *n.* A device by which a direct current component or reference is added to an alternating current signal after its reception. See also "clamping."

restriction, *n.* The denial of the capability to make an outgoing call from a PABX, either to a particular trunk group, several groups, or to all groups.

restriction, full, *n.* The denial to a PABX station of the capability to make any outgoing calls, unless they are placed by the attendant.

restriction, partial, *n.* The denial to a PABX station of the capability to make outgoing calls to city trunks, while permitting calls to other trunk groups.

restriction, toll, *n.* The action of preventing restricted PABX stations from making calls to toll or other restricted points. A restrictor in outgoing dial trunks counts the first three digits dialed and diverts calls to forbidden codes either to busy tone, to the operator, or to a recorded announcement.

restrictor, *n.* A unit of equipment for insertion in an outgoing dial trunk which counts the digits dialed and acts to restrict calls to forbidden codes. Forbidden calls are commonly diverted, either to busy tone, to the operator, or to a recorded announcement.

restrictor, toll code, *n.* A device which permits a PABX station to make outgoing trunk calls, but not toll calls. Consists of rotary stepping switches which count each of the first three digits dialed and block calls to forbidden codes.

restrictor, trunk. See "equipment, diversion."

resuscitator, mouth-to-mouth, *n.* A device used to revive a person whose breathing has stopped due to electric shock or other causes. Consists of a face mask for the victim, with a flexible tube which connects to a plastic mouthpiece. Natural breathing can be restored by rythmically expanding the victims lungs by blowing into the mouthpiece.

retard coil. See "coil, retardation."

retentivity, *n.* The property of a material measured by the amount of magnetic flux which remains after the material has been saturated with flux, and then the magnetomotive force is removed.

retractile cord, *n.* A coiled cord. An electrical cord, such as a handset cord, which is spirally wound with elastic so that it will extend as required, then restore to the tight spiral when released.

retractile spring, *n.* A restoring spring.

retrial, *n.* An attempt, after the initial attempt. The offering of a telephone call which had been attempted before, but not completed because of a busy number, busy trunk, wrong number, or no ring condition.

return, *n.* (1) A common return. (2) A negative return. (3) A ground return.—*v.* To refund a deposit to a customer at a prepay coin telephone.

return, common, *n.* A conductor which serves two or more circuits in returning a current to its source or to ground.

return, ground. See "ground return."

return, negative, *n.* A drainage wire between two points which equalizes potential differences for control of electrolysis. For instance, it may connect from main cable sheaths to a power system ground, draining stray current from the cable sheaths and returning it to the power system.

return key, *n.* The push-button key by which the operator returns coins deposited in a prepay coin telephone.

return loss. See "loss, return."

return to zero, *adj.* A method of digital signaling or recording digital signals in which the signal must return to zero after each binary digit. This type of signal restricts signaling speed.

reverberation, *n.* The persistence of sound for some time after the source is cut off, due to repeated reflections from the walls and ceiling of an enclosed area.

reverberation time, *n.* The time in seconds required for the sound energy of a particular frequency to drop by 60 db after the source of sound is cut off. Can be estimated by clapping the hands loudly once, then counting seconds until there are no audible echos.

reversal, *n.* A change (1) in the direction of current flow, (2) in the direction of transmission on a circuit, (3) in the polarity of a magnetic pole, or (4) in a stored data bit from "zero" to "one," or vice versa.

reversal, polar, *n.* A reversal in the polarity of a voltage or direction of flow of a current. A negative voltage is normally used for a marking signal, and a positive voltage for a spacing signal.

reverse battery signaling. See "signaling, reverse battery."

reverse battery supervision, *n.* A method of indicating answer of the called subscriber by causing a reversal of battery (—) and ground (+) to the tip and ring of the trunk or line, thus changing the indication from "on-hook" to "off-hook."

reverse current, *n.* The small value of current which flows when the voltage across a diode is of a polarity reversed from that for normal current flow.

reverse preemption, *n.* Preemption of a circuit by the terminal which normally receives calls to alert the terminal which normally initiates calls.

reverse voltage, *n.* Voltage of that polarity which produces the smaller current.

reverting call, *n.* The act of ringing the calling telephone, or ringing another telephone on the same line as the calling telephone, usually without the assistance of an operator. See also "reverting call switch."

reverting call switch, *n.* A special switch accessed when a party line subscriber wishes to dial another party on his line.

revertive pulsing, *n.* Pulsing over a trunk in the reverse direction. The incoming office sends open or ground pulses on the trunk to the originating office, which counts the pulses and opens the trunk when the correct number have been received.

revision, *n.* A complete publication superseding a previous edition.

rewrite, *v.* To restore a binary cell to the same state it was in just prior to being read.

R group, *n.* A one-way 48 kHz bandwidth transmission path between two points, established over radio facilities, and having terminal frequencies of 60-108 kHz.

rheostat, *n.* A resistor whose value can be changed by turning a control knob.

rhombic antenna. See "antenna, rhombic."

rhumb line, *n.* A line plotted on a map, which approximates a great circle radio path. It is a line which intersects all meridians of latitude at the same angle.

ribbon, bonding, *n.* Tinned copper strap, 1/16" x ⅜", used for interconnecting and grounding lead cable sheaths.

ribbon cable. See "cable, ribbon."

ride gain, *v.* To control the volume level on a circuit by adjusting amplifier gain while observing the level on a volume indicator, as in a broadcasting studio. (Slang).

ridged, *adj.* Describing an insulated conductor which has a raised longitudinal ridge formed in the plastic or rubber insulation. Used to designate the tip conductor.

ridge-marker, *n.* Any of one or several longitudinal ridges on the outer covering of plastic-insulated wire, used for conductor identification.

rigging, manhole pulling, *n.* A heavy channel frame, 9 to 12 feet long, into which large aluminum sheaves can be fitted and the whole adjusted to feed cable from a reel to a manhole to a cable duct. See also "sheave, manhole."

right, *adj.* Describing equipment which is on the right side of a switchboard, shelf, frame, or rack as viewed from the front.

right, pole, *n.* The right, granted by the owner of a pole, to make a single attachment to the pole, or to make attachments within a certain specified portion of the height. Usually granted in consideration of an annual rental of about one dollar per year. ·

Right-Hand Rule. See "Appendix B."

right-of-way, *n.* (1) An easement to use a specific portion of land, and to have access to it. (2) Land occupied by telephone plant but not owned by the telephone company. —*n. pl.* rights-of-way, abbrev: R/W

ring, *n.* (1) An audible signal by a bell. (2) An application of current to ring a bell or operate an alerting signal. (3) In a 2-conductor switchboard plug, the ring-shaped contact between the tip and the sleeve. (4) In paired wire, the second wire of the pair.—*v.i.* To produce a series of highly damped oscillations following shock excitation of a resonant circuit.—*v.t.* (1) To signal by applying ringing current to a circuit. (2) To apply cable rings to a cable suspension strand.

ring, bridle, *n.* A galvanized open-loop ring with a wood screw point, which can be screwed into cross-arms and poles to hold runs of bridle wires.

ring, cable, *n.* A semi-circular loop of flat spring-steel wire hooked to a suspension strand every 20 inches, and used to support an aerial cable. Now obsolescent; largely replaced by lashing wire.

ring, cable identification, *n.* A lightweight colored plastic ring placed over the bunch of pairs which constitutes one color group at a cable splice. Serves to retain the color

identification after the binder strings are torn off. Available in blue, orange, green, and brown.

ring, distributing, *n.* Insulated metal ring used to contain and route jumper wires or cable conductors on distributing frames or in cable terminals.

ring, drive, *n.* A nail-like fastening with an open loop at the head end, driven into poles or wooden surfaces to hold drop wires.

ring, jumper, *n.* A circular loop of insulated steel rod through which distributing frame cross-connections are passed to ensure an orderly arrangement.

ring, manhole adjusting, *n.* A cast iron ring, either 26, 29, or 32 inches in diameter and 2, 2½, or 3 inches high, used for raising manhole covers when the street is resurfaced with a layer of asphalt.

ring, splash. See "splash ring."

ring-around-the-rosy, *n.* Incorrect automatic routing of calls in a toll network, where a call given "lateral routing" finds itself back in the same office through which it passed earlier.

ringback, *n.* A signal used by the operator at the called end of an established connection to recall the originating operator. Operation of the called operator's ringing key sends an on-hook pulse back to the calling end where it is converted to a recall signal on the front cord of the originating operator.

ring-back switch. See "switch, reverting call."

ringback tone, *n.* An intermittent low tone, one second on three seconds off, which is returned to the calling phone to indicate that the called phone is being rung. In older connector switches, part of the actual ringing signal is bled off through a 0.04 mf capacitor and returned to the calling line. In newer offices it has been replaced with an "audible ringing tone."

ring circuit, *n.* A communication network in the form of a ring so that opening any part of the ring will not interrupt communications to any node on the ring.

ring connection, *n.* Connection of a group of components or circuit elements in series, with the output of the last connected to the input of the first so as to form a closed ring. Said also of four elements connected in a square configuration.

ring cut, *n.* Injury to an aerial cable sheath caused by rubbing on the supporting cable ring.

ringdown, *adj.* Describes a circuit or a method of signaling where the incoming signal is actuated by alternating (ringing) current over the circuit.

ringdown circuit, *n.* Circuit on which application of ringing current at one end brings in the line signal at the distant end.

ringer, *n.* (1) The alternating current bell in a subscriber's telephone set which alerts him to an incoming call. (2) A device at the terminal of a toll telephone circuit which converts the central office or switchboard ringing signal to the line ringing signal. Some examples are:

Switchboard		Line
E&M (DC)	—	SF (2600 Hz)
20 Hz	—	1000/20 Hz
20 Hz	—	135 Hz

ringer, biased, *n.* A polarized telephone bell whose armature is held at one end of its travel by a small biasing spring, so that it will respond only to pulsating current of one polarity. Pulsating current of the opposite polarity will merely attract the armature more strongly to the pole piece of the electromagnet.

ringer, coil-less, *n.* A substitute ringer for a telephone which uses a piezoelectric ceramic bender mounted as a cantilever and carrying a clapper rod at the free end.

ringer, high-impedance, *n.* A biased telephone ringer which is intended for party-line use, where it is connected from line to ground. It is therefore given a high impedance, about 160 kilohms at 1000 hertz, so that it will not unbalance the line and thereby cause the line to be noisy.

ringer, loud. See "bell, loud-ringing."

ringer, polarized, *n.* The normal bell in a subscriber's telephone set. Consists of a one or two pole high-impedance (160 Kilohms at 1000 Hz) electromagnet, biased with a permanent magnet, with a moving armature and a clapper which strikes a pair of gongs, tuned to a pleasing chord. Used in series with a capacitor which may be tuned for series resonance at the operating frequency, usually 20 Hz. The armature may have a light biasing spring to prevent bell tapping while dialing.

ringer, straight-line, *n.* A biased ringer for individual telephone lines which is connected across the line, not from one side of the line to ground. Has a relatively low impedance, and is not tuned and therefore responds to ringing frequencies ranging from 16 hertz to 30 hertz.

ringer, telephone, *n.* An electric bell which operates on low-frequency alternating or pulsating current and is associated with a telephone station to alert the user to incoming calls.

ringer, tone, *n.* Substitute for a telephone bell, using a transistor oscillator and loud-speaker to produce an alerting signal wtih strong components at 750 Hz and 1500 Hz.

ringer, tuned, *n.* Any of the several telephone bells which are capacitor-tuned to be resonant at, and to respond only to, a particular ringing frequency. Available factory-adjusted to 16.6, 20, 25, 30, 33.3, 40, 42, 50, 54, 60, and 66.6 Hz frequencies. Used on party lines which are rung with harmonic, decimonic, or synchromonic frequencies.

ringer, unbiased, *n.* A telephone bell whose armature is not held toward one end of its travel by a biasing spring. Such a bell will operate on alternating current, but will not operate well on pulsating current or superimposed (biased) ringing current.

ringer, vibrating. See "vibrating ringer."

ring forward. See "rering."

ringing, *n.* (1) The act of causing a telephone bell to ring, by application of ringing current to the line. (2) Ringing current, usually 20 Hz alternating current. (3) A damped oscillatory transient at or near the frequency of cutoff, caused by a sudden change in signal level.

ringing, code, *n.* A method of selectively calling subscribers on a multi-party line by using distinctive combinations of long and short rings.

ringing, DC, *n.* Switchboard ringing, in which the operation of a ringing key applies direct current to a ringing relay which in turn operates to place ringing current on the line.

ringing, divided, *n.* Ringing the telephone bells on a party line by connecting half of them from the tip side of the line to ground, and the other half from the ring side to ground.

ringing, harmonic, *n.* A system of selectively signaling the several parties (up to ten) on a party line using a different frequency and a tuned ringer for each party. The ringing frequencies have the following harmonic relationship: 16 2/3, 25, 33 1/3, 50, and 66 2/3 Hz. See also "synchromonic" and "decimonic."

ringing, immediate, *n.* A feature of some connector circuits which forwards a splash ring immediately when the called line tests idle, without waiting for the regular ringing cycle determined by the ringing interrupter.

ringing, machine. See "machine ringing."

ringing, manual, *n.* Switchboard ringing which continues only during the time a ringing key is held in its operated position.

ringing, selective (or full selective), *n.* System which permits ringing only one subscriber on a multiparty telephone line. Uses tuned ringers which respond to only one frequency, and ringing current of five different frequencies. See also "harmonic ringing."

ringing, semi-selective, *n.* A ringing system for four-party lines, in which two parties ring from the tip side of the line to ground, and the other two parties ring from the ring side to ground. Parties on the same side of the line have a "one ring" or a "two ring" code to distinguish between them. Thus each party hears only one ring besides his own.

ringing, superimposed. See "superimposed ringing."

ringing, thousand cycle. See "ringing, thousand/twenty."

ringing, thousand/twenty, *n.* Tone signaling method which uses 1000 Hz modulated at 20 Hz. Both the 20 and 1000 Hz circuits are sharply tuned, which avoids false operation from speech signals.

ringing, 20-cycle, *n.* Signaling on a circuit by using 20 Hz alternating current, either to ring a telephone bell or to operate a ringdown trunk equipment.

ringing converter. See "converter, ringing."

ringing current, *n.* The current which is applied to a subscriber's line to cause his telephone bell to ring. For one-party lines it is usually 20 Hz alternating current.

ringing interval. See "interval, ringing."

ringing key, *n.* Key whose operation places ringing current on the line or trunk, or which starts machine ringing on the line or trunk.

ringing period, *n.* The one-second interval during which ringing current is flowing to the called telephone.

ringing signal, *n.* (1) Any signal sent over a line or trunk to alert the party at the far end, by means of a light or bell, to the incoming call. (2) An intermittent tone heard by the calling party which indicates that the called telephone is being rung.

ring modulator, *n.* A modulator consisting of diodes connected in a closed square or ring configuration.

ring wire, *n.* (1) In paired wire, the second wire of the pair. (2) The wire which connects to the ring contact of a switchboard plug or to the ring spring of a jack. (3) The wire which is the mate of the "tip wire."

ripple, *n.* An alternating voltage superimposed on the direct current from a generator or rectifier, caused by a rough commutator on the generator or incomplete filtering in the rectifier. Percent ripple is equal to the ratio of the RMS ripple voltage to the absolute value of the total voltage, expressed in percent.

riser, *n.* Conduit or cable which runs in a vertical direction on a pole or in a building.

rise time, *n.* The time in (micro) seconds required for a pulse or other waveform to rise from 10% to 90% of its peak value.

rise time, pulse. See "time, pulse rise."

rivet, *n.* A headed fastening device having a shank end designed to be expanded, spread, or upset.

RMS amplitude. See "root-mean-square amplitude."

road side, *adv. n.* The side of a pole line toward the highway or street.

Rochelle salt, *n.* A crystalline double tartrate of potassium and sodium. It has the strongest piezoelectric effect of any material commercially available, but loses its piezoelectric properties above 68 degrees Fahr and is very sensitive to humidity.

rod, *v. t.* To push sectional duct rods through an underground duct, either to clean the duct or to insert a pulling-in wire.

rod, anchor, *n.* A long galvanized steel rod which attaches to a buried anchor and has an eye on its upper end to which anchor guys may be attached. Anchor rods are available in the following sizes: ½ in. x 6 ft., ⅝ in. x 8 ft., ¾ in. x 9 ft., 1 in. x 10 ft., and 1¼ in. x 10 ft.

rod, duct, *n.* Round hardwood rods, 1-inch diameter x 4 ft long, having hinged or screw connections on the ends by which a number of rods can be joined and pushed through an underground duct between manholes. The end rod can be equipped with a brush or root cutter to clean the duct, and a pulling-in wire is attached to the trailing rod.

rod, ground, *n.* A round steel rod, ½ " to ¾ " Diameter x 5' to 8' long, driven into the ground to provide an electrical connection to the earth.

rod, hanger, *n.* A continuously-threaded galvanized steel stud used for suspending cable runway from a ceiling, or for an angle brace of adjustable length. Available in lengths of 1, 1½, 2, 3, 4, 6, 10 and 12 feet.

rod, lightning, *n.* A pointed metal rod carried above the highest point of a pole or building, and connected to earth by a heavy copper conductor. Intended to carry a direct lightning discharge directly to earth without damage to the protected structure.

rod, sectional ground, *n.* A copper-weld ground rod made in sections, 5, 8, or 10 feet long, which may be joined by bronze couplings and driven to great depths (40 feet, or more) as required to reach moist earth.

rod, triple-eye, *n.* An anchor rod

whose eye has three thimble-like grooves, permitting the fastening of three guy strands in the same eye.

rod, twin-eye, *n.* An anchor rod whose eye has two thimble-like grooves, permitting the fastening of two guy strands in the same eye.

rodding, *n.* Threading an underground duct with a wire which can be used to pull in a cable or a winch line which will in turn pull in a cable. The pulling-in wire is threaded through the duct by tying it to jointed sectional "duct rods" which are pushed through the duct.

rods, flexible duct, *n. pl.* A set of flexible steel rods each 3 feet long which can be coupled together to form a continuous flexible rod of any required length. It is sufficiently flexible to permit its being coiled and stored on a 5½ foot diameter reel. The end of the rod can be fitted with duct rodding tools, such as an auger, a spear, or a cork-screw.

rods, ranging, *n. pl.* A set of five poles or rods of wood or aluminum tubing, usually one inch in diameter and 8 feet long, fitted with a point which can be pushed into the ground, and painted in one foot sections alternately red and white. Used for the laying out of straight pole lines by sighting past two rods to place the third rod.

roger. A word often used in voice short wave radio communications to express agreement or understanding.

roll-off, *n.* Gradually increasing attenuation of an audio system with increasing frequency.

Romex, *n.* Trade name for non-metallic sheathed cable.

roof, *n.* The top of a pole cut at an angle to shed rain water.

roof filter, *n.* A lowpass filter used in repeater and terminal equipment to attenuate the unwanted higher frequencies.

room, switch. See "switchroom."

root-mean-square amplitude (RMS), *n.* The effective value of an alternating wave (current and/or voltage) numerically equal to the direct current value that will produce the same heating effect. Can be computed as the square root of the average of the squares of all instantaneous amplitudes over a complete cycle. For sine waves, the RMS value is equal to 0.707107 times the peak value.

rope-lay, *adj.* Describing a stranded cable in which the separate wires are spirally stranded into groups before the groups are spiraled together.

rosin core solder. See "solder, rosin core."

rosin joint, *n.* A poorly soldered connection, in which the wire is held in place by the rosin flux, not by solder. It results from inadequate heating of the joint.

rotary lineswitch. See "lineswitch, rotary."

rotary out-trunk switch (ROTS). See "switch, out-trunk."

rotary step, *n.* One of the eleven possible steps the wipers of a step-by-step switch can make in moving into and through the switch bank.

rotary stepping switch, *n.* A single-motion (rotary) stepping switch having multiple double-ended wipers which rotate in one direction over a semi-circular contact bank containing 11, 16, 25, or 50 sets of contacts. It may be stepped by external pulses or driven by self-interrupted pulses. Commonly used as a lineswitch or a linefinder.

rotary switching system, *n.* A common-control switching system used extensively in Europe. All dial pulses are received by a register which controls the group selector and final selector switches. The rotary finder and rotary selector switches are power driven from a continuously rotating shaft. Instead of clutches it uses a flexible driven gear which can be driven into and out of mesh by a control magnet. Ringing, busy signal, and closing of the talking path are done by a motor-driven sequence switch.

rotator, antenna, *n.* A motor, or motor and gearing, which rotates a directional antenna to a required direction. Often the orientation is controlled or indicated by selsyns.

rotator, Faraday, *n.* A section of circular waveguide containing a ferrite slab in a magnetic field, the whole inserted as an intermediate section in a rectangular waveguide. Radio waves passing through the rotator are rotated 45 degrees. In one direction of transmission the wave is aligned perfectly with the 45 degree waveguide. In the other direction of transmission the wave is 90 degrees from the correct position, and thus is blocked and allowed to dissipate in a lossy material.

rotor, *n.* (1) The rotating armature or rotating field of an electric motor or generator. (2) The moveable plates in a variable capacitor.

rouge, jeweler's, *n.* A paste used for fine polishing, composed principally of ferric oxide.

route, *n.* The path of a pole line, a conduit, or a cable, or of a call through a telephone switching network.

route, alternate, *n.* A substitute route for a transmission path, for use when the normal route fails.

route, toll, *n.* (1) The path of a pole line or conduit run that carries toll circuits. (2) The numbered designation of a large group of toll circuits between two major points.

route control, *n.* Limiting the number of intertoll trunk links which may be used on a call by controlling the automatic alternate routing, giving preference to direct routes over switched routes, and to "forward routing" over "lateral routing."

route control digit, *n.* A digit preceding the telephone address, transmitted over intertoll trunks to (a)

control automatinc routing at the next switching center, (b) prevent "shuttle," (c) prevent "ring-around-the-rosy," and (d) allow only two successive lateral routings. These digits are:

RC Digit	Meaning
0	Employ all programmed routes.
1	Employ forward routes plus first-choice lateral routes.
2	Employ forward routes plus second-choice lateral routes.
3	Employ forward routes only.

Routine (R), *n.* The fifth highest (and lowest) ranking message precedence. It takes precedence only over "Deferred" messages.

routiner, automatic equipment, *n.* An assembly of equipment which automatically tests any of the several ranks of switching equipment in a dial central office. Connection is made to the switches in a particular rank via rotary access switches, and calls may then be outpulsed to ten different test numbers. The routiner will detect any malfunction, including absence of tone, and when a fault is detected the routining stops and an alarm is sounded.

routiner, automatic line insulation, *n.* A central office testing device which automatically scans, via test distributors and test connectors, all subscriber's lines in an office and tests them for low line insulation. Can be set to detect leakage varying from 50,000 ohms to one megohm, and can be connected to a printer to print a record of all line faults.

routiner, automatic trunk, *n.* A testing device which automatically tests each of a group of trunks in turn, automatically pulsing a test number over the trunk and receiving supervisory signals in return. These signals are checked, after which the routiner releases and reseizes the trunk to pulse a number to reach a 1000 Hz one-milliwatt test tone source in the distant office. The 1000 Hz power received from the distant office can actuate a "good-no good" registration, or print out the actual trunk loss.

routing, *n.* The process of determining and prescribing the path to be used in forwarding messages or telephone calls.

routing, alternate. See "automatic alternate routing."

routing, avoidance, *n.* The assignment of a circuit path to avoid certain critical or trouble-prone circuit nodes.

routing, diverse, *n.* The assignment of a portion of a group of circuits between two points to a path having a different physical route from that of the remaining circuits. Avoids the possibility of all circuits being disrupted by a single trouble.

routing, forward. See "forward routing."

routing indicator, *n.* A code included in the header of a teletypewritten message which gives routing instructions for its transmission. One typical indicator consists of seven characters. The first character is always "R." The next three characters denote the relay station, and the last three characters the desired terminal off of the relay station.

R supergroup, *n.* A permanently associated continuity of radio relay message units (MUR's) arranged to provide a 60-channel one-way transmission path.

RT unit. See "unit, RT."

rubber, *n.* An elastic material, natural or artificial, which is capable of rapid and repeated elastic recovery. The elasticity is such that it will stretch under low stress to at least twice its length, and then snap back to its original length upon release of the stress.

rule, B drop wire, *n.* A calculating rule consisting of a grid card, a slider to be set on the length of span, and a clear plastic curve section which enables an installer to determine what ground clearance a drop wire will have if installed with the available attachment heights at the pole and house.

rule, guy, *n.* A circular slide rule used for determining the required size and lead/height ratio of pole-to-anchor or pole-to-pole guys, when the total horizontal pull is known.

rule, pressure testing, *n.* A circular slide rule for making the computations needed when placing cables under gas pressure.

RULES. See Appendix B for a statement of the following rules:

Fermat's Principle
Left-Hand Rule
Right-Hand Rule

See also "LAWS" and "THEOREMS."

run, cable, *n.* (1) The path taken by a cable. (2) A multiple-duct conduit run which carries many cables.

run, conduit, *n.* (1) The path taken by a conduit or group of conduits. (2) A group of conduits, whether in a building or underground.

R unit. See "unit, R."

rural line, *n.* A multi-party line, frequently magneto operation, which serves customers in a rural district. May use code ringing.

ruthless preemption, *n.* The act of seizing a busy voice circuit without prior warning to the parties who are using the circuit.

RX meter, *n.* An impedance meter which measures in resistance and equivalent capacitance.

RZ signal, *n.* A discontinuous signal in which mark signals are separated by spaces which contain no signal. "RZ" signifies "return to zero."

sabin, *n.* A measure of the sound absorption of a surface. It is the equivalent of one square foot of perfectly absorptive surface. Numerically, it is equal to the fraction of the total sound energy which is absorbed by a particular material.

sabre plow. See "plow, sabre."

safety factor, *n.* The amount of additional stress a mechanical or electrical system can take, over and above the normal working stress before reaching the breakdown stress. Numerically it is equal to the breakdown stress divided by the working stress.

sag, *n.* (1) The downward curvature of a wire or cable due to its weight. (2) The vertical distance from the lowest point of the curve to a straight line joining the two points of support.—*v.i.* (3) To curve downward in the middle because of weight.—*v.t.* (4) To regulate the tension in a wire or strand by adjusting the amount of sag.

salt tablets, *n. pl.* Tablets of sodium chloride (table salt) taken to ward off heat exhaustion by persons who are working hard and perspiring profusely.

salvage, *n.* Property that is in such worn, damaged, deteriorated, or incomplete condition that it is not usable as a unit without major repairs or alterations. Salvage has some value in excess of its basic material content because it may contain serviceable components.—*v.* The saving or rescuing of condemned, discarded, or abandoned property and of materials contained therein for re-use or scrapping.

sample, *n.* An instantaneous value of a variable obtained at regular intervals.—*v.* To obtain sample values of a complex wave at periodic intervals. See also "sampling."

sampling, *n.* In pulse code modulation, the act of selecting samples of an analog wave at recurring intervals such that the original wave can later be reconstructed with reasonable fidelity from the samples.

sampling error. See "error, aliasing."

satellite, *n.* (1) A celestial body orbiting another of larger size. (2) A man-made object or vehicle intended to orbit the earth, the moon, or another celestial body. (3) A satellite central office.

satellite, active communication, *n.* A satellite which contains a source of energy, such as solar cells, and amplifies the signal it receives before transmitting it back to Earth. Examples are the Telestar and Intelsat satellites.

satellite, Atlantic II, *n.* A COMSAT synchronous satellite launched 22 March 1967, and stationed over the Atlantic.

satellite, Early Bird, *n.* A synchronous satellite of the Communications Satellite Corporation, launched 4 April 1965 and stationed over the South Atlantic. Used to relay the live TV pickup of the Gemini space capsule recovery.

satellite, Explorer I, *n.* The first United States satellite launched 31 January 1958, following the Russian Sputnik I on 4 October 1957. It had no communications relay capability.

satellite, geo-stationary, *n.* A synchronous satellite.

satellite, INTELSAT I, *n.* A synchronous satellite launched 6 May 1965 and placed in service 28 June 1965 over the Atlantic Ocean at 25 degrees west longitude. Now retired in reserve.

satellite, INTELSAT II F-1, *n.* An active communications satellite launched 26 Oct. 1966 which failed to achieve a synchronous orbit.

satellite, INTELSAT II F-2, *n.* An active communication satellite launched into synchronous orbit 11 January 1967, and placed in service 27 January 1967 over the Pacific Ocean at 174 degrees east longitude. Now in reserve.

satellite, INTELSAT II F-3, *n.* An active communication satellite launched into synchronous orbit 22 March 1967, and placed in service 7 April 1967 over the Atlantic Ocean at 6 degrees west longitude. Used principally for NASA service.

satellite, INTELSAT II F-4, *n.* An active communication satellite launched 27 Sept. 1967 into synchronous orbit, and placed in service 4 Nov. 1967 over the Pacific Ocean at 174 degrees east longitude. Now held in reserve.

satellite, INTELSAT III, *n.* Any of several satellites launched in 1968-69. All are 56 inches in diameter, weigh 250 pounds, have 160 watts of solar power, two 10-watt transmitters using despun antennas with an effective radiated power of 22 dBW. The transponders have a 225 MHz bandwidth, and can handle 1200 two-way voice channels or four television channels.

satellite, INTELSAT III F-1, *n.* An INTELSAT satellite which was destroyed shortly after liftoff on 18 Sept. 1968.

satellite, INTELSAT III F-2, *n.* An INTELSAT satellite launched 18 Dec. 1968, and placed in service 24 Dec. 1968 over the Atlantic Ocean at 30 degrees west longitude.

satellite, INTELSAT III F-3, *n.* An INTELSAT satellite launched 5 Feb. 1969 and placed in service 16 Feb. 1969 over the Pacific Ocean at 174 degrees east longitude. Repositioned 1 July 1969 over the INDIAN Ocean at 62.5 degrees east longitude.

satellite, INTELSAT III F-4, *n.* An INTELSAT satellite launched 21 May 1969, and placed in service 31 May over the Pacific Ocean at 174 degrees east longitude.

satellite, INTELSAT III F-5, *n.* An INTELSAT satellite launched 25 July 1969 which failed to reach its transfer orbit due to a Delta launch vehicle failure.

satellite, INTELSAT III F-6, *n.* An INTELSAT satellite launched Nov. 1969 and due for service over the Atlantic Ocean at 6 degrees east longitude.

satellite, Molniya, *n.* Any of a series of Soviet communication satellites, the first of which was launched on 23 April 1965. All have been in 12-hour non-synchronous orbits, and the 1969 models have a 40-watt transmitter and two steerable parabolic antennas.

satellite, Pacific I, *n.* A COMSAT synchronous communications satellite launched 11 January 1967, and stationed over the Pacific.

satellite, passive communication, *n.* A satellite designed to reflect radio signals received from the earth back to the earth, without the use of a transmitter on the satellite to strengthen them.

satellite, stationary, *n.* A "synchronous satellite," which see.

satellite, stationkept, *n.* A satellite which carries control equipment which can be energized to change its attitude or orbital velocity, so as to keep it at a particular station in its orbit.

satellite, synchronous, *n.* An artificial satellite, such as Syncom, placed in a circular orbit at a distance of 22,300 miles above the earth with a period of precisely one day. Launched toward the east (in the direction of the earth's rotation) the satellite will hover over one point on the earth.

satellite, Telestar, *n.* One of the A.T.&T. Company's active communication satellites. (1) Telestar I was placed into a non-synchronous, 3000-mile high orbit by NASA 10 July 1962. It has been used for voice and television transmission between the United States and Europe. (2) Telestar II, orbited 7 May 1963, is also non-synchronous, but in a 6702-mile high orbit.

satellite acquisition, *n.* The process beginning with location of the satellite by the search antenna, and ending when the equipment is aligned so that the antenna tracks the satellite.

satellite availability, *n.* The probability that a satellite will be available for relaying signals on a certain date.

satellite backoff. See "backoff, multiple access satellite."

satellite beacon, *n.* A radio signal from a communication satellite, tone-modulated at 120 kHz, which aids in its acquisition by the earth terminal.

satellite conjunction, *n.* The apparent passing of a satellite in front of the sun or moon, as viewed from the earth. When the satellite is in conjunction, the high gain earth antenna will pick up sufficient noise from the sun or moon to severely degrade the communication channel.

satellite downlink, *n.* The radio link from satellite to earth, including the satellite transmitter and antenna, the satellite-earth propagation path, and the earth antenna and receiver.

satellite earth station subsystem, *n.* The earth portion of a satellite communication system, consisting of an "earth terminal" and an "interconnect facility," which see.

satellite earth terminal, *n.* The assemblage consisting of directional antenna, transmitter and receiver, multiplex, modulator-demodulator, and telemetry equipment which takes the intelligence signal from the interconnect facility, modulates it, and transmits it to the satellite, and vice versa. The terminal also receives telemetry data from the satellite, acquires and tracks the satellite, and generates timing and control pulses.

satellite eclipse, *n.* The shadowing of an orbiting satellite by another. When the earth is between a communication satellite and the sun, the satellite is eclipsed and its solar battery is ineffective.

satellite ephemeris. See "ephemeris, satellite."

satellite handover, *n.* (1) The transfer of earth communication links from one satellite to another. (2) The transfer of a satellite from one pair of earth stations to another pair.

satellite interconnect facility, *n.* The terminating equipment: amplifiers, attenuators, equalizers, matching networks, etc. which take the signals from a satellite earth station and transmit them over an interconnecting link to the commercial telephone network.

satellite launch. See "launch, satellite - - -."

satellite multiple access, *n.* The capability of a communication satellite to function as a relay point between more than one pair of ground stations simultaneously.

satellite mutual visibility, zone of, *n.* The elliptical region within which a communication satellite is simultaneously visible from two or more earth stations, and is therefore available to relay communications.

satellite office, *n.* A dial central office which has trunks to only one other central office. Offices using switching-selector-repeaters are often satellite offices.

satellite orbit. See "orbit, - - -."

satellite orbit, equatorial, *n.* An orbit in which a satellite remains within the plane of the earth's equator.

satellites, Nimbus, *n. pl.* One of the two series of weather satellites.

Satellite System, Interim Defense Communications (IDCSS), *n.* A DCS system made up of a number of communication satellites at quasi-synchronous altitudes, each satellite relaying 5-12 channels.

satellites, Echo, *n. pl.* The American aluminum-coated plastic balloon satellites used to reflect radio waves for long-distance communication.

Name	Diameter	Launched	Status
Echo I	100 ft.	12 Aug. 1960	Dead
Echo II	135 ft.	25 Jan. 1964	In polar orbit

satellites, IDCSP, *n.* Seventeen (in 1968) equatorially-positioned near-synchronous satellites operated by the Defense Communication System

to provide limited wideband digital communications.

satellites, weather, *n. pl.* Any of the United States artificial satellites in the Tiros or Nimbus series, equipped with cameras and TV transmitters and used to study cloud cover and storms. The first, Tiros I, was launched 1 April 1960.

satellite space subsystem, *n.* The satellite portion of the complete satellite communication system. Consists of the satellite (the "bird") with its stabilizing system, the transmitter and receiver, the telemetry and beacon transmitters, the antennas, and solar power cells.

satellite subsystem, *n.* The satellite portion of a satellite communication system.

satellite tracking. See "tracking, - - -."

satellite uplink, *n.* The radio link from earth to satellite, including the earth transmitter and antenna, the earth-satellite propagation path, and the satellite antenna and receiver.

satellite visibility. See "zone of mutual visibility."

saturable inductor. See "inductor, saturable."

saturable reactor. See "reactor, saturable."

saturation, *n.* (1) In color TV, one of the three characteristics of color. Defines the degree to which a hue is mixed with white. Thus red may vary from high saturation crimson to low saturation pink. See also "luminance" and "hue." (2) The saturation of a magnetic core with flux. (3) A condition in which further increase in one variable produces no increase in a dependent variable. (4) The condition in an electron tube when all of the electrons the cathode can produce are going to the plate, and further increase in the plate voltage has no effect.

saw, cableman's, *n.* A short (12-inch), stiff, double-edged hand saw having fine teeth on one edge and medium teeth on the other edge. Used for cutting lead sleeves or sleeving.

saw, tree, *n.* A sabre-toothed hand saw used for cutting large tree limbs.

sawtooth wave, *n.* A recurring wave having a slow linear rise and a rapid fall, so that the waveform looks like the teeth of a saw. Useful to produce the linear scan on a television tube.

SCA channel. See "channel, SCA."

scale, gray, *n.* An optical pattern having discrete steps between light and dark.

scan, *v.* (1) To sweep an area in the sky with an antenna, as when acquiring a communication satellite. (2) To sweep an electron beam in a regular to and fro pattern, as in a television tube. (3) To periodically sample the voltages that exist at like points in a number of similar circuits.

scanner, traffic, *n.* A device which will repetitively sample each of a group of telephone circuits to determine if they are busy, and total the busy counts in a register. If the group is scanned once each 100 seconds, the register will indicate CCS (hundred call-seconds).

scanning, *n.* In television, facsimile or picture transmission, the process of analyzing or synthesizing successively the light values or equivalent characteristics of elements constituting a picture area.

scanpoint, *n.* A current detecting element, consisting of a magnetically soft but saturable ferrite, threaded by interrogate and sense wires, which can be scanned for a line off-hook indication. Substitutes for a line relay in some types of electronic switching systems.

scatter, forward, *n.* Propagation of electromagnetic waves at frequencies above the maximum usable high frequency (MUF) through use of the scattering of a small portion of the transmitted energy when the signal passes from an un-ionized medium into a layer of the ionosphere.

scatter, ionospheric, *n.* A type of scatter propagation of radio waves which depends upon scatter in the lower E layer of the ionosphere. It uses frequenoies of 35-55 MHz, and is useful for covering distances of 600-1200 miles.

scatter, tropospheric, *n.* A type of scatter propagation of radio waves which depends upon scatter in the troposphere below 30,000 feet altitude. It uses frequencies of 350-8000 MHz, and is useful for covering distances of 40-400 miles.

scattering, *n.* The diffusion of radio waves when they encounter air masses in the troposphere, producing new waves having random direction and polarization.

scattering, acoustic, *n.* The irregular diffuse dispersion of sound in many directions, caused by reflection, refraction, or diffraction.

scattering region, *n.* (1) Ionospheric. The elliptical patch in the E layer of the ionosphere which is illuminated by the radio beam from an ionospheric scatter transmitting antenna, and is also within the beam of the distant scatter receiving antenna. The E layer has a virtual height of 100 kilometers (328,000 ft.) in daytime, but at night disappears and is replaced by the F2 layer at about 200 kilometers. (2) Tropospheric. The elliptical patch in the troposphere (below 42,000 ft. altitude) which is illuminated by the radio beam from a tropospheric scatter transmitting antenna, and which is also within the beam of the distant tropo-scatter receiving antenna. There is no ionized layer in the troposphere from which radio waves are reflected; rather there is a "scatter volume" within which air turbulence causes wide changes in air density, and therefore wide changes in radio wave refraction.

scatter propagation, *n.* The transmission of UHF and VHF radio signals far beyond the radio horizon by the use of high power and a large directional antenna to beam a strong signal up to the reflecting layers in the troposphere or ionosphere where it is "scattered" and re-radiated down to a high-gain antenna at the receiving station. Typical transmitters put 10-100 kilowatts of power into 60-foot parabolic antennas, and use quadruple diversity.

scatter transmission, ionospheric, *n.* A technique of transmitting VHF radio signals long distances by the use of high power and large antennas. The 30-60 MHz signals, scattered in the ionosphere, may be received at distances of 600 to 1200 miles; about 800 miles being optimum.

scatter transmission, tropospheric, *n.* A technique of transmitting UHF radio signals for long distances by the use of high power and large antennas. The 350-5000 MHz signals are scattered in the troposphere and may be picked up at distances of 300-600 miles.

schedule, *n.* (1) A time-table for doing work. (2) A timed plan for a project. (3) For leased telephone circuits, a tariff description of the transmission-frequency capability of a certain class of circuit. See also "conditioning."

schedule, circuit, *n.* A tariff statement of the transmission, noise, and distortion requirements which will make a circuit suitable for a particular application. For examples, see "conditioning, - - -."

schematic. See "drawing, circuit schematic."

schematic, circuit. See "diagram, schematic."

schematic drawing. See "drawing, circuit schematic."

scintillation, *n.* The random fluctuation of a received radio signal around its mean value, analogous to the twinkling of stars.

scissors, electrician's, *n. pl.* A pair of heavy scissors having 1⅞-inch cutting edges (5¼ inches overall), used by cable splicers to cut wires and strip wire insulation when making cable splices.

scope, *n.* Cathode ray oscilloscope.

Scotchcast, *n.* Trade name of one brand of quick-jelling polyurethane resin for pouring into cable or wire splices to make them waterproof.

scrambler, speech, *n.* A device to provide privacy to voice communications via wire or radio. The simplest is an inverter, a modulator which changes low frequencies to high and vice-versa. For greater privacy, another privacy divides the 300-3300 Hz voice band into five equal components by the use of band-pass filters, then periodically (once each 3 minutes) interchanges the frequency position of these components.

scratch-pad memory, *n.* Temporary memory.

screen, *n.* (1) A metal partition or shield which isolates a device from external magnetic or electric fields. (2) The screen-grid electrode of an electron tube. (3) The chemically coated inside surface of the large end of a cathode-ray tube which becomes luminous when scanned by an electron beam.

screen grid, *n.* In an electron tube, a grid between the control grid and the plate. It shields the control grid from influence by the plate.

screening, tandem, *n.* The action of the completing marker in a crossbar tandem office to check whether the called office code is one within the rate area of the calling customer. If it is not, the call is denied completion.

screening, tandem code, *n.* The denying of access to specific outgoing routes by certain groups of incoming trunks while permitting access by other incoming trunk groups.

screw, cable suspension, *n.* A 9/16″ x 4-inch lag screw having a ½″ x

1½-inch stud extending outward from its head. Used to suspend light cable from poles. The washer-head lag screw is screwed entirely into the pole, and a light cable suspension clamp is placed over the protruding stud.

screw, drive, *n.* A hardened cylindrical fastener with sharp multiple spiral flutes on its shank. The tip of the shank is the same diameter as the flute root, and serves as a pilot when driven into a drilled hole.

screw, lag, *n.* A bolt having a square head and wood-screw threads. Available in sizes from ¼ ″ x 2 inches to ½ ″ x 4½ inches.

screw, Phillips, *n.* A screw which is driven by means of an indented cross in its head.

screw, residual. See "residual screw."

screw, self-tapping, *n.* An externally threaded headed hardened fastener whose thread cuts or forms its own mating thread as it is driven into a hole in the mating material.

screw-driver, cabinet, *n.* A narrow blade screw-driver whose blade and shank are the same diameter.

screw-driver, offset, *n.* A screw-driver whose shank is bent at right angles to the blade, thus enabling its use in restricted places.

screwdriver, plug, *n.* A jeweler's screw-driver having a retractile pin concentric with the screwdriver blade. Used for holding and driving the small binding screws in telephone switchboard plugs.

screw-driver, ratchet, *n.* A screw-driver whose handle contains a ratchet, thus converting oscillating rotary motion into right hand or left hand rotary motion, to drive or withdraw screws without removing the screw-driver blade from the screw head.

screw-driver, screw-holding, *n.* (1) A screw-driver whose blade is spit and exerts spring pressure outward on the slot of a screw. (2) A screw-driver having a spring clip which holds a screw in place on the blade.

Both are used to insert screws into places which are too restricted to allow entry of a hand to place or hold the screw.

screw eye, insulated, *n.* An open screw eye with the eye lined with a porcelain insulator having a slot to admit wires. Used for drop wire runs where insulation is required.

sealing, duct, *n.* The closing, with a plastic putty, of an underground duct where it enters a manhole or cable vault to prevent the entrance of gas or water.

search, idle. See "idle search."

search, polite. See "polite search."

search, preempt. See "preempt search."

search pattern, *n.* In the automatic alternate routing of toll calls, a tabular listing of the practical available alternate routes arranged in their order of preference. See also "idle search" and "preempt search."

seat, pole, *n.* An angle steel framework having a seat, which can be installed under a cable terminal where installers and repairmen must work for long periods of time when testing or installing jumpers.

secondary, *n.* (1) A secondary winding: That winding of a transformer in which the current flow is due to electromagnetic induction from current in a "primary" winding. (2) The lower-voltage conductors of a power distribution system, so called because they are fed from the secondary windings of power transformers. Often 115/230 volts, but sometimes 2400 volts.

secondary cell, *n.* A storage cell.

secondary electron, *n.* An electron driven from a material by bombardment with electrons, photons, or other high-velocity particles. Emission of secondary electrons has an important effect on the operation of electron tubes.

secondary emission. See "emission, secondary."

secondary service area. See "area, secondary service."

secondary trunk, *n.* An intra-office trunk leading to a secondary switch, such as the trunk from primary to secondary lineswitch or the trunk from selector bank terminals to a secondary out-trunk switch.

secondary voltage, *n.* (1) The voltage of power distribution circuits, commonly 115/230 volts. (2) The voltage across the secondary winding of a transformer.

secondary winding, *n.* The transformer winding that receives its energy by electromagnetic induction from the primary winding.

secretarial answering unit, *n.* A desk-top key cabinet which enables a secretary to answer and hold calls on telephone lines terminating in her office. A three-position key (OFF-ANSWER-HOLD) and a neon ringing indicator are associated with each line. A common audible signaling unit can also be provided. Available in 6, 10, and 20-line sizes.

Secretary, Electronic, *n.* One brand of telephone answering set, which see.

section, *n.* (1) A manhole section: the duct length between two adjacent manholes. (2) A loading section: the cable length between two adjacent load points. (3) A switchboard section.

section, building-out, *n.* A potted assemblage of small capacitors which may be interconnected to give a range of capacitances which may be useful in "building-out" the capacitance of a cable end section to a standard value. See also "building-out."

section, cable regulator, *n.* Two or three repeater sections of long toll cable in which the variation of transmission loss is compensated for by connection to a pilot-wire regulator.

section, cable terminal, *n.* Part of a sectional cable terminal for use in buildings, made up of several intermediate sections (back and cover) plus two end sections. Used to fabricate a terminal box to house terminal blocks as required.

section, loading, *n.* The length of cable between two load points.

section, regulator, *n.* The section of cable controlled by a single pilot-wire regulator.

section, repeater, *n.* The section of line or cable between two adjacent repeater points.

section, switchboard, *n.* One unit of a switchboard, made in one piece and normally indivisible. It may contain one, two, or three switchboard positions.

section, transposition. See "transposition section."

Sectional Center, *n.* The next to the highest rank (Class 2) toll switching center which homes on several Regional Centers (Class 1 offices).

secure voice, *n.* Digitalized and encrypted voice signals, rendered unintelligible to the extent that they may be used to convey classified (secret) intelligence.

security, communication, *n.* The art and science of processing signals so that their information content can be extracted only by those authorized and equipped to do so.

seize, *v.i.* To stick together by cohesion.—*v.t.* To access or connect to a circuit, at the same time making it busy to prevent intrusion.

selectance, *n.* A measure of the falling off in response of a resonant device with departure from resonance, expressed as the ratio of the amplitude of response at the resonant frequency to the response at some frequency differing from it by a specified amount.

selective calling, *n.* A method of calling one particular station on a mobile radio system, in which a unique multi-frequency code is sent which actuates a unique set of tuned reed relays at the called station.

selective fading, *n.* Fading of a radio signal which does not affect all frequencies equally, and is caused by multipath transmission. See also "multipath fading."

selective ringing, *n.* A party line ringing system whereby only the bell of the desired party is rung.

selective signaling, *n.* The alerting of one subscriber on a multiparty line by ringing only his bell. Superimposed ringing systems can discriminate between four parties per line, and frequency timed ringing between eight parties per line.

selectivity, *n.* The ability to select one particular signal from other signals at nearby frequencies.

selector, *n.* An electromechanical switching device which can be electrically directed or driven to connect a single input circuit to any one of many (usually 100) output circuits.

selector, absence-of-ground searching, *n.* A step-by-step selector whose wipers hunt across a dialed level until they reach an ungrounded control bank contact.

selector, battery-searching, *n.* A step-by-step selector which continues to hunt across a dialed level until the wipers reach an idle trunk having battery or resistance-battery on the control bank contact.

selector, digit-absorbing, *n.* A type of step-by-step selector having a vertical bank by which each level can be separately marked to absorb a dialed digit by stepping to the dialed level and then dropping to start over on the following digit. Several markings are possible Viz:
A—Absorb once, then unlock the bank
AR—Absorb repeatedly
None—Cut into the bank

selector, Gill, *n.* A type of stepping switch used to select a particular party on a railway "message line." At each waystation, a Gill selector is bridged across the line and controlled by coded polar pulses (at 3½ pulses per second) from keys at the operator's position. All selec-

tors step simultaneously as three successive digits are sent. Certain switches restore at the completion of each digit, and at the end only the called station is selected and signaled.

selector, group, *n.* In an electronic central office, a switching unit controlled by a marker which provides access from "line groups" and "trunk groups" to switching levels.

selector, MDA, *n.* A step-by-step selector having multiple-digit absorbing capabilities. For any particular digit dialed, it can either (CI) cut into the bank, (A) absorb once and unlock the bank for following digits, (AR) absorb repeatedly, unless preceded by an "A" or "CA" marked digit, (CA) cut in if the first digit, or act as an "A" digit if it is the second or later digit, or (CR) cut in if the first digit, or act as an "AR" digit if it is the 2nd or 3rd digit.

selector, special third, *n.* One of a group of selectors used in step-by-step offices to give access to special service codes:
    113—Information
    114—Repair Service
    116—Emergency
    117—Fire, etc.

selector, step-by-step, *n.* An automatic switching mechanism actuated by DC pulses to select one of ten groups of trunks, after which it hunts and connects to an idle trunk in the group.

selector, Strowger, *n.* An automatic selector which is stepped vertically to one of ten levels, after which its wipers hunt horizontally into a semi-circular bank of contacts and select (stop on and connect to) the first idle set of trunk contacts.

selector, telegraph. See "selector, Gill."

selector, toll transmission, *n.* The final selector in a toll switch train which connects to a "combined toll and local connector" and which gives the operator control of the ringing.

selector, transfer. See "transfer selector."

selector, 2-5. See "selector, MDA."

selector, waystation. See "selector, Gill."

selector, X-Y, *n.* An automatic step-by-step selector in which the bank contacts and the wipers are all in the same plane. The step-by-step pulses carry the wipers across the front of the set of bank contacts, then the wipers advance into the bank to hunt a set of idle trunk contacts.

selector-connector, *n.* A two-motion step-by-step switch which can be wired to operate as a selector on certain levels and as a connector on the other levels. As a selector, a single digit selects a particular level after which the switch automatically hunts for an idle trunk on that level. As a connector, two digits select first a level and then a particular terminal on that level.

selenium, *n.* A gray, crystalline, semi-metallic appearing element of the sulfur group. Its electrical conductivity increases with the brightness of light by which it is illuminated.

selenium rectifier, *n.* Rectifier consisting of multiple iron discs coated with a thin layer of metallic selenium, then with a soft metal which forms the other electrode. Current will flow from the iron to the selenium, but not in the reverse direction. Rectifiers made thus have an efficiency of about 75%, and a voltage regulation of about 15%, with a very long life.

self-bias, *n.* A manner of operating an electron tube in which the proper grid bias is provided by the voltage drop across a resistor in the cathode circuit.

self-excited, *adj.* Said of a generator which provides the current for its own field coils.

self-impedance, *n.* At any pair of terminals of a network, the ratio of the applied voltage to the resultant current, all other network terminals being open.

self-inductance, *n.* The property of an electrical circuit which determines, for a given rate of change of current in the circuit, the electromotive force which is induced in the same circuit.

self-induction, *n.* Generation of a counter-electromotive force in a circuit by a change of current in the same circuit.

self-interrupted, *adj.* Said of a step-by-step switch which provides its own energizing pulses. Each time the rotary magnet operates it opens its own circuit, and in falling back steps the wipers using spring energy. Rotary action continues until the wipers find a potential which operates a relay to open the rotary magnet circuit.

selsyn, *n.* A single-phase self-synchronous rotary machine which converts mechanical position into electrical signals, or vice versa.

semiconductor, *n.* A material whose resistivity is between that of conductors and insulators, and whose resistivity can sometimes be changed by light, an electric field, or a magnetic field. Current flow is sometimes by movement of negative electrons, and sometimes by transfer of positive holes. Used in transistors, diodes, photodiodes, photocells, and thermistors. Some examples are: silicon, germanium, selenium, and lead sulfide.

semiconductor, acceptor-type. See "semiconductor, p-type."

semiconductor, donor-type. See "semiconductor, n-type."

semiconductor, extrinsic, *n.* A semiconductor whose electrical properties are dependent upon impurities.

semiconductor, intrinsic, *n.* A semiconductor which is a pure crystal without donor impurities.

semiconductor, n-type, *n.* A semiconductor material, such as germanium or silicon, which has a small amount of impurity, such as antimony, arsenic, or phosphorous, added to increase the supply of free electrons. Such a material conducts electricity through movement of electrons.

semiconductor, p-type, *n.* A semiconductor material which has been doped so that it has a net deficiency of free electrons. It therefore conducts electricity through movement of "holes," which see.

semiconductor device, *n.* A device making use of electronic conduction which takes place within a semiconductor.

semiconductor diode. See "diode."

semiconductor integral circuit, *n.* A combination of interconnected circuit elements inseparably associated on or within a continuous semiconductor substrate.

semiconductor switch. See "silicon controlled switch."

semi-duplex, *n.* A method of operation of a communication circuit where one end is duplex and one end is simplex. Sometimes used in mobile systems with the base station duplex and the mobile station simplex.

semi-postpay coin telephone service, *n.* Service on coin telephones which enables a customer to dial a number without depositing a coin, but requires the coin before the talking circuit is cut through to the called party.

semiselective ringing. See "ringing, semiselective."

sender, *n.* A device in a common-control switching system which receives address information from a register or routing information from a translator, and outpulses the correct routing digits to a trunk or to the local equipment. Frequently combines the functions of register and sender in a single device.

sender, alarm. See "alarm sender."

sender, crossbar, *n.* A switch which combines both register and sender functions. (#4A TSS).

sender, incoming, *n.* The switch in a #4A toll office which receives either dial pulses (DP) or multifrequency pulses (MF) over incoming trunks, obtains code conversion (translation) as required, then outpulses the proper routing digits DP or MF directly to the outgoing trunks, or DC key-pulses directly to outgoing senders. These senders usually have 11-digit capacity, and code conversion capability.

sender, intermarker group, *n.* The switch in a #5 crossbar office which is used for traffic between two different marker groups located in the same building. It serves as an outgoing sender for the calling marker and as an incoming register for the called marker. These intermarker group senders transfer information from one marker group to the other by simultaneous pulses on large groups of leads called connectors.

sender, outgoing, *n.* The switch in a #5 crossbar office which furnishes pulses over an outgoing trunk to control operation of the switching equipment in a distant office. The pulses may be:

DC dial pulses (DP)
Multifrequency (MF)
Revertive pulses (RP)
Panel call indicator (PCI)

sender signal, *n.* A lamp signal which lights when the equipment has selected and connected a sender, indicating that the equipment is ready for dialing or key pulsing.

senior multiple, *n.* Type of cabinet used for multiple switchboards in which the multiple repeats on every fifth panel (4-panel multiple). Consists of 1-position, 2-panel sections.

sensation, auditory, *n.* The perception of sounds by the ear. It is limited on the low-level end by the "threshold of audibility," and on the high-level end by the "threshold of feeling."

sense, *n.* Direction or polarity.—*v.* To detect the presence of holes in data cards or punched tape.

sense wire, *n.* A wire threaded through a magnetic memory core which detects whether a "one" or "zero" is stored in the core when the core is interrogated by a "read" pulse.

sensitivity, *n.* (1) Of a radio receiver, the minimum input required to produce a specified output having a specified signal-to-noise ratio. (2) Of a voltmeter or other meter, the current required to produce a full-scale deflection.

sensitivity, klystron deflection, *n.* A measure of the linearity of a klystron. The variation with frequency of the ratio of frequency deviation to repeller voltage.

sensitivity, radio receiver, *n.* The minimum input signal (stated in microvolts) at which the receiver will produce a specified adequate output signal having a specified adequate signal-to-noise ratio.

sensor, *n.* Any device that can detect the presence, or a change in the state of, a light, radio, or sound wave.

sent-paid call, *n.* A telephone call for which the originator will pay all charges.

separate channel signaling, *n.* Signaling arrangement on a carrier system where the signaling leads for all channels are combined and multiplexed on one of the voice channels. Used with the TASI system.

separately excited, *adj.* (1) Describing a generator which obtains its field current from another generator. (2) Using a separate oscillator to generate the carrier frequency for a radio transmitter.

separation filter, *n.* A filter composed of bridged low-pass and high-pass sections, used to separate one frequency band from another, as voice frequencies from carrier frequencies.

separator, battery, *n.* The microporous sheet insulator which separates the positive and negative plates in a storage battery.

sequence switch, *n.* A power driven relay using a number of cam disks to close sets of contact springs. Permits a large number of permutations.

sequential answering, *n.* Answering of incoming calls at a switchboard in the same sequence or order in which they arrived. A feature of "automatic call distribution" systems.

sequential pulsing, *n.* A method of sending numerical information over a circuit by interrupting the direct current flow, or interrupting a single AC tone. The value of each digit is indicated by the number of interruptions. Dial pulsing is sequential pulsing.

sequential transmission. See "transmission, serial."

serial, *adj.* Said of pulses which are sent separately, one after the other. The opposite of "parallel."

serial-to-parallel converter, *n.* Device which converts a single serial signal into several simultaneous parallel signals. For instance, changing a 2400 bits per second serial signal into sixteen 150 bits per second parallel signals.

serial transmission, *n.* Transmission of signals one after the other over a single transmission channel.

series, number, *n.* Ten thousand or less nonconflicting telephone line numbers between 0000 and 9999. They may be associated with one, two, or three office code groups.

series circuit, *n.* A circuit having all its components connected end-to-end so that the total current flows through all of them in sequence.

series connection, *n.* Elements in an electrical circuit are said to be connected in series when the same current flows through all of them in sequence.

series excitation, *n.* Obtaining the field current for a generator or motor by connecting the armature in series with the field.

series feed, *n.* (1) An arrangement of

power supply to multiple units of equipment such that the current that flows through one unit will flow through the other units in their turn. (2) Application of the plate supply voltage to a vacuum tube through the load that carries the output signal, rather than through a plate supply choke. (3) Feeding the radio frequency energy to one end of an antenna.

series multiple, *n,* A wiring arrangement on the older small multiple switchboards where each jack has a pair of lamp cutoff springs. See also "bridged multiple."

series-parallel connection, *n.* A connection, of cells in a battery or other elements, where several identical series-connected groups are all connected in parallel.

series resonance. See "resonance, series."

series-wound, *adj.* Describing a generator or motor whose armature and field windings are connected in series.

service, *n.* (1) The aggregate of all the acts performed by a telephone company in providing communications to its customer. (2) the quality of that which is provided. (3) A measure of the traffic adequacy. See also "service, grade of."

service, answering. See "answering service, telephone."

service, checking. See "checking service."

service, dictation. See "dictation service."

service, direct line. See "direct line service."

service, extended area, *n.* Telephone service in an area outside of the normal base rate area within which toll-free calling is permitted in return for payment of higher metropolitan area rates.

service, fixed, *n.* A radio communication service between specified fixed points.

service, flat-rate, *n.* Local telephone service for which a stipulated monthly charge covers all message use to stations within the specified local service area.

service, foreign exchange, *n.* Local telephone service furnished from a central office which is outside of the exchange area in which the customer is located.

service, full period, *n.* A communication channel furnished for a subscriber's exclusive use twenty-four hours of every day.

service, grade of, *n.* The ability of a telephone system to connect one subscriber with another (a) without having the call blocked by busy trunks or (b) without causing the call to wait longer than an acceptable time, both expressed as the probability that the blocking or unacceptable delay will occur.

service, house, *n.* The work required to keep a building clean and repaired.

service, measured rate, *n.* Telephone service in which a subscriber's calls are counted automatically and a charge made based on their number.

service, message waiting. See "message waiting service."

service, mobile, *n.* A radio communication service between land base stations and mobile stations, or between mobile stations.

service, night answering. See "night answering service."

service, off-hook. See "off-hook service."

service, private line. *n.* (1) A point-to-point communication service furnished to a subscriber for his exclusive use. (2) Incorrectly used to designate an "individual line," a line to the public telephone system used exclusively by one subscriber.

service, private line teletypewriter. See "private line teletypewriter service."

service, secretarial, *n.* A telephone service similar to an off-premises extension, but with the extension line terminated on a switchboard of an organization providing contract secretarial service.

service, short period, *n.* A communication service between specific locations and set up over normal telephone, data, or teletypewriter message facilities for short periods of time, usually in multiples of 15 minutes and recurrent at the same time on specified days.

service, standard frequency, *n.* A service of the National Bureau of Standards which broadcasts from radio stations WWV, WWVB, WWVL (Ft. Collins, Colorado) and WWVH (Puunene, Maui) the following accurate radio frequencies: 20, 60 kHz, 2.5, 5, 10, 15, 20, and 25 MHz, and the following accurate audio frequencies: 440, 600, and 1000 Hz, plus accurate time signals. Broadcasts are every hour. For more information write the National Bureau of Standards, Boulder, Colorado 80302.

service, telephone, *n.* The act of providing the public with the use of telephones which meet all reasonable communication needs, current with the state of the art as economics permit, and at a reasonable cost—all done in a manner which creates customer satisfaction.

service, telephone answering. See "Telephone Answering Service."

service, teletypewriter exchange (TWX), *n.* Service given by a telephone company which provides a subscriber with a teletypewriter connected to a teletypewriter switchboard or switching center, and thus enables him to call and exchange messages with other distant subscribers to the same service.

service, time. See "time-of-day."

service, wide area data. See "Wide Area Data Service."

service, wide area telephone. See "Wide Area Telephone Service (WATS)."

service area. See "area, service" and "coverage."

service area, primary. See "area, primary service."

service channel, *n.* A band of frequencies, usually including a voice channel, utilized for maintenance and fault indication on a communication system.

service life. See "life, service."

service observation, *n.* Measurement of the quality of telephone service by observing a representative sample of calls. Accomplished by a trained service observing operator working at a special monitoring turret. See also "board, service observing."

servicing, *n. v.t.* To make fit for continued service, by inspecting, adjusting, repairing, or refueling.

serving, *n.* (1) A wrapping of wire on the end of a steel strand to keep the strands from unraveling. (2) A wrapping of thread or yarn over a relay coil to protect it from damage.

servisleeve, *n.* A small metal clip which substitutes for the wire serving required when a guy strand loops through an eyebolt or strain insulator.

servo system, *n.* An electromechanical system including a feedback loop which can accurately transmit mechanical position information over an electrical circuit.

set, *n.* An assembly of electrical components or sub-assemblies which are interconnected to perform a specific function.—*v.* To place a binary digit in a memory cell.

set, antisidetone, *n.* A telephone set having a balancing network connected so that only a small portion of the transmitter power reaches the receiver.

set, card dialer telephone. See "card dialer telephone set."

set, combined telephone, *n.* A desk telephone set which includes in a single housing all of the components required for a complete telephone set except for the handset which it supports.

set, common battery, *n.* A subscriber's telephone set designed to be powered from the battery in the central office.

set, composite, *n.* An assembly of coils and capacitors used to derive two grounded direct current telegraph circuits from one two-wire telephone circuit, without mutual interference. See also "composite, set, - - -" and "composite signaling equipment."

set, cradle, *n.* Outmoded term for a hand telephone set, on which the handset is held (cradled) on the mounting when not in use.

set, current-flow test, *n.* A portable DC milliammeter and lever switch assembly designed to measure and control the "operate" and "non-operate" current fed to a telephone relay under test. Facilitates the adjustment of relays.

set, cut closed test, *n.* A small test set enabling cable splicers to make pair transfers of working lines without interrupting service. Contains battery operated 500 Hz and 50 Hz tones which alert the splicer if the connections are not properly made.

set, data, *n.* Device which accepts serialized DC data signals from a business machine and converts them to frequency or phase modulated tones for transmission to the line facilities, and vice versa. Sometimes provides other features, such as: alternate voice communications, a clock for timing signals, regeneration, a separate voice communication channel, recovery of timing signal, alarm sending, or automatic answer.

set, explosion-proof telephone, *n.* A telephone set designed for security against ignition of an ambient explosive atmosphere. All elements of apparatus which might produce a spark or an arc are completely enclosed.

set, fire-reporting telephone, *n.* A manual telephone without ringer, in a red cast metal case for wall or pole mounting. Used by the public for reporting fires directly to a central "fire-reporting switchboard."

set, four-wire terminating, *n.* A unit of equipment used to connect four-wire lines to two-wire central office equipment. It commonly includes a hybrid coil and a balancing network.

set, hand, *n.* Properly one word. See "handset."

set, hand telephone, *n.* A telephone designed for hand-held use and complete except for ringer and switch hook functions. Sometimes one-piece, sometimes two-piece consisting of a handset and separate dial and switchhook housing.

set, head telephone, *n.* Telephone set designed to be worn by a telephone operator. Consists of a receiver with headband, a transmitter on an arm, and a cord with a 4-conductor plug.

set, key telephone, *n.* A desk telephone set having six illuminated push-button keys across the set below the dial. The keys may be connected for different functions: (1) hold, (2) pick up a central office line, or (3) pick up an intercom line. Requires separate relay equipment composed of "key telephone units."

set, lineman's test, *n.* A portable set in a case with shoulder strap which a lineman can carry to a pole top and use for talking, ringing, and testing. Contains a telephone handset, magneto-generator, test lamp, test-leads with clips, a battery for talking, and sometimes an exploring coil.

set, local battery talking common-battery signaling telephone, *n.* A telephone set which uses dry cells to supply the transmitter current but uses loop signaling into a common-battery central office.

set, loudspeaker, *n.* Housing for desk mounting containing a loudspeaker, amplifier, and loudness control. Used for projecting both sides of telephone conversations to a small group of people.

set, magneto telephone, n. A local-battery telephone set which uses dry cells to supply the transmitter current, and signals the central office with ringing current from a magneto hand generator.

set, motor-generator, n. An electrical machine consisting of one or more motors coupled mechanically to one or more generators.

set, multiple key telephone, n. A complete key telephone set in a plastic housing with a sloping front panel on which is mounted a dial and either three key units (18 buttons) or five key units (30 buttons). Requires separate relay units. See also "key telephone set."

set, noise measuring, n. An instrument used to measure the noise level on a communication circuit, in terms of decibels above a reference noise. Contains several "weighting networks," which see.

set, operator's telephone, n. A lightweight transmitter and receiver assembly used by telephone operators and testboardmen. It connects by a cord and plug to the operator's telephone circuit in the switchboard or testboard. Consists of two types: (a) A type (52) designed to be worn on the head continuously and supported by a headband, and (b) a type (53) designed to be hand held.

set, sidetone telephone, n. A telephone set which does not have a balancing network which reduces sidetone.

set, sound-powered telephone, n. A telephone set in which the transmitter is a dynamic microphone requiring no power other than that of the voice.

set, subscriber, n. (1) A metal box for wall mounting which contains a ringer, capacitor(s), and an induction coil or network. Used with a "hand telephone set" to form a complete unit of telephone station equipment. (2) Any box used with a telephone or data set to contain auxiliary equipment.

set, telephone, n. A complete telephone in one unit, including: a handset with transmitter and receiver, connected by a cord to a base which contains a hookswitch, dial, induction coil or network, ringer, and capacitors.

set, telephone answering, n. An electromechanical device which answers a telephone in the subscribers absence, plays a recorded message, and then records a 30-second message from the caller before disconnecting. When the subscriber returns he can rewind and play back all messages recorded in his absence.

set, terminating test, n. A network of resistors and adjustable capacitors, sometimes with a hybrid coil, used to provide a compromise termination to 600-ohm or 900-ohm two-wire or four-wire trunks.

set, test. See "test set."

set, Touch-Tone telephone, n. The Bell System's designation for a telephone set using a push-button multifrequency dial.

set, wall telephone, n. A complete telephone set designed to be mounted on the wall. The dial and switchhook project through the cover. The associated handset is connected by a retractile cord.

set, weather-proof telephone, n. A telephone set in a cast-metal case with inner and outer doors. All components except the dial and handset are in an inner sealed compartment. When not in use, the self-closing gasketed outer door protects the dial and handset from the weather.

set, 3B noise measuring, n. A compact, transistorized meter to measure noise in dbrn on message and program circuits. Has a choice of C-message and 3 KC flat or Program and 15 KC flat weighting networks. Powered from the 48 volt central office battery.

set, 13A transmission measuring, *n.* A small, portable, 60 Hz AC powered, 600-ohm transmission receiving set. Consists of a 3-stage, negative-feedback amplifier and a rectifier-type meter. Measures 30-15000 Hz over a range of —45 dbm to +10 dbm. Used with a #19C Oscillator.

set, 20C test, *n.* A portable test tone generator consisting of a vibrator-type tone source, a motor-driven interrupter, an induction coil and four #6 dry cells, all in a wooden carrying case. Provides a high-current audio tone for use in tracing buried cable or in locating cable faults.

set, 21A transmission measuring, *n.* A portable, 60 Hz AC powered, test set combining oscillator and detector functions. The oscillator will supply 20-20,000 Hz at levels from —50 dbm to +20 dbm. The detector has a sensitivity of —70 dbm to +30 dbm.

set, 23A transmission measuring, *n.* A simple, passive, portable meter which can be used to measure levels of —25 dbm to +10 dbm over a range of 300-5000 Hz on both 600-ohm and 900-ohm circuits.

sferics, *n.* Interference to a radio receiver from atmospherics, or static.

shaft, *n.* A cylindrical rod which supports a rotating member, and is supported by bearings in which it rotates.

shape, *v.* To alter the waveform of an electric wave by filtering or limiting.

shaping, pulse, *n.* Taking a pulse through a low-pass filter to remove some of the high frequency components, thus making it easier to send over a transmission facility.

shaping network, *n.* A network which provides complementary compensation or equalization for the loss-frequency characteristic of a line or its equipment.

shears, cable, *n. pl.* (1) A pair of lopping shears, used to cut up waste cable for salvage. (2) A pair of electrician's scissors.

shears, lopping, *n. pl.* A pair of heavy pruning shears with short curved blades and 30-inch handles, used for cutting heavy brush or lead-covered cable.

shears, splicer's. See "scissors, electrician's."

sheath, *n.* The protective outer gastight covering of a cable, not including any protective wrappings. It is commonly of polyethelene or of lead.

sheave, manhole, *n.* A large, round-groove pulley, of diameters from 10 to 25 inches, used to feed cable into a manhole and then into a duct. Rotates on adjustable shafts held in a channel framework. See also "rigging, manhole pulling."

sheet, cut, *n.* (1) A written order to change crossconnections on a distributing frame, or in a cross-connecting terminal. (2) a written order specifying the transfer of pair groups in cable splicing.

shelf, distributing frame, *n.* The aggregate of horizontal steel bars on the horizontal side of a distributing frame, on which the crossconnections lie as they run horizontally.

shelf, jumper-type, *n.* A switch shelf on which the switch jacks are interconnected with jumper wire instead of locally-formed cable. Facilitates trouble shooting and rearrangements.

shelf, plug, *n.* The fixed back portion of the lower horizontal part of a switchboard, through which the plugs and cords protrude.

shelf, switch, *n.* A steel framework for horizontal mounting on a central office switch bay, which will hold a row of 10, 11, 16, 20, or 21 switches. Jack contacts at the back of the shelf make contact with matching plugs on the backs of the switches.

shelf life, *n.* The length of time under

specified conditions that a material or product retains its usability.

shellac, *n.* A thin clear varnish made by dissolving natural lac resin in alcohol. Used to insulate cable forms having textile insulation.

shield, *n.* A metallic covering over a circuit or equipment component which intercepts electrostatic or electromagnetic fields, and conducts the currents they induce to ground. Magnetic fields are shielded by magnetic material such as iron; electric fields are shielded by materials which are good conductors, such as copper.—*v.* To protect from stray electric or magnetic fields.

shield, cable, *n.* That metallic layer applied over insulation covering a cable core, composed of woven, braided or served wires, foil wrap, or metal tube, which acts to prevent electromagnetic or electrostatic interference from external fields.

shield, cable duct, *n.* A split tube of nylon six inches long having a wide rounded flange. Inserted in the end of a conduit to protect the cable from sharp edges. Also called a "cable protector."

shield, electron tube, *n.* A metal shield placed around an electron tube to act as an electrostatic shield and/or to assist in radiating heat from the tube.

shield, electrostatic, *n.* A metallic enclosure or screen placed around a device to ensure that it will not be affected by external electric fields.

shield, lead. See "anchor, wood screw."

shield, magnetic, *n.* An enclosure made from high permeability magnetic materials which can protect the circuits or equipment it encloses from the effects of external magnetic fields.

shield, manhole, *n.* A expandable, cylindrical, sheet-steel curb, 6-8 inches high which is placed in an underground manhole rim when necessary to prevent entry of water, snow, or dirt during splicing operations.

shielded pair, *n.* A paired insulated wire surrounded by an electrostatic shield consisting of braided copper wires or a wrapped metallic foil.

shield factor, See "factor, shield."

shield wire. See "wire, shield."

shift, case, *n.* The change of a teletypewriter from letters case to figures case, and vice versa.

shift, phase. See "phase shift."

shifter, strand, *n.* A chain hoist device used to raise cable which is supported on tensioned strand, particularly at poles on which there is a corner.

shiner, *n.* The end of a wire or skinner from which the insulation has been stripped to permit its connection to a terminal.

shock, *n.* A sudden stimulation of the nerves and convulsive contraction of the muscles caused by a discharge of electricity through the body. The severity depends upon (a) the amount of current, (b) whether the path of the current is through a vital organ, and (c) the duration of the current.

shock, acoustic, *n.* The physical pain, dizziness, and sometimes nausea caused by hearing a sudden loud sound. The threshhold of pain is about 120 dbm.

shock, effects of electric. The probable effects of electric shock to the human body are:

Current (Milliamps)	Effects
0-1	Perception
1-4	Surprise
4-8	Mild discomfort
8-20	Serious discomfort
21-40	Muscular inhibition
40-up	Respiratory block and death

shock excitation, *n.* The sudden application of a momentary steep-wavefront voltage to a circuit which causes a damped oscillation.

shock mounting, *n.* A cradle used to mount delicate equipment and insulate it from mechanical shock. Usually supported on rubber or wire spring shock isolators.

shoe, *n.* A plug-type device which can be clamped to electrical terminals for the purpose of making a temporary test connection.

shoe, reversing, *n.* A device inserted in a central office protector to reverse the line, ie: to connect the tip conductor of the central office equipment to the ring conductor of the outside cable, and vice versa.

shoe, test, *n.* Spring device to make contact with the springs of an MDF protector, or with the lugs on a terminal block.

shoes, ladder, *n. pl.* Rubber-faced, swivel pads that can be attached to the bottom of ladder rails to prevent the ladder from slipping.

short, *n.* A short circuit.

short circuit, *n.* An accidental or intentional near zero resistance connection between two sides of a circuit. It disrupts transmission, and may cause an excessive current flow.

shorted, *adj.* Prevented from operating by a short circuit.

short-haul carrier, *n.* Carrier system designed for use over distances of 10-200 miles.

short-period circuit, *n.* A circuit used only for a specified period each day. See also "on-call circuit."

short wave, *adj. n.* An indefinite term applied to a radio wave having a short wavelength. Generally considered to be a wavelength shorter than 200 meters, equivalent to 1500 kilohertz.

shovel, pole-hole. See "spoon" and "spud."

shunt, *n.* (1) An alternate path in parallel with a part of a circuit. (2) A bypass or parallel path which diverts current from a circuit. (3) A standard resistor, of low resistance and high accuracy, used with a millivoltmeter to permit the measurement of currents in amperes.—*v.* (1) To place a circuit element in parallel with another. (2) To bypass a portion of a circuit.

shunt, brush. See "pigtail."

shunt, instrument, *n.* A low-resistance highly-accurate resistor which is bridged across a millivoltmeter to enable the measurement of currents in amperes.

shunt, magnetic, *n.* A moveable piece of magnetic material which can divert a portion of the flux in a magnetic circuit from its customary path. Used to adjust the degree of magnetic coupling.

shunt feed, *n.* A method of applying direct voltage to the anode of an electron tube by feeding it through a choke coil that excludes the signal current.

shunt-wound, *adj.* Describing a direct current generator or motor whose armature and field are connected in parallel.

shuttle, *n.* Incorrect routing in a toll switching network in which a call, finding all "forward routing" trunks busy, is routed back to the office from whence it came.—*v.* To route a call out on the same trunk group on which it arrived.

sibilants, *n. pl.* The hissing sounds in speech: s, sh, z, zh, j, and ch.

side, field, *n.* The side of a pole line away from the roadway.

side, road, *n.* The side of a pole line towards the roadway.

sideband, *n.* A band of frequencies on each side of the carrier frequency of an amplitude modulated wave. The upper sideband contains frequencies which are the sums of the carrier and modulation frequencies, and the lower sideband contains the difference frequencies. Each sideband contains all of the information which was in the modulating wave.

sideband, double (DSB), *adj.* Describing a form of amplitude modulation of a carrier signal in which both the upper and lower sidebands which result are transmitted.

sideband, lower, *n.* In carrier transmission, the band of frequencies which is lower than the carrier frequency, and which is the difference between the instantaneous values of the carrier frequency and the modulating frequency.

sideband, single (SSB), *adj.* Describing a form of amplitude modulation of a carrier in which only one of the two resulting sidebands is transmitted.

sideband, twin, *n.* (1) A modulated radio frequency signal containing both upper and lower sidebands, both of which carry the same intelligence. (2) A term sometimes used improperly when "independent sideband" is meant.

sideband, upper, *n.* In carrier transmission, the band of frequencies which is higher than the carrier frequency, and which is the sum of the instantaneous values of the carrier frequency and the modulating frequency.

sideband, vestigal, *n.* In amplitude modulated transmission, the transmitted portion of one sideband which has been largely suppressed by a filter having a gradual cut-off in the neighborhood of the carrier frequency.

sidebands, *n. pl.* The bands of spectral energy at frequencies higher and lower than the carrier frequency which result from a modulation process.

side circuit, *n.* One of the two 2-wire metallic circuits which comprise a phantom group, and from which a phantom circuit is derived.

side cutters, *n.* A pair of lineman's pliers (slang).

sidetone, *n.* The hearing of one's own voice, or room noise, in the receiver when talking into the transmitter of a telephone.

sidetone circuit. See "circuit, sidetone."

sidetone path, *n.* A medium-loss transmission path from the transmit to the receive side of a four-wire telephone which provides sidetone for the talker.

sidetone telephone set. See "set, sidetone telephone."

side-to-side coupling, antenna, *n.* The fraction, expressed in db, of the power transmitted from an antenna which would be received by a second similar antenna located at the side of the transmitting antenna.

siemens, *n.* The new international standard unit of conductance which replaces and is identical to the "mho." It is the reciprocal of resistance in ohms.

sigma, *n.* Designation for a group of telephone conductors, usually the majority of the conductors of the path, treated as a single conductor which serves as the return for noise or residual currents. Used in the measurement of noise or current balance ratio.

signal, *n.* (1) An electrical wave used to convey information. (2) An alerting signal. (3) An acoustic device such as a bell or a visual device such as a lamp which calls the attention.—*v.* To transmit an information signal or alerting signal.

signal, alerting, *n.* An indication of an incoming call to a phone or switchboard. The signal may be visual as a lamp or annunciator, or audible as a bell, buzzer, or tone.

signal, analog, *n.* A nominally continuous electrical signal that varies in amplitude or frequency in response to changes of sound, light, heat, position, or pressure.

signal, answer. See "answer signal."

signal, audible ringing, *n.* Tone signal of 440 Hz + 480 Hz at a level of + 16 dBm per frequency, used to indicate that the called line has been reached and ringing has started. (Previously used 420 Hz modulated by 40 Hz).

signal, bidirectional. See "signal, polar."

signal, bipolar, *n.* A type of direct current signal in which consecutive marks are of opposite polarity, and a space is represented by zero voltage.

signal, busy, *n.* (1) A low tone, interrupted at 60 IPM, which indicates that the called line is busy. (2) A busy visual.

signal, coin collect, *n.* A +110 volts (sometimes +130 volts) negative grounded potential applied to both sides of the loop to the pay telephone which operates the coin relay to collect any coins which may have been deposited.

signal, coin return, *n.* A —110 volts (sometimes —130 volts) positive grounded potential applied to both sides of the loop to the pay telephone which operates the coin relay to refund any coins which may have been deposited.

signal, color picture, *n.* An electrical signal which includes all color picture information, but excluding all synchronizing signals. One form of color picture signal consists of a monochrome component plus a subcarrier modulated with information which specifies the colorimetric difference between the specified color and a pure white of equal luminance.

signal, common-audible, *n.* A feature available on multi-line telephones by which a single signal unit in the telephone provides an audible signal for an incoming call on any of the several lines.

signal, delay pulsing, *n.* An off-hook signal returned to the calling end of a trunk as soon as the called end receives a connect (off-hook) signal, to indicate that it is not ready to receive pulses.

signal, digital. See "digital signals."

signal, disconnect, *n.* An on-hook signal transmitted toward the called end of a trunk which exceeds 300 milliseconds, and notifies the called

end that the established connection is no longer needed and should be released.

signal, end-of-dialing. See "end-of-dialing signal."

signal, error, *n.* A signal whose magnitude and sign are used to correct error or deviation in a controlled device or signal.

signal, facsimile framing, *n.* A signal used for adjustment of the picture to a desired position in the direction of line progression.

signal, go, *n.* An on-hook signal transmitted toward the calling end of a trunk following a stop signal, indicating that the called end is ready to receive additional digits.

signal, high level digital, *n.* A DC signal of the type used as a data or teletypewriter line signal, and having the following level:

Neutral: 120 volts, 60 milliamperes.
Polar: Plus or minus 60 volts, 20 milliamps.

signal, high tone. See "tone, high."

signal, incoming call lamp, *n.* A 60 ipm flashing line lamp used on key telephones to indicate an incoming call.

signal, intelligence, *n.* Any signal which carries information, whether in analog or digital form.

signal, key. See "key, cryptographic."

signal, line, *n.* A steady lamp signal which indicates an incoming call on·the line jack associated with the lighted line lamp.

signal, line permanent, *n.* A signal which appears to be an attempted call, which results when a telephone is left "off-hook" or when a subscriber's line is short-circuited. It is considered to be permanent if no dial pulses have been received 30 seconds after the off-hook signal is received.

signal, low level digital, *n.* A DC signal used within a teletypewriter or data switching center which is at a low level to prevent crosstalk. It is a plus-or-minus 6 volts, one milli-ampere polar signal.

signal, mark. See "mark."

signal, monochrome, *n.* In television, whether in monochrome or color, the signal which controls the luminance of the picture.

signal, no circuit, *n.* A low tone (480 Hz + 620 Hz) interrupted at 120 IPM (on 0.2 second, off 0.3 second) which indicates that no toll circuit is available.

signal, non-return to zero. See "NRZ signal."

signal, no such number. See "no such number signal."

signal, off-hook. See "off-hook."

signal, on-hook. See "on-hook."

signal, permanent, *n.* The condition caused by operation of a line relay which is followed by no dialing, or by incomplete dialing. After a measured interval, the customer's line is usually connected to a permanent signal trunk.

signal, polar, *n.* A signal whose information is contained in current reversals in the circuit, one direction of flow being considered a marking signal and the opposite direction a spacing signal.

signal, pseudo-random, *n.* (1) A complex signal composed of many multiplexed telegraph or voice signals having a frequency distribution which is approximately random. (2) A cryptographic key generated by logic devices which produce a digital signal having a logical pattern which may not repeat for a period of 1000 hours, and therefore approximates a random signal.

signal, pseudo-ternary. See "signal, bipolar."

signal, quasi-analog, *n.* A digital signal which is suitable for transmission over an analog (voice) channel. Implies that the frequency, bandwidth, distortion, and noise requirements can be met by a voice channel.

signal, recall, *n.* Any cord lamp signal requiring an answer or challenge.

signal, reorder. See "reorder signal."

signal, ringing, *n.* (1) Any signal sent over a line or trunk to alert the party at the far end, by means of a bell or light, to an incoming call. (2) A ringback tone.

signal, ringing start, *n.* A signal provided to start the ringing on circuits using controlled ringing, such as toll switching trains and delayed pulsing senders. The SX ringing start signal is +130 volts applied on a simplex basis to both conductors for a minimum of 0.1 second. The 20 Hz ringing start signal consists of 105 volts AC ringing current applied on a loop basis for a minimum of 0.35 second.

signal, space. See "space."

signal, speech-simulated, *n.* A signal composed of loud components of the voice signal which act to cause false operation of tone-operated supervisory equipment.

signal, spurious, *n.* An undesired false signal generated within the equipment. See also "response, image."

signal, start dialing. See "start dialing signal."

signal, stop, *n.* An off-hook signal transmitted toward the calling end of a trunk which occurs after a part of the digits have been received at the called end, and which indicates that the called end is not yet ready to receive the remaining digits.

signal, supervisory, *n.* (1) A signal, such as "on-hook" or "off-hook," which indicates whether a circuit or line is in use. (2) A lighted supervisory lamp on a switchboard cord circuit, which indicates that the party on that cord has hung up his phone.

signal, television, *n.* In the United States, a signal of 6 MHz bandwidth, with an amplitude-modulated composite picture and synchronizing signal on a video carrier located 1.25 MHz above the lower boundary, plus a frequency-modulated audio signal on an aural carrier 4.5 MHz above the video carrier. For color transmission, the luminance information is transmitted as in black-and-white, and chrominance information is phase and amplitude-modulated on a subcarrier located 3579.545 kHz above the video carrier. Different colors or hues are indicated by phase-modulating the color subcarrier, while the saturation or richness of of the color is indicated by amplitude-modulating the subcarrier.

signal, time. See "time signal."

signal, timing. See "timing signal."

signal, tone. See "signal, single-frequency" and "signal, multi-frequency."

signal, unidirectional. See "signal, neutral."

signal, video. See "signal, television" and "television standards."

signal, wink. See "wink signal."

signal-guard circuit, *n.* A circuit which prevents false signaling caused by signal frequencies present in the voice. When the circuit detects a pure 2600 Hz tone a negative signaling voltage is produced. If any other frequencies are also present, the circuit produces a positive inhibit voltage.

signaling, *n.* A procedure for indicating to the receiving end of a communication circuit that intelligence is to be transmitted.

signaling, battery and ground, *n.* A popular type of loop signaling which doubles the current available for signaling by using battery and ground at both ends of the loop, but with opposite polarities at the two ends. It doubles the signaling range—and the impulse noise!

signaling, carrier, *n.* Built-in signaling capability that exists on some types of carrier, such as the "N," "O," and "ON." Uses 3700 Hz tone on when idle. The 3700 Hz modulates the carrier frequency of the voice channel for which it signals.

signaling, CCIS. See "common channel interoffice signaling."

signaling, CCITT #6, *n.* A proposed international standard for interoffice signals, probably very similar to the Bell System's CCIS, which see.

signaling, closed circuit, *n.* A type of direct current signaling in which the circuit remains closed at all times and signaling is accomplished by varying the current flow.

signaling, common-battery, *n.* A method of passing supervisory and telephone address information from a telephone to its serving central office by closing and opening the line at the telephone. See also "signal, off-hook" and "signal, on-hook."

signaling, composite, *n.* A DC signaling system similar to full duplex telegraph. It uses a single line conductor for each signaling channel. A balanced polar relay is used at each end of the signaling section in a symmetrical arrangement which allows full duplex operation. A filter arrangement called a composite set separates frequencies above 100 Hz (voice) from the signaling currents. Two composite channels can be derived from one pair of wires, and four from a phantom group. Composite channels not used for telephone signaling may be used for DC telegraph or teletypewriter circuits.

signaling, confirmation, *n.* A mode of signaling used to ensure accurate reception of MF 2/6 address signals. When the distant office receives an MF 2/6 signal it returns the same tone pair to the sending office. If confirmed correct, the sending office sends an interdigital tone which the distance office returns as notice that it is ready for the next digit.

signaling, dual tone multi-frequency, *n.* A method of sending numerical address information from a telephone or PBX switchboard by sending simultaneously a combination of two tones out of a group of eight. The eight frequencies are:

697, 770, 852, 941, 1209, 1336, 1477, and 1633 Hz.

signaling, duplex (DX), *n.* An excellent, modern signaling system using a balanced symmetrical polar relay circuit that is identical at both ends. Uses the same cable pair as the talking path and does not require a filter, or any earth potential compensation. A single DX signaling section is limited to 5000 ohms loop resistance, but several sections can be used in tandem.

signaling, E&M, *n.* A method of signaling between the central office trunk equipment and a separate signaling equipment unit over two leads: an "M" lead which transMits near-end conditions to the signaling unit, and an "E" lead which recEives indications of far-end conditions from the signaling unit. The signals and corresponding conditions are:

Near-end on-hook — GROUND on M lead
Near-end off-hook — BATTERY on M lead
Far-end on-hook — OPEN on E lead
Far-end off-hook — GROUND on E lead

signaling, E-type, *n.* The use of a single-frequency in-band (2600 Hz) line signal. Signaling units may use either loop or E&M signaling on the central office side of the unit.

signaling, high-low, *n.* A method of signaling in which a high resistance shunt is used to indicate on-hook, and a low resistance shunt to indicate off-hook. An obsolete method of signaling.

signaling, inband, *n.* A type of signaling using an AC signal (usually 2600 Hz) within the normal voice band. This signal can be transmitted from end to end of a long voice circuit without any intermediate signaling equipment. Since the signal is audible, the signaling equipment must be arranged for "tone on when idle" operation.

signaling, loop, *n.* Any of the three signaling methods which use the metallic loop formed by the trunk conductors and the terminating equipment bridges. Loop signals are transmitted by:

a. Opening and closing the direct current path around the loop.
b. Reversing the voltage polarity.
c. Changing the value of the equipment resistance.

signaling, magneto, *n.* Ringdown signaling from a magneto telephone to its switchboard, accomplished by spinning the magneto generator in the telephone.

signaling, multi-state, *n.* Any of the multifrequency pulsing systems (two-out-of-five, two-out-of-six, or two-out-of-eight) which are suitable for transmitting numerical address signals.

signaling, 135 cycle, *n.* Ringdown signaling using a low-frequency current of 135 Hz.

signaling, open-circuit, *n.* A type of direct current signaling in which signals are sent by opening and closing the circuit, and in which no current flows when the circuit is in the idle condition.

signaling, out-of-band, *n.* An AC tone signaling system which uses a frequency (usually 3825 Hz) which is within the pass band of the transmission facility, but outside of the voice band. Compandors are not affected by such a tone and signaling can, if required, take place during the talking condition. The type "N," "O," and "ON" carrier equipments use out-of-band signaling.

signaling, polar-duplex. See "signaling, duplex."

signaling, positive-negative, *n.* Battery-and-ground signaling, which see.

signaling, reverse battery, *n.* A very common method of loop signaling which uses open and closed loop signals from the calling end, but reverses battery and ground on the tip and ring of the loop to give an "off hook" signal when the called party answers.

signaling, ringdown, *n.* A method of signaling in which an alternating (ringing) current is transmitted over the circuit to operate (ringdown) the drop or relay at the far end.

signaling, selective. See "selective signaling."

signaling, separate channel, *n.* In carrier telephone transmission, the practice of setting aside certain voice channels to handle only signaling functions. These channels will be equipped with telegraph or data carrier to derive from 16 to 26 signaling channels each.

signaling, simplex, *n.* Signaling over a "simplex circuit," which see.

signaling, single-frequency, *n.* A signaling system which uses a 2600 Hz in-band signal on the voice path. The tone is on in the idle condition, pulsed for dialing, and off when the circuit is in use.

signaling, T carrier, *n.* A signaling system used with pulse code modulated carrier systems, such as the T1, which uses one of the code bits associated with each channel for sending the "off" or "on" signaling state of that channel.

signaling, 1000 cycle, *n.* Ringdown toll line signaling using a voice frequency tone (1000 Hz, interrupted twenty times per second) which passes through voice repeaters and does not require any intermediate signaling equipment.

signaling, time division, *n.* In time division multiplex, all of the voice channels share a common signaling channel on which time-division provides the separation between signaling channels. This system is also used on "common channel interoffice signaling," which see.

signaling, tone, *n.* The use of voice frequency tones to transmit alerting, address, and supervisory signals over a telephone voice circuit.

signaling, tone-on-when-idle, *n.* Inband signaling, which see.

signaling, 20 cycle, *n.* Ringdown signaling using a 20 Hz signal.

signaling, two-state, *n.* Any of the systems of signaling which transmit only two states, *i.e:* "off" and "on," or "off hook" and "on hook," and thus are suitable for transmitting supervisory signals or dial pulses.

signaling, variable resistance. See "signaling, high-low."

signal - plus - noise - to - noise (S+N)/N. See "ratio, signal-plus-noise-to-noise."

signal station, *n.* An unattended station which, upon receipt of a ring, automatically indicates that it has answered, gives a series of audible signals equivalent to a message, and then a disconnect signal.

signal-to-noise ratio, *n.* A ratio, expressed in db, which gives the relative levels of useful signal and masking noise. To be specific, the method of measurement must be stated. The most common method is as follows: A 1000 cycle test tone "signal" with a power of 0 dbm at a zero transmission level point is compared with the total unweighted noise in a 3 kc band.

silence, radio, *n.* A short period each hour during which marine radio transmitters must be silenced to permit reception of weak distress signals.

silent period, *n.* The four-second interval between the individual rings of interrupted ringing current. During the silent period, only direct current is flowing through the loop to the called telephone.

silica gel, *n.* A colloidal form of silica which will absorb moisture from the air. Small bags of silica gel are packed with electronic equipment when it is shipped to protect it from moisture.

silicon, *n.* A dark-gray, hard, crystalline solid, second most abundant among the elements in the earth's crust. Used in making transistors, and in alloying with iron in making steel for transformer cores.

silicon controlled switch (SCS), *n.* A pnpn semiconductor with all four regions connected to leads, providing an anode, cathode, anode gate, and cathode gate. The gates give versatile control of current flow under a variety of conditions.

silicon diode, *n.* A semiconductor diode that uses silicon as the rectifying element.

silicone, *n.* Any of several polymeric (long chain molecule) materials in which the recurring chemical group contains silicon and oxygen atoms as links in the main chain. Produces resins, oils, greases, plastics, etc., which have a high resistance to temperature changes and to water.

silk-and-cotton cable, *n.* A type of terminating cable, using silk and cotton yarns to insulate the conductors, which is no longer manufactured. See "cable, terminating."

simplex circuit, *n.* A signaling path over a dry talking circuit which uses the two sides of the circuit in parallel, derived by connecting to the midpoints of repeating coils or retardation coils which are across the circuit.

simplex operation, *n.* Operation of a circuit such that the transmission is in only one direction.

sine wave, *n.* A wave whose amplitude varies as the sine of an angle proportional to time or distance or both.

singing, *n.* A continued whistle or howl in a repeatered (amplified) telephone circuit. It occurs when the sum of the repeater gains exceeds the sum of the circuit losses, and occurs most often in the frequency ranges 200-500 Hz and 2500-3200 Hz.

singing, repeater, *n.* A undesired self-sustaining oscillation of a repeater circuit caused by either (a) excessive gain, or (b) unbalance of the hybrid coil terminations.

singing margin, *n.* The gain which, if added to a working repeatered voice circuit, would just start singing. This singing margin should be at least 10 db.

singing point, *n.* The point, measured by repeater gain, where a voice repeater will just start to sing. The actual total gain should be about 10 db below the singing point to provide a stable working circuit.

single-channel amplifier. See "amplifier, single-channel CATV."

single-channel office, *n.* An office at which customers dial the code "O" to reach an operator for both dial assistance and toll calls.

single-frequency signaling unit, *n.* A device which converts DC supervisory and control signals on the E and M leads into 2600 Hz tone signals on the voice path, carrier or wire pair. The tone is on in the idle condition, and off when the circuit is in use.

single hop, *adj. n.* (1) Describing a radio system without intermediate repeater stations. (2) Describing a radio wave which is reflected from the ionosphere only once in its path from transmitter to receiver.

single-phase, *adj.* Describing any electrical circuit in which there is a single sinusoidal voltage.

single-pole double-throw (SPDT), *adj.* Describing a three terminal switch which can connect terminal A to either terminal B or terminal C.

single-pole single-throw (SPST), *adj.* Describing a two-terminal switch having two positions: open or closed.

single sideband. See "sideband, single."

single sideband (SSB) modulation, *n.* A form of amplitude modulation of a radio signal in which only one of the two sidebands is transmitted. Either of the two sidebands may be transmitted, and the carrier may be transmitted, reduced, or suppressed.

single-wire circuit. See "circuit, ground return."

sink, data, *n.* A memory or recording device in which information can be stored for future use.

sink, heat, *n.* A mass of metal having fins or ribs on which a circuit component which produces heat can be mounted. Absorbs and radiates the heat to maintain a safe working temperature for the component.

sinusoidal, *adj.* Varying with time in proportion to the sine of an angle, as in an alternating current.

skew, *n.* Distortion of a facsimile signal due to lack of synchronism between the scanner and the receiver, which destroys the rectangularity of the received copy.

skin effect, *n.* The tendency for a high-frequency current to travel on the outside "skin" of a conductor, rather than being distributed uniformly throughout the conductor. Skin effect causes an increase in the "effective resistance" of a conductor at high frequencies.

skinner, *n.* (1) In a sewed cable form, that portion of the wire which extends from the sewed portion of the form to the end of the wire. (2) In fanned cable forms, either (a) that portion of the wire which extends from the butt of the cable, or (b) that portion which extends from a sewed cable form located between the cable butt and the end of the wire.

skinner connection, extended, *n.* A connection between adjacent terminals which is established by extending the bare end of a skinner between the terminals. Used to avoid the use of a separate strap or loop.

skinner length, *n.* (1) In a sewed form, the wire length from the sewed portion to the point of connection to the terminal, as measured from the inside edge of the cable. (2) In a fanned form, the wire length from the cable butt or cable form breakout to the point of connection to the terminal on which the skinner is terminated.

skinning, *n.* The operation of removing insulation from skinners.

skip distance, *n.* The distance out from a radio transmitter within which a sky wave reflected from the troposphere or ionosphere does not appear. Communication by scatter transmission is not practical to points within the skip distance.

skirt, *n.* The flared bottom of a pin insulator which keeps the leakage path to the pin clean and dry. See also "petticoat."

sky wave, *n.* That portion of a radio wave which is reflected from the ionosphere in its path between transmitting and receiving antennas.

slack, *n.* (1) Any excess length of wire or aerial cable between two supports which allows excessive sag. (2) An excess length of cable, compared with the length of its supporting messenger strand, which allows the cable to take a snaky position.

slackmaker, cable, *n.* A slack puller, which see.

slack puller, *n.* Device used by a cable splicer to remove the tension from aerial cable. A three-point clamp which is placed on the suspension strand and forces it out of a straight line.

slant distance, *n.* The true distance between two points which are not at the same elevation.

slave carrier terminal. See "terminal, slave carrier."

slave intercom station, *n.* An intercom station capable of receiving calls from any interconnected master station, and of answering them by speaking into the loudspeaker which also acts as a microphone. The slave station may have also a push button to initiate calls to its master station.

sleeve, *n.* (1) The sleeve, or control wire. (2) A lead tubing, used to cover splices in lead cables. (3) Cotton or plastic tubes, used to cover wire joints in cable splices. (4) A copper tube around a relay core, used to delay changes in the magnetic flux. (5) A short piece of copper or bronze tubing used to make compression splices in line or drop wires. (6) The long cylindrical contact member on a switchboard plug.

sleeve, compression. See "sleeve, splicing."

sleeve, cotton. See "sleeve, waxed cotton."

sleeve, double wall, *n.* A two-ply waxed cotton sleeve used for insulating conductor splices in toll cables. Available in 5/32 and 1/4-inch size, each about 3 1/4 inches long.

sleeve, filled plastic splice, *n.* A color-coded polyethelene tube about 2 1/2 inches long, closed on one end and then filled with silicone grease. Used to insulate and protect exposed twisted splices in wires. Available in yellow, green, blue, clear, and red, and in 3/32, 7/64, 1/8, 9/64, and 5/32-inch diameters.

sleeve, heat-shrinkable, *n.* A split cable sleeve of irradiated heat-shrinkable polyethelene which can be placed around a repair splice and then shrunk with a hot air blower to form a water-tight closure.

sleeve, lead, *n.* A piece of lead pipe slipped over a cable splice and wiped to the lead cable sheath on either side of the splice to make a weather-tight enclosure. Available from 3/4-inch to 8-inch inside diameter, in lengths from 15 inches to 24 inches.

sleeve, Nicopress. See "Nicopress."

sleeve, Nicotap. See "Nicotap."

sleeve, prepared cotton, *n.* A waxed cotton sleeve, factory prepared by boiling in paraffin, punching to open to a cylinder, and packing in a waterproof cardboard box. See also "sleeve, waxed cotton."

sleeve, relay, *n.* A conducting tube, usually copper, around a relay core which constitutes a short-circuited winding which acts to retard operation or release of the relay.

sleeve, repair, *n.* A very long split lead cable sleeve used to make a duct splice or to replace a section of damaged lead cable sheath.

sleeve, single wall, *n.* The normal waxed cotton sleeve used for insulating conductor splices in exchange cable. Available in 3/32, 1/8, 5/32, and 1/4-inch sizes, all about 3 1/4 inches long.

sleeve, splicing, *n.* A short piece of copper or bronze tubing which is used to make compression splices in line and drop wires. The sleeve is compressed around the wire by a plier or roller tool.

sleeve, split, *n.* A lead cable splicing sleeve which has been split down one side with a V-cut by a shave hook. The sleeve can then be opened and be placed over an existing splice, bent to close, and a solder seam floated in the V-cut. Used to replace a sleeve removed from an existing splice.

sleeve, waxed cotton, *n.* A woven tube of cotton, impregnated with an insulating wax, and punched to open it to a cylinder. Used to cover conductor splices in cables. Available in both single wall and double wall types, which see.

sleeve wire, *n.* The third control wire associated with every circuit in an automatic switching center.

sleeving, cotton, *n.* A braided, knitted, or woven cotton tubing. Formerly used by the splicer to make the paraffin impregnated sleeves with which he covered the wire joints in a cable splice.

sleeving, lead, *n.* A six-foot mill length of lead pipe which can be cut as required to make lead splicing sleeves.

slicer, *n.* A circuit which combines the functions of both clipper and limiter, in limiting both positive and negative peaks of its output wave.

slicing level, *n.* Of a signal representing a binary digit, the signal level below which the bit is judged to be a space, and above which it is judged to be a mark.

slide, chassis, *n.* Metal supports used in pairs on the side of an equipment chassis which enable the chassis to be pulled out of its mounting rack as a drawer is pulled out. Sometimes when the chassis is fully out it can then be rotated for maximum accessibility in making repairs.

slider, *n.* A sliding contact.

slide rule, *n.* A hand calculating tool consisting of several sliding scales divided in proportion to the logarithm of the numbers they represent. Permits rapid calculations by manually adding or subtracting logarithms.

sling, rope, *n.* A rope harness with snap fasteners used like a safety belt by a lineman when working in trees.

sling, wire rope, *n.* A piece of wire rope, 4 to 6 feet long, with a loop on each end. Used to place a sling around a pole to permit lifting it with a pole derrick.

slip *n.* The difference between the actual speed of an induction motor and synchronous speed (usually 1800 rpm). Slip increases as the load increases.

slip ring, *n.* One of a set of concentric cylindrical copper rings mounted on the shaft of a generator and used, with stationary brushes, to make connection to the rotor winding.

slitter, figure-8 cable, *n.* A pliers-like tool having cutting jaws which permit separating the messenger and cable of figure-8 cable without damage to either.

slitter, parallel wire, *n.* A metal block having a slot the size of parallel drop wire and having a razor blade centrally placed. Used to slit drop wire in the exact center between the conductors.

slitter, switchboard cable, *n.* A hand tool having a hooked blade that can be inserted under the jacket of switchboard cable, and pulled to slit the jacket lengthwise and allow its removal.

slope, *n.* The variation of attenuation (or gain) with frequency.

slot, *n.* (1) A narrow band of frequencies. (2) Any of the several narrow passages which hold the windings in a generator or motor armature. (3) A narrow groove between two adjacent segments of a commutator. (4) A time slot.

slot, time, *n.* A channel on a time-division multiplex system. Any of the many recurring time intervals during which the gate for a particular channel is open.

slotted line. See "line, slotted."

slow-operate relay, *n.* A relay with a copper slug or collar at the armature end of its core, which delays the operation of the armature momentarily after its operating winding is energized.

slow-release relay, *n.* A relay with a copper slug or collar at the heel-piece end of its core which delays the release of its armature momentarily after its operating winding is de-energized.

slug, *n.* A heavy copper sleeve placed over a relay core to make the relay slow in operating or releasing. A slow operate relay has the slug on the armature end of the core. Sometimes called a "collar."

slug tuning, *n.* Adjusting the resonant frequency of a coil by moving a powdered iron or ferrite slug in or out of the coil to change its inductance. Also called "permeability tuning."

slumber time. See "diversion, slumber time."

smearing, television image, *n.* A defect of a television image in which the vertical images are blurred along the horizontal axis. Caused by frequency distortion in the middle video range, from about 150 kHz to about 1 MHz.

Smith chart, *n.* A patented chart based on the circle diagram which facilitates the calculation of radio-frequency transmission line problems.

smooth, *adj.* Not lumpy. Describing a transmission line whose inductance, capacitance, and resistance are distributed uniformly along the line.

sneak current, *n.* A current which is of a magnitude only slightly higher than normal, and which will not cause harmful effects unless prolonged. Is of a magnitude too low to operate the ordinary telephone fuses.

sneak current fuse, *n.* (1) A fuse of very low amperage rating. (2) A heat coil made to replace a fuse where sneak current protection is needed.

sniffer, cable, *n.* Device which detects leaks in pressurized cables by detecting ultrasonic hiss of escaping gas. Consists of a microphone probe, amplifier, frequency convertor, audio amplifier, and loud speaker.

sniffer, radio-frequency, *n.* A device which detects RF leaks around shielding. Consists of a broadband RF receiver with an output meter and loudspeaker.

snips, splicer's. See "scissors, electrician's."

soak, *v.* To increase the current through a relay winding until the core is saturated with flux, and hold the magnetization at that level for a prescribed time.

socket, lamp, *n.* A tubular mounting device with springs to hold a slidebase switchboard lamp, and with an open end to receive a lamp cap. Part of a switchboard lamp strip.

socket, tube. *n.* A mounting into which an electron tube can be pushed. Spring terminals in the socket base contact the electron tube base pins, and hold the tube firmly.

soft, *adj.* (1) Compressible. (2) Lacking hardness. (3) Said of any plastic material or any metal not work-hardened or case-hardened and having a Brinell hardness less than 86. (4) Said of an electron tube which is gassy.

soft tube, *n.* An electron tube which does not have a high vacuum, either intentionally or because of occluded gases.

software, *n.* (1) Any of the routines, programs, and instructions required to use directors, translators, and computers. (2) The programs associated with automatic data processing and computer systems. A written statement of the procedures to be used and the format of the data at every step.

solar cell, *n.* A device which will generate low voltage direct current from the radiant energy in sunlight. Consists of a silicon p-n junction in which photons of light energy penetrate a thin layer of n-type silicon and create electron-hole pairs at the p-n junction. These travel to the terminals and produce a useful external current.

solar cycle. See "sunspot cycle."

solder, *n.* A metal alloy that can be melted and used for joining metal parts.—*v.i.* To become joined by solder.—*v.t.* To join with solder.

solder, aluminum tinning, *n.* A low melting point alloy of 90% Tin and 10% Zinc, used to tin aluminum sheath cables in preparation for soldering.

solder, arsenical wiping, *n.* A soft solder especially designed for cable wiping. An alloy containing 37% Tin, 63% Lead, and a small amount of arsenic. The arsenic makes it solidify more slowly, so that it has a finer grain and greater strength.

solder, eutectic, *n.* Solder which has the lowest possible melting point for its combination of elements. Eutectic tin-lead solder is composed of 63% tin and 37% lead, and melts at 361 degrees Fahrenheit. Eutectic tin-silver solder has 96.5% tin with 3.5% silver, and melts at 430 degrees Fahrenheit.

solder, hard, *n.* An alloy which melts at red heat. Used for joints which must withstand heat or stress. The following are two of many types:

a. For joining iron, copper, or brass. 55% Copper, 45% Zinc. Melts at 1600 degrees F.

b. For joining iron, copper, silver. 33% Copper, 10% Zinc, 57% Silver. Melts at 1800 degrees F.

solder, rosin core, *n.* A tin-lead solder in the form of a hollow wire filled with pockets of rosin flux, so that the required flux is always supplied with the molten solder.

solder, sealing, *n.* A low melting point bismuth solder composed of 40% Bismuth, 20% Tin, and 40% lead. Melts at 232 degrees F. A stick of sealing solder is rubbed over a newly wiped lead joint, melts, flows into and seals any minute pores in the lead wiping.

solder, seam, *n.* A solder consisting of 50% tin and 50% lead, used for running seams on split lead sleeves. Also used to enrich wiping solder when a higher tin content is desired.

solder, silver, *n.* A hard solder used to join silver, copper, or iron. Consists of 57% silver, 33% copper, and 10% zinc. Melts at 1800 degrees F.

solder, soft, *n.* A low melting point alloy of lead and tin. The following three are used in the telephone industry.

Use	Alloy	Melts at
Soldering copper	50% lead, 50% tin	300° F
General soldering	60% lead, 40% tin	340° F
Wiping lead joints	63% lead, 37% tin	370° F

solder, stearine core, *n.* A tin-lead solder in the form of a hollow wire filled with pockets of stearine flux. Used when soldering lead with a soldering iron. Not used for soldering copper conductors.

solder, wiping, *n.* A soft solder composed of 63% lead and 37% tin, used by cable splicers to wipe lead

sleeves to a lead cable sheath. See also "solder, arsenical wiping."

soldering, *n.* The process of uniting or patching metals by fusing a lower melting point alloy (a solder) around them.

soldering flux. See "flux, - - -."

soldering iron. See "iron, soldering."

solenoid, *n.* A tubular coil of wire which, when energized with electric current, will pull a moveable iron core into a central position in the coil.

solid, *adj.* (1) Describing a wire which consists of a single conductor, not of multiple strands. (2) Describing a ground connection which does not have any inserted resistance.

solid-state, *adj.* Denoting the use of semiconductors, such as diodes and transistors, instead of vacuum tubes.

solid-state circuit, *n.* An integrated circuit in which all circuit elements: transistors, diodes, resistors, capacitors, etc., are formed on a single block of semi-conductor material.

solution, pressure testing, *n.* A solution of soap in water, alcohol, and glycerine. Sprayed or painted on suspected portions of pressurized cables to check for leaks. Leaking gas will blow bubbles.

SONAD, *n.* Speech-operated noise adjusting device inserted in the receiving branch of a mobile radio base station which provides reduction of noise during the silent intervals between speech.

sone, *n.* A unit of loudness. A pure tone of 1000 hertz, 40 decibels above a listeners threshold, produces a loudness of one sone.

sonic, *adj.* (1) Having to do with sound. (2) Having a speed roughly equal to that of a sound wave, or roughly 1100 feet per second.

sonics, *n.* The technology of analyzing processing, and utilizing sound for any purpose.

sort, *v.t.* To arrange data cards in

some desired order of the information contained in a particular card field.

SOS, *n.* The internationally recognized radio distress signal in International Morse code: three dots, three dashes, three dots.

sound, *n.* (1) An oscillation in pressure, stress, particle displacement, and particle velocity in an elastic or viscous medium. (2) The auditory sensation which is evoked by an oscillation of audio frequency.

sound, velocity of. See "velocity of sound."

sounder, ionospheric, *n.* A device for determining the potential quality of HF radio transmission over a particular path at any frequency. Consists of an electrically-tuned HF pulse transmitter and a distant scanning HF receiver. The transmitter emits short pulses of HF energy sequentially on each of 120 discrete frequencies in the 4-32 MHz band. The receiver tuning is stepped in synchronism, and the received pulses are displayed on a storage oscilloscope. By inspection, the operator can determine the LUF, MUF, and probable multipath distortion.

sounder, local telegraph, *n.* A telegraph sounder having low resistance coils (4 or 50 ohms) operated with local battery from the contacts of the main-line relay. A mark signal produces a sharp "click," and a space signal a dull "clack."

sounder, main-line telegraph, *n.* A telegraph sounder having 120 ohm coils, and designed to produce an adequate sound volume when connected in series with a 60 milliampere telegraph line. Avoids the use of a main-line relay.

sounder, Morse, *n.* Device consisting of an electromagnet with a spring-loaded armature, used for the reception of Morse coded signals. The start of a mark signal produces a sharp "click;" the end of the signal a "clack."

sounder, telegraph. See "sounder, Morse."

sounder test cord, *n.* Single cord on a local test desk, equipped with a telegraph sounder and battery supply. Used to connect to a pair under observation, and serves to indicate when the pair is shorted, or when anyone is working on the far end of the pair.

sound-powered telephone, *n.* A telephone in which the voice sound waves operate a moving coil or variable-reluctance transmitter to produce the current waves which are transmitted to the telephone line. No battery power is used, but the output level is lower than that of a battery-powered phone.

sounds, unvoiced. See "unvoiced sounds."

sounds, voiced. See "voiced sounds."

South pole, *n.* The pole of a magnet which seeks the south magnetic pole of the Earth. The lines of force within the magnet are assumed to have entered at its south pole.

space, *n.* (1) In digital transmission, the binary state "zero," when any of the following conditions exist:
  (a) Current or tone is "off."
  (b) The loop is open.
  (c) There is a negative voltage, line to ground.
  (d) FSK system is on the upper frequency.
  (e) There is no hole in the paper tape.
(2) The continuous three-dimensional expanse outside the Earth's atmosphere. (3) The expanse between electrodes in a vacuum tube.

space, climbing, *n.* The vertical space reserved up the side of a pole or tower to permit the lineman to have ready access to conductors or equipment at the higher levels.

space, deep, *n.* The region beyond near space, which includes the Moon.

space, near, *n.* The space above the earth in which communication satellites will travel, beginning at an altitude of about 120 miles.

space diversity. See "diversity, space."

spacer, cable, *n.* A moulded plastic or lead separator used to maintain space between the strand and cable at splices in lashed cable, or to maintain space between two cables entering a splice case.

spacer, jack, *n.* In a switchboard face equipment, a wooden or plastic strip the same length as a strip of jacks and either ½, 1, or 1½-inch high. Used to fill a space intended for 1, 2, or 3 future jack strips.

spacer, wire, *n.* Plastic rod with the ends bent at 90 degrees and spirally formed. For application to open line wires in mid-span to prevent swinging short circuits by maintaining the normal 10 or 12-inch wire spacing.

spacing, load coil, *n.* The distance in feet between successive load coils inserted in a cable circuit. Several loading systems have been used, with spacing designated by an initial letter, as follows:

Designation	Spacing, Feet
A	700
B	3,000
C	929
D	4,500
E	5,578
F	2,787
H	6,000
J	640
M	9,000
X	680
Y	2,130

spacing, repeater, *n.* The distance between successive telephone repeaters or carrier repeaters, designed to give a satisfactory signal-to-noise ratio.

S-pad, *n.* A switching pad.

spaghetti, *n.* Linen or cotton fabric tubing impregnated with insulating material and baked. Used to insulate short lengths of bare wires.

span, *n.* (1) A length of wire, cable, or suspension strand between two poles. (2) A length of cable or conduit between two manholes.

span clamp, drop wire. See "clamp, drop wire span."

spare. *adj.* (1) Not in use. (2) Not reserved for a future requirement. (3) Available, or can be made available, for use.

spare pair, *n.* (1) An extra pair in a cable which is continuous from the central office main distributing frame, and can be picked up and terminated for use when needed. (2) A pair which is terminated, but not in use.

spares, running, *n. pl.* The aggregate of spare parts required to keep a particular equipment or machine operating (running) for a period of about 90 days, or for a period long enough to replenish the parts stock. Normally includes only those parts which are expected to have a high failure rate.

spare wire, *n.* Any of the extra wires placed in switchboard or other cables for use when some of the regular wires are broken and are not available for use.

spark, *n.* The brief flash of light from the arc which results when contacts carrying current are opened.

sparking, *n.* Spark discharges between the brushes and commutator of a generator or motor when the brushes are not adjusted to the proper part of the commutator.

spark killer. See "suppressor, spark."

spark suppression, *n.* The use of a small capacitance or high resistance across contacts which break currents in inductive circuits, to prevent excessive sparking when the contacts break. A capacitor and resistance in series is also used as a suppressor.

spark test, *n.* A test used by a manufacturer to locate pin-holes in insulated wire by grounding the wire conductor and drawing it between electrodes charged with a high voltage.

speaker, *n.* (1) One who speaks, or talks. (2) A loudspeaker.

Speakerphone, *n.* A telephone having a transistorized voice-switched microphone-speaker system which permits hands-free conversation.

special billing telephone number, *n.* A telephone number assigned to certain PBX customers for billing purposes. Either a 10-digit number with "1" or "ø" as the first digit and the Revenue Accounting Office (RAO) code as the last three digits, or a 7-digit number with "Q" or "Z" as the second digit when "1" or "ø" is not the first digit. Obviously, such numbers cannot be called. It may be given to the CAMA or OUTWARD operator as the calling number on an outward paid call, or may be used as a "third number billed" on a collect call.

special collect toll call, *n.* A call to a special number of a customer at a toll point who has made previous arrangements to accept charges on all calls to that number.

special-grade, *adj.* Said of a communication circuit which is conditioned to handle special services requiring a better-than-average transmission circuit. Conditioning may be to reduce attenuation deviation, delay distortion, or noise.

special instruction call, *n.* A type of toll telephone call requiring specialized handling, such as "credit card" and "bill-to-third-number" calls.

special-service trunk, *n.* A trunk over which a customer reaches "information," "repair," "time-of-day" or other like services.

specifications, *n. pl.* A published set of instructions for doing work in a uniform, standard manner. See also "practices."

specific gravity, *n.* A measure of the density of a substance. For liquid solutions it is the ratio of the weight of that solution to the weight of an equal volume of pure water at the same temperature. Measurements of specific gravity are used to determine the state of charge of a lead-acid storage battery. A fully charged cell will have a specific gravity of 1.215; a discharged cell of 1.150.

specs. *n. pl.* Specifications.

spectrum, *n.* A continuous range of frequencies, wide in extent, within which waves have some specified characteristic in common, *e.g:* audio spectrum, radio spectrum, etc.

spectrum, audio, *n.* The range of frequencies which can be detected as a sound by the human ear, ranging from about 15 hertz to about 20,000 hertz.

spectrum, microwave, *n.* The spectrum of frequencies suitable for microwave radio communication, lying between 300 megahertz and 300 gigahertz.

spectrum, radio, *n.* The total band of frequencies useful for radio communication, lying between 8 kilohertz and about 300 gigahertz.

spectrum, voice, *n.* The total fundamental frequency range of the human voice. The several types of voice have the following average ranges:

	Range	Hertz
Bass	$D\#_2 - F_4$	78 - 349
Baritone	$G_2 - G_4$	100 - 392
Tenor	$C_3 - B_4$	131 - 494
Contralto	$E_3 - B_5$	165 - 988
Soprano	$D_4 - F_6$	294 - 1397

spectrum analyzer. See "analyzer, spectrum."

specular reflection, *n.* The sharply directional reflection of light, radio, or sound waves from a mirror-like surface. See also "diffuse reflection."

speech, coded, *n.* Speech that has been converted into a multi-level digital signal.

speech interference level (SIL). See "level, speech interference."

speech-only, *adj.* In the transmission of broadcast programs, describes a circuit adequate for voice transmission but not for music.

speech-plus, *n.* Arrangement of carrier channel filters to enable a 4 kHz carrier channel to carry voice from 200-3400 Hz, plus a teletypewriter or supervisory signal at 3700 Hz.

speech-plus telegraph, *n.* A voice circuit on which a half-duplex telegraph or teletypewriter channel has been derived. Both may be used simultaneously.

speed, data transmission, *n.* Rate of transfer of information over a data channel. Normally given in either bauds or in cards per minute. Assuming an eight-level code and transmission of standard IBM cards, 100 cpm = 1,200 bauds.

speed, telegraph signaling, *n.* Rate of transferring information over a telegraph or teletypewriter channel. Given either in bauds or in words per minute. If one assumes a seven-level teletypewriter code and six character-intervals per word, then the relation between the two units is as follows:

60 wpm = 44.7 bauds
75 wpm = 55.9 bauds
100 wpm = 74.5 bauds

speed calling, *n.* Abbreviated dialing. See "calling, abbreviated."

speed dialing, *n.* Dialing at a speed greater than the normal ten pulses per second.

spike, *n.* A pulse of short duration, and of greater amplitude than the average pulse.

spill, *n.* In automatic switching, the full complement of digits which is received from the preceding office.

spill-forward, *v.* In automatic switching, to transfer full control on a call to the succeeding office by sending forward the complete telephone address of the called party.

spilling, no-skip, *n.* Action of a dial office in outpulsing on an outgoing trunk all of the digits it has received from the subscriber or from an incoming trunk.

spilling, skip-3, *n.* Action of a dial office or tandem switching center in deleting the first three of the 10 or 7 digits it has received before outpulsing the remaining 7 or 4 digits over a trunk to the next switching point.

spilling, skip-6, *n.* Action of a dial office or tandem switching center in deleting the area code and the central office code before outpulsing the remaining four digits over a trunk to the end office.

spilling, variable, *n.* Action of a dial office or tandem switching center in deleting part of the digits it has received before outpulsing over a trunk to the next switching point, which may not require the complete number to complete the connection. The number of digits spilled depends upon the route selected.

spill office, *n.* An intermediate automatic toll office which receives the full telephone address on calls incoming from another office, and then treats these calls as if they had been originated by its own subscribers.

spin, electron, *n.* The precession of the axis of a rotating electron when the electron is in a magnetic field and a radio frequency field which are mutually at right angles.

spinner, *n.* A cable lasher, used to lash aerial cable to its supporting strand.

spin-stabilized, *adj.* Describing a communication satellite which spins about its axis at about 150 rpm, as a means of keeping its axis and its antennas oriented in a particular direction.

spiral-four *n.* A quad in which the four conductors are twisted about a common axis, with opposite conductors being used as pairs.

spiral wrap, *n.* The helical wrap of a tape or binder over a cable core.

splash ring, *n.* Momentary application of ringing current, often applied immediately on switching to an idle trunk or line without waiting for initiation of automatic ring through the ringing interruptor.

splash tone, *n.* A short spurt of audio tone, usually 400 or 500 Hz, applied to a trunk to indicate readiness to accept an order, or to indicate class of service. Often called "zip tone."

splice, cable, *n.* The joining of two or more cables together by splicing the conductors pair-for-pair, then covering the whole with a weather-tight sleeve or case.—*v.t.* To make a cable splice.

splice, capacitance unbalance. See "splice, final test," and "splice, semi-final test."

splice, compression, *n.* A splice made by placing the wire ends to be spliced into a bronze or copper tube which is then compressed around the wires, using a plier or roller tool.

splice, conductor, *n.* An electrical joint which connects two conductors together, and has both good conductivity and adequate mechanical strength.

splice, duct, *n.* A long, slender cable splice which will fit inside a 3¼-inch conduit, but allow the cable and splice to be pulled from the conduit if necessary. Used when repairing cable trouble in the middle of a conduit run.

splice, final test, *n.* In splicing quadded cable, the splice where the quad capacitance unbalances (phantom-to-side, and side-to-side) are adjusted to a satisfactorily low value for the loading section, either by matching unbalances of opposite sign in the two halves of the load section so that they will neutralize, or by splicing in balancing units. The final test splice is made at the mid-point of the loading section.

splice, preformed, *n.* Tubular steel cable formed of spirally-wound wires. Can be used to butt-splice steel strand by winding individual splice wires around the strand.

splice, random, *n.* In splicing cable, a splice where pairs from the two ends are spliced, within each color group, without regard for their theoretical pair count, and even with deliberate mixing.

splice, rotation, *n.* A cable splice in which pairs from the two ends are joined, pair-for-pair, by starting at a marker pair then going around the core and splicing each pair in sequence.

splice, semi-final test, *n.* In splicing quadded cable either of the splices at the one-quarter and three-quarters points of the loading section where the quad capacitance unbalances in the quarter-sections are spliced so as to neutralize, or are "built" for neutralization at the final test splice.

splice, tag, *n.* A cable splice in which each pair is identified and tagged with its pair number, after which the splicing proceeds in accordance with the job instructions.

splice, Western Union. See "joint, Western Union."

splice, Y, *n.* A splice in which two cables in one direction are spliced to a single cable in the other direction.

splice case. See "case, splice."

splice coat. See "coat, splice."

splicing chamber, *n.* A compartment whose removable cover is the floor in front of the main distributing frame, in which tip cables can be spliced to the entrance cables. Used in offices which are too small for a cable vault, or where the main distributing frame is several floors above the cable vault.

split-phase, *adj.* Describing any device, such as an induction motor, which derives a second phase from a single-phase alternating current source by tapping it off through a capacitive or inductive reactor.

splitter, *n.* A radio-frequency hybrid which takes one 75 ohm cable input and divides it equally between two, four, or eight 75 ohm outputs, while maintaining isolation between outputs. Used in CATV work.

splitter, band, *n.* A frequency dividing network which will take a broadband radio signal and divide it into two bands, one of higher frequency than the other. Used in CATV work.

splitter, phase. See "phase splitter."

splitting, *n.* The action of an operator in dividing a cord circuit or link circuit into two parts, so that she may talk to only one of the two parties to the connection (calling or called; trunk or extension). See also "cord-splitting" and "key, splitting."

S-pole, *n.* A junction pole between two open wire transposition sections. See also "pole, junction" and "transposition, junction."

spoon, *n.* A long-handled (7-9 ft.) shovel having a bent spoon-shaped round point blade. Used for removing the dirt from the bottom of a pole hole or anchor hole.

sporadic, *adj.* Occurring occasionally, and at random intervals. Infrequent. A characteristic of impulse noise.

sporadic E layer. See "E layer, sporadic."

sporadic propagation, *n.* Abnormal and unpredictable radio transmission which occurs only occasionally. Caused by unusually intense ionization in some part of the E layer of the ionosphere.

spreader, lead sleeve, *n.* A double wedged tool looking somewhat like a carpenter's plane, but with a knob handle. The lower and smaller wedge will open a split sleeve ½ inch, and the upper wedge will increase the opening to 1 inch.

spread spectrum. See "modulation, spread spectrum."

spring, contact, *n.* A resilient flat strip of metal, usually phosphor bronze, which is the contact or

supports a contact in a jack, key, or relay.

spring, retractile, *n.* (1) A restoring spring. (2) a coil spring which has been stressed by elongation.

spring adjusting tool, *n.* Small hand tool used for bending the springs of jacks and relays.

spring pile-up, *n.* An assembly of all the contact springs which are operated by one relay armature lever, or by one key cam or roller.

springs, impulse, *n. pl.* In a rotary telephone dial, the pair of springs whose contacts are opened and closed at a 10 pps rate to produce the dial pulses.

springs, normal post. See "normal post springs."

springs, shunt, *n. pl.* In a rotary telephone dial, the group of springs which close when the dial is first moved and remain closed until the dial returns to normal. These springs place a short across the receiver to prevent clicks during dialing, and a short across the transmitter to remove its resistance from the dialing path.

spud, *n.* A long-handled (8-10 ft) shovel with a straight round-point blade. Used for loosening the dirt at the bottom of a pole hole or anchor hole.

spudger, *n.* A pencil-sized wooden or fibre stick having one end conically pointed and the other end shaped like a screwdriver blade. It has numerous uses, including the cleaning of solder from terminals.

spurious emission, *n.* Any emission from a radio transmitter outside of its assigned frequency band.

spurious response. See "response, spurious."

spurs, *n.* (1) The wedge-shaped points on a lineman's climbers. (2) The climbers themselves (slang).

sputter, *n.* The very rapid (200-300 Hz) change in fading on a radio wave traversing high latitudes. This is equivalent to amplitude modulation with noise, caused by doppler interference associated with rapid changes of ionization in the aurora.

sputtering, cathode, *n.* The depositing of thin films of metal (typically tantalum) onto an insulator (typically an integrated circuit substrate) in a low-pressure argon atmosphere by connecting a negative 5000 volts potential to a metal (tantalum) electrode, thus causing a glow discharge and releasing metal atoms which condense on the insulator forming a thin conducting film. Used to form thin films for integrated circuits.

square wave. See "wave, square."

square wave testing, *n.* The use of a square wave signal, which contains an infinity of odd harmonics, to test the frequency response of a wide band device. Observation of the output wave on an oscilloscope will show how much the square wave was distorted in passing through the device.

squelch, *v.* To reduce the gain of a radio receiver automatically when its input signal is not modulated. Used to suppress noise on mobile telephone receivers.

squelch circuit. See "suppressor, noise."

squirrel-cage winding, *n.* The permanently short-circuited copper bar winding used on the rotor of an induction motor.

stability, *n.* The ability to remain stable, without drift, oscillations, or variations.

stability, frequency, *n.* The ability of a device, such as an oscillator, transmitter, receiver, etc., to maintain its designed frequency for a long period of time.

stability test, *n.* A test obtained by dialing a connector test number which automatically applies open, short, or termination conditions for ten seconds each. Used to test the stability of carrier-derived or negative-impedance repeatered circuits.

stabilizer, voltage, *n.* A cold-cathode gas diode bridged across a power supply which acts to hold its output voltage to a nearly constant value.

stack, *n.* A pileup of plates in a dry-disc rectifier.—*v.* To place one channel, or group or supergroup, above another in a frequency-division multiplex system.

stack, rectifier, *n.* The series of metal discs having oxide coatings which form the rectifying element of a "dry disc rectifier." The discs have a hole in the center and are compressed on a threaded rod.

stacked, *adj.* Describing carrier channels which are placed (stacked) one above another in the frequency spectrum.

stacked array, *n.* A group of several identical microwave antennas placed one above the other and connected in proper phase relationship so that their signals are additive. Used to increase the gain of an antenna.

stage, *n.* A single section of a multisection circuit or device.

stage, originating, *n.* That portion of a telephone switching process whereby a connection is extended from the selected intraoffice trunk to the originating line.

stage, switching, *n.* A group of selector switches, crossbar switches, or a matrix which will receive a call through a single inlet and connect it to a particular outlet within a group of outlets.

stage, terminating, *n.* The switching process which extends a connection from a selected intraoffice trunk to the called line.

staggered twist, *adj. n.* A method of constructing paired telephone cables in which adjacent pairs always have a different length of pair twist. Used to reduce crosstalk.

staggering, carrier frequency, *n.* The practice of reducing crosstalk within a four-wire carrier system by using one carrier frequency for the East-West direction, and another for the West-East direction.

stagger tuning, *n.* The production of a wide-band response in a multi-stage frequency-selective device, such as an intermediate frequency amplifier, by tuning each of the stages to a slightly different frequency.

stalpeth, *adj. n.* A type of telephone cable sheath having an 8-mil corrugated aluminum tape applied longitudinally without overlap over the core, followed by a corrugated steel tape applied longitudinally with a soldered seam, then a polyethelene jacket overall.

stand, desk, *n.* An outmoded form of telephone having a circular base supporting a column with a transmitter at the top. A switchhook on the column held the receiver when not in use, and a rotary dial was set in the base.

stand, mounting, *n.* A floor-mounted metal frame which may be used to support apparatus mountings when located on a subscriber's premises.

standard, primary, *n.* A standard of voltage, current, frequency, etc. precisely defined by the National Bureau of Standards, against which portable secondary standards are calibrated.

standard frequency service. See "service, standard frequency."

standard test tone. See "tone, standard test."

standby communication facility, *n.* A facility maintained primarily as a readily available alternate communication facility.

standby generator. See "generator, emergency engine."

standing wave, *n.* A wave caused by two waves of exactly the same frequency moving in opposite directions on the same transmission line. At points where the voltages of the two waves add, there will be a voltage antinode. At points where the voltages subtract, there will be a voltage node. These nodes and anti-nodes do not move, and the resultant wave is called a "standing wave." The second wave is often a reflection of the first wave from an impedance discontinuity.

standing wave ratio (SWR), *n.* A property of a standing wave which is a measure of the reflection at an impedance mismatch. It is the ratio of the amplitude of the standing wave at an anti-node to the amplitude at a node.

stapler. See "gun, stapling."

star connection, *n.* Three windings or network elements with one terminal of each connected to a common node.

Starlight, *adj.* A registered trademark of Automatic Electric Co. for a line of small telephones having electro-luminescent dial number plates.

start dialing signal, *n.* A keyshelf lamp signal, provided in some offices, which lights to indicate to the operator that she may dial on the connection as long as the lamp remains lighted.

starter, automatic, *n.* A motor starter which takes the several steps required to start a large motor automatically, requiring only the pushing of a start button.

start lead, *n.* The wire, or lead, over which the first electrical pulse is transmitted to activate a circuit. For instance: "linefinder start," "ringing start."

start of message indicator (SOM), *n.* A designation required on messages passed through automatic digital switching systems to indicate the start of message and to activate the automatic message switching equipment.

start signal, *n.* A pulse or battery connection which initiates action. An example is the signal which initiates hunting of a linefinder.

start-stop, *adj.* An asynchronous mode of teletypewriter operation in which the receiving teletypewriter operates on a character basis, starting at the beginning of a character, receiving the five serial bits which encode the character, stopping, and starting again on receipt of the start pulse which precedes the following character. The speed of sending may be quite variable, since there is no synchronization except with the character.

start-stop teletypewriter, *n.* A method of teletypewriter operation in which the operating mechanism is operated for one revolution at a time, during which time it transmits, or selects and prints, one complete character.

state, *n.* Either of the two conditions of a bistable device, the "one state" or the "zero state."

static, *n.* (1) An electric charge which does not move, such as the bound charge on a capacitor plate. (2) Crackling or hissing sounds which disturb radio reception. (3) White flecks on a television screen which interfere with television reception. —*adj.* (1) Without movement. (2) Having no moving parts.

static, precipitation, *n.* Radio static caused by the impact of electrically-charged rain drops or dust particles on a receiving antenna.

static charge, *n.* An electric charge held on the surface of an object, particularly on a dielectric.

station, base. See "station, mobile base."

station, extension, *n.* A telephone station connected to the same telephone line and having the same telephone number as an associated main station. The extension station may be identical to the main station, or it may lack a ringer. See also "extension, - - -."

station, left-in, *n.* A telephone station which has been disconnected but left in place after the subscriber moved out. This is a practice for avoiding re-installation costs.

station, main, *n.* A telephone station which is connected directly to a central office and which has a unique telephone number. Not an extension station.

station, master intercom. See "master intercom station."

station, mobile base, *n.* Any of the several scattered fixed radio stations which transmit to and receive telephone messages from mobile stations in automobiles.

station, off-premises, *n.* A PBX station which is not located on the same contiguous property with the PBX.

station, public telephone, *n.* A telephone station available for use by the general public upon payment of a fee which is deposited in a coin collector or paid to an attendant.

station, pushbutton, *n.* An assembly of one or several pushbutton switches in a mounting, which is mounted and wired as a unit.

station, radio relay, *n.* A station containing radio receivers and transmitters which receives signals on one radio link and retransmits them on another.

station, receiver, *n.* A place where radio receivers with associated antennas receive transmissions from a distant station and send them over local cable or microwave circuits to a remote communication center.

station, repeater, *n.* An intermediate (usually every fifty miles) station on a toll cable, equipped with voice repeaters which are connected into the toll circuits.

station, signal. See "signal station."

station, slave intercom. See "slave intercom station."

station, tape-relay. See "tape relay, - - -."

station, telephone, *n.* An installed telephone with its associated wiring and auxiliary equipment.

station, teletypewriter, *n.* The group of equipments used to give teletypewriter service to a customer. It may include (a) a receiving page teletypewriter, (b) a monitoring teletypewriter, (c) a tape perforator, and, (d) a tape transmitter.

station, toll. See "toll station."

station, transmitter, *n.* A place where radio transmitters and associated antennas, usually keyed from a remote communication center, extend the radio circuit to a distant receiver station.

station, way. See "waystation."

stationary wave, *n.* A standing wave, which see.

station call, *n.* A station-to-station call, as distinguished from a person-to-person call.

stationkept, *adj.* A stationkept satellite carries control equipment such as gas jets which can be activated to change the orbital velocity or altitude of the satellite, thus enabling it to keep its position above a fixed point (station) on the Earth's surface.

station signaling rack (SSR), *n.* The unit of central office power equipment which provides ringing current, various tones (direct and interrupted), and interrupted ground.

station-to-station call, *n.* (1) A call on which the calling party says he will talk to anyone at the called number. (2) A call on which the calling party does not specify that he wishes to talk with a particular person, nor with a particular extension, department or office to be reached through a PBX attendant.

stator, *n.* That portion of a rotating electrical machine consisting of the stationary portion of the magnetic circuit and its associated windings.

steady-state, *n.* The condition of a current or voltage when switching transients have ceased and the current or voltage has reached its regular unvarying level.

stearin, *n.* A white waxy substance, glyceryl stearate, found in the solid portion of most fats. Its derivative, stearic acid, is used by cable splicers as a flux when soldering or wiping lead joints. Furnished as stubby candles 4 inches long, weighing 1/6 pound.

steatite, *n.* A dense ceramic having a dielectric constant of 6.0, low moisture absorption, and low dielectric losses in the megacycle range. Fabricated from magnesium silicate talc with added barium and calcium carbonates to reduce losses. Much used to make insulating parts requiring close mechanical tolerances.

steep wavefront, *adj.* Having a wave whose voltage rise is very rapid.— *n.* A voltage wave which rises from zero to a finite value in a very short time measured in microseconds. Implies the presence of many odd harmonic frequencies in the wave.

steerable antenna, *n.* A multi-element antenna in which the phase relationship between the elements is electronically adjustable, thus enabling the antenna beam to be steered in direction and adjusted for beamwidth.

Stefan-Boltzmann Law of Radiation. See "Appendix B."

step, *n.* (1) One unit of movement of a stepping switch. A vertical step or a rotary step. (2) A pole step. —*v.* To move the wipers of a stepping switch from one bank level to another (vertical step), or from one contact to another in the same bank level (rotary step).

step, detachable pole, *n.* A removable formed steel step which slips over a permanently installed pole plate. Prevents climbing of the pole by any except authorized workmen who carry the detachable step.

step, metal pole, *n.* A 5⁄8″ diameter screw-pointed step 9 inches or 10 inches long placed at 3-foot intervals on cable terminal poles, starting at 6½ feet above the ground.

step, pole, *n.* A foot support on the side of a pole, enabling installers and repairmen to climb the pole without the use of climbers. There are both wooden and metal pole steps, which see.

step, rotary. See "rotary step."

step, vertical. See "vertical step."

step, wooden butt, *n.* A creosoted wooden wedge, 1¾ x 2¾ x 7 inches, nailed to the butt of a terminal pole at 3½ feet above the ground line. It allows access to the higher metal steps, but is not a hazard to pedestrians.

step-by-step, *adj.* Describing an automatic switching system in which the call is extended progressively step-by-step to the desired terminal under direct control of pulses from a subscriber's dial, or from a sender.

step down, *v.* To decrease the value of an electrical quantity, such as a voltage.

step up, *v.* To increase the value of some electrical quantity, such as a voltage.

stereo, *adj.* Stereophonic.—*n.* A system for the reproduction of stereophonic sound.

stereophonic, *adj.* Describing sound which is transmitted from two different sources or heard over two different paths so as to give the effect of auditory perspective.

stereophonic transmission. See "transmission, stereophonic."

stick, orange. See "spudger."

sticks, *n. pl.* The test shoes used on main distributing frame protectors and on terminal blocks to make test connections. (slang)

stile strip, *n.* The vertical strip on the face of a switchboard which separates the panels and carries the number plates.

stitch, F, *n.* A supplementary stitch on a local cable form used to separate wires of the same color.

stochastic, *adj.* At random; proceeding by guesswork.

stop, finger, *n.* A hook-shaped device which hangs over the finger wheel of a rotary telephone dial and limits travel of the finger wheel. The older large diameter dials have a fixed finger stop. The newer small dials have a moveable finger stop, which enables elimination of the large space between the digits 1 and 0.

stop-dial, *n.* An off-hook condition returned from the far end of a dial trunk during the interdigital interval, as a signal that the incoming switching equipment cannot accept additional digits.

stop signal. See "signal, stop."

storage, *n.* The portion of a translator or computer which stores digital information for later use.

storage, magnetic drum. See "drum storage."

storage battery, *n.* A group of storage cells connected in series. See also "cell, (type) storage" and "battery, central office."

storage capacity, *n.* The amount of information, expressed in bits or words, that can be retained in a memory system.

storage cell. See "cell, storage."

store, *n.* A storage unit. A memory unit in which information can be accumulated until needed for future use.—*v.* To insert a binary digit into a register or memory unit.

store, call, *n.* (1) A storage unit where information is placed temporarily until it can be placed in a semipermanent memory unit. (2) A storage unit which is used for transient information regarding calls in progress.

store, flying-spot, *n.* A memory device for a common-control dial office consisting of a rectangular matrix of square conducting spots, scanned by a flying electron beam which can read or write electrostatic charges on the spots. Now replaced by the twistor store.

store-and-forward, *adj. n.* (1) In data communication, a technique in which a message is received from the originator and held in storage until a circuit to the addressee becomes available. (2) In satellite communication, a technique in which a message is received from one earth terminal and held in storage in the satellite until the satellite is in view of the second earth terminal, at which time the message is retransmitted.

store-and-forward switching. See "switching, message."

stored program. See "program, stored."

storm, ionospheric, *n.* An ionospheric disturbance characterized by wide variations from normal in the state of the ionosphere, including effects such as turbulence in the F region, increases in absorption and often decreases in ionization density and increases in virtual height. The effects are most marked in high magnetic latitudes and are associated with abnormal solar activity.

storm, magnetic, *n.* A disturbance in the earth's magnetic field occurring concurrently with ionospheric storms; probably caused by intense particle radiation from the sun.

storm guys. See "guys, storm."

storm loading. See "loading, storm."

straggler message, *n.* A teletypewritten message which has been inadvertently automatically transmitted with the preceding message because the first message did not have a proper end-of-message indicator.

straightforward call completion, *n.* Plan of traffic handling in which the called number is passed by an "A" operator to a "B" operator over the same circuit that is used for completing the call. See "straightforward trunk."

straightforward trunk, *n.* A trunk between two manual switchboards arranged so that insertion of a plug in the trunk jack by the originating operator automatically signals the operator at the terminating switchboard. Straightforward trunks are usually equipped with "order tone," and with through supervision.

straight-line capacitance, *adj.* Describing a variable capacitor in which the moveable plates are shaped so that the capacitance varies directly with the angle of rotation. Used in measuring equipment.

straight-line frequency, *n.* Describing a variable capacitor whose moveable plates are so shaped that the frequency of the circuit the capacitor tunes varies directly with the angle of rotation. Used in radio-frequency equipment.

strain insulator. See "insulator, strain."

strand, *n.* A bundle of wires that are twisted together to form a flexible cable capable of withstanding large tensile stress. The most common strands are composed of seven galvanized steel wires.

strand, bunch, *n.* A stranded conductor in which all the individual wires are bunched and twisted in the same direction, without any care to place them in layers.

strand, Copperweld, *n.* Guy and suspension strand made of copper-clad steel wires. See also "Copperweld."

strand, galvanized steel, *n.* A guy or suspension strand composed of galvanized steel wires.

strand, guy, *n.* A mechanical cable used for guying poles, composed of seven or three strands (wires) of galvanized steel, copperweld steel, or alumoweld steel. Available in sizes roughly 5/16", 3/8", 7/16", and 1/2" which in the "Utilities Grade" have breaking strengths of 6,000; 10,000; 16,000; and 25,000 pounds.

strand, messenger, *n.* Cable suspension strand.

strand, suspension, *n.* Cable made of steel wires twisted together, supported by poles and used to carry an aerial cable which is lashed to it.

stranded conductor. See "conductor, stranded."

stranding, concentric, *n.* The twisting together of bare wires to form a core surrounded by one or more spirally-wrapped layers. Used to make flexible single-conductor wire.

strandlink, *n.* A patented automatic compression sleeve which permits making splices in steel strand by simply pushing the ends of the strand into the link, where internal conical wedges grip the strand ends.

strandvise, *n.* A patented device for the automatic dead-ending of guy strand or messenger strand. Consists of a sleeve containing an internal conical wedge which grips the strand, and a stainless steel bail which can be placed through the eye of a thimbleye bolt or of an anchor rod.

Stranterm, *n.* One company's name for a strand-mounted cable terminal.

strap, *n.* (1) A bare or insulated conductor run from terminal to terminal of the same or adjacent components, but not included in a sewed form. (2) A connecting link or wire between two terminals.—*v.* To interconnect two or more terminals with strapping wire.

strap, cable, *n.* A strap of semi-circular cross section having two ears with mounting holes. Placed over a cable to fasten it to a flat surface.

strap, safety, *n.* Strong nylon strap, adjustable for length, and fitted with safety snaps on each end for securing to the lineman's tool belt. Encircles the pole, and provides safe support for a lineman.

strap, sleeved, *n.* A strapping between two terminals made with sleeved wire.

strap, wall, *n.* A heavy metal strap for fastening to a building wall, having an eye for terminating a messenger strand.

strapping, *n.* An interconnecting strap or straps.

straps, climber, *n. pl.* Leather straps with buckles, 1-inch wide by 22 inches long, used to fasten climbers to the legs of the user.

strategic communications, *n.* Long-haul, point-to-point, fixed station communications, whether owned or leased. (DCS)

stratification. See "duct, atmospheric."

stratosphere, *n.* The layer of atmosphere above the troposphere, located from about 10 to 50 miles above the surface of the earth.

stray capacitance, *n.* Any of the small unintentional capacitances which exist between wires or components in a circuit, particularly capacitance to ground. Although not an intentional part of the circuit, they can seriously affect its operation at the higher frequencies.

stray current. See "current, ground-return."

stray magnetic field, *n.* Stray magnetic flux from nearby transformers or inductors which can link with conductors or other inductors to produce undesired noise voltages.

streaking, television image, *n.* A defect in a television image in which a dark streak trails a bright object, or a light streak follows a dark object. Caused by poor video response below about 150 kilohertz.

strength, dielectric. See "dielectric strength."

strength, field. See "field strength."

strength, radio field. See "intensity, radio field."

strength, tensile, *n.* The pulling stress required to pull a material in two. Stated in pounds of stress per square inch of cross-sectional area.

strength, yield. See "yield strength."

stress, voltage, *n.* The force exerted on a dielectric which is in an electric field.

stretcher, line, *n.* A section of coaxial line which telescopes and can be extended or retracted.

striking voltage, *n.* The value of voltage required to start current flow through a gas tube.

stringing, *n.* The work of placing wire, strand, or cable in position on the poles.

strip, *n.* A long narrow piece. (See the listed varieties which follow.)—*v.* To remove the insulation from a wire.

strip, barrier terminal, *n.* A terminal strip having insulating ridges between adjacent pairs of terminal screws.

strip, busy-designation, *n.* A designation strip placed directly over the circuit busy lamps. A small hole in the bristol-board backing permits the light from the busy lamp to be seen through the translucent designation strip.

strip, designation, *n.* A small mounting used to hold designation cards on a switchboard. Consists of a flat metal channel which will accept a strip of Bristol board on which circuit designations can be printed. Includes a transparent face strip to cover and protect the Bristol board.

strip, distributing. See "block, connecting."

strip, fanning, *n.* A narrow maple strip having a number of ⅜″ D smooth holes through which cross-connecting wires can be brought for orderly termination on a terminal block or terminal strip.

strip, holly. See "holly strip."

strip, stile, *n.* The narrow vertical metal strip between jack fields on a switchboard or testboard.

strip, terminal, *n.* An insulating mounting for interconnected pairs of terminal screws.

strip test, *n.* A strip of starched canvas or fibre having numbered holes through which a cable splicer passes each pair or quad at a test splice as he identifies it by number.

stripe, hash mark, *n.* A color stripe applied helically to a conductor insulation for wire or pair identification, but which is not continuous.

stripe, helical color, *n.* A continuous colored stripe for wire or pair identification, applied spirally on the conductor insulation.

stripe, longitudinal color, *n.* A colored stripe on a conductor insulation running with the axis of the conductor, and used for wire or pair identification.

stripe, tracer. See "tracer, stripe."

stripline, *n.* Strip transmission line. A type of microwave transmission line used in integrated circuits. Consists of a narrow flat conductor sandwiched between and insulated from wider flat grounded conductors.

stripper, *n.* (1) That portion of the end of a cable from which the outer covering is stripped or removed. (2) Any of the individual wires within that portion of the cable.

stripper, double, *n.* That portion of a cable between two points from which the outer covering has been stripped or removed.

stripper, insulation, *n.* (1) A hook-shaped flat metal tool having a wedge-shaped slot which can be used to pull insulation from the ends of wires. (2) A plier-type tool which holds the wire while a pair of jaws pulls the insulation from the end of the wire.

stripper, single, *n.* That portion of the end of a cable from which the outer covering has been stripped or removed.

stripper, splice, *n.* A double stripper, which see.

stripper, wire. See "wire stripper."

stripping, *n.* The operation of removing the outer sheath or covering of a cable together with any inner wrapping, thus exposing the insulated wires.

strips, terminal. See "block, terminal."

stroboscope, *n.* A high-intensity flashing light whose rate of flashing can be precisely controlled, so that the light can be used to observe rotating or vibrating objects while making them appear to stand still.

Strowger switch, *n.* The original, two-motion (up and around), step-by-step switch, named for its inventor, Almon B. Strowger.

structural coordination. See "coordination, structural."

stub, *n.* (1) A cable stub. (2) A guy stub. (3) A radio-frequency stub. (4) A terminal stub cable.

stub, cable, *n.* A short (within the manhole) branch cable from a large underground cable. It brings out pairs from the main cable to avoid entering the main cable splice if pairs should be needed later.

stub, guy, *n.* A short stubby pole which carries both an overhead guy and an anchor guy. Used when the anchor guy must be placed a span away from the pole requiring guying.

stub, matching, *n.* A reactance, consisting of a section of transmission line less than one-quarter wavelength long with its free end either open or shorted as required, used to match a transmission line to the impedance of an antenna.

stub, quarter-wave, *n.* A section of radio-frequency transmission line which is shorted at the far end and is one-quarter wavelength long at the operating frequency. It therefore has a high impedance at the operating frequency and all odd harmonics, but is an effective short at all even harmonics.

stub, radio-frequency, *n.* A short section of radio frequency transmission line, adjustable in length and usually shorted at the far end, which can be bridged on a longer transmission line and used to tune it to an impedance match with an antenna or transmitter.

stub, terminal, *n.* The short (6-10 feet) cable which terminates on the binding posts of a cable terminal and extends for connection into the cable.

stub, tuning. See "stub, matching" and "stub, radio-frequency."

stub out, *v.t.* To connect a cable stub to pairs in a main cable, thus avoiding the necessity to open the large main cable splice at some future time in order to obtain use of the pairs.

stub pole, *n.* A short pole used to terminate an overhead guy. The top of the stub pole is in turn guyed to an anchor in the ground.

Stubs Iron Wire Gauge, *n.* An older designation for the scale of measuring ferrous (iron) wires, now known as the Birmingham Wire Gauge (BWG). See also "gauges, wire."

stud, *n.* A fastener consisting of a headless rod with external threads, but without any provision to turn it or lock it.

stud, powder actuated, *n.* A pointed, hardened steel rod having bolt threads on its outer end. Can be powder-power driven into a masonry or steel surface, leaving the threaded bolt protruding for use in fastening to the surface.

stud, residual. See "residual stud."

Styleline telephone, *n.* Trade mark of the Automatic Electric Company's brand of dial-in-handset.

stylus, *n.* The diamond or sapphire point on a phonograph pickup which rests in the phonograph record grooves and transmits their modulations to the pickup elements where they are converted into audio-frequency currents.

subassembly, *n.* A portion of a complete equipment which has one particular function, and whose components are combined into a single unit for ease of replacement.

subcarrier, *n.* A carrier band which is applied as modulation on another carrier wave.

Sub-Cycle converter, *n.* Registered name of a device which will supply 20 Hz or 30 Hz ringing power when energized with 60 Hz commercial power. Consists of a transformer with a secondary resonant at 20 Hz (or 30 Hz), and whose primary is shock-excited at a 20 Hz (or 30 Hz) rate from the 60 Hz supply.

Subcycle ringing generator. See "generator, sub-harmonic" and "generator, transistor ringing."

sub-group, trunk, *n.* A portion of a large group of selectors, all of which have access to trunks to the same destination.

subharmonic, *n.* A harmonic tone whose frequency is less than that of the fundamental tone, being the fundamental frequency divided by an integral number.

submarine cables. See "cable, - - - submarine."

submarine cable system, Type SB, *n.* A system using two 0.620 inch diameter armored coaxial cables with flexible vacuum-tube repeaters spaced 38.7 nautical miles to provide 48 two-way 3 kHz voice channels, on a baseband of 20-164 kHz. The maximum system length is 2200 nautical miles.

submarine cable system, Type SD, *n.* A system using a single 1-inch diameter armorless coaxial cable with rigid vacuum tube repeaters spaced 20 nautical miles to provide 128 two-way 3 kHz voice channels on basebands of 108-516 and 648-1052 kHz. The maximum system length is 3500 nautical miles.

submarine cable system, Type SF, *n.* The current (1971) system using a single 1½ inch diameter armorless coaxial cable with rigid transistorized repeaters spaced 10 nautical miles to provide 720 two-way 3 kHz voice channels on basebands of 564-2788 and 3660-5884 kHz. The maximum system length is 4000 nautical miles.

sub-office, *n.* A small dial central office which has only (a) line equipment, (b) linefinder or lineswitch equipment, (c) pulse repeaters, and (d) connectors. All selector equipment is located in the "master office." Sub-offices are obsolescent.

subscriber, *n.* A person or agency subscribing for telephone service, as distinguished from a user who obtains his service through a subscriber.

subscriber's line. See "line, subscriber's."

subscriber's loop, *n.* Circuit between a local office and a subscriber's telephone set.

subscriber's multiple. See "multiple, subscriber's."

subscriber's telephone set. *n.* A complete telephone set used by a subscriber for originating or receiving telephone calls.

subscription music channel (CATV). See "channel, subscription music."

subset, *n.* (1) A subscriber set. (2) A subscriber's telephone set.

subsidiary carrier authorized. See "channel, SCA."

subsidiary conduit. See "conduit, subsidiary."

substitution, code, *n.* Code conversion, which see.

substrate, *n.* That part of an integrated circuit which acts as a support. It may be a ceramic insulator to which an integrated circuit is attached, or a semi-conductor chip within which an integrated circuit is fabricated. Typical substrates bearing complete complex integrated circuits are 0.05 inch square.

sub-system, *n.* A major portion of a complete system. Usually includes a complete function in itself, such as "transmission sub-system," "power sub-system," etc.

sudden ionospheric disturbance (SID), *n.* A sudden increase in absorption of radio waves in the lower HF and upper MF frequencies, caused by high ionization density in the upper atmosphere, in turn caused by ultra-violet light from a solar flare, which disrupts HF radio communications badly.

sulfuric acid, *n.* An oily, colorless, heavy, extremely corrosive liquid used, in a dilute form, as the electrolyte in central office storage batteries.

sum, vector. See "vector sum."

sump, manhole, *n.* A hole, or cast-iron fitting, about 12 inches in diameter x 4 inches deep, placed in the low point of a manhole floor. Allows drainage from the manhole, and forms a pocket where a pump suction hose can be placed to pump the manhole dry.

sun, active, *n.* A condition of the sun characterized by spots and flares, and by large variations in radio-frequency radiations.

sunspot, *n.* A dark spot on the sun,

in some way responsible for the disturbances in the ionosphere which severely affect radio communication.

sunspot cycle, *n.* The period of about eleven years during which sunspots and solar flares pass through one cycle—minimum to maximum to minimum occurrences. The last minimum occurred in 1964. The 1968 maximum was the twentieth observed since 1760.

sunspot number, *n.* Number of visible spots on the face of the sun. Useful in predicting high-frequency radio propagation. The number is taken from a smoothed graph of all observed data.

superconduction, *n.* The property of certain metals which cause them to lose all apparent electrical resistance when cooled to a few degrees above absolute zero (0 degree K or —459.7 degrees F). A current started in a superconducting loop will circulate for years without measureable attenuation.

supergroup, carrier, *n.* A grouping of five 12-channel carrier groups, translated from the band 60-108 Hz to occupy adjacent positions in a frequency spectrum from 312 Hz to 552 Hz.

superheterodyne receiver, *n.* A radio receiver which converts the incoming radio wave to an intermediate frequency and amplifies the signal at the intermediate frequency before detection. See also "detection" and "frequency, intermediate."

superimposed ringing, *n.* Ringing in which the 90 volt 20 Hz ringing current is biased by being superimposed on (connected in series with) 48 volt DC power. Provides a ring trip voltage during silent intervals in the ringing period, and makes possible furnishing semi-selective ringing on party lines.

Superposition Theorem. See "Appendix B."

supersonic, *adj.* Traveling at a speed greater than the speed of sound.

Do not confuse this term with "ultrasonic" which describes sound at frequencies above the audio range.

supervision, answer, *n.* Indication received at the calling end of a circuit that the called end has answered. It is initiated by the called end changing from the "on-hook" to the "off-hook" condition after the ringing cycle has begun. See also "supervision, reverse-battery."

supervision, disconnect, *n.* Indication that a circuit is no longer in use, given by each end changing from an "off-hook" to an "on-hook" condition.

supervision, reverse-battery. See "reverse-battery supervision."

supervisor, *n.* (1) Any telephone operator who supervises the work of other operators. (2) Any employee who supervises the work of others.

supervisory control, *n.* The supervision and control of devices at a distance. For instance: a Power Company can monitor operation of a substation and connect or disconnect circuits; a Pipeline Company can monitor a pumping station and open or close valves.

supervisory lamp, *n.* A lamp associated with a cord which indicates to the operator whether she has a circuit or an off-hook telephone connected to that cord. A lighted supervisory lamp indicates that the customer has hung up, or that the circuit has been disconnected.

supervisory relay, *n.* A relay which is effectively connected in series with a telephone line and is operated by line current to indicate whether the line is in an "off-hook" or "on-hook" condition.

supervisory signal, *n.* A signal, such as "on-hook" or "off-hook," which indicates whether a circuit or line is in use.

supplement, *n.* A supplement is a separate publication, related to a basic publication, and prepared for purposes of promulgating additional information.

supply, *n.* The procurement, distribution, maintenance while in storage, and salvage of supplies, including the determination of kind and quantity of supplies to stock.

supply, power, *n.* (1) The commercial AC power provided by a power company. (2) A rectifier or other device which provides power for communication equipment.

supply, short, *n.* An item is in short supply when the total stock on hand and anticipated receipts during a given period is less than the total estimated demand during that period.

supply voltage, *n.* The voltage at which AC power is supplied for use by the customer. The customer may use it at the supply voltage, or step it down to a lower "utilization voltage."

support, hand set, *n.* Plastic device with a removable pad which may be assembled to the hand set to permit it being supported on either the left or right shoulder. Permits hands-free use.

support, tangent, *n.* (1) A device placed over a through-bolt on a pole, used to support figure-8 cable. It combines a "J" hook to support the cable during placing and tensioning, plus clamping plates for permanent fastening. The clamping plates are flared to permit their use on poles having corners up to 35 degrees. (2) A stiff steel wire formed into a long spiral which can be wound onto a drop wire or small cable where it passes a pole. Reinforces the wire or cable so that it does not bend excessively at the support.

support facility, *n.* Any item, such as land, buildings, roads, standby power plant, reserve fuel storage which is in direct support of a communication facility.

suppressed carrier, *adj.* Describing any carrier transmission system in which the carrier frequency is eliminated from the transmitted wave, leaving only one or both sidebands.

suppressed zero, *adj.* Describing a meter in which the zero position is below the end of the scale markings.

suppression, noise, *n.* The capability of a radio receiver circuit to automatically reduce the noise output when no carrier is being received.

suppression, spark. See "spark suppression."

suppressor, blockless echo, *n.* An echo suppressor which generates a signal to cancel the echo, rather than inserting loss in the echo path.

suppressor, echo. See "echo suppressor, - - -."

suppressor, full echo, *n.* An echo suppressor installed at only one end of toll circuits of 1500-2500 miles in length, which can insert suppressor loss in either the transmit or receive leg of the circuit, and thus can suppress echos from either talker. It cannot be applied to circuits over 2500 miles in length because the round-trip echo path is twice the length of the circuit, and the echo delay becomes unacceptably long for longer circuits.

suppressor, noise, *n.* (1) A device which limits noise. See "limiter." (2) A squelch circuit which blocks the output of a radio receiver when no radio frequency carrier signal is received, and therefore limits background noise.

suppressor, radio frequency, *n.* A circuit for absorbing radio frequency energy generated by sparks or arcs, at its source so that it will not be radiated and interfere with radio reception. An example is the RF suppressor (filter) used on a telephone dial.

suppressor, spark, *n.* A capacitor and resistor in series, placed across contacts to inhibit sparking and to short-circuit noise voltages from the sparks.

suppressor, split echo, *n.* An echo suppressor which can insert suppressor loss only in the transmit leg of the circuit, and thus must be installed at both ends of the circuit. The split echo suppressor operates only for the talker at the far end of the circuit. Used on circuits over 2500 miles long, on which the transmission time is so long that it would be difficult for one party to interrupt the other if a full echo suppressor were used.

suppressor grid, *n.* In a pentode electron tube, a grid placed between the screen grid and the plate. Usually connected to the cathode. Prevents secondary electrons emitted from the plate from flowing to the screen grid.

surcharge, *n.* An additional charge, over the station-to-station rate, sometimes applied to the first few minutes of overtime on person-to-person calls.

surface duct. See "duct, surface."

surface leakage, *n.* The passage of a small current over the boundary surface of an insulator, rather than through the insulator.

surface noise, *n.* The noise output from a phonograph pickup due to dust or scratches on the record.

surface resistivity. See "resistivity, surface."

surface wave, *n.* (1) A wave that travels along the interface between two media without radiation, such as an electric wave on the surface of a wire surrounded by air. (2) A ground wave.

surface wave line. See "line, surface wave."

surge, *n.* A short-duration increase of current or voltage in a circuit.

surge admittance. See "admittance, surge."

surge impedance. See "impedance, surge."

survey, route, *n.* A detailed survey for a pole line, along the path suggested by a preliminary sketch, incorporating modifications necessary for competition of construction plans.

survivability, *n.* The capacity of a communication network to provide adequate service after major damage to portions of the network.

susceptance, *n.* The reciprocal of reactance, and the imaginary component of admittance. Specified in "mho." See also "admittance."

susceptiveness, *n.* The tendency of a telephone system to pick up noise and low frequency induction from a power system. It is determined by telephone circuit characteristics as follows: (a) circuit balance, (b) isolation from ground, (c) wire spacing, and (d) transpositions. See also "influence" and "coupling."

suspension, *n.* The wire torsion or spring element which supports the moving coil of a galvanometer or meter.

suspension strand. See "strand, suspension."

swab, antiseptic, *n.* Antiseptic, either bactine or merthiolate, hermetically sealed in a glass ampoule with an applicator tip. A component in all first-aid kits.

swab, insect sting, *n.* A sealed glass ampoule containing a medicine giving relief from stings of bees, hornets, wasps, ants, and mosquitos. Contained in the first aid kits used by the outside plant forces.

swamp anchor, *n.* A large screw anchor having sufficient area to be effective in swampy ground. See also "anchor, screw."

sweep, *vt.* To test a transmission facility by sending into it a test signal whose frequency repetitively varies so as to scan the whole transmitted band. By observing the reflections of that signal on an oscilloscope one can estimate the location and magnitude of any impedance irregularities.

sweep circuit, *n.* The oscillator and amplifier that generate the sawtooth waveform which is used to produce the scan in a television tube.

sweeper, *n.* A sweep-frequency generator.

sweep frequency, *adj.* Describes an oscillator whose output frequency is swept over a band of frequencies.—*n.* An audio or radio frequency which is repetitively varied over a band of frequencies. Provides a test signal for wide-band devices.

swept cable. See "cable, swept coaxial."

swing, *n.* (1) The total variation of voltage, current, or frequency. (2) The arc traversed by the needle of a meter. (3) A swinging short.

swinging choke. See "choke, swinging."

swinging short, *n.* A come-and-go short, like that produced by a pair of wires swinging together in the wind.

switch, *n.* (1) A mechanical-electrical device which can be controlled to interconnect two circuits. (2) A switching center.—*vt.* (1) To interconnect two circuits. (2) To transfer a connection from one circuit to another.

switch, analog, *n.* A switching center which handles analog (voice) traffic.

switch, band, *n.* A switch used to select one of several frequency bands in a radio receiver, radio transmitter, or signal generator.

switch, busy. See "busy switch."

switch, circuit, *n.* A switching center which interconnects lines and trunks. Compare with "switch, message."

switch, coaxial, *n.* A single-pole multi-throw switch which switches coaxial conductors without inserting an impedance irregularity. Used to switch one radio receiver to any of several antennas, etc.

switch, concentrating. See "out-trunk switch."

switch, connector. See "connector, step-by-step."

switch, crossbar, *n.* A selective, multi-unit, two-stage relay, configured with 10 or 20 horizontal paths and 10 or 20 vertical contact paths. A two-stage operation is used to close any crosspoint. First a selecting magnet shifts all springs in a horizontal row, then a holding magnet shifts a vertical actuating card to close the selected contacts.

switch, crossbar trunk, *n.* (1) A crossbar switch which terminates 16 trunks on 8 horizontal levels. Each of the levels 2 to 9 terminates two 3-wire trunks (appearances "A" and "B"). The select magnet "0" selects "A" appearances, while select magnet "1" selects "B" appearances. (#5 X Bar) (2) A type of switch used in small crossbar PAX's which is associated with a particular central office trunk, and which serves as a finder on outgoing calls and as a connector on incoming calls extended to a PAX station.

switch, digital, *n.* An automatic switching center which is capable of switching digital signals. It may be either a "circuit switch" or a "message switch."

switch, electrolysis drainage, *n.* A high-current automatic switch placed in an electrolysis drainage wire which connects to a trolley bus negative return. Permits drainage of current from the cable, but opens if the current should reverse and flow toward the cable.

switch, end-cell, *n.* A switch of high ampere capacity which maintains circuit continuity during operation. May be operated manually, by solenoid, or by electric motor. Used to switch the central office battery load from 23 cells to 26 cells, and vice versa.

switch, homing type, *n.* An automatic stepping switch which always restores to its normal at-rest position when not in use.

switch, inspector's ring-back, *n.* A reverting-call switch, specifically for the use of telephone installers and repairmen.

switch, instrument, *n.* A switch used to connect or disconnect a measuring instrument, such as a voltmeter, or to transfer it from one circuit or phase to another.

switch, knife, *n.* An open switch in which hinged metal blades may be swung to meet stationary spring contacts.

switch, lever. See "key, lever."

switch, line. See "lineswitch, - - -."

switch, linefinder. See "linefinder."

switch, master. See "masterswitch."

switch, mercury, *n.* An evacuated glass tube having sealed-in contacts and a pool of mercury which bridges the contacts when the tube is tilted.

switch, message, *n.* An automatic switching center which receives a data or teletypewriter message on an incoming circuit, and retransmits it to its destination on an outgoing circuit without interconnection of the incoming and outgoing circuits.

switch, minor, *n.* A 10-point, single-motion stepping switch, whose wipers return to the "home" position when released.

switch, non-homing. See "non-homing switch."

switch, non-numerical. See "non-numerical switch."

switch, numerical. See "numerical switch."

switch, out-trunk, *n.* One of several outgoing secondary trunk switches, rotary or plunger, used between selector levels and pulse repeaters on outgoing trunks, for the purpose of concentrating the traffic so that it can be carried on fewer trunks.

switch, plunger line. See "lineswitch, plunger."

switch, quick-break. See "quick-break switch."

switch, repeater. See "repeater, impulse."

switch, reverting call, *n.* A switch in a dial central office used to provide ringing current back to the line from which the call came. When accessed from a selector level it holds the connection after the calling party has hung up, then returns ringing current to the calling line. Used by repairmen to facilitate the adjustment of telephone ringers.

switch, rotary, *n.* An automatic switch having 25 sets of contacts spaced around a semi-circular arc, traversed by double-ended wipers rotating in a single direction. Usually energized by self-interrupted pulses.

switch, rotary line. See "lineswitch, rotary."

switch, rotary out-trunk. See "switch, out-trunk."

switch, safety, *n.* A power switch completely enclosed in a metal box, and operable without opening the box.

switch, selector. See "selector."

switch, sensitive, *n.* A snap-action toggle switch which will operate from a very small movement of the actuator. See also "Micro Switch."

switch, sequence. See "sequence switch."

switch, series-parallel, *n.* A double-pole double-throw switch connected so that it can be used to change the connection of two devices from series to parallel.

switch, silicon controlled, *n.* A four-layer semiconductor device having all layers brought out to terminals. Can be used as a "silicon controlled rectifier" or as a gate which can be turned on and off like a switch.

switch, slide, *n.* A very small switch which is operated by sliding a button.

switch, snap-action, *n.* A small switch, usually SPST or SPDT, having a toggle contact which operates very fast with only a small movement of the actuator. One brand is called "Micro Switch."

switch, step-by-step, *n.* An automatic switch whose wipers move over a bank of contacts one step at a time until the desired terminal is reached. Each step may be under the control of external pulses, or local self-interrupted pulses. See also: "switch, rotary," "switch, Strowger," "switch, X-Y."

switch, stepping, *n.* Generic term for any switch which electro-mechanically steps its wipers across a bank of contacts. See also "switch, rotary" and "switch, step-by-step."

switch, Strowger, *n.* A step-by-step automatic switch with a semi-cylindrical bank of contacts having ten pairs of contacts on each of ten levels. The first motion is vertically to the desired level under control of dial pulses. The second motion is circular, into the bank to the desired pair of contacts. In a one-digit switch (selector), the second motion is energized by self-interrupted pulses. In a two-digit switch (connector), the second motion is under control of dial pulses.

switch, 3-digit, *n.* A step-by-step automatic switch, such as a 200-line connector switch, which receives three digits to determine its operation. The first digit, either a "1" or "2" determines which of two banks will be accessed. The last two digits select the desired pair of contacts in that bank.

switch, time, *n.* An electric clock-controlled switch which can be set to turn a circuit on and off at predetermined times.

switch, toggle, *n.* A small panel switch whose lever can be flipped up or down to operate it. A spring-operated toggle provides quick operation.

switch, transfer, *n.* A double-throw switch, which disconnects one or more wires of circuit A from cir-cuit B, and connects them instead to circuit C.

switch, wideband, *n.* An automatic switching center which is capable of switching wideband (75-100 kHz) signals without degrading them.

switch, X-Y, *n.* A step-by-step automatic switch whose bank contacts are in a horizontal plane of ten rows and ten columns. In the first motion the wipers travel across the bank to the desired column (level). In the second motion the wipers enter the bank to the desired terminal. Normally the switch includes only the "X" and "Y" operating magnets and the release magnet, with all relays which determine the circuit functions located separately on a circuit plate.

switchboard, *n.* A cabinet having a vertical face mounting line and trunk jacks with associated line and busy lamps, and a horizontal keyshelf mounting cords, supervisory lamps, and keys for talking and ringing. An operator uses the cords to interconnect lines and trunks, and supervises the connections.

switchboard, A, *n.* A switchboard where subscriber's lines appear for answering and calling.

switchboard, attendant's. See "attendant's switchboard."

switchboard, B, *n.* A switchboard used only for completing calls which come in on trunks from an "A" board, or from the toll switchboard. The incoming trunks are commonly "plug ended" for call circuit operation. The subscriber's line multiple jacks are not equipped with line or busy lamps.

switchboard, common battery, *n.* A manual switchboard which serves common battery telephone sets.

switchboard, cordless, *n.* A small manual, desk-top, switchboard so constructed that connections between station loops, and between loops and trunks, are made by the operation of lever type keys.

switchboard, dial assistance. See "switchboard, DSA."

switchboard, dial system B (DSB), *n.* A switchboard auxiliary to a dial system used for completing incoming calls received from operators over straightforward or call circuit trunks.

switchboard, DSA, *n.* Dial service auxiliary switchboard. A manual switchboard associated with an automatic central office, and used to give operator assistance, and to serve any manual lines. Sometimes also serves as the Telephone Company PBX.

switchboard, emergency reporting, *n.* A one-position PBX which can receive calls from 100 police or fire call boxes, accept reports, and dispatch police, ambulance or fire emergency vehicles. The single position can be split for the use of two operators. A supervisory relay in each station line gives instant indication of line trouble.

switchboard, fire-reporting, *n.* A manual cord switchboard used at a central fire station to receive reports of fires from public fire phones. Each line is equipped with a line lamp to indicate incoming calls, and an alarm lamp to warn if the line to that fire phone should go open.

switchboard, magneto, *n.* A manual telephone switchboard in which all signaling is ringdown. Inward signaling is to a "magneto drop," and outward signaling is sometimes from a "magneto" generator.

switchboard, manual, *n.* A telephone switchboard at which the connections are made manually, between plugs and jacks or through keys.

switchboard, monocord, *n.* A small local battery switchboard in which a switchboard jack and a single cord ending in a plug are permanently connected to each loop or trunk. A connection is made by connecting the cord of the calling line to the jack of the called line.

switchboard, multiple, *n.* A manual telephone switchboard on which each line and trunk appears on several jacks spaced along the length of the switchboard so that they are within reach of every operator.

switchboard, non-multiple, *n.* A small manual switchboard on which each loop and trunk has but one appearance on a jack in front of the operator. Two positions is the maximum practical size which permits each operator to reach every jack.

switchboard, power, *n.* A switchboard for controlling AC power circuits, including main circuit switching and interrupting devices, and their interconnections.

switchboard, telephone answering, *n.* Switchboard made for use at a telephone answering bureau. The lines appearing on this switchboard are normally one-way incoming, so that outgoing calls cannot be made. See "answering service, telephone."

switchboard, teletypewriter, *n.* An operator's switchboard having cord circuits which will handle teletypewriter lines. Used to give exchange teletypewriter (TWX) service.

switchboard, toll, *n.* A switchboard at which toll telephone connections are established, supervised, and timed. See also "toll, inward," "toll, outward," and "toll, through."

switchboard drop. See "drop, switchboard."

Switched Circuit Automatic Network (SCAN), *n.* A nationwide subscriber's direct distance dialing network for the Department of Defense. Now replaced by AUTOVON.

switch frame. See "frame, switch."

switchhook. See "hookswitch."

switching, circuit, *n.* A method of handling message traffic in which circuits are interconnected (switched) to provide a direct connection between the calling and called stations.

switching, machine, *n.* An electromechanical system for automatically switching telephone calls.

switching, manual, *n.* The switching of telephone calls by operators at a switchboard.

switching, message, *n.* The operation by which messages are transmitted link by link, using a store-and-forward technique, through a communication network of switching centers.

switching arrangement, common control, *n.* A communication network provided by the Bell System for handling the private line communication needs of its large business customers.

switching center, *n.* Location at which telephone traffic, either local or toll, is switched or connected from one circuit or line to another. A local switching center may be comprised of several central office units.

switching-selector-repeater, *n.* A step-by-step switch which combines the functions of a selector and a pulse repeater. It serves as a selector on local calls, and as a pulse repeater on trunked calls to other offices. Switching can be on the first, second, or third digit, and until that decision is made, the incoming selector at the far end of the associated trunk steps (and drops) in unison with the switching-selector-repeater.

switchman, central office, *n.* A person who maintains and repairs the switching equipment in an automatic central office.

switchroom, *n.* That part of a central office which houses automatic switching equipment. It may also house relay equipment associated with a switchboard, and the ringing and tone supplies, the battery, and battery charging equipment.

switchtrain, *n.* A series of selecting switches through which a telephone call moves in sequence.

switchtrain, transfer, *n.* One or more "transfer selectors" in tandem.

swivel, pulling line, *n.* A pair of metal eyes connected with a ball-bearing rotatable joint. Inserted between a winch line and wire, cable, or strand being pulled, to relieve any tendency to twist.

symbols, *n. pl.* Conventional designs used on drawings and records to represent circuit components and plant elements. A circle represents a pole, a rectangle a manhole, a line a conduit or cable, etc.

sync, *v.t.* Slang expression meaning "to synchronize," *i.e.:* to cause to agree in rate or speed.—*n.* Synchronization.

syncable, *adj.* Capable of being synchronized.

synchro, *n.* Any of several self-synchronous devices, of which the "selsyn" is the most common.

synchromonic frequencies, *n.* Frequencies used for party line selective ringing which are in the series 16, 30, 42, 54, and 66 Hz.

synchronization, *n.* The operation of two systems or two AC generators, or two oscillators at the same frequency and with the same phase relationship.

synchronize, *v.* To cause two systems or machines to operate at precisely the same frequency or speed, so that they are "in phase."

synchronizing pilot. See "tone pilot."

synchronizing pulse, *n.* A sharp pulse which causes two or more circuits to start operating at the same instant.

synchronous, *adj.* Describing a device whose speed of operation or rotation is controlled by other devices, such that they operate at the same speed.

synchronous converter, *n.* A rotary converter. See "converter, rotary."

synchronous operation, *n.* A method of on-line transmission of telegraphic or encrypted signals in which the sending and receiving terminal equipments are kept in step by a timing device, whether traffic is being passed or not.

synchronous system. See "system, synchronous."

SYNCOM II, *n.* A synchronous communication satellite placed in orbit over the mid-Pacific by NASA and operated by the Department of Defense. It has a capacity of two voice channels, and is expected to last until 1976. Presently (1970) has one ground terminal and one shipboard terminal.

synthesis, network, *n.* The derivation of the configuration and element values of a network with given electrical properties.

synthesizer, frequency, *n.* A highly precise crystal oscillator with frequency divider used to provide the precise radio frequency for carrier suppressed radio transmission. A typical synthesizer can be set to any 100 Hz step within the 2-30 MHz band, and will produce an output accurate in frequency to one part in 100 million.

syringe, hydrometer, *n.* A glass tube fitted on one end with a rubber bulb by which liquid can be drawn into the tube, and later be ejected. Used to withdraw a sample of the electrolyte from a storage cell in order to measure its specific gravity. See also "hydrometer."

system, all-relay, *n.* A switching system which uses only relays to accomplish the switching.

system, automanual telephone, *n.* A telephone system in which operators receive orders verbally from the calling parties, and then establish connections by using automatic switching equipment.

system, automatic switching, *n.* Any of the many systems for the automatic switching of circuits under the control of the person originating the call, or of switching (routing) digital messages under the

control of a message header. See also "circuit switching" and "message switching."

system, automatic telephone, *n.* A switching system through which telephone calls are routed automatically under control of the caller's dial.

system, automatic transmission measuring (ATMS), *n.* A system which automatically makes noise and two-way transmission measurements on two-wire or four-wire trunks, and prints out the actual deviation from the expected value.

system, balanced polyphase, *n.* A polyphase power system in which both the currents and voltages are symmetrical.

system, balanced three-wire, *n.* A three-wire electrical distribution system in which no current flows in the neutral conductor.

system, cable. See "cable system, - - -."

system, carrier, *n.* A system which enables passing a number of communication channels over a single comunication facility. See also "carrier system, - - -."

system, command conference, *n.* A circuit which permits a control station to originate a conference call to a group of PBX stations. If any of the called stations are busy, a tone is applied to the connection but the station is not cut off. When the connection is released, the station is immediately connected to the conference circuit.

system, crash alarm, *n.* A circuit which permits a control station to originate a conference call to a group of PBX stations which cuts off the PBX line equipment, then connects to and rings each conference station. As each station answers the conference call one of a group of supervisory lamps at the control station is lighted.

system, crossbar, *n.* An automatic telephone switching system using a crossbar switch. A common-control system having lines and trunks terminating on link frames, and interconnected by junctors under the control of markers. Its advantages are:

  a. Complete availability of large trunk groups.
  b. Decreased maintenance cost.
  c. Improved transmission due to precious metal contacts in the transmission path.

First used (#1) at Brooklyn, N.Y. in 1938.

system, dynamic gas pressure, *n.* A cable protection system which permits small leaks, but continuously feeds dry air into the cables at a pressure of 8 pounds per square inch from a compressor-dehydrator at the central office. The pressure is not permitted to drop below 2-3 lbs/square inch at the ends of the cables.

system, equivalent four-wire carrier, *n.* A two-wire carrier system which uses different frequency allocations for the West-East and East-West directions.

system, #5 crossbar switching, *n.* A 2-wire, local switching system for medium-sized areas (2000-20,000 lines) using crossbar switches and common-control equipment. It can interface with all present local, tandem, and toll-switching offices except some 2-wire panel offices.

system, #4A switching, *n.* A system for the four-wire switching of intertoll traffic using crossbar switches and common-control equipment.

system, gas pressure, *n.* (1) A network of cables, kept filled with dry gas under pressure. (2) A method of preventing moisture from entering cables by keeping them filled with dry gas under pressure. Both dry air and dry nitrogen are used.

system, grounded, *n.* An electrical system in which one conductor or a neutral point is intentionally grounded, either solidly or through a "grounding device."

system, group alerting, *n.* Central office equipment to provide emergency alerting to a pre-selected group of stations. When dialed from a control station, it makes a busy test on the lines to be alerted, rings those found idle, and sends 14 seconds of group alerting tone to the busy lines. Busy lines will be camped-on and connected to the alert when they become idle. All transmission is one way from the control station to the alerted stations. The alerted stations cannot communicate with each other or with the control station.

system, key telephone, *n.* A versatile station switching system located on the customer's premises, consisting of one or more multibutton (6, 12, 18, 24 or 30) telephone sets and associated relay equipment. Permits mutual access to and control of a number of central office lines. Provides pick-up, hold, signal, and intercommunication features.

system, loading, *n.* Any of the arrangements of loading coils applied to cables, designated by the following sequence of letters and numbers: (a) A number specifying the cable wire gauge, (b) a letter indicating the spacing between load coils, (c) a number specifying the pair or side circuit coil inductance in millihenries, and (d) a number specifying the phantom circuit inductance in millihenries. Typical systems are:

Exchange	Use
D-88	Loop & trunk
H-88	Loop & trunk
Toll	
H44-25	Four-wire toll
H88-50	Two-wire toll
H174-63	Two-wire toll

See also "spacing, load coil."

system, master reference, *n.* A primary reference telephone system for determining, by comparison, the performance of telephone systems and components with respect to loudness and articulation. This is done by adding loss to a distortionless standard system until its performance is equivalent to the system under test.

system, microwave relay, *n.* A multichannel communication system using radio transmission in the 2, 4, or 6 gigahertz bands, relayed every 20-30 miles. See also "system, TD microwave" and "system, TH microwave."

system, neutral telegraph. See "neutral telegraph system."

system, panel dial, *n.* An automatic switching system developed by the Bell System about 1920 for very large offices which is now obsolescent. Large banks of terminals on double-sided vertical panels are accessed by brushes moved up and down on vertical rods driven through magnetic clutches from continuously rotating electric motors. Uses revertive pulsing extensively.

system, panel switching, *n.* A two-wire local switching system using common-controlled motor driven selector brushes hunting over banks which are 500 trunks high. Now considered to be obsolescent.

system, Pentaconta switching. See "Pentaconta switching system."

system, primary distribution. See "primary distribution system."

system, public address, *n.* An assembly of microphones, amplifiers, and loud speakers, properly positioned, interconnected, and adjusted used for addressing large audiences, indoors or outdoors.

system, radio relay, *n.* A microwave radio system which uses a number of radio links in tandem to transmit for a considerable distance.

system, rotary switching. See "rotary switching system."

system, static gas pressure, *n.* A cable protection system where the terminal stub cables are plugged and all small leaks are repaired. Then the cables are filled with dry nitrogen gas at a pressure of 8 lbs/sq. in. and sealed. No gas flows through the cable, but the pressure

remains until a leak occurs. The cable pressure may require recharging periodically.

system, step-by-step, *n.* An automatic telephone switching system in which each call is extended progressively through a central office by a succession of switches which move step-by-step to the desired terminal under the direct control of the subscriber's dial, or a sender.

system, synchronous, *n.* A system in which the sending and receiving instruments operate at the same frequency and are maintained, by correction if required, in a uniform phase relationship.

system, TD-2 microwave, *n.* Long lines microwave used by Bell System between 1950-1960 which had 6 or 12 RF channels with triode amplifiers operating at 4 GHz. Each RF channel had a capacity of 500 voice channels.

system, TD-2A microwave, *n.* A Bell System long lines microwave system applied starting 1968 which has 12 RF channels with triode amplifiers working at 4 GHZ. Each RF channel has a capacity of 1000 voice channels.

system, TD-3 microwave, *n.* A solid-state version of the TD-2 microwave system.

system, telephone, *n.* A complete system for telephonic communication, including telephone sets, subscriber's loops, switching centers, and trunks.

system, TH microwave, *n.* Long lines microwave used by Bell System between 1961-1966 which had 8 RF channels with traveling wave tube amplifiers operating at 6 GHz. Each RF channel had a capacity of 1860 voice channels.

system, TH-3 microwave, *n.* A newer version of the TH microwave system which is entirely solid-state except for the traveling wave tube.

system, transmission. See "transmission system."

system, transposition, *n.* One of

many orderly schemes for interchanging the position of wires on an open wire line in order to reduce crosstalk and noise induction.

system, Unigauge. See "Unigauge system."

system, working reference. See "working reference system."

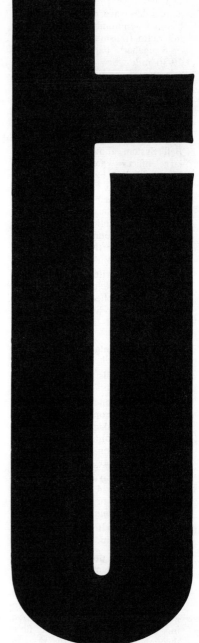

table, trunk adjustment, *n.* Tabular data showing the number of trunks which should be added (or may be subtracted) from a given-sized trunk group to provide a desired traffic grade of service, as related to the number of ATB, LTB, or OF conditions experienced.

table, truth. See "truth table."

tabulator, *n.* (1) An electromechanical temporary memory device which receives data on automatically ticketed toll calls from a ticketer, sorts this information into the proper sequence, then transfers it to the tape perforating equipment. (2) An electromechanical device that reads punched cards, sorts the information, and produces tabulated lists.

tacker, *n.* Staple gun used for fastening inside wires and small cables.

tag, *v.t.* To identify cable pairs by pair number, usually by passing the pair through a numbered hole in a tag board.

tag, cable, *n.* (1) Round or octagonal tags of 1/16-inch sheet lead, with a ⅛-inch hole for lashing wire. Are stamped with (a) cable size and gauge, (b) cable number, and (c) pair count, then tied to cables in manholes as a designation. Octagonal tags are used for toll; round for exchange cables. (2) Rectangular tag of 3/64-inch sheet lead, made with a tongue and eye for fastening around a terminal stub cable.

tag, duct splice, *n.* A lead tag, to be soldered around a cable in the manholes at each end of a section containing a duct splice, and stamped with the distance in feet from the end wall of the manhole to the duct splice.

tag, pair identification, *n.* White plastic tag, about 1 x 2 inches, with a split hole for snapping over wires or binding post screws. Will accept pencil or pen designations.

tag, pole, *n.* A strip aluminum tag to be nailed to a pole, and embossed with the following minimum data: (a) The initials of the company· owning the pole, and (b) the serial number of the pole.

tag, terminal, *n.* A metal tag placed around a cable terminal stub cable and embossed with the terminal pair count.

tag board, *n.* A strip of cloth, fiber, or leather with 26 or 51 numbered holes, used to establish pair number identity during cable splicing operations.

tagging, *n.* In cable splicing, the act of numbering cable pairs as they are identified, by passing them through a numbered hole in a "tag board."

tailing, *n.* Hangover of a pulse.

talk-back circuit, *n.* Any of the several arrangements to povide sidetone to persons using four-wire telephones. It usually is an isolation amplifier connected from the transmit to the receive leg of the same four-wire circuit.

talk key. See "key, talk."

talk-off, *n.* The false disconnection of circuits due to the high energy of voice signals momentarily simulating an on-hook signal.

tamper. See "bar, tamping."

tandem, *n.* A switching arrangement, in which the trunk from the calling office is connected to a trunk to the called office through an intermediate point known as a tandem switching center.

tandem, toll. See "control switching point."

tandem office. See "office, tandem."

tandem trunk, *n.* A trunk to or from a tandem office.

tangent support. See "support, tangent."

tank, gas, *n.* A heavy-walled steel tank in which gas (nitrogen, acetylene, propane, etc.) can be stored at a pressure sufficient to keep the gas in a liquid state.

tank circuit, *n.* A circuit composed of lumped inductance and capacitance capable of storing electrical energy over a band of frequencies centered around the resonant frequency of the circuit.

tap, *n*. (1) A branch circuit. (2) A connection brought out from an intermediate point of a coil or winding.—*v*. To make a tapped connection.

tap, bridged, *n*. Any portion of the cable pair which is not in the useful path of the circuit. For instance: an extension of a cable beyond the point where the circuit ends, or a branch cable which is bridged on the same cable count. A bridged tap impairs transmission, for it acts like a capacitor bridged across the working circuit.

tap, CATV back-matched, *n*. A CATV tap which uses transformer isolation, and thus provides excellent impedance matching and avoids "ghosts."

tap, CATV capacitive, *n*. A device for tapping a subscriber's drop from a CATV cable which incorporates a capacitor-resistor network which causes a higher loss at the lower frequencies, thus compensating for the opposite slope of the subscriber's drop cable.

tap, CATV directional, *n*. A wye junction for insertion in a CATV cable which gives a low loss (0.2 db to 1.0 db) to the through cable, but gives maximum isolation (20-35 db) for the tap.

tap, CATV pressure, *n*. A fitting for a CATV cable having a threaded pointed probe which penetrates the coaxial shield and contacts the center conductor. Used to make a tap from a CATV cable without cutting it.

tap, compression, *n*. A solderless connector which can be used to clamp a branch power conductor to a main power conductor without cutting it.

tap, distribution wire, *n*. A compact, pole-mounted, w e a t h e r p r o o f wire terminal through which rural dis-

tribution wires pass and are terminated without cutting on a terminal block, to which drop wires can be bridged. Available in 6, 11, 12, and 16 pair sizes, with and without arresters.

tap, gutter, *n*. A solderless compression connector which can be used to clamp a branch power conductor onto the main conductor. Can then be taped and left in the wiring gutter.

tape, *n*. (1) Magnetic tape. (2) Punched tape. (3) A relatively narrow strip of fabric, paper, or plastic, woven or cut, with or without an adhesive coating. Many types are used, such as: friction tape, lead tape, muslin tape, plastic tape, rubber tape.

tape, aluminum, *n*. A ½-inch wide tape of soft, pure aluminum having a pressure-sensitive adhesive on one side. Used to provide an electrostatic shield at splices in shielded cable, or to provide a moisture barrier.

tape, AMA (Automatic message accounting), *n*. Oil impregnated 3-inch wide paper tape with space for 28 holes punched across the tape. The tape is advanced 0.1 inch after each punch. These punch marks encode all of the information needed for billing the telephone call.

tape, chad, *n*. A punched tape in which the paper at the perforations is completely removed, leaving a. clean round hole.

tape, chadless, *n*. A punched tape in which the paper at the perforation is not completely severed, but is left as a flap, thereby permitting the alphanumeric characters represented by the perforations to be printed on the tape.

tape, cigarette wrap, *n*. An insulating tape, often of Teflon, applied longitudinally rather than spirally to a conductor or cable.

tape, closure sealing, *n*. Sealing compound provided in 1½-inch wide tape, used to make the end seals around a cable where it enters a splice case closure.

tape, DR, *n.* A wide rubber tape which has a layer of white unvulcanized tacky rubber bonded to a colored ply of vulcanized rubber. A removable protector covers the tacky side. Used for temporarily closing incomplete splices. Available in ¾-inch and 2-inch widths.

tape, electrical, *n.* Any tape which, because of its insulating and voltage-breakdown characteristics, can substitute for the normal insulation of an electrical conductor at splices.

tape, fish, *n.* A spring-tempered narrow steel tape having a loop on one end. Can be pushed through a conduit or building partition and then used to pull (fish) a wire or cable from the far end.

tape, friction, *n.* An impregnated adhesive cloth tape used to hold insulation in place. Available in ¾-inch and 2-inch widths.

tape, laminated, *n.* An insulating tape consisting of two or more layers, usually of different materials.

tape, lashing, *n.* A flat, extruded nylon tape about 5/16-inch wide used for the lashing of aerial cable. Particularly useful in salt spray and corrosive atmosphere areas.

tape, lead serving, *n.* Tape of metallic lead, 1/32 inch thick by 1½ inch wide. Used to wrap around cable sheaths to protect them from cutting by grade clamps, or to build up the cable diameter when it is too small for the clamp.

tape, magnetic, *n.* A plastic tape having one side smoothly coated with magnetizable iron oxide particles, in which audio or radio frequencies can be recorded as variations of the magnetization. The common size is ¼-inch wide, but other widths to 1-inch are used.

tape, marker, *n.* A longitudinal tape under the sheath of a cable which shows the manufacturer's name and the cable specification number.

tape, measuring, *n.* A long narrow band of linen, fiberglass, or steel graduated in feet, and the feet graduated in tenths or twelfths, used to make accurate measurements of length. Usually arranged so that it can be coiled up inside a case when not in use.

tape, plastic electrical, *n.* A tape having a stretchy, rubber-like vinyl plastic backing that enables it to substitute for both rubber and friction tape.

tape, punched, *n.* A paper tape, 11/16-inch to 1-inch wide, on which data or information is coded with punched holes. There may be from five to eight holes across the tape, plus a line of tiny sprocket drive holes. A punched hole indicates a "mark," and lack of a hole indicates a "space."

tape, rubber, *n.* Tape of new live rubber which is tacky both sides, and is therefore rolled with an interleaved varnished cloth tape. Used to insulate splices in rubber-insulated power conductors, and is then covered with a layer of friction tape. Available in ¾-inch and 2-inch widths.

tape, sealing, *n.* Tape used to assist in making a gas-tight seal on the ends of splice cases.

tape, skived, *n.* Tape made by shaving a thin layer from a cylindrical block of material.

tape, #22 electrical, *n.* A heavy-duty vinyl plastic tape of 0.010 inch thickness, available in widths of ¾ ", 1", and 2 inches. Used to seal and insulate splices on rubber and plastic cables, to wrap bus bars, and to provide moisture and oil protection on flexible conduit.

tape, #27 electrical, *n.* A flame-resistant glass cloth tape having a pressure-sensitive thermosetting adhesive. Sets at high temperatures to form a strong permanent bond. Available in 1-inch width.

tape, #88 electrical, *n.* A general purpose, all-weather, flame-retardant, tough vinyl plastic which has high electrical, mechanical, and tensile strength. Available in ¾ ″, 1 ″, 1½ ″, and 2-inch widths.

tape deck. See "transport, tape."

tape perforator. See "perforator, tape."

taper, *n.* The type of resistance distribution in a potentiometer, whether linear, left-hand, or right-hand. With linear taper, resistance increases uniformly with rotation of the knob. With left-hand taper, there is little change at the left end, but an increasing rate of change as the knob is turned to the right. A right-hand taper starts with a large change which gets progressively smaller as the knob is turned to the right.

tape reader. See "reader, paper tape."

tape recorder, *n.* A mechanical-electrical device that records signals by selective magnetization of iron oxide particles which are coated on a thin plastic tape.

tape relay. See "relay, tape."

tape relay, automatic, *n.* A method of store-and-forward teletypewriter operation which stores incoming messages, automatically routes to their destination, and forwards when the proper circuit is idle.

tape relay, manual. See "tape relay, torn-tape."

tape relay, semi-automatic, *n.* A teletypewriter message switching system in which an operator at a push-button console directs incoming messages to the proper outgoing channel.

tape relay, torn-tape, *n.* A manual method of store-and-forward teletypewriter operation which receives incoming messages on paper tape, which is then torn off and carried to a transmitter on the appropriate outgoing circuit.

tape relay center. See "center, tape relay."

tapes, intercalated, *n. pl.* Several tapes, applied spirally to a cable core in such a manner that a portion of each tape overlays a portion of another.

tape speed, *n.* The speed, in inches per second, that magnetic tape is drawn past the recording and playback heads on a tape recorder. Normal speeds are 1⅞, 3¾, and 7½ inches per second, but 15 and 30 inches per second are also used where very high fidelity reproduction is required.

tape wrap, *n.* A tape material spirally or longitudinally wrapped around a wire or cable core. Used either as insulation or as a mechanical barrier.

tapped resistor, *n.* A fixed resistor which has one or more intermediate terminals between those at the two ends. Used as a voltage divider, or to obtain a neutral voltage (center-tap) point.

tapping, wire. See "wiretapping."

tariff, *n.* A document filed by a Communication Company with the Public Utilities Commission which lists the communication services offered by the Company and gives a schedule of rates and charges.

tarnish, *n.* A discoloration or stain on the surface of a metal, caused by exposure to chemicals or to the atmosphere.—*v.t.* To dull or destroy the lustre of a metal.

tarp, *n.* A tarpaulin (Slang).

tarpaulin, *n.* (1) A canvas canopy. (2) A rectangle of heavy, waterproof canvas duck used to spread over materials to keep them from getting wet. Usually equipped along the edge with grommets for rope ties.

technical load, *n.* The portion of total power load which is necessary for uninterrupted communications. Usually the load of communications equipment, but may include also indispensable lighting and air conditioning.

tech rep, *n.* Technical representative. A manufacturers representative who gives advice and assistance in the application, use, maintenance, and repair of his company's products.

tee, hybrid. See "hybrid tee."

tee junction, *n.* A junction of waveguides in which the branches are in the shape of a letter "T." The waveguide which continues through the junction is the main guide, while the waveguide which terminates is the branch guide.

Teflon, *n.* Dupont's name for tetrafluorethylene, a tough heat and chemical-resistant plastic used as a radio-frequency insulator.

telautograph, *n.* A record communication system in which writing movement at the transmitting end causes corresponding movement of a writing instrument at the receiving end.

telecast, *n.* A television broadcast.

telecommunication, *adj.* Pertaining to the art and science of telecommunication.—*n.* (1) Communication over a distance by telephone, radio, telegraph, etc. (2) Any transmission, emission, or reception of signs, signals, writing, images, or sounds, or intelligence of any nature by wire, radio, visual, or other electromagnetic systems. (DCS)

telecommunications, *n. pl.* (1) The aggregate of several modes of conveying information, signals, or messages over a distance. (2) The art and science of communicating at a distance. (Note: TELECOMMUNICATIONS is a plural noun, never an adjective. The adjective is "telecommunication," without the terminal "S,")

Telecommunications Service Request (TSR), *n.* An 80-column punched card form used by the Defense Communications Agency (DCA) for transmitting requests for new telecommunication service.

telecon, *n.* A teletypewriter conference.

telegram, *n.* Written matter intended to be transmitted by telegraphy. This term also normally includes a radiotelegram.

telegraph, *n.* A system of communication using coded signals. Several types are recognized:

(a) Manual telegraph, using keys and sounders, with wire lines.
(b) Printing telegraph. such as the stock ticker.
(c) Teletypewriters.
(d) Radio telegraph.

telegraph, bridge-duplex, *n.* A duplex telegraph system in which the separation of send and receive currents is accomplished with a Wheatstone bridge circuit. The receive relay is bridged between points which are of equal potential for the sent currents.

telegraph, differential duplex, *n.* A system which enables simultaneous two-way transmission over a single wire grounded telegraph circuit. Each terminal consists of two relays. The send relay, operated from a local keying circuit, provides polar reversals to the mid-point of the receive relay where the current divides to line and network without affecting the receive relay. At the far end of the circuit, the line current operates the receive relay which controls a local sounder circuit.

telegraph, inverse-neutral, *n.* A system of telegraph transmission in which no current flows during marking intervals, and current flows during spacing intervals.

telegraph, neutral, *n.* The telegraph system in which signals are transmitted by opening and closing the circuit. A closed circuit (current flowing) provides a mark signal, while an open circuit (no current) provides the space signal.

telegraph, polar, *n.* The telegraph system in which signals are transmitted by reversing the direction (polarity) of current flow in the telegraph line.

telegraph carrier. See "carrier, voice-frequency telegraph."

telegraph concentrator. See "concentrator, telegraph."

telegraph hub circuit. See "hub, telegraph."

telegraph key, *n.* A hand-operated

switch, which can be opened and closed rapidly to form the dots and dashes of the Morse code.

telegraph leg, balanced. See "leg, balanced telegraph."

telegraph repeater. See "repeater, regenerative," "repeater, single-line telegraph," "repeater, telegraph," and "repeater, telegraph loop."

telegraph selector. See "selector, Gill."

telegraph transmission coefficient. See "coefficient, telegraph transmission."

telegraphy, *n.* The art of communicating at a distance by means of coded current pulses sent over wire circuits. See also "code, Morse," "sounder, - - -," and "telegraph key."

telegraphy, carrier, *n.* A method of telegraph transmission in which a carrier wave is modulated by telegraph signals, and the modulated wave is transmitted.

telegraphy, multiplex printing, *n.* A multi-channel form of printing telegraphy in which one telegraph line serves several telegraph channels in sequence by time division.

telegraphy, printing, *n.* Any system of telegraph operation in which the received signals are automatically recorded in printed characters.

Tele-Lecture, *n.* Bell System designation for an educational system to provide two-way amplified voice communication between a lecturer and scattered remote classrooms.

telemeter, *v.* To transmit the readings of measuring instruments at a remote location to a central control point, by electrical means.

Telepak, *n.* (1) Acronym for "telephone package." (2) A schedule of bulk discount rates for multiple private line services between a given pair of points. (3) A tariff offering which provides substantially lower rates when a subscriber contracts for all the channels of a carrier system. The packages are in several sizes:

Telepak A — 12 channels
Telepak B — 24 channels

Telepak C — 60 channels
Telepak D — 240 channels

telephone, *n.* A system for conveying speech over a distance by converting the sound energy into electric waves, transmitting these waves to the distant point, and there re-converting them into sound waves reproducing the original speech. In addition to the telephone instruments and transmission facilities, it uses switching facilities, signaling devices, and central direct current power supplies.

telephone, antisidetone, *n.* A telephone set having a balancing network arranged so that only a fraction of the transmitter power reaches the receiver.

telephone, coin, *n.* A telephone for paystation use. A wall telephone having a heavy cast locking case equipped with a coin chute and coin receptacle in addition to the usual handset, hookswitch, dial, and transmission unit. Uses a separate ringer box, if required.

telephone, common battery, *n.* A telephone instrument which is designed to be powered from a "common battery" at the central office.

telephone, desk, *n.* Any telephone, single line or multiple key, suitable for use on a desk. Single line desk telephones usually contain all the components of a complete telephone.

telephone, field, *n.* A portable telephone intended for use in the field. Usually capable of working on either common-battery or magneto lines.

telephone, fire-reporting, *n.* A red weatherproof manual telephone, pole or pedestal mounted, and connected directly to a fire-reporting switchboard. See also "switchboard, fire-reporting."

telephone, hands-free. See "telephone, speaker-type" or "Speakerphone."

telephone, hand test. *n.* A telephone handset whose cord is terminated in test clips or in a test plug, for use in central office or outside plant testing. The handset may include a dial and a monitoring capacitor.

telephone, hard-of-hearing, *n.* A telephone set having a transistor amplifier, powered with line current, which amplifies the signal into the receiver.

telephone, hazardous location. See "telephone, mine."

telephone, key. See "set, key telephone."

telephone, local battery, *n.* A telephone instrument whose transmitter current is furnished from a pair of dry cells at the telephone. It may use either "common-battery signaling" or "magneto signaling."

telephone, magneto, *n.* A telephone instrument which has a magneto hand generator for signaling the switchboard to which it is connected.

telephone, message waiting, *n.* A desk telephone for hotel or motel service which has a small lamp in its base which can be lighted from a central control cabinet as a notice to call the desk for a held message. See also "message waiting service."

telephone, mine, *n.* A combined telephone set for use in mines, oil refineries, and other locations which may have an explosive atmosphere. All components which might produce sparks, such as the dial and hookswitch are enclosed in a gastight housing.

telephone, multiline, *n.* A desk telephone equipped with keys in the base which enable the pickup, and sometimes the holding, of two or three separate PBX or central office lines.

telephone, outdoor, *n.* A telephone in a cast metal case for pole or wall mounting, and having a hinged watertight door to cover the handset and dial. Used at taxi stands, etc.

telephone, panel, *n.* A flush-mounting wall telephone, which fits into a steel box recessed 2 inches into the wall. All of the telephone components mount on the back of a 9x12 inch panel except the handset and the dial, either rotary or touch-tone. The hookswitch protrudes through the front of the panel.

telephone, railroad, *n.* A local-battery magneto telephone for use on railroad party lines.

telephone, sound-powered. See "sound-powered telephone."

telephone, speaker-type, *n.* A telephone having a transistorized voice-switched microphone and speaker system which permits hands-free conversation.

telephone, wall, *n.* A telephone designed for surface mounting on a wall. See also "telephone, panel."

Telephone Answering Service (TAS), *n.* A company whose business is answering telephone calls for customers at times when the customer is away from his office.

telephone answering set. See "set, telephone answering."

telephone central office. See "central office."

telephone channel. See "channel, voice."

telephone dial. See "dial, subscriber's."

telephone exchange. See "exchange."

Telephone Influence Factor (TIF), *n.* The reading obtained on a "TIF Meter" which gives a relative indication of the harmonic content of the voltage wave of the power circuit to which it is connected, and therefore of the power circuit influence. Used to estimate the interference which may result on an exposed telephone circuit. See also "influence," "coupling," and "susceptiveness."

telephone line. See "line, subscriber's."

telephone number, *n.* The seven-digit number assigned to a telephone, comprised of a 3-digit central office code (or central office name and numeral) and a 4-digit station number.

telephone operator. See "operator."

telephone package (TELEPAK). See "Telepak."

telephone receiver. See "receiver, telephone" and "earphone."

telephone ringer. See "ringer."

telephone set. See "set, - - -."

telephone station. See "station, telephone."

telephone switchboard. See "switchboard, - - -."

telephone system. See "system, telephone."

telephone transmitter. See "transmitter, telephone."

telephony, *n.* The art and science of conveying speech sounds over distances by converting them into analog electrical signals which can be transmitted over wires or via radio.

telephony, carrier. See "carrier telephony."

telephoto, *n.* The transmission of pictures by wire or radio.

teleprinter, *n.* (1) A teletypewriter. (2) An electromechanical device which prints alphanumeric characters on a paper tape, such as a stock "ticker."

Telering converter, *n.* Registered name of a device which will supply 20 Hz ringing power when energized with 60 Hz commercial power. Consists of a transformer whose secondary is resonant at 20 Hz.

TELESTAR I, *n.* The first active communication satellite, launched 10 July 1962 and still orbiting. It weighed 170 pounds and carried a traveling wave tube transmitter powered by nickel-cadmium batteries charged by solar cells. It was silenced by radiation damage on 21 February 1963, after 226 days of use. Its orbital period was 158 minutes, with an apogee of 3531 miles, and a perigee of 592 miles.

TELESTAR II, *n.* The second active communication satellite, launched 7 May 1963, and still orbiting. Its transmitter was turned off 16 May 1965. Its orbital period was 225 minutes, with an apogee of 6713 miles and a perigee of 604 miles.

Teletype, *n.* The registered trade mark of teletypewriter products produced by the Teletype Corporation.

Teletypesetter (TTYS), *n.* A special type of teletypewriter equipment which is linked to a Linotype machine and which sets the message in lead type.

teletypewriter, *n.* An electric typewriter device which generates a coded signal corresponding to the typed character. This electrical signal may be passed over transmission facilities and used to control a similar teletypewriter at a distance.

teletypewriter, start-stop. See "start-stop teletypewriter."

teletypewriter code. See "code, Baudot" and "code, ITA #2."

teletypewriter conference. See "conference, teletypewriter."

teletypewriter exchange service (TWX), *n.* A service given by the Telephone Company whereby a customer's leased teletypewriter is connected to a "TWX" switchboard, and from there can be connected over the regular toll circuits to a teletypewriter of any customer in the United States who subscribes to similar service.

televise, *v.t.* (1) To scan with a television camera. (2) To transmit a television signal.

television, *n.* A system for the conversion of transient visual images into electrical signals which can be transmitted by radio or wire to distant receivers where the signals can be reconverted to the original visual images.

television, community antenna, *n.* A system to supply television program signals to a community of homes via a network of distribution cables. Consists of a central well-situated tower with antennas to pick up television and FM radio signals, combiners and amplifiers, a distribution coaxial cable with spaced line amplifiers, and taps for the subscriber's drop cables.

television, master antenna, *n.* A system to supply television program signals to a concentration of television sets, such as in an apartment building. Consists of one or several antennas which pick up the television signals, feed them through a hybrid to a broadband amplifier, then through splitters (signal dividers) to the individual television outlets.

television broadcast band. See "band, broadcast."

television cable. See "cable, coaxial."

television demodulator. See "demodulator, television."

television modulator. See "modulator, television."

television signal, *n.* The radio frequency signal which contains both aural and visual intelligence, or the sound and the picture. See also "signal, television" and "television standards."

television standards, *n.* Television in the United States is in accordance with CCIR Standard M, as follows:

Lines per frame	— 525
Interlace	— 2 to 1
Frames per second	— 30
Video bandwidth	— 4.2 MHz
Radio bandwidth	— 6.0 MHz
Audio modulation	— F3
Polarization	— Horizontal
Horizontal scanning (B&W)	— 15,750 Hz
Horizontal scanning (color)	— 15,734 Hz
Vertical scanning (B&W)	— 60 Hz
Vertical scanning (color)	— 59.94 Hz

Television in Canada, Mexico, Panama, Japan, Korea, Iran, Saudi Arabia, and the Netherlands Antilles uses these same standards.

television translator. See "translator, television."

Telewriting, *n.* Bell System designation for an educational TV system to supplement Tele-Lecture.

Telex, *n.* Western Union's name for its teletypewriter exchange service.

temperature, noise. See "noise temperature."

temperature coefficient. See "coefficient, temperature."

temperature compensation, *n.* (1) The process of making some important characteristic of a circuit independent of temperature changes. (2) The practice of having some component in a circuit, usually a capacitor, change with temperature in such a way as to compensate for temperature changes in other components, and thereby keep the frequency of the circuit constant.

temperature inversion. See "inversion, temperature."

temperometer, *n.* An indicating thermometer, direct reading on a 2½ inch diameter dial. The stainless steel stem can be inserted in hot paraffin or wax, and be read at a distance. Calibrated for the range 200-1000 degrees Fahrenheit.

tensile strength, *n.* The pulling stress required to break a material, such as a wire. Stated in pounds of stress per square inch of cross-sectional area.

tension, *n.* (1) Electric-potential or potential difference. Voltage. (2) Mechanical stress caused by forces which tend to stretch the material stressed.

tent, splicers aerial, *n.* A white 10-oz. canvas tent, 4 ft. square by 8 ft. high, supported by a three-ribbed metal framework which fastens to the cable strand. Side openings lace from the inside. Used to protect the splice and splicer when working on an aerial platform.

tent, splicer's ground, *n.* A white 10-oz. canvas tent, 6 ft. high, 3 ft. square at the top, 6 ft. square at the bottom, with a sod flap except at the opening. Supported with an iron pipe framework. Used to place over the manhole opening when making underground cable splices in inclement weather.

tera-, *n.* The metric prefix meaning one million million. Abbreviated T.

terminal, *n.* A point at which a circuit

element may be directly connected to one or more other elements.

terminal, aerial cable, *n.* A cable terminal which mounts on the cable suspension strand near the pole, or on the pole, and is spliced to the distribution cable.

terminal, buried cable, *n.* A cable terminal in which pairs of a buried cable are terminated. Usually held in a pedestal through which the buried cable loops.

terminal, cable, *n.* A weatherproof housing with a cover, containing binding posts which are connected via a stub cable to a distribution cable. Makes the cable pairs available for use as required.

terminal, crossconnecting, *n.* A cable terminal at a junction of two cables which terminates pairs from both cables so that they can be crossconnected when needed. Often used at the junctions between a feeder cable and the distribution cables it serves.

terminal, data, *n.* The aggregate of equipment employed at the end of a transmission system for the transmission or reception of data, including the end instrument and data sets or signal converters.

terminal, dispatch, *n.* A direct connection from a customer's phone to a mobile radio switchboard to facilitate connections to the mobile radio system.

terminal, East. See "East terminal."

terminal, gas-tight, *n.* A cable terminal having a pressure plug in its stub cable, so that it can be used on a pressurized cable without loss of gas pressure.

terminal, in-and-out, *n.* A cable terminal at which some or all of the pairs are cut and terminated in both directions. A pair so terminated can be used at the in-and-out terminal free from the bridged tap loss of the cable which continues, or can be connected "through" for use at another more remote terminal.

terminal, L.D., *n.* Appearance directly

on a toll switchboard of a line from a subscriber's phone or PBX. Used for placing toll calls expeditiously.

terminal, looping, *n.* A terminal used on plastic cables, in which the cable is looped through the terminal without cutting. The sheath is removed from the cable within the terminal, and the desired pairs are connected to the terminal studs.

terminal, master carrier, *n.* A carrier terminal whose operating frequencies are determined by a very stable oscillator (plus or minus one part per million for 30 days) which sends a 96 kHz pilot signal over the carrier line to synchronize the slave terminal at the far end of the circuit.

terminal, mobile radio control, *n.* A control unit connected between dial switching equipment and base station radio units which performs control, signaling, and switching functions, regulates speech levels and provides a two-wire to four-wire transition.

terminal, protected cable, *n.* A cable terminal in which each cable pair is protected against excessive voltage by a pair of carbon blocks.

terminal, protected crossconnecting, *n.* A crossconnecting cable terminal which inserts a pair of 7-ampere fuses in the crossconnection.

terminal, quick-connect, *n.* A strip of 2-6 tin-plated spring clips, electrically and mechanically common, held in a moulded terminal block. A special tool presses the insulated conductor into the slot of the quick-connect clip. The clip cuts away the insulation to make contact, and the tool follow-through seats the conductor and trims off the excess wire.

terminal, ready-access, *n.* A moulded plastic splice closure which has one or more 6-pair terminal blocks mounted inside.

terminal, slave carrier, *n.* A carrier terminal whose operating frequencies are synchronized by a highly stable 96 kHz pilot signal received from the "master carrier terminal."

terminal, solderless, *n.* A terminal or lug which holds the conductor it terminates by screw compression.

terminal, splice case, *n.* An aerial cable terminal mounted on and forming a part of a splice case closure.

terminal, strand-mounted, *n.* A cable terminal which is supported by being clamped to the cable supporting strand rather than being fastened to the pole. Permits replacing the pole without disturbing the terminal.

terminal, toll. See "toll terminal."

terminal, underground cable, *n.* A waterproof cable terminal designed for installation in an underground manhole. Equipped with a watertight gasketed clamped cover. Service cables leave the terminal through stuffing boxes.

terminal, unprotected cable, *n.* A cable terminal which does not have either carbon block or fuse protection.

terminal, watchcase, *n.* A small single pair wire terminal which clamps onto the support wire, and serves to make connection between a drop wire and multi-pair distribution wire. Consists of a round plastic base with molded-in binding posts, and having a flexible snap-on neoprene cover.

terminal, West. See "West terminal."

terminal, wire, *n.* A terminal without a stub cable, used to terminate multi-pair distribution wire. Available in protected and unprotected types, in sizes from 6 pairs to 26 pairs.

terminal, wire-wrap, *n.* A terminal of square cross-section having sharp corners and suitable for wrapped connections.

terminal assembly, distributing. See "distributing terminal assembly."

terminal block. See "block, terminal."

terminal (grade) circuit, *n.* A toll circuit between an end office and a toll center, whose high loss limits its use to terminal traffic only.

terminal equipment, *n.* (1) Equipment at the terminal of a communication circuit. (2) Equipment at a subscriber's or user's terminal. May include telephones, key systems, PBXs, etc.

terminal net loss (TNL). See "loss, terminal net."

terminal pair, *n.* The designation of a particular pair of binding posts in a terminal, used to simplify the work of telephone installers and repairmen. A 16-pair terminal has terminal pairs 1 through 16, even though they may terminate cable 2601, pairs 1025-1040.

terminal-per-line, *n. adj.* A party-line system which assigns only one connector terminal to each party line. A 3-digit connector selects the ringing frequency of the desired party.

terminal-per-station, *n. adj.* A switching system which uses a connector terminal for each party on a party line. A two-digit connector is used. Frequency selection may be by using different connector shelves, or by using a special terminal-per-station connector with a 400-point bank, on which the EC lead is connected to matched pulse bunching block to select the proper ringing frequency. Two-party divided ringing may also be used.

terminal repeater, *n.* A repeater, either voice or pulse, used at the end of a trunk, as distinguished from an intermediate repeater.

terminal room, *n.* In a manual central office, the room which contains the distributing frames and the relay equipment associated with the switchboard. In a dial office that equipment is combined with the switching equipment in a "switchroom."

terminals, *n. pl.* Of any equipment or circuit, the screws or soldering lugs to which an external circuit can be connected.

terminate, *v.t.* (1) To connect a line to a terminal, distributing frame, switch, or matrix. (2) To bridge an impedance onto a line so as to remove impedance irregularities and stabilize voice repeaters which otherwise might sing.

terminated, *adj.* (1) The condition of a wire or cable pair which is connected to (terminated on) binding posts or a terminal block. (2) The condition of a circuit which is connected to a network which has the same impedance the circuit would have if it were infinitely long. See also "iterative impedance."

terminating link, *n.* A toll connecting trunk: one which connects a toll office to a local "end" office. See also "toll connecting trunk."

terminating set, *n.* A network of resistors and adjustable capacitors, sometimes with hybrid coils, used to provide a compromise termination to 600 ohm or 900 ohm two-wire or four-wire trunks. Assembled in a can for relay rack mounting.

terminating toll center (TTC), *n.* The toll center through which the called telephone is reached.

termination, *n.* (1) The connection of a line to (a) a terminal, (b) a distributing frame, (c) a switch, or (d) a matrix. (2) An iterative impedance connected to the end of a line while it is being tested. (3) An idle line termination, which see.

termination, balanced, *n.* For a network or circuit having two output terminals, a load which presents the same impedance to ground for each of the output terminals.

termination, balance test, *n.* A unit which is connected to the far end of a line in order to test it for balance.

termination, idle line, *n.* An electrical network that is bridged across the terminal of a carrier or repeated circuit in the idle condition which maintains the hybrid balance, and ensures that the circuit will not sing when idle.

termination, matched, *n.* (1) Terminating a line in its iterative impedance. (2) Terminating a line so that, from the sending end, it appears to be of infinite electrical length.

termination, midcoil, *n.* The ending of a loaded cable at a load point, one full loading section away from the adjacent load point, but terminating it in a loading coil having one-half the inductance of the other loading coils.

termination, mid-section, *n.* The termination of a loaded cable at an office such that the loading end section is one-half the length of the normal loading section.

termination, mid-series, *n.* The termination of a network, consisting of a number of "T" sections in series, at the mid-point of a series element.

termination, mid-shunt, *n.* The termination of a network, consisting of a number of "pi" sections in series, such that the termination is a shunt element of double the impedance of the normal shunt element.

term set, *n.* A terminating set (Slang). See also "set, four-wire terminating."

tertiary circuit, *n.* A third circuit, through which crosstalk currents flow in traveling from the disturbing circuit to a disturbed circuit.

tertiary winding, *n.* A third winding on a transformer or relay coil.

test, *n.* A procedure or sequence of operations and tests to determine whether a circuit is operating properly and, if not, the type and location of troubles.

test, busy, *n.* An automatic or manual test to determine whether a circuit is busy. An automatic switch may search for "absence of ground" on a control contact which indicates the circuit is not busy. An operator may touch the tip of a plug to a jack sleeve and detect a busy by a click in her head receiver.

test, capacitance unbalance, *n.* A test

made on a quadded cable at a test splice point to determine the capacitance unbalance which exists between the three circuits: (a) white side to black side, (b) white side to phantom, and (c) black side to phantom. The two sections of cable will then be spliced together so that the unbalances in one section of cable neutralize those in the other section. See also "splice, final test" and "splice, semi-final test."

test, coin, *n.* In a crossbar office, a test made either by the originating register or by a coin supervisory circuit to detect the presence of a coin in the trap of a coin telephone.

test, friendly busy, *n.* To test a circuit to determine if it is busy without taking any action to disturb a call in progress.

test, hostile busy, *n.* To test a circuit to determine if it is busy, and if found busy to automatically preempt after giving a warning of preempt tone.

test, stability. See "stability test."

test, tank, *n.* A voltage dielectric test for wire or cable in which the specimen is submerged in a liquid (usually water) and a high voltage applied between the conductor(s) and the grounded liquid.

test, tip-busy, *n.* A method of testing a switchboard jack to determine whether its associated circuit is busy. To make the test, the operator takes a cord to which her operator's telephone circuit has been connected and touches the "tip" of the plug to the "sleeve" of the jack. If the circuit is busy, battery potential on the sleeve of the jack will cause a click in her receiver.

testboard, *n.* A manual switchboard equipped with instruments for testing both the outside plant and the inside plant. See "testboard, toll" and "test desk, local."

testboard, toll, *n.* A manual board on which all of the toll cable pairs entering a toll center appear on "LINE" and "EQUIP"(ment) jacks.

The board is equipped with primary and secondary test cords, a 150V voltmeter circuit, and a Wheatstone bridge, enabling testing and location of troubles, and rerouting or substitution of circuits by patching. See also: "patchboard" and "board, test and control."

test center. See "center, test."

test clip, *n.* Terminal for a testing lead consisting of a pair of spring-closing metal jaws which can be clamped on any terminal to which a temporary test connection is required. Sometimes equipped with needle points for making connection through the insulation.

test desk, local, *n.* A manual switchboard at a local dial office, equipped with instruments to test subscriber loops with their phones, and toward or through the central office equipment. Has a 48V voltmeter circuit, dial speed and percent break meter, and a howler. The testman tests all lines reported to repair service, and directs repairmen in clearing the trouble.

testdeskman, *n.* A workman at a local test desk who receives reports of telephone trouble from the repair clerk, tests the faulty line, and dispatches a repairman, central office repairman, or cable splicer to clear the trouble.

tester, B voltage, *n.* Field testing device which permits linemen, installers and repairmen to check for the presence of a harmful foreign voltage on wires and pole hardware before working on or near them.

testing, remote, *n.* The testing, from a centrally-located local test desk, of subscribers lines in a remote central office. Requires a master control unit and one or more remote control units, each connected to the master unit over a dedicated facility. It is essentially a telemetering system using multifrequency (15 frequencies) tone signaling.

tests, acceptance, *n. pl.* Tests required

to prove that a new communication facility meets all applicable performance or contractual specifications. Before acceptance, the facility should be operating at peak performance.

test set, *n.* Any instrument or device, other than a voltmeter or ammeter, which is used to test circuits or equipment for particular functions. See also "set, - - -."

test, set, call-through, *n.* An automatic test set used in step-by-step central offices which originates test calls through the switching equipment, monitors the progress of the call, and sounds an alarm while holding the switch train if trouble is encountered.

test set, dial speed and pulse ratio, *n.* A component of a local test desk used to remotely check the pulse speed and percent make of telephone dials. It consists of a dual scale indicating meter and associated circuit.

test turret, *n.* A small table-top cabinet holding a voltmeter, dial speed test set, keys, and a telephone set which functions as a small local test desk.

tetrafluorethylene, *n.* Teflon. A heat-resistant plastic insulator suitable for radio frequency use. Used in some coaxial cables.

tetrode, *n.* A four-electrode electron tube containing an anode, a cathode, a control grid, and an additional electrode that is usually a grid.

THEOREMS. See Appendix B for a statement of the following theorems:

Compensation Theorem.
Fourier's Theorem.
Maximum Power Transfer Theorem.
Norton's Theorem.
Reciprocity Theorem.
Superposition Theorem.
Thévenin's Theorem.

See also "LAWS" and "RULES."

theoretical number. See "number, theoretical."

thermal noise. See "noise, thermal."

thermionic, *adj.* Pertaining to the emission of electrons or ions from an incandescent body.

thermistor, *n.* A semi-conductor resistor whose resistance decreases as its temperature rises. Used in circuits to compensate for the effects of temperature variations, or as a non-linear circuit element.

thermocouple, *n.* A thermoelectric thermometer consisting of a pair of dissimilar wires (copper and iron, or antimony and bismuth) joined at one end. An EMF is generated if the joined end is heated above the temperature of the other end of the wires. Can be joined with a heater wire and used to measure radio-frequency currents.

thermoelectricity, *n.* The flow of electricity produced when two thermoelectric junctions in the same series circuit are at different temperatures, one heated and one cooled.

thermoelectric junction, *n.* Any of the junctions between dissimilar wires in a thermocouple or thermopile, where a potential difference is created by the application of heat.

thermomagnetic, *adj.* Pertaining to two effects: (a) the heating of a body by changes in magnetization, and (b) the destruction of magnetization by heating a magnet.

thermometer, *n.* An instrument for indicating temperatures, used with a central office storage battery to ensure that the temperature never exceeds 100 degrees F.

thermophone, *n.* A device used to calibrate microphones which produces a sound wave of exact volume by audio frequency electric heating of a wire.

thermopile, *n.* A number of thermoelectric junctions connected in series to provide a useful output voltage.

thermoplastic, *adj.* A classification of resin which can be readily softened and resoftened by repeated heating.

thermosetting, *adj.* A classification of resin which cures by a chemical reaction initiated by heating and, when cured, cannot be resoftened by heating.

thermostat, *n.* A device which controls temperature by automatically controlling a heater or air-conditioning unit. Consists of a bimetallic element which moves to close or open a contact when the temperature is too low or too high.

Thévenin's Theorem. See "Appendix B."

thimble, *n.* A grooved metal ring inserted in a loop of rope to prevent wear of the rope.

thimble-eye, *adj.* Describing an anchor rod or through-bolt equipped with a thimble eye.—*n.* An elongated grooved eye which fits a rope or strand and prevents it from being over-stressed in bending or compression.

thimbleyelet, *n.* A thimbleye attachment which can be used under the head or nut of a through-bolt. Its mounting hole slips over the bolt and is not tapped.

thin film circuit, *n.* A circuit whose elements are films formed on an insulating substrate. A thin film is one which is only several molecules thick.

third harmonic, *n.* A component of a complex wave whose frequency is three times that of the fundamental wave. The third harmonic on a 60 hertz power circuit is 180 hertz. See also "triple harmonics."

third wire, *n.* The sleeve wire, which see.

thousand/twenty. See "ringing, thousand/twenty."

three-phase, *adj.* Describing an alternating current circuit in which there are three sinusoidal voltages differing in phase by 120 electrical degrees, or one-third of a cycle.

three pole, *adj.* Describing a switch or relay which switches three circuits simultaneously.

three-way calling. See "calling, three-way."

threshold, AM, *n.* Noise threshold, which see.

threshold, FM improvement, *n.* In an FM receiver, the point at which the peaks of the incoming RF signal exactly equal the peaks of the internally generated thermal noise power. A baseband signal-to-noise ratio of about 30 dB is obtained at the FM improvement threshold, and this improves about one dB for each one dB increase of the RF signal above the FM improvement threshold.

threshold, noise, *n.* In a radio receiver, the radio-frequency input level at which the signal power exactly equals the internally generated thermal noise power.

threshold practical, *n.* FM improvement threshold, which see.

threshold, tangential, *n.* Noise threshold, which see.

threshold of audibility, *n.* For a specified frequency of signal, the minimum sound pressure which can be heard a specified fraction of the trials.

threshold of feeling, *n.* For a specified signal, the minimum effective sound pressure which in a specified fraction of the trials will stimulate the ear to the point where there is a sensation of feeling, tickle, discomfort, or pain.

thrift-pak, long-distance, *n.* Tariff item giving a 20% reduction in charges for long-distance calls between 5 PM and 7 AM, providing total long-distance usage is over $10 per month.

through circuit, *n.* A circuit suitable for a (built-up) connection which requires the use of more than one toll circuit. Also called a via circuit.

through-group, *n.* In carrier telephone transmission, a group of twelve voice channels which goes through a carrier repeater point as a unit, without being broken down to voice frequency.

throughput rate, data. See "efficiency, data transmission."

through-supergroup, *n.* In carrier telephone transmission, a group of sixty voice channels which goes through a carrier or radio repeater point as a unit, without being broken down to group or channel frequencies.

through-supervision, *n.* Complete supervision of a toll call by the originating operator through intermediate switching points to the called party.

through toll. See "toll, through."

thump, *n.* The very low frequency noise heard in a telephone circuit, coming from a telegraph circuit derived from the same pair.

thump killer, *n.* An inductance used with most polar duplex signaling sets to reduce the sudden surge of current which occurs when the transmit relay changes the "M" lead from battery to ground, and vice versa.

thyratron, *n.* A hot-cathode gas tube in which one or more control electrodes can initiate a current flow, but thereafter cannot control it.

thyristor, *n.* A high-current transistor used in power rectifier circuits. Its control lead can initiate high currents which then flow uncontrolled during the remainder of the half-cycle. See also "thyratron," its vacuum tube counterpart.

thyrite, *n.* A material used in voltage-sensitive devices. The resistance of thyrite decreases as the voltage applied to it increases, making it useful for protecting devices from high voltages.

ticker, stock, *n.* A printing telegraph which prints a record of stock market transactions in alphanumeric characters on a paper or transparent film tape. Transparent film can be fed into an optical projec-

tion system which projects the image of the tape onto a screen.

ticket, cable repair, *n.* A small printed form used to report pairs in trouble, the nature of the trouble, and the pair substitutions and/or materials which will be needed for permanent repairs.

ticket, mark-sense toll, *n.* A standard 80-column data card arranged so that it can be used by an operator to record details of a toll call, using slanting marks with a conductive pencil within designated "bubble" areas. A machine card reader can then read the called area code and telephone number and the calling telephone number.

ticket, toll, *n.* A paper ticket, 2½" wide x 5" high, used by the operator to record details of a toll call. She records the place, telephone number, and name of the person calling and called, notes the route to be used, whether collect and accepted, reports made, and lost time due to disconnects. The back of the ticket is used for a calculagraph stamping showing the total elapsed time of the call.

ticket, trouble, *n.* Any of many varieties of tickets used to report actual or potential trouble.

ticketer, *n.* A device which automatically prints toll tickets, using information dialed by the calling telephone and from the "charge computer."

ticket filing position, *n.* The desk, table, or position where message tickets are accumulated, and collated before being sent to the Accounting Department.

ticketing, automatic, *n.* Method of obtaining a printed toll ticket by using the sender to control a message ticketer in the trunk circuit. Elapsed time information is added by a timer in the trunk. This printed ticket requires the same accounting treatment as a manually written toll ticket.

ticketing, toll. See "automatic toll ticketing."

ticket operator, *n.* The operator at the ticket position who maintains a file of delayed tickets, furnishes information regarding these tickets on request, and sends the tickets to the switchboard for further action.

ticket position, *n.* A desk, table, or position where delayed toll tickets are held pending further action, but not for completion at the position at which the call originated.

tick, time, *n.* A time signal, which see.

tickle, *n.* The auditory sensation which is experienced when sound level at the ear exceeds the threshold of feeling.

tickler, *n.* A coil connected in series with the plate circuit of an electron tube and inductively coupled to a grid-circuit coil in order to establish feed-back or regeneration in a radio circuit.

ticktone, *n.* A light clicking noise used on some PABX trunks to indicate that any digit dialed will be repeated to the central office, and that dial "1" or dial "0" transfer should not be attempted.

tie, *n.* (1) An electrical connection or strap. (2) A tie point. (3) A tie wire.—*v.t.* To fasten an open line wire to its supporting insulator using a short (18-30 inch) tie wire, which is wrapped around both.

tie, wire, *n.* The wrapping of a "tie wire" around both an open line wire and the insulator on which it is supported.

tie down, *v.t.* To terminate a jumper wire onto a terminal block.

tie line, PBX, *n.* A trunk between two private branch exchanges.

tie point, *n.* An insulated terminal on a mounting plate to which several wires can be connected.

tie trunk, *n.* A trunk between two private branch exchanges. Usually called a "PBX tie line."

tie wire, *n.* A piece of wire, 20 to 30 inches long and of the same material as the line wire, used to tie open line wire to its insulator.

TIF. See "Telephone Influence Factor."

tight coupling. See "coupling, close."

tile, *n.* Hard-baked clay pipe or conduit placed underground for conducting cable. See "conduit."

tile, multiple, *n.* Hard-baked clay conduit containing several ducts. Available in the following configurations: 1x2, 1x3, 2x2, 2x3, 2x4, and 3x3 ducts. Standard tiles are 36 inches long, but short lengths are available.

tile, sewer, *n.* Common commercial cylindrical vitrified tile with bell-and-spigot joint, which may be used to construct subsidiary ducts.

tile, split, *n.* Clay tile conduit, either single duct or multiple duct, which is scored so that it can be split on the job and used to repair or replace conduit around existing underground cables.

tilt, *n.* The angle of an antenna axis above the horizontal, measured in degrees. See also "slope."

tilt angle (of a rhombic antenna), *n.* One-half of the obtuse angle between the antenna leg connected to the feed line and the leg connected to the load termination.

tilt control, *n.* A control on a broadband amplifier which changes the slope of the gain-frequency characteristic. Enables a high gain at higher frequencies to compensate for higher cable loss at the higher frequencies.

timbre, *n.* That attribute of a sound by which a listener can judge that two sounds are unlike, even though they have the same loudness and pitch. Timbre depends principally upon the waveform of the sound.

time, answering, *n.* The time in seconds which elapses between the appearance of a signal on a switchboard and the response by the operator. For a line signal, the time in seconds from the time the line lamp is lighted until it is extinguished.

time, attack, *n.* The time, usually measured in milliseconds, required to initiate an effect after start of a cause. Example: In an echo suppressor, the time required to suppress transmission in one direction on a four-wire circuit after receipt of transmission in the other direction.

time, busy, *n.* The total time in seconds that a circuit is busy on a call. On manual calls this includes the operator's work time, the customer's conversation time, and the disconnect time.

time, compressor attack, *n.* The interval in seconds between the instant when the compressor input signal increases from —16 dBmO to —4 dBmO, and the instant when the compressor output signal voltage reaches 1.5 times its final steady-state value. Normal attack time is about three milliseconds.

time, compressor recovery, *n.* The interval in seconds between the instant when the compressor input signal is reduced from —4 dBmO to —16 dBmO, and the instant when the compressor output signal voltage reaches 0.75 times its final steady-state value. Normal recovery time is about 13.5 milliseconds.

time, connection, *n.* From the time the last digit of the telephone number is dialed until the called telephone rings.

time, daylight saving, *n.* A time which is arbitarily one hour earlier than standard time.

time, decay, *n.* The time taken for a voltage or current to decline to a specified fraction of its original value. This fraction is usually $1/e = 1/2.7183 = 0.367879$.

time, deductible, *n.* The time in seconds during which a toll call was interrupted or otherwise made unusable. At the discretion of the operator, such time is deducted

from the calculagraph time to obtain a "net elapsed time," on which the toll charge will be based.

time, down. See "downtime."

time, elapsed, *n.* (1) The total time in seconds during which a circuit is usefully occupied. (2) The time printed on a toll ticket by a Calculagraph, for which charges will be made. See also "time, deductible."

time, hangover, *n.* The time required for a circuit to return to normal after an inhibiting cause has been discontinued. Example: In an echo suppressor, the time required to remove suppression after transmission stops.

time, holding, *n.* The total time in seconds that a circuit is in use on a call. For manual calls this includes the operator's work time, the customer's conversation time, and the disconnect time.

time, interdigital. See "interdigital time."

time, isolation, *n.* That portion of maintenance time during which the least-replaceable-unit is isolated.

time, localization, *n.* That portion of maintenance time required to locate the portion of the system which is faulty. It does not identify the exact faulty component.

time, memory access, *n.* The time interval between the instant at which information is requested from a memory unit and the instant at which this information begins to be available.

time, net elapsed, *n.* The total time, from start to finish of a toll call, minus the time deducted because the call was interrupted.

time, operate. See "operate time."

time, pulse decay, *n.* The time required for the instantaneous amplitude of an electrical wave to go from 90% to 10% of the peak amplitude.

time, pulse rise, *n.* The time required for the instantaneous amplitude of an electrical wave to go from

10% to 90% of the peak amplitude.

time, real, *adj.* (1) Instantaneous. (2) Not subject to storing before transmission.

time, recovery, *n.* The length of time that a condition remains in effect after the control signal which initiated the effect has disappeared. See also "delay, hangover."

time, release. See "release time."

time, repair, *n.* That portion of maintenance time during which the least-replaceable-unit is replaced, or readjusted in place.

time, reverberation, *n.* The time in seconds required for the average energy of a sound to decay (decrease) from an initial value to an energy value 60 dB less. Although not accurate, it is common practice to judge reverberation time by clapping the hands loudly once and counting seconds until the sound has decayed to inaudibility.

time, rise, *n.* The time, in microseconds, required for a pulse or other steep front wave to rise from 10% to 90% of its peak value.

time, standard, *n.* The local civil time of the standard meridian which applies to all points within 7½ degrees east and west of the standard meridian. There are 24 standard meridians, 15 degrees apart, reckoned from 0 degrees at Greenwich, Great Britain.

time, transit, *n.* In an electron tube, the time required for an electron to pass from the cathode to the plate. See also "transit time effect."

time, warmup, *n.* The time interval between the first application of power to a communication equipment or system and the time when voltages have stabilized and the equipment is ready for operation.

time, zulu, *n.* Time at the 0 degree meridian, or Greenwich standard time.

Time Assignment Speech Interpolation (TASI), *n.* On the average voice circuit, audible speech is only present about 45% of the time. The efficiency of costly overseas channels is improved by TASI: detecting a talker's speech and assigning him an unused channel within milliseconds, so that very little of the initial syllable is lost. The talker will keep that channel until he is silent and his channel is needed for another. During light load periods, TASI does little or no switching. During heavy load periods, the efficiency will be improved from 45% to 75-80%.

time constant, *n.* The time in seconds required for an electrical voltage or current to rise to 63.21% of its final value or to fall to 36.79% of its initial value. The time constant of a capacitor of C farads in series with a resistor of R ohms is RC. The time constant of an inductance of L henries in series with a resistance of R ohms is L/R.

time delay, *n.* The time required for a signal to travel between two points, on a circuit or through space.

time delay relay. See "relay, dashpot," "relay, slow operate," "relay, slow release," and "relay, slow operate and release."

time-division multiplex, *n.* Arrangement where several signals share a single transmission facility, each being connected in sequence for a short period of time.

timed release, *n.* Release of a circuit which has mal-functioned, after a delay interval. The amount of delay is usually regulated by a dashpot relay.

time gate, *n.* A transducer which has an output only during selected time intervals.

time-of-day, *n.* A service by the Telephone Company which enables a customer to dial a service code (844) or a special number (such as 447-1212) and be connected to a machine which announces the correct time every ten seconds. Calls to "time service" are chargeable.

time-out, *n.* (1) The automatic release of equipment or circuits on calls which do not proceed to completion. (2) A delayed decision, in which a circuit waits for a predetermined interval (from milliseconds to minutes) before operating. Used to delay trouble alarms, lock-out, etc.—*v.* To disconnect after a certain preset time interval.

timer, AMA master, *n.* Clock device which keeps a running record of the time by month, day, hour, minute, and tenths of a minute. It supplies a running record of the time within each hour to each AMA recorder for use in recording the answer and disconnect time entries. (#5 X Bar)

timer, initial-period-reminder, *n.* An electric timer which the operator starts when she places a call from a coin telephone. The timer alerts her a few seconds before she must request additional coins from the caller if he wishes to continue.

timer, toll. See "Calculagraph," "clock, switchboard," and "timer, initial-period-reminder."

time sharing. See "multiplex, time division."

time signal, *n.* A standard, very accurate time signal broadcast hourly by radio stations WWV, WWVH, WWVB, and WWVL. These broadcasts are at 2.5, 5, 10, and 15 megahertz. Used to adjust time-of-day equipment.

time-temperature. See "announcer, time-temperature."

timing, permanent. See "permanent timing."

timing allowance, *n.* A number of minutes which is deducted from the elapsed time of a toll call before charges are computed, based on disconnections, interruptions, or poor transmission.

timing signal, *n.* Signal used to ensure synchronization of interconnected digital equipments. Usually a symmetrical square wave signal.

tin, *n.* A silver-white metal with a bluish tinge, softer than zinc and harder than lead. Used to make solder, and to provide a protective plating on ferrous metals and on copper wires.

tinned, *adj.* Covered with a coating of metallic tin to inhibit corrosion and facilitate soldering.

tinned wire, *n.* Copper wire used for strapping or in switchboard cables which has been coated or plated with metallic tin to facilitate soldering to terminals.

tinsel conductor, *n.* A very flexible conductor made by serving one or more thin ribbon conductors over a nylon cord core. Used in the construction of telephone cords.

tip, *n.* (1) The ball-shaped contact at the end of a telephone plug. (2) The first wire in a pair of wires, commonly uncoded. (3) Cable, such as textile-insulated, spliced to a paper-insulated cable to allow it to be terminated as on a distributing frame.

tip, cord, *n.* A terminal soldered or squeezed onto the end of a cord conductor, which permits a mechanical and electrical connection. May be either a brass pin, a solder lug, or a spade tip.

tip, silk and cotton, *n.* Tip cable having conductors insulated with silk and cotton wrappings. Has been superseded by plastic-insulated terminating cable.

tip, spade, *n.* A metal terminal for a wire lead, spade-shaped with an open-end slot so that it can be clamped under a binding post nut.

tip-busy. See "test, tip-busy."

tip cable. See "cable, terminating."

tip jack. See "jack, pin."

tip wire, *n.* (1) The first wire of a pair, of which the second wire is called the "ring." (2) The wire which connects to the tip conductor of a switchboard plug.

Tiros satellites, *n. pl.* One of two series of weather satellites.

T network, *n.* An unbalanced network

composed of two series branches whose common midpoint connects to a shunt branch, the whole resembling the letter "T." The ends of the two series branches form an input and an output. The free end of the shunt branch is the other input and output.

tolerance, *n.* An amount of permissible variation from a standard, often expressed in percent.

toll, *adj.* Describing any component of telephone plant which is used principally for giving toll service.— *n.* A charge for service, or for extra service such as a long-distance telephone call.

toll, foreign area, *n.* Toll calls directed to a different area code than that of the originating office.

toll, home area, *n.* Toll calls within the same area code as the originating office.

toll, inward, *n.* Toll calls which come in over intertoll trunks from other toll offices, and are directed to phones in that office or to phones in connecting tributary offices.

toll, outward, *n.* Toll calls which originate at a toll center or its tributary offices, and which are directed to outgoing intertoll trunks.

toll, through, *n.* Toll calls which arrive over intertoll trunks and are switched to other intertoll trunks leading to their destination.

toll board, *n.* A switchboard used to establish telephone connections over toll lines.

toll call, *n.* Any call to a point outside the local service area, the income from which is credited to toll revenue, as distinguished from local and inter-zone calls whose income is credited to exchange revenue. See also "call, person-to-person" and "call, station-to-station."

toll center (TC), *n.* (1) A Class 4C toll office. (2) A toll office where operators are present and assistance in completing incoming calls is provided in addition to other traffic operating functions. (3) A toll office

of any rank where inward operator service code (121) functions are provided.

toll center office, *n.* A central office used primarily for completing and supervising toll calls. A toll center may be designated as an originating toll center (OTC), intermediate toll center (ITC), or terminating toll center (TTC), depending on its function in the handling of a specific call.

toll circuit, *n.* A circuit between two toll switching units, regardless of their class. Also called an intertoll trunk.

toll connecting trunk, *n.* Trunk between a local office (end office) and a toll center. Also called a "terminating link." Its transmission loss should not exceed 4 dB.

toll cord, *n.* The cord on which a toll circuit is connected. At an outward switchboard, it is the front cord; at an inward switchboard, it is the back cord.

toll dial assistance operator (TDA Opr), *n.* An operator who assists in the completion of incoming, through, and outward toll dialed calls.

toll dial assistance position (TDA Pos), *n.* A switchboard position to which incoming, through, and outward toll calls are routed when the originating operator requires assistance in the completion of the call.

toll diversion. See "restriction, toll" and "equipment, diversion."

toll line. See "line, toll."

toll message, *n.* A completed toll call.

toll office, *n.* (1) A center for the switching of toll calls. (2) An office where toll calls are filed.

toll point (TP), *n.* (1) A Class 4P office. (2) An office where operators handle only outward toll calls, or where there are no operators present, such as in a CAMA tributary office.

toll restriction. See "restriction, toll."

toll station, *n.* A telephone, either private or public, connected directly to the toll board, or bridged onto a ringdown toll circuit. See also "LD terminal."

toll switching centers. See "centers, toll switching."

toll switching operator, *n.* A "B" operator who completes connections between incoming toll switching trunks and telephone lines.

toll switching position, *n.* A "B" position in a local central office at which incoming toll switching trunks terminate, and at which connections from the toll office to called lines are established.

toll switching trunk, *n.* A trunk outgoing from a toll office to a local (end) office, used for completing calls to subscriber's lines.

toll tandem. See "control switching point."

toll terminal, *n.* A direct line from the subscriber's premises to the toll switchboard for the purpose of placing and/or receiving toll calls. Also called "LD terminal."

toll terminal loss. See "loss, toll terminal."

toll ticketing. See "automatic toll ticketing."

toll train. See "train, toll."

toll trunk. See "toll circuit."

tone, *n.* (1) A sound wave capable of exciting an auditory sensation having pitch. (2) An electrical wave of audio frequency. (3) A sound that is distinct and identifiable by its regularity of frequency, or constant pitch. It may be a single frequency, or several frequencies which have a fixed harmonic relation.

tone, all trunks busy, *n.* A low tone (480 + 620 Hz) interrupted at 120 IPM (On 0.3 second, off 0.2 second) which indicates that local switching paths or equipments are busy.

tone, beep. See "beep tone."

tone, busy, *n.* A tone returned to the calling party telephone to indicate that the called line is in use (60 IPM), or that all trunks are busy (120 IPM).

tone, call-waiting. See "call-waiting tone."

tone, class-of-service, *n.* Short splashes of tones (usually 400 or 500 Hz often called "zip tones") used at switchboards to indicate to the operator the class-of-service of the calling customer when several classes are served by the same trunk group.

tone, coin collect, *n.* A low tone (480 Hz + 620 Hz) used to inform the originating operator that a coin control circuit or a B operator has collected the coin(s).

tone, coin return, *n.* A high tone (480 Hz) used to inform the originating operator that the coin control circuit or a B operator has returned the coin(s).

tone, dial, *n.* A tone signal informing the calling subscriber that the central office equipment is ready to accept dial pulses. Dial tone consists of 350 Hz plus 440 Hz at a level of —13 dBm per frequency. The 90 Hz difference (440—350= 90 Hz) frequency gives this tone its low-pitched sound. (Previously 600 Hz modulated by 120 Hz when supplied by a tone alternator, or 600 Hz modulated by 133 Hz when supplied by an interrupter.)

tone, high, *n.* A tone signal consisting of 480 Hz at a level of —17 dBm. (Previously 500 Hz when supplied from a tone alternator, or 400 Hz from an interrupter.)

tone, high frequency test, *n.* A supersonic test tone used with a remote detector by cable splicers for identifying pairs in working cables without disturbing the service.

tone, hold and trace, *n.* A low-level (—10 dBm) 2100 Hz tone interrupted 120 IPM applied through a holding repeating coil to a faulty circuit. Holds the circuit connection while the circuit is traced by a repairman.

tone, idle marking, *n.* Tone placed on

the next available idle channel of a mobile radio system at the base transmitter. All idle mobile sets hunt over their channels until the idle tone is detected, and then camp on that marked channel. The next call in either direction is then established over that channel.

tone, line busy, *n.* A low tone (480 + 620 Hz) interrupted at 60 IPM (On 0.5 second, off 0.5 second) which indicates that the called subscriber line has been reached, but that it is busy. Previously 600 Hz modulated by 120 Hz, interrupted at 60 IPM.

tone, low, *n.* Low tone consists of 480 Hz plus 620 Hz at a level of —24 dBm per frequency. The 140 Hz difference (620—480=140) frequency gives it the low-pitched sound. Used for line busy, reorder, and no-circuit tone signals reached by the subscriber.

tone, no circuit, *n.* A tone which indicates a lack of idle trunks at an intermediate switching point. The NC tone is 600/120 Hz, interrupted 120 times per minute. (Older offices may still use 30 IPM.)

tone, no such number. See "no such number signal."

tone, order, *n.* Short spurts of high tone sent back over a trunk to indicate to the originating operator that she should pass the order (destination, or called telephone number), and to indicate to the receiving operator that the order is about to be passed.

tone, out-of-order. See "out-of-order tone."

tone, overflow. See "tone, all trunks busy."

tone, paths busy. See "tone, all trunks busy."

tone, paystation identification, *n.* A short spurt of tone which the operator receives when she answers a call on a paystation trunk which notifies her that the call originated at a paystation.

tone, pilot. See "pilot tone."

tone, precise dial, *n.* A mixture (not a modulation) of 350 hertz and 440 hertz tones, selected so that they will not interfere with DTMF dialing.

tone, preempt, *n.* Tone applied to each end subscriber to indicate that their line or trunk has been preempted. The 440+620 Hz tone at —10 dBm level is maintained until the subscribers hang up.

tone, pure, *n.* (1) A sound sensation which is characterized by its singleness of pitch. (2) A sound wave, the instantaneous sound pressure of which is a simple sinusoidal function of time.

tone, recorder warning, *n.* When recording equipment is used, a "beep" of 1400 Hz tone is connected to the line for a 0.5-second interval every 15 seconds to inform the distant party that the conversation is being recorded.

tone, reorder, *n.* A low tone (480+ 620 Hz) interrupted at 120 IPM (On 0.2 second, off 0.3 second) placed on a toll circuit to indicate to the operator one of the following conditions:

  a. No toll circuit available.
  b. A sender timed-out.
  c. That an unassigned code was dialed.

tone, ringback, *n.* An audible signal, consisting of 400 Hz modulated by 40 Hz, which indicates to the calling party that the called line has been reached, and that ringing has started.

tone, ringing. See "tone, ringback" and "audible ringing tone."

tone, second dial, *n.* Any dial tone received after the first, and during the dialing period. Provided when accessing another office via its line equipment, or in any condition when the inter-digital time is too short for the following equipment to prepare to receive dial pulses.

tone, splash, *n.* A short spurt of audio tone, usually 400 or 500 Hz, applied to a trunk to indicate readiness to accept an order, or to indicate class of service. Sometimes called "order tone" or "zip tone."

tone, standard test, *n.* The standard tone for the transmission testing of voice frequency circuits is 1000 Hz, applied at a level which will send one milliwatt of power into a 600 ohm impedance.

tone, test, *n.* (1) The interrupted low-frequency buzzer tone (20-C) used by cable splicers for identifying pairs. (2) The 1000 Hz tone used for transmission tests. (3) Any other tone used for specialized testing.

tone, trunk busy, *n.* A 600+120 Hz tone interrupted at 120 IPS returned to the calling subscriber or operator to indicate that all trunks are busy.

tone, warble. See "warble-tone."

tone, woo-woo, *n.* No-such-number tone.

tone, zip. See "tone, splash."

tone generator, *n.* An oscillator or rotary generator which generates a single audio-frequency signal used for any of the following:

   a. Dial tone.
   b. Busy tone.
   c. Ringback tone.
   d. Single-frequency (2600 Hz) signaling.
   e. Transmission test tone (1000 Hz).

tone jacks, *n.* A group of jacks in the switchboard trunk multiple to which various signals and tones are wired for demonstration.

tone ringer, *n.* Incoming ring indicator for a telephone consisting of a small loudspeaker actuated by an audio-frequency signal over the telephone loop circuit.

tones, class of service. See "class of service tones."

tones, coin denomination, *n. pl.* The tones produced at a coin telephone as nickels, dimes, or quarters are deposited. May be produced by a tone generator, or by a bell and gong in the coin chute. If the latter, a special transmitter near the coin chute picks up the tones and sends them to the line. Coins produce the following tones:

   Nickel—One bell
   Dime—Two bells
   Quarter—One gong

tones, supervisory, *n. pl.* Tones which indicate circuit conditions. Examples are:

Dial tone	— 600/120 Hz
Busy tone	— 600/120 Hz at 60 IPM
Trunk busy tone	— 600/120 Hz at 120 IPM
No such number tone	— 500 Hz alt 600/120 Hz at 60 IPM
Audible ringing	— 400/40 Hz
Pre-empt signal	— 480 Hz

tone signaling, *n.* The use of voice frequency tones to transmit alerting, address, and supervisory signals over a voice telephone circuit.

TONLAR, *n.* Tone-operated net loss adjuster. A system for adjusting and stabilizing the net loss of a telephone circuit by use of a tone transmitted between speech signals.

tool, coinbox sealing, *n.* A plier-like compression die used to crimp the lead seal on coin receptacles.

tool, connector crimping, *n.* A plier-like tool for squeezing wire splicing connectors.

tool, drive. See "tool, multi-use."

tool, impact, *n.* An electric or compressed-air powered tool for use with drills and wrenches. It imparts rotary motion by a series of rapidly repeated impacts, the force of which is accurately spring controlled. The force on the drill or wrench never exceeds the force required.

tool, multi-use, *n.* A drive rod and chuck assembly with a rubber protective hand grip. Used to hold any of an assortment of hardened drive pins and threaded studs so they can be driven into masonry walls.

tool, Nicopress, *n.* A plier-like tool for compressing Nicopress sleeves onto wires. See also "Nicopress."

tool, powder-powered, *n.* A pistol

type device used for driving hardened steel drive pins or threaded studs into masonry or steel. The gas produced by a gunpowder explosion drives a piston against the pin or stud to be driven. The powder charges are in .22 caliber or .25 caliber cartridges, color coded to indicate the weight of the powder charge, from sub-light to extra heavy.

tool, quick-connect, *n.* A hand tool having a plastic handle containing a reversible metal blade. The blunt end is for connecting a looped conductor to a quick-connect terminal; the sharp end for cutting off the excess wire. (WECo #714 tool)

tool, relay blocking, *n.* A small plastic tool having two wedge shaped points of different sizes. A wedge of proper size is inserted under a relay armature to block operation of the relay.

tool, sheath constriction, *n.* A splicer's hand tool having a round rod bent into a half-circle. This is placed on a lead or stalpeth cable sheath and beaten with a hammer to form a constricting groove in the sheath.

tool, spring adjusting, *n.* A small hand tool used to bend the springs of jacks, keys, and relays.

tool, wire connecting. See "tool, quick-connect."

tool, wire raising, *n.* A metal head to be used on a tree-pruner pole, having a U-shaped metal end used to lift drop wires over obstructions or to guide wires through trees.

tool, wire wrapping, *n.* A small hand tool, 5/16"D x 4½" long, used to wrap connecting wires around the square, sharp, solderless terminals designed for that type of connections. (WECo #635B tool)

topographic map. See "map, topographic."

torn-tape relay, *n.* A tape relay station at which an operator must tear off the perforated tape of an incoming message and physically feed it into the tape transmitter on the proper outgoing channel.

torn tape relay center. See "tape relay, manual."

toroid, *n.* An inductor or transformer wound on a doughnut-shaped magnetic core. All loading coils are wound as balanced toroids.

toroidal coil, *n.* A coil wound on a doughnut-shaped core, so that the winding has the form made by bringing together the ends of a coil spring.

torr, *n.* The standard unit for expressing pressure or vacuum, equal to one millimeter of mercury, or 1/760 of a standard atmospheric pressure.

touch calling, *n.* A type of high-speed address signaling in which numbered buttons in a bank of ten can be depressed to give one of a group of audio tone pairs for signaling directly over the circuit. See also "signaling, dual tone multifrequency."

TOUCHTONE, *adj.* A registered trade-mark used by the Bell System to describe their method of using a keyset to generate dual-tone multifrequency address signals.

Touch-Tone telephone set, *n.* The Bell System's designation for a telephone set using a push-button multifrequency dial.

tourmaline, *n.* A natural piezo-electric mineral which is a complex silicate of aluminum and boron. It occurs in hexagonal prismatic crystals colored pink, rose, green, blue, brown, or black.

tower, antenna, *n.* A tall metal structure used as a support for one or more antennas, or as one of the supports for a very large antenna.

tower radiator, *n.* A tall metal structure which of itself constitutes a transmitting antenna.

T pad. See "T network."

trace, *n.* The visible glow left on the fluorescent screen of a television tube by the moving beam of electrons.

trace, return, *n.* On a cathode ray or television tube, the path of the scanning spot during the interval when it returns to its starting point. During the return interval its brightness is reduced to a minimum.

tracer, *n.* (1) A colored mark on the insulation of a wire, either a dye mark on polyethylene or a colored thread woven in textile insulation, which identifies the wire and distinguishes it from others in the same group. (2) A tracer pair.

tracer pair, *n.* In concentric-lay telephone cables, one pair in each layer which has insulation of a distinctive color. It provides a starting point from which pair numbers can be counted within that layer.

tracer quad, *n.* In concentric-lay quadded telephone cables, one quad in each layer which has a distinctive color, usually orange-red. Provides a starting point from which quad numbers can be counted within that layer.

tracer stripe, *n.* In the color coding of wires, the first stripe is the base stripe and other narrower stripes are called tracer stripes.

tracking, *n.* (1) The following of a phonograph record groove by the stylus of the pickup. (2) The maintaining of all tuned circuits in a radio receiver at the same frequency as the receiver is tuned across the band. (3) The following of a satellite in its path by the earth terminal antenna.

tracking, automatic, *n.* Automatic tracking of a satellite by a servomechanism which points the earth antenna in the direction from which the radio signal arrives, and continually corrects this pointing.

tracking, programmed, *n.* Automatic satellite tracking by servomechanisms controlled by a program developed from calculated orbit parameters. Not entirely satisfactory due to fortuitous ionospheric refraction.

traffic, *n.* (1) The messages sent and received over a communication channel. (2) A quantitative measure of the total messages and their length, expressed in hundred call-seconds (CCS) or other units.

traffic, telephone, *n.* The sum of the holding times of all calls in progress over a particular group of circuits. Usually expressed in CCS—the total amount of traffic in seconds divided by 100.

traffic overflow reroute control, automatic (TORC), *n.* A control system in regional toll centers which automatically reroutes overflow traffic to alternate regional centers when final trunk groups become overloaded.

traffic service position (TSP), *n.* A toll switchboard position configured as a pushbutton console.

traffic table, probability. See "probability traffic table."

traffic unit, *n.* A unit of telephone traffic which is numerically equal to percentage occupancy. Also called "Erlang."

trailer, cable reel, *n.* A two-wheeled, rubber-tired vehicle designed to be towed behind a construction truck and to carry a full reel of cable. Cable can be payed from the reel while it is mounted on the trailer.

trailer, cable splicer's. See "cart, cable splicer's."

trailer, pole, *n.* A steel frame equipped with a pair of rubber-tired wheels, and used to support the butt of a pole while it is being towed behind a line construction truck. A drawbar is fastened to the top end of the pole to provide an attachment to the towing hook of the truck.

train, *n.* A series of like pieces of equipment through which a call moves in sequence, such as a "switch train."—*v.t.* To point a directional antenna.

train, pulse, *n.* A succession of pulses which follow each other closely, usually at equal intervals.

train, switch, *n.* A series of selecting

switches through which a call moves in sequence to its destination.

train, toll, *n.* A switch train used to establish a connection from a toll board to a subscriber's line.

transceiver, *n.* A single small unit which combines both radio transmitter and radio receiver functions, with some of the circuitry common to both functions.

transceiver, mobile, *n.* A transmitter-receiver unit in an automobile which transmits telephone calls to and receives calls from a "base station," where connection is made to the local telephone system.

transconductance, *n.* A rating of an electron tube obtained by dividing a small change in plate current by the smaller change in control grid voltage which produced it. Also called "mutual conductance."

transcription, *n.* A phonograph record, especially the 33-1/3 rpm 16-inch record used to record broadcast programs.

transducer, *n.* A device which receives a wave from one transmission system or medium and transmits a wave containing equivalent information to a different system or medium.

transducer, active, *n.* A transducer whose output waves receive their power from a separate power source, controlled by the input waves to the transducer.

transducer, gas pressure, *n.* A device which can be permanently connected to a pressurized cable in the field, and will enable the gas pressure at that point to be read from the central office. A change in pressure from 0 psig to 7 psig will cause a typical transducer resistance to change from 100 kilohms to 568 kilohms.

transducer, magnetostriction, *n.* A loudspeaker element used for underwater sound ranging. Multiple magnetostrictive elements in parallel are used to convert electrical energy into sound energy for radiating underwater.

transducer, passive, *n.* A transducer whose output waves derive their power solely from the input waves.

transducer, pressure, *n.* Device whose resistance varies proportional to a gas pressure. When connected at a remote location on a pressurized cable, permits reading the cable pressure at that point over a cable pair from the central office.

transender, *n.* A type of register-sender which has only a partial register and no capability for party station and directory number identification. It is used only on direct-distance-dialed calls, and therefore can depend on the automatic toll ticketer for the register and identification functions.

transfer, *n.* (1) The work of moving a group of working circuits from one group of pairs to another in the same cable, or to another cable. (2) The transferring of pole attachments (cables, crossarms, etc.) from an old pole to a new pole at the same location.—*v.* (1) To move circuits, pair counts, pole attachments, or data from one place to another. (2) To disconnect circuit A from circuit B, and connect it instead to standby circuit C.

transfer, automatic power, *n.* The automatic transfer of a power load from a power source which has failed to an alternate power source.

transfer, call, *n.* A service available at some PABX's and centrex offices where a station receiving an incoming call can transfer it to any other station in the same group without the assistance of an operator.

transfer, dial "1," *n.* Feature of some PABXs which enables any station receiving a trunk call to transfer the call by dialing "1," then the other station number. When station #2 answers and station #1 hangs up, station #2 will be connected to the trunk.

transfer, dial "0", *n.* A feature of

some PABXs which enables any station receiving a trunk call to transfer the call to the operator by dialing "0."

transfer, information, *n.* The transmission of a signal bearing intelligence, whether between teletypewriters over a long circuit, or between register and sender. See also: "transfer, parallel information" and "transfer, serial information."

transfer, maximum power, *n.* The condition whereby the power transferred from a source to a load is the maximum possible. This condition exists when the source impedance and the load impedance are conjugate impedances (which see). If the magnitude of the impedance can be controlled but not its angle, then maximum power transfer occurs when the load impedance is equal to the source impedance.

transfer, parallel information. *n.* The transmission of all 8-12 bits comprising one alpha-numeric character simultaneously over 8-12 parallel transmission paths. This method is used between colocated data processing machines.

transfer, power failure, *n.* Feature of some PABX systems which automatically transfers all PABX trunks to pre-assigned stations in the event of failure of PABX power. This could occur if standby battery power is not provided.

transfer, serial information, *n.* The transmission of items of information, either bits or characters, sequentially one after the other. The teletypewriter uses bit-serial transfer. Data processing machines generally use bit-parallel character-serial transfer.

transfer impedance. See "impedance, transfer."

transfer key. See "key, transfer."

transfer relay, *n.* A relay which acts to substitute a stand-by unit of equipment when the unit in service fails. Example: ringing machine transfer.

transfer selector, *n.* Separate selector used by the attendant or stations of a PABX to accomplish dial "1" and dial "0" transfers.

transfer service, subscriber, *n.* Optional service available to business subscribers. Before leaving his office the subscriber can, by turning a key on his telephone, transfer incoming calls to his home, or to an answering service.

transfer switchtrain, *n.* One or more "transfer selectors" in tandem.

transfluxor, *n.* A two-aperture ferrite core having unequal size apertures, used as a memory element having non-destructive readout capability.

transform, *v.* (1) To pass through a transformer. (2) To change data or equations from rectangular to polar coordinates, or vice versa. (3) To change data from one code to another without changing its meaning.

transformer, *n.* A device with two or more windings linked by a common magnetic circuit. Variations of current in a primary winding are converted, by mutual induction, into variations of current and voltage in a secondary winding. Used extensively in telephony, where it is commonly called a "repeating coil" or an "induction coil."

transformer, audio, *n.* A transformer designed specifically to pass audio frequencies with a minimum of loss and distortion.

transformer, balanced-to-unbalanced. See "balun."

transformer, bell-ringing, *n.* A small iron-core transformer having a 115 volt 60 Hz primary and a 10-15-20 volt secondary. Used to provide low voltage AC power for the operation of bells, buzzers, or chimes.

transformer, bridge, *n.* A hybrid coil, which see.

transformer, constant current, *n.* A transformer which will supply a constant current to a varying load. Regulation is either (a) by varying the separation between primary and secondary windings, or (b) by use of a resonant network.

transformer, constant voltage, *n.* A small power transformer which will supply a constant voltage to an unvarying load, even with changes in the primary supply voltage.

transformer, coupling, *n.* A transformer used to couple two circuits by means of its mutual impedance.

transformer, current. See "current transformer."

transformer, delta-matched, *n.* A radio-frequency impedance matching device which uses delta-matched transmission line. See also "delta-matched."

transformer, hybrid. See "coil, hybrid."

transformer, ideal, *n.* A transformer which can change the magnitude of the load impedance without altering its phase angle, and which introduces no losses into the circuit.

transformer, impedance-matching, *n.* A transformer which transforms the impedance of one circuit to exactly match the impedance of a second circuit, thus enabling maximum power transfer at their junction.

transformer, input. See "input transformer."

transformer, instrument. See "instrument transformer."

transformer, intermediate-frequency, *n.* A tuned transformer used for inter-stage coupling in an intermediate-frequency amplifier.

transformer, isolation, *n.* A transformer used to separate two sections of a circuit, often to prevent longitudinal currents by separating a grounded section from an ungrounded section.

transformer, line, *n.* A transformer inserted in a communication line for the purposes of impedance matching, isolation, or deriving additional circuits.

transformer, matching, *n.* An inequality ratio transformer used between unequal impedances to provide an impedance match and enable maximum power transfer.

transformer, output, *n.* An audio frequency transformer used to match the power output stage of an audio frequency amplifier to a low impedance load.

transformer, potential, *n.* A step-down transformer having no leakage flux and capable of carrying only a very small current. Used to measure the voltage of a high voltage power circuit, the primary being connected to the power circuit and the secondary to a low-voltage voltmeter.

transformer, pulse, *n.* A transformer capable of passing a wide band of frequencies, and thus of passing a pulse without unacceptable distortion.

transformer, push-pull, *n.* A transformer having a balanced center-tapped winding for use in a push-pull amplifier, which see.

transformer, quarter-wave, *n.* A section of coaxial line or waveguide, about one-quarter wavelength long, used to match a transmission line to an antenna or load.

transformer, radio-frequency, *n.* A transformer designed for impedance matching at radio frequencies. It is likely to have only an air core or a ferrite core.

transformer, step-down, *n.* A transformer used to reduce an alternating voltage. Its secondary voltage is less than the primary voltage.

transformer, step-up, *n.* A transformer used to increase an alternating voltage. Its secondary voltage is greater than the primary voltage.

transformer, Subcycle. See "generator, sub-harmonic."

transformer, tuned, *n.* A transformer designed to be resonant at the frequency with which it will be used, thereby causing the secondary voltage to build up to high values. An intermediate-frequency (IF) transformer is one example of a tuned transformer.

transformer, variable, *n.* A power transformer, either an autotransformer or a two-winding transformer, whose output voltage can be varied over a considerable range. See also "Variac."

transformer, voltage. See "voltage transformer" and "instrument transformer."

transformer, voltage-regulating. See "regulator, voltage."

transformer coupling. See "coupling, inductive."

trans-hybrid loss. See "loss, trans-hybrid."

transient, *n.* A rapid, sometimes violent, fluctuation of voltage or current in a circuit, usually of short (several hertz) duration. Caused by switching, changes in load, or by momentary crosses or grounds.

transient, switching, *n.* A rapid fluctuation of voltage or current in a circuit, caused by switching operations which change the current flowing in the circuit.

transient regulation, *n.* The degree of freedom of a system from variations in voltage and frequency caused by sudden loud changes, operational switching, emergency power transfers, system faults, reflected power changes, etc.

transient response. See "response, transient."

transistor, *n.* A very small, active, semi-conductor device which can perform the same functions as electron tubes, such as amplification, control, and rectification. It has three or more electrodes including the base, collector, and emitter. Conduction is accomplished by the transport of electrons or holes.

transistor, common-base. See "common-base."

transistor, common-collector. See "common-collector."

transistor, common-emitter. See "common-emitter."

transistor, field-effect, *n.* A tiny bar of n-type semiconductor having opposite spots of p-type material. Application of a negative bias to the p-type regions controls their space charge region which controls the through resistance of the n-type bar.

transistor, unijunction, *n.* A transistor having two connections to the base plus an emitter connection. It has a negative resistance characteristic, and is useful as an oscillator, in timing circuits, voltage and current sensing circuits, and in digital logic circuits.

transistorized, *adj.* Using transistors instead of vacuum tubes. This requires a complete redesign, not a one-for-one replacement.

Transite, *n.* Johns-Manville's registered trademark for its brand of asbestos-cement conduits. Transite "C" duct is for direct burial. Transite "B" duct has a thinner wall, for encasement in concrete.

transition, signal, *n.* (1) The point of change from a mark signal to a space signal. (2) The point of zero current in a polar signal.

transition loss. See "loss, transition."

transit time, *n.* In an electron tube, the time required for electrons to pass from the cathode to the plate.

transit time effect, *n.* A phenomenon which occurs when electron tubes are used at the higher microwave frequencies, in which the period of one-half cycle of the signal applied to the control grid of the tube is less than the time it takes an electron to travel from the cathode to the plate. Under such conditions, the signal on the control grid may reverse before the electrons in transit reach the plate, and the tube therefore becomes ineffective. Transit time effect thus limits the upper frequencies which may be applied to electron tubes.

translate, *v.* (1) To shift up or down in frequency, usually by a modulation process. (2) To change telephone address digits into call routing digits.

translation, *n.* (1) The shifting in the frequency spectrum by which channels are formed into groups, groups into supergroups, and supergroups into a baseband. (2) The conversion of a telephone address (10 or 7-digit telephone number) into routing instructions for the automatic switches.

translation, digit, *n.* The conversion, in a translator, of a telephone address into routing instructions for the automatic switches.

translation, frequency, *n.* The transfer, as a block without altering its bandwidth, of signals occupying a definite frequency band from one position in the frequency spectrum to another. For instance: translating a voice channel (0-4 kHz) to carrier channel #12 (60-64 kHz).

translation, 3-digit, *n.* In a common-controlled switching center, determining the routing of the call on the basis of the first three digits received, which may be a central office (NNX) code, or a numbering plan area (NPA) code.

translation, 6-digit, *n.* In a common-controlled switching center, examining the first six digits received on calls to another numbering plan area (NPA) to determine the routing digits required.

translation matrix. See "decoder."

translator, *n.* In a common-controlled dial central office, the device which accepts the telephone address digits dialed by the customer and changes them into equipment routing digits. There may be more or less routing digits than address digits.

translator, AMA, *n.* Device used by the transverter to convert the calling line and party information received from the outgoing sender into the subscriber's directory number for recording on the AMA tape. (#5 X Bar)

translator, card, *n.* Translator which stores code-conversion information

on 5″ x 10½″ coded metal cards. Input codes are coded by tabs on the bottom 10½″ edge. Routing information is coded by punching holes in the center of the card. Code bars select the card corresponding to the input code. The card is then dropped and the routing information is read on a bank of photo-transistors, energized by 400 Hz modulated light shining through the holes in the card.

translator, foreign area, *n.* Translator which provides information on different AMA charge treatments where several destination codes are reached over a single trunk route to another national numbering area. (#5 X Bar)

translator, television, *n.* A television repeater station which picks up television signals, and then rebroadcasts them over the air on TV channels which are locally unused. No CATV cable is involved. This provides excellent local reception without interference from the original signal.

translator, VHF-to-VHF CATV, *n.* A device used at a CATV head end which receives a television signal on one VHF channel, down-converts it to an intermediate frequency (such as 45 MHz) and amplifies it, then up-converts it to a different VHF channel and transmits it to the cable network.

translator, UHF-to-VHF CATV, *n.* A device used at a CATV head end which receives a television signal on an ultra-high frequency (UHF) channel, down-converts it to an IF, amplifies it, up-converts it to a very-high frequency (VHF) channel, then transmits it to the cable network. It enables persons who have only a VHF television set to receive programs broadcast only on UHF channels.

transmission, *n.* The science dealing with the transferring of information in electrical signals over a distance without unacceptable attenuation, distortion, masking by noise, crosstalk, or echo, and without losing information content.

transmission, asynchronous, *n.* A digital transmission process such that between any two significant signal transitions in the same character or data block there is always an integral number of unit intervals. Between two significant signal transitions located in different characters or in different data blocks there probably will not be an integral number of unit intervals.

transmission, beam, *n.* The sending of a unidirectional flow of radio waves concentrated into a small solid angle in space, as from a high-gain directional antenna.

transmission, carrier. See "carrier transmission."

transmission, double-current, n. Polar telegraph transmission in which a positive current denotes a mark, and a negative current denotes a space.

transmission, free-space. See "free-space transmission."

transmission, parallel, *n.* The simultaneous transmission of a number of signal elements, either as tones (MF 2/6 signaling) or as DC pulses (register to translator to sender).

transmission, radio, *n.* The transmission of signals through space by radiation of an electromagnetic wave at radio frequencies, which may vary from 6000 hertz to 300 gigahertz.

transmission, scatter. See "scatter transmission, - - -."

transmission, serial, *n.* A method of transferring information in which the code elements are sent sequentially, one after another.

transmission, sideband. See "sideband, double," "sideband, single," and "sideband, twin."

transmission, stereophonic, *n.* Radio transmission of stereophonic sound covering the band 50-15000 hertz, with harmonic distortion not exceeding 3.5%, using a horizontally-polarized FM broadcast signal carrying a 23-53 kilohertz subchannel. The main FM carrier is frequency modulated by the sum of the left and right stereo channels. The subcarrier is amplitude modulated by a signal equal to the difference between the left and right channel signals.

transmission, suppressed carrier. See "suppressed carrier."

transmission, synchronous, *n.* A digital transmission process such that between any two significant signal transitions in the overall stream of pulses, there is always an integral number of unit intervals.

transmission, video, *n.* The transmission without distortion of frequencies in the band from 30 Hz to 4.5 MHz, adequate for both color and monochrome signals. See also "signal, television."

transmission bridge, *n.* A circuit (such as used in a connector switch) which couples two lines (calling and called) electrostatically for the transmission of voice currents, but separates the two lines for the feeding of separate talking battery supplies. Consists of two bridged battery feed coils connected together by a pair of balanced capacitors in series with the line between the battery feed coils.

transmission distributor, CATV, *n.* A directional coupler used with a bridging amplifier for supplying signals to several branching CATV cables.

transmission facilities. See "facilities, transmission."

transmission gain. See "gain, transmission."

transmission level, *n.* The level of power, in dbm, which should be measured at a particular point (TLP) in a transmission system when one milliwatt (zero dbm) of 1000 Hz tone is transmitted as a reference (TLP).

transmission level point (TLP), *n.* Any point in a transmission system where a power level measurement is made.

transmission line. See "line, transmission."

transmission loss. See "loss, transmission."

transmission measuring set (TMS). See "set, 13A transmission measuring," or "set, 23A transmission measuring."

transmission mode, *n.* In a wave guide, one of the field patterns in a plane transverse to the direction of propagation. See also "mode, TE," "mode TM," and "mode, dominant."

transmission system, *n.* The complex aggregate of electronic equipment and wire, carrier, or radio facilities which provide a multiplicity of channels over which are transmitted customer's messages and associated signaling information.

transmit, *v.t.* To send information or data, by voice, telegraph, teletypewriter, or card.

transmitter, *n.* (1) A person who transmits. (2) A telephone transmitter. (3) A radio transmitter. (4) A tape transmitter.

transmitter, coin-signal, *n.* A small transmitter, located in the upper housing of a coin telephone, used to transmit bell and gong signals to an operator during coin deposit.

transmitter, land, *n.* Fixed radio transmitter in a mobile, or ship-to-shore radio system.

transmitter, mobile, *n.* A radio transmitter for installation on a vehicle such as an auto, or on an aircraft or boat.

transmitter, noise-cancelling, *n.* A transmitter which can be substituted for the standard handset transmitter in noisy areas. Ambient noise reaches both sides of the transmitter diaphragm, and thus is cancelled out. The voice sound wave reaches principally the front of the diaphragm, and thus is transmitted.

transmitter, radio, *n.* The assembly of equipment which generates a radio frequency signal, modulates it with an intelligence signal, amplifies it to a higher power, and efficiently couples it to an antenna for radiation into space.

transmitter, tape, *n.* A mechanical-electrical device which accepts a previously punched paper tape and transmits serially the coded signals which are on the tape. Permits transmitting at a fast uniform rate from tapes which were hand punched at a slower rate.

transmitter, telephone, *n.* A transducer which uses voice sound pressure on a diaphragm to compress carbon granules between electrodes. The resulting resistance variation modulates a battery current flowing between the electrodes, thus translating the acoustic message into an analog electrical signal.

transmitter-distributor (TD), *n.* A motor-driven device which translates teletype code combinations from punched paper tape into electrical impulses, and transmits these impulses to one or more receiving stations.

transmitting equipment, radio, *n.* The oscillator, amplifiers, modulator, tuned circuits, and high voltage rectifier which comprise a radio transmitter.

transparent, *adj.* Said of a circuit which is suitable for the transmission of digital signals without the use of regenerative repeaters, or of any signals without unacceptable degradation.

transponder, *n.* A device (usually a radio transmitter) which initiates action, after being triggered by an interrogator, to send a confirming or identifying message or to release stored messages. Used on communication satellites.

transponder, satellite, *n.* The equipment in a communication satellite which receives signals from earth, then amplifies, translates, and retransmits these signals back to earth.

transport, tape, *n.* The portion of a tape recorder which holds the reels of magnetic tape, and draws the tape at a constant speed past the recording and playback heads. It does not include amplifiers or loudspeakers.

transportable, *adj.* Describing communication equipment which is configured or broken into separate units so that it can be readily transported by truck or aircraft. Implies equipment which is assembled and wired in weatherproof shelters which can be quickly interconnected to make the equipment operational.

transpose, *v.t.* To interchange, at systematic intervals, the pin positions of wires on an open-wire telephone line for the purpose of reducing crosstalk.

transposition, *n.* The interchanging, by rules, of wire positions on an open-wire lead for the purpose of reducing coupling, and therefore crosstalk, between circuits.

transposition, floating. See "bracket, span transposition."

transposition, junction, *n.* A transposition located on the junction pole between two transposition sections. When several sections of the same type of transpositions are used in tandem, some pairs may need to be transposed at the junction pole.

transposition, phantom circuit, *n.* A transposition in the phantom circuit. There are four types of phantom transpositions: (a) Type 1 transposes the phantom and both side circuits, (b) Type 2 transposes the phantom and side 1 but not side 2, (c) Type 3 transposes the phantom and side 2 but not side 1, and (d) Type 4 transposes the phantom only.

transposition, point, *n.* An interchanging of the pin position of open wire conductors at a single bracket, on the pole or mid-span. The usual

transposition requires two spans. Point transpositions are used either (a) for transposing carrier circuits, or (b) where long spans make mid-span transpositions necessary.

transposition, rolled, *n.* A transposition in which the conductors of an open wire line are physically rotated in a substantially helical manner. With two wires a complete transposition is executed in two consecutive spans.

transposition, side circuit, *n.* A transposition within a phantom group which affects only the side circuit, not the phantom circuit.

transposition interval, *n.* Any of the 32 equal segments of a transposition section.

transposition pattern. See "transposition type."

transposition section, *n.* An arbitrary length of open wire line that can be divided into 32 equal segments called transposition intervals. The transposition scheme is complete within each transposition section, and therefore the ends of the section can be termination or junction points in the wire line.

transpositions, *n. pl.* The interchanging of the pin position of open wire conductors within their crossarm and phantom group for the purpose of reducing noise induction and crosstalk.

transpositions, coordinated, *n. pl.* Transpositions placed in both communication and power circuits to obtain the maximum reduction of inductive coupling.

transposition type, *n.* Any of the 32 transposition patterns which have been standardized by the Bell Telephone Laboratories for use in designing transposition systems. Each type is designated by a letter or pair of letters, for example:

Type	Transpositions per Section
P	0
O	1
N	2

M   3
L   4
K   5
J   6

transposition type, relative, *n.* The transposition type which corresponds to the relationship of two pairs, each of which is transposed. The relative of a type O pair and a type N pair is a type M. The relative of a type O pair and a type L pair is a type K.

transender, *n.* A combined register-sender.

transistor, *n.* A tiny electronic device, similar in its functions to an electron tube, but using point or layer contacts on a semiconductor such as germanium or silicon. Conduction is by electrons or "holes" (which see). Uses small operating voltages, and has a large amplification factor.

transistor, junction, *n.* A transistor without point contacts having three layers of semiconductor material, either n-p-n or p-n-p.

transistor, n-p-n, *n.* A junction transistor having a thin layer of p-type semiconductor between two pieces of n-type material. The center layer is the base, and is positive with respect to the emitter and negative with respect to the collector. Conduction is by the movement of electrons.

transistor, p-n-p, *n.* A junction transistor in which a thin layer of n-type semiconductor (the base) is sandwiched between two pieces of p-type material. Conduction is by the movement of holes, therefore the emitter is positive to the base, and the collector is negative to the base.

Transite, *n. adj.* One brand of asbestos-cement products much used for telephone conduit. See "conduit, asbestos-cement."

transverse wave. See "wave, transverse - - -."

transverter, AMA, *n.* Device which receives from an outgoing sender

the details of an outgoing call, converts it to recording format, then seizes the recorder which controls perforation of this information in the AMA tape.

transverter, ANI, *n.* A circuit which furnishes the calling party's directory number to a centralized message accounting operator. It receives the calling line equipment number from the outgoing sender, calls in a translator to convert it to the directory number, then transfers the directory number to the outgoing sender.

trap, annoyance call, *n.* Central office equipment (H-85908), which can be actuated by a person receiving an annoyance call, which holds up the switch train and gives an alarm so that an attendant can trace the connection.

trap, tuned, *n.* A series resonant circuit bridged across a circuit or line which effectively shorts it at the resonant frequency.

trap, wave, *n.* A tuned trap, which see.

traveling wave. See "wave, traveling."

traveling wave tube. See "tube, traveling wave."

tray, cable, *n.* A steel mesh or ladder-like trough hung horizontally below the ceiling in equipment buildings to support equipment cable runs. Sometimes made by inverting ladder-type cable rack.

tray, storage battery, *n.* A glass, plastic, or lead tray placed under one or more storage cells as a precaution against leaking or spilled battery acid.

treatment, *n.* Any of the several actions a telephone company takes on telephone bills which are overdue.

treatment, acoustic, *n.* The application of sound-absorbing materials to the ceiling or walls of a room to reduce reverberation.

treatment, rate. See "rate treatment number."

treatment, service, *n.* Certain routing,

conditioning, precedence, etc. actions by the switching equipment which are activated by class marks on the individual subscriber line or trunk.

treble, *adj.* Denoting those musical tones written in the treble clef in musical notation, and therefore above middle C or 256 hertz.

tree, *n.* (1) A network or relay circuit configuration in which there are connected branches but no meshes (closed loops). (2) A decoder.

tree wire. See "wire, tree."

trencher, *n.* A self-propelled machine on wheels or crawler tracks which uses a toothed steel digging chain or wheel to dig a trench, 3-4 feet deep, in which to bury cable or wire.

triangulate, *v.* To make a measurement by triangulation when only one end of the circuit to be measured is available to the tester.

triangulation, *n.* A method of measuring the resistance of one wire or the transmission loss of one circuit, when testing at only one end of the circuit. Take any three good wires or three good circuits. Call them A, B, and C. Loop the wires (or circuits) at the far end and measure A+B, A+C, and B+C. Substitute the measurements in, and solve this formula:

$$(A+B) + (A+C) - (B \quad C) = 2A$$
$$2A/2 = A$$
$$(A+B) - A = B$$
$$(A+C) - A = C$$

tributary office, *n.* A local office, some or all of whose toll calls are ticketed and timed at a toll center. A Class 5 toll switching center, or "end office."

trickle charge. See "charge, trickle."

trigger, *v.* To initiate an action which will then continue or proceed to completion, and cannot be stopped by the triggering mechanism or circuit.

trigger circuit, *n.* A circuit in which

a small input can initiate an abrupt change, as from non-conduction to conduction. A flip-flop is a common type of trigger circuit.

trimmer, *adj.* A term describing a small capacitor, inductor, or resistor which is screwdriver adjustable, placed in parallel or series with a larger capacitor, inductor, or resistor and used to tune the circuit precisely.

trimmer, tree. See "head, pruner."

trimming, tree, *n.* The work of cutting back trees or brush to provide clearance for a telephone pole line. Before cutting trees, check with the Right-of-Way Agent to determine if there is an easement, or if permission must be secured.

triode, *n.* A three-electrode electron tube which contains an anode, a cathode, and a control electrode which is usually a grid.

trip-free, *adj.* Describing the property of a power circuit breaker which will trip out and clear a faulty circuit, even when its operating handle is being held closed.

triple, *n.* Three insulated wires twisted together.

triple (alternate routing). See "direct triple" or "alternate triples."

triple harmonics, *n. pl.* Any of the harmonics on a Y-connected power circuit whose frequencies are multiples of three times the fundamental frequency (180, 360, 540, 720 Hz etc). These make an important contribution to telephone line noise, unless shorted out by a delta-connected power transformer.

tripler, frequency, *n.* An electron tube circuit in which the plate circuit is tuned to a frequency which is three times that of the frequency in its grid circuit.

tronic, *adj.* Slang term for "electronic."

tropopause, *n.* The boundary between the troposphere and the stratosphere.

troposphere, *n.* That portion of the

earth's atmosphere in which temperature generally decreases with altitude, clouds form, and convection disturbances occur. It extends to a height of about 25,000 feet at the poles, and to about 55,000 feet at the equator.

tropospheric scatter. See "scatter transmission, tropospheric."

tropospheric wave. See "wave, tropospheric."

trouble, *n.* Failure of a system, an equipment, a circuit, or a circuit element to operate or to perform within standard limits.

trouble intercepting trunk, *n.* In a dial office, a trunk connected to the terminating equipment of an out-of-order line so that calls for that line are routed to an intercepting position. Paired with a "trouble observation and test trunk."

trouble observation and test trunk, *n.* In a dial office, a trunk connected to the originating (line) equipment of an out-of-order line so that attempted calls from that line are brought to the attention of a testman. Paired with a "trouble intercepting trunk."

trouble operator, *n.* Operator who "plugs up" and holds lines or trunks reported to her as out of order, and who assists the Plant forces in clearing the trouble.

trouble-shoot, *v.* To investigate a trouble report and determine the basic cause of the trouble, and (usually) to make at least a temporary repair.

trough, wiring. See "wireway."

trunk, *n.* (1) One telephone communication channel between (a) two ranks of switching equipment in the same central office, (b) between central office units in the same switching center, or (c) between two switching centers. A trunk is for the common use of all calls of one class between its two terminals. (2) The DCS term meaning "trunk group."

trunk (DCS definition), *n.* A single or multichannel communications medium between two successive terminal facilities (except unattended relays) with DCS access, where channels may be tested, rerouted, dropped out, or switched to another route.

trunk, automatic signal. See "automatic signal trunk."

trunk, CLR, *n.* Combined Line and Recording trunk. The trunk you seize when you dial the toll operator. Over it the operator records the details of the call, and then completes the call to the called party without the calling party leaving the line. The CLR trunk has a low transmission loss.

trunk, dial-back. See "dial-back trunk."

trunk, direct toll. See "trunk, end office toll."

trunk, end office toll, *n.* A toll trunk which interconnects two Class 5 offices. Its transmission loss must not exceed 8.0 dB, and preferably should be its VNL plus 5 dB.

trunk, extendable information, *n.* Type of trunk circuit available in some PABXs which enables the operator to connect a call from a restricted station on a "O" level trunk directly to an outgoing central office trunk, thus enabling the station to dial his own city numbers.

trunk, foreign exchange, *n.* A trunk connecting a PBX to a central office other than its normal serving central office.

trunk, incoming, *n.* A trunk incoming to a local central office switching unit for use in terminating calls on the subscriber lines of that unit. Also a trunk incoming to a toll, tandem, or PBX switchboard or switching unit.

trunk, inspector's *n.* An incoming trunk to a local test desk, for use by repairmen, inspector's, etc.

trunk, intermarker group, *n.* A trunk used to handle traffic between two crossbar marker groups located in the same building. The traffic may be subscriber to subscriber, trunk to subscriber, or subscriber to trunk. These trunks have terminations in both marker groups, and handle the traffic more efficiently than if routed over regular interoffice trunks.

trunk, interoffice, *n.* A trunk between two switching units regardless of type. The term should be restricted to trunks between local offices in the same exchange area.

trunk, interposition, *n.* A trunk which interconnects two positions of a large switchboard so that a line or trunk appearing on one position can be connected to a trunk or line appearing on the other position.

trunk, interswitch, *n.* A trunk between switching centers.

trunk, intertandem, *n.* A trunk between two tandem offices.

trunk, intertoll, *n.* Trunk between two toll offices.

trunk, intra-office, *n.* (1) A trunk between two ranks of switches within the same central office unit. (2) A trunk between two central office units in the same switching center.

trunk, listed number, *n.* A seven digit telephone number, listed in the telephone company's directory, which gives access to a PABX operator.

trunk, no-test. See "no-test trunk."

trunk, outgoing, *n.* A trunk used for telephone calls terminating outside the switching unit.

trunk, PBX, *n.* A trunk between a private branch exchange and a Telephone Company central office. See also "tie line, PBX."

trunk, plug-supervision. See "plug-supervision trunk."

trunk, primary, *n.* The trunk from a primary switch (lineswitch or line-finder) to a first selector.

trunk, recording, *n.* A trunk to the toll operator used only for accepting and recording details of a proposed call. Used on high traffic days when delays are being quoted on outgoing toll calls. Recording trunks may not have the low transmission loss needed to complete toll calls.

trunk, recording-completing, *n.* A CLR trunk; a toll trunk which has a low transmission loss so that it can be used both for recording the ticket information and for completing the call.

trunk, reverting call, *n.* A trunk used to set up a talking path for a reverting call.

trunk, secondary, *n.* (1) A trunk to a secondary switch, such as to a secondary lineswitch or secondary out-trunk switch. (2) Sometimes used improperly when a "direct trunk" is meant.

trunk, secondary intertoll, *n.* A trunk used to connect a toll switching machine to its associated manual assistance switchboard in the same or adjacent building. Its loss shall not exceed 0.5 db.

trunk, special-service. See "special-service trunk."

trunk, straightforward. See "straightforward trunk."

trunk, tandem, *n.* A trunk to or from a tandem office.

trunk, tie, *n.* A trunk between two private branch exchanges. Usually called a "PBX tie line."

trunk, toll, *n.* A single voice communication circuit used for carrying toll calls from one toll office to another. Also called an "intertoll trunk."

trunk, toll connecting, *n.* A trunk which connects a Class 5 local office to any higher ranking toll office. Its loss will not be greater than 4.0 dB, and preferably VNL + 2.5 dB.

trunk, toll switching, *n.* A one-way trunk from a toll switchboard to a local central office (end office) over which the operator establishes an incoming toll call. It has a low transmission loss.

trunk, tone, *n.* A trunk which supplies tone to a calling customer. The marker attempts to route a customer to a tone trunk for conditions of line busy on an intraoffice call, overflow, partial dial, or vacant code.

trunk, tributary toll, *n.* A toll circuit connecting a tributary office with its toll center.

trunk, trouble intercepting. See "trouble intercepting trunk."

trunk, trouble observation and test. See "trouble observation and test trunk."

trunk, TX, *n.* A trunk that has its terminating end in front of a TX operator.

trunk, verification. See "verification trunk."

trunk board, *n.* A switch frame, which see.

trunk busy tone, *n.* A tone which indicates a trunk busy condition to an operator. It consists of dial tone (600/120 Hz) interrupted 120 times per minute.

trunk finder. See "finder, trunk."

trunk group, *n.* A group of trunks between the same two points, which are electrically similar and are used for the same purpose.

trunk-hunting, *adj.* Describing a selector (or connector) which searches from one terminal to another until an idle trunk (or idle station line within a group) is found.—*n.* The act of searching for an idle terminal.

trunk-hunting connector. See "connector, trunk-hunting."

trunk loss. See "loss, trunk."

trunks, final, *n. pl.* The group of trunks which takes the overflow traffic from a group of direct "high-usage" trunks.

trunks, high-usage, *n. pl.* A group of trunks which is the primary direct route between two points, and is engineered to carry the maximum traffic at all times. To provide an acceptable grade of service, an al-

ternate "final group" must be provided for the overflow traffic.

truth table, *n.* A logic table which lists all possible input conditions, and for each of them gives the output.

tube, ballast. See "lamp, ballast."

tube, cable, *n.* Lined tunnel of 7-foot diameter circular cross-section used in Great Britain to supplement or substitute for underground conduit where underground cable runs are exceptionally heavy.

tube, cathode-ray (CRT), *n.* Any electron-beam tube similar to the picture tube in a television receiver.

tube, cold-cathode, *n.* An electron tube containing a cathode which operates at room (ambient) temperature.

tube, electron, *n.* An electron device in which conduction by electrons takes place through a vacuum or gas within a gas-tight envelope.

tube, gas, *n.* An electron tube in which the contained gas or vapor performs an essential function in the operation of the tube.

tube, hard, *n.* An electron tube which has been highly evacuated and therefore contains no residual gases to impair its operation.

tube, lighthouse. See "lighthouse tube."

tube, mercury-vapor, *n.* A gas tube in which the electron carrying gas is mercury vapor.

tube, metal, *n.* An electron tube having a metal housing, with the electrode leads passing through glass seals in the base.

tube, numerical read-out. See "Nixie tube."

tube, plastic entrance, *n.* Replacement for porcelain tube previously used to insulate drop wires where they go through building walls. Available in 3/8" ID and lengths of 4, 6, 8, 12, and 16 inches.

tube, porcelain entrance, *n.* A flanged porcelain tube used to insulate drop wires where they go through building walls. Available in ⅜-inch inside diameter, and lengths from 4 to 12 inches.

tube, soft, *n.* An electron tube (not a "gas tube") containing residual gas which adversely affects its operation.

tube, traveling wave (TWT), *n.* A wideband microwave electron tube amplifier in which a stream of electrons moves with an electromagnetic wave down the length of the tube and interacts in such a way that there is a transfer of energy from the electron stream to the radio wave.

tube, tungar. See "tungar tube."

tube, vacuum, *n.* An electron tube which has been evacuated to such a degree that residual gas or vapor does not affect its electrical characteristics.

tube, velocity-modulated, *n.* An electron tube in which the velocity of the electron stream is alternately increased and decreased during the transit time between cathode and anode.

tube, voltage regulator, *n.* A gas tube in which the tube voltage drop is approximately constant over the range of operating current. Used to stabilize the voltage of a power supply.

tubing, electrical-metallic (EMT). See "conduit, thin-wall metallic."

tubing, flexible nonmetallic, *n.* A mechanical protection for a conductor consisting of a flexible, cylindrical tube woven of non-conducting fibrous material.

tubing, heat shrinkable, *n.* A tube of irradiated polyolefin or polyvinylchloride plastic which will shrink to half its diameter when heat is applied. Used to provide close-fitting insulation over electrical terminals.

tubing, lead, *n.* Lead pipe, ¼-inch ID, used for bypasses and valve extensions in pressurized lead-sheathed cable.

tubing, plastic, *n.* Pipe of black polyethylene plastic, ¼-inch OD, used for bypasses and the piping of dry air to pressurized plastic-sheathed cables.

tubing, poly-cor, *n.* A plastic sheath covering 3, 5, or 10 plastic tubes. Used to pipe dry air from a meter panel to cables in a cable vault.

tubing, temporary closure, *n.* Plastic tubing which can be opened and closed by means of a longitudinal plastic zipper. Used to protect bundles of wires, or for temporary covering of unsheathed cable.

tubing, varnished. See "spaghetti."

tune, *v.t.* (1) To adjust for resonance at a selected frequency. (2) To adjust for the best operation.

tuned circuit, *n.* A circuit which will resonate at a selected frequency. The circuit contains both capacitance and inductance, one of which is adjustable.

tuned radio frequency, *adj.* Describing a radio receiver in which the radio frequency amplification is done at the carrier frequency, rather than at a lower intermediate frequency.

tuned relay, *n.* A relay which is mechanically resonant at, and responds only to, a particular frequency. The 135 Hz ringing relay is an example.

tuned ringer, *n.* Any of the several telephone bells which are capacitor tuned to be resonant at, and to respond only to, a particular ringing frequency. Available factory adjusted to these frequencies: 16.6, 20, 25, 30, 33.3, 40, 42, 50, 54, 60, 66, and 66.6 Hz. Used on party lines which are rung with harmonic, decimonic, or synchromonic frequencies.

tuner, radio, *n.* The forward end of a radio receiver which provides a low-level audio output, without audio amplification.

tuner, stub. See "stub, matching."

tuner, waveguide, *n.* An adjustable device added to a waveguide for the purpose of changing its impedance. See also "waveguide slug tuner" and "waveguide stub tuner."

tungar tube, *n.* A high current rectifier tube used for 6 and 12 volt battery charging. Consists of a tungsten filament cathode and a carbon disk anode in an argon filled glass bulb.

tungsten, *n.* A steel-gray, brittle, hard metal which melts at 3370 degrees C. Used in the making of electron tube filaments, and for alloy steels.

tuning, *n.* The act of adjusting a circuit to resonance, or for the best performance at a particular frequency.

tuning, broad, *n.* Tuning which is not sharply resonant, and therefore not selective. See also "tuning, stagger."

tuning, core. See "core tuning."

tuning, electron, *n.* Adjusting the frequency of a device, such as a reflex klystron, by changing its electrode potentials.

tuning, ganged, *n.* The simultaneous tuning of two or more circuits by a single control. Usually accomplished with a "gang capacitor."

tuning, permeability, *n.* Tuning a coil to resonance by moving a ferrite or powdered iron core in or out of the coil, thereby changing its inductance.

tuning, sharp, *n.* Tuning of a circuit so that it is resonant over a very, narrow bandwidth, and is therefore very selective. Sharp tuning requires a "high Q" circuit.

tuning, slug. See "tuning, permeability."

tuning, staggered, *n.* A method of tuning an intermediate-frequency amplifier by tuning each stage to a slightly different frequency in order to widen the overall amplification-frequency curve.

tuning core, *n.* A powdered iron or ferrite core that can be moved in and out of a coil to vary its inductance.

tuning indicator, *n.* A small voltmeter in a radio receiver, used to indicate when the receiver is tuned accurately.

tuning screw, *n.* In a cavity or wave-guide, an impedance adjusting element consisting of a threaded rod whose depth of penetration into the cavity or waveguide is adjustable.

tuning stub. See "stub, matching."

tunnel diode. See "diode, tunnel."

turnstile. See "antenna, turnstile."

turntable, *n.* The circular table, precisely rotated at 33-1/3, 45, or 78 rpm, on which a phonograph record is placed for playing.

turret, test, *n.* A table-top cabinet having test circuits with a voltmeter, dial speed test set, and an operator's telephone circuit which functions as a small local test desk.

turn, *n.* One conductor making one complete loop around a magnetic circuit.

turn over, *v.* To reverse a line, tip for ring and ring for tip.

turns ratio, *n.* In a transformer, the number of turns in the secondary winding divided by the number of turns in the primary winding. Under normal circumstances, it is also the voltage ratio.

turret, attendant's, *n.* A PABX attendant's switchboard, made in the form of a small key cabinet for top-of-desk mounting. May use either a handset or an operator's headset.

turret, information. See "information board."

turret, test. See "test turret."

tweeter, *n.* A small horn-type loud-speaker designed to reproduce high audio frequencies from 3500 to 20,000 hertz. Requires a "crossover network," which see.

twine, lacing, *n.* A 6-ply or 8-ply waxed linen cord used to lace cable conductors. See also "cord, nylon lacing."

twine, linen, *n.* The traditional lacing twine is 6-ply or 8-ply waxed linen cord. See also "cord, nylon lacing."

twine, marline. See "marline."

twin-channel carrier, *n.* Carrier using independent sideband modulation in which the adjacent channels are upper and lower sidebands of the same carrier frequency. The Bell System "O" open wire carrier system is an example.

twin-line, *n.* A type of balanced radio frequency transmission line having two parallel insulated conductors spaced ¼-inch, and separated by a web of the insulating material. Has an impedance of 300 ohms, and is widely used as a television lead-in cable.

twin sideband. See "sideband, twin."

twist, *n.* The component of the attenuation-temperature characteristic of a toll cable which varies with frequency.

twist, staggered. See "staggered twist."

twist, waveguide, *n.* A section of waveguide in which the cross-section progressively rotates about the longitudinal axis.

twisted pair, *n.* A pair of insulated conductors twisted together, without a common covering.

twister, sleeve, *n.* A plier-like tool having parallel grooves in the jaws which fit and hold the twin sleeves used for splicing line wire. One twister is used at each end of the sleeve, and they are rotated around the sleeve to make the twisted joint.

twistor, *n.* A magnetic memory device which is bistable, permitting the storage or sensing of binary information. Fabricated by helically wrapping a very thin magnetic tape around a core of tinned copper wire. Each short length of twistor encompassed by a small wire-wound solenoid represents one memory bit.

two-party line. See "line, party."

two-phase, *adj.* Describing an alternating current circuit in which there are two sinusoidal voltages differing in phase by 90 electrical degrees, or one-quarter of a cycle.

two-tone keying, *n.* Frequency-shift keying, which see.

two-way, *adj.* Describing a trunk which can be used for calls which pass in either direction. When it is seized

for a call in one direction, the other direction is made busy.

two-wire line, *n.* A two-conductor metallic circuit used for one-way or two-way transmission.

two-wire repeater. See "repeater, two-wire."

TX operator, *n.* Operator who makes subsequent attempts to complete delayed calls.

tying-in, *n.* The work of fastening open wire to its supporting insulators, using tie wires.

type, transposition. See "transposition type" and "transposition type, relative."

Type eleven, *adj.* Designation of step-by-step C.O. equipment using "universal" trunk boards 5'-11" long, 1'-0" deep and 7-6, 9-0 or 11-8 high. Shelves mount on rear of trunk board upright.

Type 11A, *adj.* See "35E97."

U guard. See "guard, U cable."

UL approved, *adj.* Designating a product or device which has been inspected, tested, and approved by the Underwriter's Laboratories, Inc.

ultimate, matrix, *n.* The maximum size of a space-division electronic switch, as determined by the size of the B-B stage of the switching matrix.

ultrahigh frequency (UHF), *n.* Any of the frequencies in the band 300-3,000 megahertz. Also called a "microwave frequency."

ultrasonic, *adj.* Describing frequencies higher than can be heard by the human ear, therefore above 20,000 Hertz.

ultra-violet degradation. See "degradation, ultra-violet."

umbrella, cable splicer's, *n.* A 5½-ft. diameter umbrella on a 6 ft. wooden pole, used to protect an aerial cable splice from sun and summer showers.

unattended, *adj.* Said of a facility, such as a telephone central office, which does not normally have maintenance personnel in attendance, even during the normal working hours. Maintenance personnel visit periodically to perform routines and as required to clear trouble.

unbalanced circuit, *n.* A two-wire circuit whose two sides are not alike electrically, either from the standpoint of series resistance, series inductance, shunt leakage resistance, or shunt capacitance to ground.

unbalanced line, *n.* A transmission line of which one side is at ground potential, such as a coaxial line.

unbalanced output, *n.* An electrical output of which one of the two terminals is at ground potential.

unbiased, *adj.* (1) Said of a ringer whose armature is not held at one end of its travel by a spring. (2) Said of an electron tube grid which is at the same potential as the cathode.

unclassified, *adj.* Describing information which does not have a security classification.

undamped wave, *n.* A wave having constant amplitude.

underbunching, *n.* A condition in a klystron or traveling wave tube in which there is less than optimum bunching.

undercurrent relay, *n.* A relay designed to operate when the current it is monitoring drops below a preset value.

underground, *adj.* (1) Describing communication conduit installed under the surface of the earth. (2) Describing communication cable installed in underground conduit so it can be removed without digging. —*adv.* Under the ground.—*n.* Underground conduit and manholes.

undervoltage alarm, *n.* An aural alarm in a central office which indicates the battery voltage being supplied to the equipment is too low.

undervoltage protection, *n.* The automatic action of circuit breakers to disconnect power loads when the AC power voltage is too low for safe operation. Prevents damage to motors, and unloads the power circuit to facilitate recovery of the normal voltage.

undervoltage relay, *n.* A moving coil voltmeter-type relay which is designed to close an alarm contact when the voltage across it drops to a pre-set level.

Underwriter's Laboratories, Inc., *n.* A non-profit laboratory sponsored by the National Board of Fire Underwriters which examines and tests devices, materials, and systems whose action may effect casualty, fire, and life hazards.

ungrounded, *adj.* Without any connection to ground.

unicoupling device, *n.* A balun, which see.

unidirectional, *adj.* (1) Receiving or radiating electromagnetic waves in only one direction (antenna). (2) Flowing in only one direction (current).

unifilar, *adj.* Using only a single wire.

uniform line, *n.* A transmission line which has identical electrical properties for each unit of its length.

Uniform System of Accounts. See "Accounts, Uniform System of."

Unigauge central office. See "central office, Unigauge."

Unigauge system, *n.* A new system of designing subscribers loop plant which the Bell System applies in #5 crossbar offices. Its principal features are:

(a) Use of 26 AWG cable loops to 30,000 feet.

(b) Inductive loading on loops over 24,000 feet, but no loading coils within 15,000 feet of the central office.

(c) Range extenders in the central office on loops over 15,000 feet.

unijunction transistor. See "transistor, unijunction."

Uni-Pair, *adj.* Describing a patented method of constructing a plastic-insulated paired cable in which the two insulated wires comprising a pair are joined by a thin web of polyethylene and are twisted. Since the two wires of the pair are exactly the same length, the mutual capacitance of this cable is very uniform.

unipole, *n.* An isotropic antenna, which see.

uni-switch, *n.* A type of crossbar switch usage in which all equipment units which have a matrix appearance are connected in the same switch.

unit, answer-back, *n.* An electromechanical device used with a teletypewriter set to transmit a predetermined message of not more than 21 characters in response to a request signal. It can transmit either a 5-level 7.42 unit code or an 8-level 11.0 unit code at speeds up to 100 words per minute.

unit, balancing, *n.* (1) A small adjustable capacitor used for balancing the capacitance of office wiring in toll offices. (2) Capacitor consisting of helically coiled parallel insulated wire which can be cut in length to give the desired capacitance and added at quadded cable splices to adjust wire-to-wire capacitances to a low value.

unit, battery test load, *n.* A testing unit consisting of a bank of heavy-duty resistors which can be switched in parallel to simulate a particular load on a 2-volt cell of a storage battery. Usually contains a 0-400 ampere ammeter.

unit, cable, *n.* A group of pairs which are stranded together as a unit in the construction of a multi-pair cable. A later method than concentric layer construction.

unit, central office, *n.* A unit of automatic telephone switching equipment whose maximum capacity is 10,000 lines.

unit, central processing (CPU), *n.* The subsystem which is the brain of an electronic central office. It receives instructions from the program section of the memory, executes the instructions, analyzes the result, and decides what step to take next.

unit, cgs, *n.* Any of the metric units of measurement based on the centimeter-gram-second system.

unit, circuit, *n.* A section of toll circuit having zero transmission loss, used as a patching facility. It can substitute for any similar facility without disrupting the transmission layout of the overall circuit.

unit, crosstalk, *n.* The unit of crosstalk coupling, in which the current in the disturbed circuit is one-millionth of that in the disturbing circuit. One unit of crosstalk (coupling) is equal to 120 dB of loss.

unit, DX signaling, *n.* A duplex signaling unit which applies E & M lead signals via A & B leads onto the same cable pair that carries the voice message.

unit, intercom selector, *n.* A key telephone unit which includes a rotary selector switch used to direct a ringing signal to a particular intercom station. See also "intercom, telephone."

unit, key service, *n.* A complete, factory pre-wired, apparatus mounting containing relay equipment (key telephone units) and power supply equipment required to give key telephone service to a group of lines. (WECo #311A, #501AW, 550A Units)

unit, key telephone, *n.* Assemblage of apparatus such as relays, capacitors, coils, resistors, etc., on a metal panel, surface wired to a terminal panel. Performs one of many functions required for key telephone service.

unit, L, *n.* A permanently associated continuity of coaxial line facilities between adjacent switching stations or combining equipments. It extends from the input of the line hybrid at one station to the output of the flat gain amplifier at the next station, and includes intermediate amplifiers.

unit, labor, *n.* The length of time, in hours or fractions of an hour, which an average trained man will take to perform a particular item of work.

unit, line building-out, *n.* An impedance compensator, which modifies the impedance of a loaded cable pair to closely approximate that of a 2 mf capacitor in series with 900 ohms, and makes the loading end section look like an 0.8 end section. Used on repeatered circuits to reduce the mismatch between the cable and the office equipment.

unit, message, *n.* A unit for the measurement of telephone service which combines the length of call in minutes with the distance called. One message unit usually equates to a local call lasting for three minutes.

unit, noise, *n.* An outmoded unit for measuring the interfering effect of circuit noise. It is the arbitrary amount of energy of mixed random frequencies as generated by a #1-A Noise Standard (not white noise) which equals, in interfering effect on a telephone conversation, a 1000 Hz tone at a level of 98.5 db below one milliwatt. For modern noise standards see "dba" and "dbrnC."

unit, power, *n.* An assemblage of transformer, resistors, capacitors, inductors, diode rectifiers, etc. in a case for wall or relay rack mounting. Used to provide ac and dc power for key telephone systems, small PBX's, etc.

unit, protector, *n.* Protector blocks, or protector blocks and heat coils, assembled into a split metal sleeve holder provided with a color-coded plastic cap. Provides a replaceable over-voltage and over-current protector element for main distributing frame protectors. Used also in telephone station protectors and protected cable terminals.

unit, R, *n.* A permanently associated continuity of radio facilities providing a one-way transmission path between adjacent main radio stations, between a repeater bridging point and a main station, or between a repeater bridging point and a user's location. Extends from the input of the exciter at the transmitting end to the output of the combiners and baseband amplifiers at the receiving end.

unit, radio relay message (MUR), *n.* A microwave radio relay or tropospheric scatter facility assigned for use in one direction between those stations where channels are added or dropped.

unit, receiver, *n.* The working parts of a telephone receiver: diaphragm, electromagnets, permanent magnet, and varistor, sealed in a small moisture-proof capsule which forms a part of a handset or head telephone set.

unit, remote scanner and encoder, *n.* A remote electromechanical scanner which monitors up to 200 traffic points, five at a time, to determine whether they are idle or busy. This information is then encoded into data words and transmitted via a data link to a centralized control unit which stores it in memory registers, from where it can be used to actuate a printer.

unit, repeater gain, *n.* The amplifying unit of a repeater, which must be combined with impedance matching, equalizing, hybrid, and balancing networks to make a complete repeater.

unit, RT, *n.* A low capacity unit, powered from 115 volt 60 Hz AC, which supplies 20 Hz ringing power and 20-24 volts DC talking power for small PBX or key systems installations. Some types also supply 10 volts, 60 Hz signal lamp power.

unit, secretarial answering, *n.* A small key cabinet, available in 6, 10, and 20-line sizes, which enables a secretary to pick up or hold any of the telephone lines bridged in it. The unit does not require external relay equipment.

unit, SF signaling. See "single-frequency signaling unit."

unit, signaling, *n.* The line signaling device associated with a switchboard drop, as distinguished from a "ringer."

unit, T, *n.* Talking battery unit. A small capacity rectifier, powered by 115 volts 60 Hz AC, which supplies 20-24 volt DC talking power.

unit, telegraph coupling, *n.* Any of several units which are used as an interface between portions of a telegraph circuit which would otherwise be incompatible because of different voltages or types of operation. For instance: (a) Interface between a neutral line repeater or polar line repeater and a hub circuit operating at +60 volts mark and —30 volts space. (b) A two-path unit serving to interface one-way sending and one-way receiving loop repeaters to sending and receiving hub circuits. (c) A two-path unit used to interconnect half-duplex hub circuits of the same concentration group, or for interfacing one-way hub circuits (+60 volts mark, —30 volts space) with a full duplex hub circuit (—10 volts mark, —60 volts space).

unit, traffic, *n.* A measure of telephone traffic which is numerically equal to percentage occupancy. In Europe it is called the "Erlang." See also "occupancy."

unit, traffic work, *n.* An interval of time, 15.65 seconds, used to represent one unit of work by an operator.

unit, transmission, *n.* (1) A pre-connected network of induction coil, line balancing network, and talking capacitor potted in a single case with screw terminals. Used in telephone sets. (2) A unit of transmission loss, now superseded by the "decibel." Abbreviated "TU."

unit, transmitter, *n.* A carbon-type telephone transmitter sealed in a moisture-proof capsule which forms the transmitter portion of a handset, head telephone set, and similar devices.

unit, trouble, *n.* The decimal fraction which indicates the percentage number of cases of trouble which can be expected from a particular class of plant during a unit of time, usually a year.

unit, volume, *n.* An empirical measure of useful speech power, being the reading on an rms-reading voltmeter having a flat frequency response and closely specified inertial properties, when the meter is read in a carefully specified manner.

Unit call, *n.* The same as "hundred call seconds" (CCS).

unitized power equipment, *n.* Central office power equipment grouped into three major units, as follows: (a) A "power control unit," with associated "rectifier enclosure unit," (b) "station signaling rack," and (c) an "equipment supervisory rack."

unit of property, *n.* A single item of telephone plant, such as: a pole, a manhole, a foot of cable, as defined by the Uniform System of Accounts.

unity coupling, *n.* The condition existing in a perfect transformer, where all of the magnetic flux generated by the primary winding passes through the secondary winding.

unity power factor, *n.* A power factor of 1.0, which condition exists in an alternating current circuit when the voltage and the current are in phase. The power factor of a pure resistance load is 1.0.

universal motor, *n.* A commutator-type electric motor which will operate almost equally well on single-phase alternating current and direct current.

universal night answer. See "answer, universal night."

unloaded, *adj.* Describing a telephone circuit from which inductive loading has been removed. "Unloaded" is not a synonym for "non-loaded."

unmodulated, *n.* Without modulation, as a carrier when the modulating signal has been removed.

unstable, *adj.* Describing an electrical circuit which can be easily unbalanced, as a circuit which is on the verge of singing.

untuned, *adj.* Not tuned to be resonant at a particular frequency.

unvoiced sounds, *n. pl.* Speech sounds formed without the use of the vocal cords, and therefore not having a fundamental frequency or pitch. Very similar in composition to "random noise." See also "sibilants."

unweighted, *adj.* Flat weighted.

upconverter, *n.* A modulator whose input is an intermediate frequency and whose output is a radio frequency.

update, *v.t.* To modify or change information which is in storage, or programmed into a translator.

upgrade, *v.* (1) To improve a transmission facility by (a) reducing transmission loss, (b) reducing noise, or (c) increasing bandwidth. (2) To improve telephone service by changing from a 4-party to a 2-party line, or from either to an individual line.

uplink. See "satellite uplink."

upper sideband, *n.* The higher of the two bands of frequencies produced by an amplitude modulation process. Its frequencies consist of the sum of the carrier frequency and the modulating frequencies.

upset duplex, *n.* A method of telegraph circuit working between two duplex sets which uses polar signals in one direction and neutral signals in the opposite direction. The neutral signals are sent by opening and closing the line, which upsets the duplex balance on the receiving end of the circuit.

usage, *n.* (1) The percentage time that a telephone circuit is in use. (2) The total traffic that a circuit (or group of circuits) carries, usually expressed in hundred call-seconds (CCS).

usage, air, *n.* The volume of dry air or nitrogen fed to a pressurized cable. Usually measured in cubic feet per day.

usage count, *n.* A count of the number of times a circuit tests busy during a definite interval. If tested every 100 seconds, the counter will read CCS.

usage meter. See "meter, usage."

use, joint, *n.* The utilization of the same poles by two or more utility companies (telephone, power, street light, CATV) by mutual agreement.

useful bandwidth, *n.* In a carrier or radio system, that portion of the channel spacing which remains after the necessary guardbands are deducted. A carrier channel spacing of 4 kc. may give a useful bandwidth of 200-3200 cps.

user, *n.* Any individual who uses a communication service, as distinguished from a subscriber who contracts for that service from the Telephone Company.

utility power load, *n.* Administrative, support, and air-conditioning power loads which can be interrupted without immediate adverse effect on communications.

utilization factor, *n.* Of an electric power system, the ratio of the maximum demand to the rated capacity of the system.

utilization voltage, *n.* The voltage required to provide directly the input voltage requirement of a specific group of equipment.

vacant number, *n.* A telephone number which cannot be used because there is no terminating equipment in the central office. See also "nonworking number."

vacuum, *n.* The condition of a space, such as within an electron tube, from which air has been pumped until the small amount of gas remaining will not adversely affect operation of the device which is in the vacuum.

vacuum relay, *n.* A relay having contacts sealed in a vacuum, to achieve: (a) sparkless breaking of high voltages, (b) great reliability, or (c) long life.

vacuum tube, *n.* An electron tube, capable of acting as a diode, an amplifier, an oscillator, a modulator or demodulator, or rectifier.

vacuum-tube voltmeter. See "voltmeter, vacuum-tube."

valence electron, *n.* An electron in the conduction band of a semiconductor, where it is free to move under the influence of an electric field.

valley, *n.* A dip, or low point, in a curve which plots the electrical characteristics of a circuit.

value, analog, *n.* A value which is continuously variable.

value, average. See "average value."

value, effective. See "effective value."

value, instantaneous. See "instantaneous value."

value, peak. See "peak value."

valve, *n.* An electron tube (British).

valve, C pressure testing, *n.* A tire valve having ¼-inch —20 USS threads at the end of the stem, by which it can be screwed directly into a lead sheath or splice sleeve without using a flange.

valve, F pressure testing, *n.* An ordinary tire valve having ⅛-inch male pipe threads by which it can be screwed into a C or D pressure testing flange.

valve, gas admission, *n.* In the gas pressurizing of cable systems, a valve designated for use in connecting gas tanks for routine recharging of the cable system with gas.

valve, gas bypass, *n.* A gas valve, having a control stem with screwdriver slot, inserted in a bypass connection of a pressurized cable so that the bypass can be opened and closed at will. Also equipped with pressure testing valves on each side of the bypass valve.

valve, gas pressure relief, *n.* A valve which opens automatically to relieve excessive dry air pressure in a cable. Available to relieve pressures of over 3 pounds, 9 pounds, and 15 pounds.

valve, P pressure testing, *n.* A tire valve having a 1-inch long x ¼" OD stem which allows it to be soldered into the end of a ¼-inch lead pipe to provide a valve extension.

valve, pressure testing gas, *n.* A valve exactly like that used on auto tires, connected to a cable so that the gas pressure in the cable can be measured.

Van Allen belts, *n. pl.* Radiation belts situated around the earth, and consisting of electrons and protons at high energy levels. The inner, more energetic, belt is centered at 1900 miles above the earth; the outer at 9900 miles.

vaportight, *adj.* So enclosed that vapor will not enter the enclosure.

varactor, *n.* A semiconductor diode used as a variable capacitor. Varying the reverse bias varies its internal capacitance over a range of 0.2-260 picofarads. Used as harmonic generators, frequency multipliers, and as amplifiers utilizing energy from a pump signal input.

variable capacitor, *n.* A capacitor whose capacitance can be varied by moving one set of plates with respect to the other.

variable coupling. See "coupling, variable."

variable-frequency oscillator (VFO), *n.* An oscillator whose frequency can be varied over a considerable range. Usually either a beat-frequency oscillator, or an RC-tuned oscillator.

variable inductance. See "inductance, variable."

variable-mu, *adj.* Describing an electron tube in which the amplification factor (mu) varies with a control-grid voltage.

variable-reluctance, *adj.* Describing any of a number of transducers, such as microphones, phonograph pickups, etc., in which the input is made to vary the reluctance of a magnetic path.

variable spilling, *n.* Capability of a sender in a switching system to delete certain digits when they are not required to be outpulsed.

Variac, *n.* Registered trade name of one brand of continuously adjustable autotransformer. A typical Variac has an input of 120 volts AC, and an output continuously variable between 0 volts and 140 volts.

variation, *n.* The degree or extent of change from the normal or average.

variation, net loss, *n.* The change, over a specified period of time, of the overall net transmission loss between the terminals of a circuit.

variation, seasonal, *n.* The amount of change between wet and dry seasons, or between hot and cold seasons. Often called "annual variation."

variations, transmission. See "annual transmission variations."

varicap, *n.* A varactor diode used as a voltage-variable capacitor. See also "varactor."

varindor, *n.* An inductor whose inductance varies considerably with variation of the current through its winding.

variocoupler, *n.* A radio-frequency transformer arranged so the coupling between the primary and secondary is adjustable. In practice the two windings were tubular coils with the secondary coil supported on a brass rod track so that it could slide into, and out of, the primary coil. Not used today.

variolosser, *n.* A balanced attenuator whose attenuation is controlled by a signal obtained by rectification of the signal which passes through it. It can be connected so to increase or decrease the attenuation with an increase in input signal strength. Together with an amplifier, a variolosser constitutes a compressor or an expandor.

variometer, *n.* A variable radio-frequency inductor having two concentric spherically-shaped coils in series. The inductance is varied by rotating the inner coil inside the outer coil, thus varying the inductance from a value equal to the difference between the individual coil inductances to a value equal to their sum.

varistor, *n.* A pair of diodes, either copper-oxide or silicon, connected in parallel but with opposing polarities. Used as a voltage limiting device since its resistance drops as the applied voltage is increased. One important application is to bridge it across a telephone receiver to prevent acoustic shock.

Varley, *n.* The measure, in ohms, of the amount of resistance unbalance between two sides of a circuit.

Varley, three-wire, *n.* A measurement of the resistance unbalance of a circuit which uses a third wire (instead of ground) connected from the Wheatstone bridge to the shorted far end of the pair. Also called "metallic Varley."

vault, cable, *n.* A long, narrow, locked room in a central office building, usually in the basement directly under the main distributing frame, where outside plant cables enter and are spliced to tip cables which extend up to the protectors on the main distributing frame.

vector, *n.* A quantity represented by a line having both length and direction. Used to portray the amplitude and phase relationships of alternating voltages and currents.

vector diagram, *n.* A diagram showing, by the use of vectors, the magnitudes and phase relationships of voltages and currents in an alternating current circuit.

vector sum, *n.* The sum of two vectors which are 90 degrees apart (as resistance and reactance) is a vector whose length is the square root of the sum of the squares of the two vector quantities.

velocity, apparent wave, *n.* Phase velocity, which see.

velocity, escape, *n.* A velocity, of 37,000 feet per second, which a rocket launching a satellite needs to attain in order to overcome the earth's force of gravity.

velocity, group, *n.* The velocity with which a modulated radio-frequency signal is propagated through a waveguide.

velocity, phase, *n.* In a waveguide, the apparent wavelength divided by the frequency of a wave which propagates through the waveguide. Phase velocity can greatly exceed the velocity of light.

velocity modulate, *v.* To modulate an electron stream, as in a klystron or traveling wave tube, so that some electrons are accelerated while others are retarded. This results in the electrons being crowded together in bunches.

velocity modulation. See "bunching," "klystron," "modulation, velocity," "tube, velocity-modulated."

velocity of light, *n.* The velocity of light in a vacuum is 2,997,925. meters per second = 186,280 miles per second. For rough calculations the figure of 3,000,000 meters per second is generally used.

velocity of propagation. See "propagation, velocity of."

velocity of sound, *n.* The velocity of sound varies with temperature and the transmission medium. Here are several examples:

Medium	Degrees Centigrade	Velocity Ft/Second
Air	0	1088

Air	20	1129
Water	15	4714
Lead	20	4026
Steel	20	16360
Glass	20	18000

verification, *n.* The act of an operator who dials a busy subscriber line over a switching trunk to equipment which will connect to a busy line. She does this to (a) establish the fact that the line is in use, not out of order, or (b) to complete an emergency call, or (c) to verify the correctness of the telephone number given her by a party she has on another cord.

verification trunk, *n.* A trunk to the terminating switching equipment of a central office which enables an operator to obtain access to a subscriber's line even though it is busy. Sometimes called "no-test trunk."

vernier, *n.* Any device which makes it possible to read a measuring instrument with greater precision, or to make a finer adjustment of a moving control.

vertex, *n.* A network node, which see.

vertical, crossbar, *n.* The armature associated with one hold magnet of a crossbar switch.

vertical, distributing frame, *n.* (1) One unit of length of a main distributing frame or of an intermediate distributing frame. (2) The vertical steel member of a distributing frame, on which protector strips or terminal blocks are mounted.

vertical brace. See "brace, vertical."

vertical conductor, *n.* Any wire or cable extending in an approximately vertical direction on a supporting pole or structure.

vertical step, *n.* One of the ten units of vertical movement a step-by-step switch can make in moving from the at-rest position to a specified bank level.

very high frequency (vhf), *adj.* Referring to any of the radio frequencies in the band between 30 and 300 megahertz.

very low frequency (vlf), *adj.* Referring to any of the radio frequencies in the band between 3 and 30 kilohertz.

vest, safety, *n.* A vinyl vest, of fluorescent orange color, worn by telephone workmen who are exposed to auto traffic.

vestigal-sideband, *adj.* Referring to a type of amplitude-modulated radio signal in which most of one sideband is eliminated, leaving the other sideband intact. Used for the composite picture and synchronizing signal in television broadcasting.

via (grade) circuit, *n.* (1) A "through circuit." (2) A toll circuit whose transmission loss is low enough so that it can be used for built-up connections.

via net loss (VNL), *n.* The lowest loss at which trunk facilities can be operated, as limited by their inherent characteristics and achievable return losses. The VNL in db is obtained by multiplying the Via Net Loss Factor by the circuit length in miles and adding 0.4 dB.

via net loss factor (VNLF), *n.* A dB per mile constant, dependent upon the speed of propagation over the specified transmission facility.

vibrating circuit. See "circuit, vibrating."

vibrating rectifier, *n.* AC buzzer-type device which rectifies an alternating current by reversing the connections between the alternating supply and the load in step with the alternations of the supply. The load reversing contacts are on a permanent-magnet-biased armature which is in the field of an electromagnet across the AC supply, and thus vibrates in step with the AC alternations.

vibrating reed frequency meter. See "frequency meter, vibrating reed."

vibrating ringer, *n.* An electro-mechanical device for changing 48 volts of direct current to 90-100 volts of 20 Hz or 135 Hz alternating ringing current. It consists of a DC buzzer mechanically tuned to the output frequency, whose vibrating armature carries contacts which periodically reverse the current to a transformer primary. The output of the secondary is alternating current at the desired ringing frequency. It is not a sine wave, but has numerous odd harmonics.

vibration, *n.* (1) A rapid rhythmic motion back and forth. (2) A motion like that of a pendulum. (3) A mechanical oscillation.

video, *adj.* (1) Pertaining to the signal which carries a television picture. (2) Describing the four megahertz wide band of frequencies which constitutes a television signal.

video pair, *n.* A balanced video (TV) transmission line consisting of two #16 AWG solid copper conductors, twisted, insulated with foam polyethylene, covered with helically wrapped polyethylene tape, then helically wrapped copper tape. One to six such pairs are combined in a lead or polyethylene sheathed cable, and used for remote TV pickups, closed circuit TV, or telephone carrier circuits.

video signal. See "signal, television" and "television standards."

video transmission. See "transmission, video."

vinyl resin, *n.* A synthetic resin formed by polymerization of the radical CH_2CH. Widely used for phonograph records.

virtual height, *n.* The apparent height of a layer in the ionosphere. The height of a plane producing a pure reflection which would give the same total transit time (Earth-to-layer-to-Earth) as the compound refraction which actually occurs. Virtual height is determined by an ionospheric sounder which directs a pulsed radio wave vertically and then measures the time for the reflection to return from the ionosphere.

vise, strand. See "strandvise."

visual, busy, *n.* A magnetic signal used to indicate a busy condition on the toll trunk jack with which it is associated. Made to occupy the same space as a busy lamp, and preferred because it produces much less heat at the switchboard.

vocoder, *n.* A device which converts analog voice signals to serial binary digital signals, and on the receiving end of the circuit converts the digital signals to reconstructed intelligible analog speech.

VODAS, *n.* "Voice-operated device, anti-sing." A device for preventing singing on a two-way radiotelephone circuit by disabling one direction of transmission when it detects strong voice signals in the other direction.

VOGAD, *n.* "Voice-operated gain adjusting device." A voice-operated device used to provide a constant volume output for a wide range of voice inputs.

voice, artificial, *n.* A small loudspeaker mounted in a shaped baffle which is proportioned to simulate the acoustical constants of the human head; used for calibrating and testing close-talking microphones.

voice, secure, *n.* Telephone communications that are protected against compromise by use of an approved encryption system.

voice channel. See "channel, voice."

voice coil, *n.* The coil of wire at the apex of a loudspeaker cone which carries the voice currents and, being in a strong magnetic field, moves the speaker cone in unison with the voice currents.

voiced sounds, *n. pl.* Speech sounds formed by the vibrating vocal cords, characterized by having a fundamental frequency or pitch, plus harmonics.

voice frequency, *n.* (1) Any of the frequencies present in the human voice, from 82 Hz to 20,000 Hz. (2) Any of the frequencies in the band 300-3400 Hz which must be transmitted to reproduce the voice with reasonable fidelity.

voice grade, *adj.* Said of a communication channel which is nominally 4000 Hz wide and capable of passing speech signals in the band 300-3000 Hz.

Voice-Operated Device, Anti-Singing (VODAS), *n.* A voice-operated device to eliminate singing on transoceanic radio circuits by disabling one direction of transmission while the other direction is in use.

Voice-Operated Gain Adjusting Device (VOGAD), *n.* A voice-operated device used on transoceanic radio circuits to maintain the modulation at its optimum point, even with varying voice inputs. Similar to a compressor, but more restrictive in its action.

Voice-Operated Loss Control and Suppression (VOLCAS), *n.* A voice-operated circuit that controls echo and singing by varying the transmission loss inserted in the inactive direction of transmission. A more sophisticated circuit than the "echo suppressor," which see.

voice-switched, *adj.* Describing a voice transmission system which is activated by the sound of a voice but turns off during silent intervals in the speech.

volatile, *adj.* Describing information held in a memory which is lost if power is not continuously supplied to the memory.

VOLCAS, *n.* Voice-operated loss control and suppressor. A voice-operated device which switches loss out of a transmitting branch and inserts loss in a receiving branch under control of a subscriber's speech.

volt, *n.* The unit of electromotive force or pressure. One volt will force a current of one ampere through one ohm.

voltage, *n.* The electric pressure that exists between two points, and which will force a current to flow through a circuit between the points. Synonymous with the terms "potential," "potential difference," and "voltage drop."

voltage, avalanche. See "zener voltage."

voltage, average, *n.* Of an alternating voltage wave, the average of all of the instantaneous voltages which occur during one-half cycle of the wave. If the wave is a sine wave, the average value is 0.63662 times the peak voltage or 0.90090 times the effective voltage.

voltage, breakdown, *n.* (1) The voltage at which there is a disruptive current discharge through insulation or a dielectric. (2) Avalanche breakdown in a semiconductor.

voltage, bucking, *n.* An opposing voltage, having opposite polarity to that of another voltage which it opposes.

voltage, effective, *n.* Of an alternating voltage, the square-root-of-mean-square voltage. If the alternating voltage is a sine wave, the effective value is the peak value multiplied by 0.7071.

voltage, forward, *n.* Voltage of that polarity which produces the greater current.

voltage, high, *n.* A voltage higher than is commonly used for power distribution circuits. The Bell System classes everything over 5000 volts as high voltage, while the National Electrical Safety Code places the lower limit at 8700 volts.

voltage, inverse, *n.* Voltage of that polarity which produces the smaller current.

voltage, line, *n.* Utilization voltage.

voltage, peak, *n.* Of a time-varying voltage, the maximum value which occurs during a period of time. If the voltage is a sine wave, the peak value is 1.4142 times the effective value. See also "period."

voltage, plate, *n.* The D.C. voltage existing between the anode (plate) and the cathode of an electron tube.

voltage, residual, *n.* In an unbalanced

polyphase power circuit, the vector sum of the voltages of the several phases.

voltage, reverse, *n.* A voltage of that polarity which produces the smaller current.

voltage, striking, *n.* The value of voltage required to initiate current flow through a gas tube.

voltage, utilization. See "utilization voltage."

voltage, working. See "working voltage."

voltage, zener. See "zener voltage."

voltage amplification, *n.* The ratio of the voltage across an amplifier load to the voltage at the amplifier input, expressed in decibels.

voltage amplifier, *n.* An amplifier designed to greatly increase the voltage of a signal, but having a high output impedance and supplying little power.

voltage divider. See "divider, voltage."

voltage doubler. See "doubler, voltage."

voltage drop, *n.* (1) The decrease in electric potential as a current flows through a resistance. (2) The voltage measured across a resistor through which a current is flowing.

voltage efficiency. See "efficiency, voltage."

voltage fed, *adj.* Describing an antenna which is energized by a feeder connected at a point of maximum voltage.

voltage gradient, *n.* (1) The voltage per unit distance across an insulator, which determines when there will be a disruptive flashover. (2) The voltage existing across individual capacitors which are connected in series.

voltage reference circuit, *n.* A circuit which provides an extremely stable voltage to which an unknown voltage may be compared.

voltage reference tube. See "tube, voltage regulator."

voltage regulation. See "regulation, voltage."

voltage standing wave ratio (VSWR), *n.* A standing wave ratio measured with respect to points where voltage is a maximum. See also "standing wave ratio."

voltage to ground, *n.* The highest voltage existing between any conductor of a circuit and the earth.

voltage transformer, *n.* A highly accurate, well-insulated instrument transformer having a high-voltage primary and a low-voltage secondary, permitting the measurement of high voltages with a low voltage voltmeter. See also "instrument transformer."

voltages, telegraph hub, *n. pl.* The voltages which appear on telegraph send and receive hubs for various conditions are as follows:

+60v   Mark
—30v   Space
—60v   Double space

On the send hub only when a regenerative repeater is used, the potential is —30 volts for both the space and double-space conditions.

voltammeter, *n.* A measuring instrument having terminals and scales permitting it to be used either as a voltmeter or as an ammeter.

volt-ampere (VA), *n.* The unit of apparent power in an alternating current circuit, equal to the voltage across the circuit in volts times the current through the circuit in amperes.

volt-amperes, reactive. See "reactive volt amperes."

Volta's Law. See "Appendix B."

voltmeter, *n.* An indicating instrument for measuring electrical pressure in volts.

voltmeter, frequency-selective, *n.* Voltmeter capable of measurements over a wide frequency band, fitted with a tuneable narrow-band input filter to ensure that the voltmeter reads only voltage at the frequency of interest, rejecting spurious frequencies and noise.

voltmeter, vacuum-tube (VTVM), *n.*

A voltage measuring instrument which uses the amplifying and rectifying properties of a vacuum tube to measure either direct or alternating voltages. Its accuracy is excellent since its input impedance is very high.

voltmeter relay. See "relay, voltmeter."

volt-ohm-milliammeter, *n.* A multipurpose test meter having a single meter element with a number of scales, and a rotary switch with which one can select any of a number of voltage, current, and resistance ranges.

volume, *n.* (1) The strength of loudness of sound. (2) The magnitude of a complex audio-frequency wave as measured in a standard manner on a standard volume indicator, expressed in volume units (vu).

volume compressor. See "compressor."

volume control, *n.* A potentiometer voltage-divider used to adjust the loudness of an audio signal, particularly at the input to an amplifier.

volume expander. See "expander."

volume indicator, *n.* An indicating voltmeter having the impedance and dynamic characteristics prescribed in American Standards Association Standard C16.5, calibrated in volume units (vu) and, when read in a prescribed manner, used to measure the magnitude of an audio-frequency signal.

volume limiter. See "limiter."

volume unit (VU), *n.* An empirical measure of useful speech power, defined as the reading on a carefully specified rms-reading volume indicator having a flat frequency response, called a VU meter, when the meter is read in a carefully specified fashion.

V-Permendur, *n.* A cobalt-iron-vanadium alloy ((49%-49%-2%)) having a high remanence (14,000 gauss), used for receiver diaphragms.

WADS. See "Wide area data service."

wafer, *n.* A thin slice of semiconductor material, upon which an integrated circuit can be constructed.

walkie-talkie, *n.* A small portable transceiver, hand-held or back pack, which can be used for radio voice communication over short distances. Uses "citizen's band" frequencies: 27.255 MHz or 462.55-469.95 MHz, for which no license is required.

wall distributing frame, *n.* A small, single-sided, distributing frame designed to be installed against a wall.

wall phone. See "set, wall telephone."

wand, tuning, *n.* A plastic rod having a ferrite plug in one end and a brass plug in the other end. Used to check the tuning of radio frequency circuits. When inserted in a coil, the ferrite increases the inductance while the brass decreases the inductance.

warble-tone, *n.* An audio-frequency tone whose frequency is varied over a small range periodically at a slow (1-20 Hz) rate.

warmup. See "time, warmup."

washer, B sealing, *n.* Round polyethylene washer having a round concentric hole and a radial slit. Used to place around a cable sheath to provide a gas-tight seal between the cable and a splice case or cable terminal case.

washer, C sealing, *n.* Round lead washer used in the end seals of large mechanical splice cases to adapt them to smaller cables.

washer, D sealing, *n.* Round polyethylene washer having concentric grooves permitting cutting to make a B sealing washer. Also used to seal a vacant hole in the splice case or terminal case.

washer, E sealing, *n.* Round lead washer having a recess in which B or D sealing washers can be inserted to provide a seal for very small cables entering large splice cases or terminal cases.

washer, round, *n.* A general-purpose round galvanized steel washer much used in pole line construction. Available in the following sizes:

Washer	Hole	For Bolt
1 " OD	7/16"	⅜ "
1¼ " OD	9/16"	½ "
1⅜ " OD	9/16"	½ "
1¾ " OD	11/16"	⅝ "

washer, square, *n.* A square galvanized steel washer used in pole line construction where a large bearing surface against wood is required. Available in the following sizes:

Washer	Hole	For Bolt
2 " x 2 "	9/16"	½"
2 " x 2 "	11/16"	⅝"
2¼ " x 2¼ "	13/16"	¾ "
3 " x 3 "	7/8"	⅝" or ¾ "
4 " x 4 "	7/8"	⅝" or ¾ "
4 " x 4 "	1 1/8"	1"

washer, square curved, *n.* A 2½ ", 3" or 4-inch square washer with hole for a through bolt, curved with a 4½-inch radius so that it bears against the pole.

wash item, *n.* In a comparative cost study, any item whose costs are identical for the several plans studied.

water, battery, *n.* Distilled water, or water which has been made mineral-free by passing through a demineralizer.

waterblocked cable. See "cable, waterblocked."

WATS. See "Wide area telephone service."

WATS, inward, *n.* Inward "wide area telephone service" permits a customer, for a monthly charge, to receive incoming station-to-station calls from telephones within prescribed service areas or in six interstate bands, without charge to the calling party.

WATS, outward, *n.* Outward wide area telephone service permits a customer, for a monthly charge, to place outgoing station-to-station paid calls to telephones within prescribed service areas or in six interstate bands, not including Alaska or Hawaii.

watt, *n.* The unit of electric power, equal to the rate of work when a current of one ampere flows under a pressure of one volt. For direct currents, it is equal to the product of the voltage and current, or the product of circuit resistance by the square of the current. For alternating currents it is equal to the product of effective volts and effective current times the circuit power factor.

wattage rating. See "rating."

watt-hour, *n.* A unit for measuring electrical energy. It is the work done by one watt acting for one hour. The kilowatt-hour, one thousand watthours, is the unit commonly used.

watthour constant, *n.* Of a watthour or kilowatthour totalizing meter, the number of watthours represented by one revolution of the rotor.

watthour meter, *n.* A totalizing meter which registers the total electrical energy used, usually in kilowatthours.

wattless power, *n.* Reactive power, which see.

wattmeter, *n.* An indicating meter which indicates the rate at which electrical energy is being used, in watts.

wave, *n.* (1) A periodic variation of an electric voltage or current. (2) A wave motion in any medium: mechanical as in water, acoustical as sound in air, electrical as current waves on wires, or electromagnetic as radio and light waves through space.

wave, backward, *n.* A wave, such as in a traveling wave tube, whose phase velocity is opposite to the direction of flow of the electron stream.

wave, carrier, *n.* The sinusoidal sin-

gle-frequency wave which is modulated by a complex intelligence wave (called the modulating wave) to obtain a modulated wave capable of carrying much intelligence over a single channel.

wave, circularly polarized. See "polarization, circular."

wave, complex. See "complex wave."

wave, continuous (CW). See "continuous wave."

wave, damped, *n.* A wave whose amplitude diminishes during each succeeding period.

wave, direct, *n.* That portion of a radio wave which travels in a direct path from transmitting to receiving antenna without reflections or refractions.

wave, electromagnetic, *n.* A wave capable of propagating energy through space at the speed of light, consisting of electric and magnetic fields at right angles to each other and to the direction of propagation. Depending upon its frequency it may be known as a radio wave, a light wave, or an x-ray.

wave, elliptically polarized. See "polarization, elliptical."

wave, forward, *n.* A wave whose group velocity is in the same direction as the motion of the electron stream.

wave, free-space. See "free-space wave."

wave, ground, *n.* The portion of a radio wave which travels in the earth. Except at low frequencies, it is completely attenuated within a short distance of the transmitting antenna.

wave, ground-reflected, *n.* The portion of the "space wave" which is reflected from the ground.

wave, guided, *n.* A wave which is concentrated between materials having different properties, and is propagated within those boundaries. See also "surface wave" and "waveguide."

wave, horizontally polarized, *n.* An

electromagnetic wave whose electric field is everywhere parallel to the earth's surface.

wave, intelligence, *n.* A complex electrical wave which contains information.

wave, interrupted continuous (ICW), *n.* A continuous wave that is interrupted at a constant audio frequency rate.

wave, ionospheric, *n.* A radio wave that is propagated by reflection from the ionosphere. See also "wave, sky."

wave, light. See "light."

wave, modulated, *n.* A carrier wave, either sinusoidal or pulsed, whose amplitude, frequency, or phase has been varied in step with a modulating intelligence wave.

wave, modulating, *n.* The complex intelligence wave which modulates a sinusoidal carrier wave to gain the advantages of transmission at the higher carrier frequency.

wave, periodic, *n.* A wave which repeats itself at regular intervals of time.

wave, plane-polarized, *n.* An electromagnetic wave whose electric field vector at all times lies in a plane which also contains the direction of propagation.

wave, radio, *n.* An electromagnetic (having both electric and magnetic components) wave which travels through the sky at the speed of light. Produced by energizing an antenna with radio-frequency current.

wave, sawtooth. See "sawtooth wave."

wave, short. See "short wave."

wave, sine, *n.* A wave whose amplitude varies as the sine of an angle proportional to time or distance, or both.

wave, sky, *n.* The portion of a radio wave which travels up into the ionosphere, where it may or may not be scattered and returned to earth.

wave, sound, *n.* A traveling wave in air or other elastic medium produced by audio-frequency vibrations. The velocity of a sound wave in air is about 1100 feet per second; in water about 4800 feet per second.

wave, space, *n.* That portion of a radio wave which travels through the atmosphere immediately above the earth, and is therefore useful for low-powered radio transmissions. It consists of two components: a "direct wave" and a "ground-reflected wave."

wave, square, *n.* A periodic wave which takes alternately a positive value and then an equal negative value, and changes from one value to the other instantaneously. A square wave contains every odd harmonic of the fundamental wave, and therefore is useful for testing the response of wideband circuits or equipment.

wave, standing. See "standing wave."

wave, stationary. See "standing wave."

wave, surface, *n.* A component of "ground wave" radiation that travels entirely along the surface of the earth. See also "wave, space."

wave, transverse electric (TE mode), *n.* A mode of wave propagation in a waveguide in which the electric field vector is everywhere perpendicular to the direction of propagation.

wave, transverse electromagnetic (TEM), *n.* A wave in which both the electric vector and the magnetic vector are perpendicular to the direction of propagation. This is the mode commonly excited in coaxial and open-wire lines, but it cannot be propagated in a waveguide.

wave, transverse magnetic (TM mode), *n.* A mode of wave propagation in a waveguide in which the magnetic field vector is everywhere perpendicular to the direction of propagation.

wave, traveling, *n.* A plane wave,

each of whose frequency components has an expotential variation of amplitude and a linear variation of phase in the direction of propagation.

wave, tropospheric, *n.* An ultra-high or super-high frequency radio wave which is returned from the troposphere by scatter propagation.

wave, undamped, *n.* A wave having a constant amplitude.

wave, vertically polarized, *n.* An electromagnetic wave whose electric field is everywhere perpendicular to the earth's surface.

wave analyzer. See "analyzer, wave."

wave antenna. See "antenna, wave."

waveband, *n.* The band of frequencies comprising an electrical wave.

wave filter. See "filter."

waveform, *n.* The characteristic shape of a periodic wave, as determined by what harmonics it contains. May be seen on a cathode ray oscilloscope, or reconstructed by Fourier synthesis of the analyzed wave.

waveform analyzer, *n.* A frequency-selective voltmeter which can be used to determine the frequency and amplitude of each sine-wave component of a complex wave.

wave front, *n.* A surface at right angles to rays which proceed from the wave source. The surface passes through those parts of the wave which are in the same phase and travel in the same direction. For parallel rays, the wave front is a plane; for rays which radiate from a point, the wave front is spherical.

wavefront, steep. See "steep wavefront."

waveguide, *n.* A hollow metal pipe, usually rectangular in cross-section but sometimes round or elliptical, which is precisely dimensioned to enable it to carry radio-frequency energy from one point to another. Used to carry frequencies of 1700 MHz and above, with a loss approximating 2 dB per 100 feet. Typical waveguide dimensions are:

Range, Megahertz	Cutoff, Megahertz	Dimensions, Inches
3300-4900	2590	2.418x1.273
4900-7050	3710	1.718x0.923
7050-10000	5260	1.250x0.625

waveguide, circular, *n.* A waveguide whose cross-section is a circle.

waveguide, dielectric, *n.* A waveguide which consists solely or principally of a dielectric structure.

waveguide bend, *n.* A section of waveguide in which the longitudinal axis is bent. If the narrow side of the waveguide is bent, it is an "E-plane bend." If the wide side of the waveguide is bent, it is an "H-plane bend."

waveguide slug tuner, *n.* A dielectric slug used for tuning a waveguide to its load. It projects about one-quarter wavelength into the waveguide, which penetration is adjustable for tuning.

waveguide stub tuner, *n.* A waveguide stub having an internal adjustable piston for tuning of the stub.

waveguide twist. See "twist, waveguide."

wave interference. See "interference, wave."

wavelength, *n.* The distance between three consecutive nodes of a wave, equal to 360 electrical degrees. It is equal to the velocity of propagation divided by the frequency, when both are in the same units.

wavelength, cutoff, *n.* Of a waveguide, the free-space wavelength which corresponds to the waveguide cutoff frequency.

wavelength, effective, *n.* The wavelength in a broad-band radiation chosen such that the total energy in the band at longer wavelengths equals the total energy at shorter wavelengths.

wavelength, radio, *n.* Wavelength is equal to the volocity of propagation divided by the frequency. The wavelength in meters is equal to 300,000 divided by the frequency in kilohertz, or 300 divided by the frequency in megahertz.

wavemeter, *n.* A device for measuring the wavelength of a radio wave.

wave trap, *n.* A tuned parallel resonant circuit for the purpose of eliminating one undesired frequency from the circuit to which it is connected.

wax. See "beeswax" and "paraffin."

waystation, *n.* One of the local battery telephones bridged on a multiparty line, such as used for railway dispatching. Signaling is ringdown from telephone to operator, and by use of Gill selectors from operator to a particular station. See also "line, message."

weatherproof, *adj.* (1) So constructed or protected that exposure to the weather will not prevent proper operation. (2) Describing a conductor which is covered with braids of fibrous material and impregnated with a moistureproof compound.

weatherproof phone. See "set, weatherproof telephone."

weathertight, *adj.* So constructed that exposure to a driven rain will not result in the entrance of water.

wedge, lead cable, *n.* A small lead casting, shaped to wedge securely between two cables at a "Y" splice.

wedges, multiple, *n. pl.* Pairs of smooth wooden wedges, 16″ long x 3″ high, used to seperate switchboard multiple cables when it is necessary to get behind them to repair a jack strip or lamp strip. (WECo #410 tool)

weight, handline throwing, *n.* A pear-shaped lead weight similar to a fisherman's sinker, having a heavy rubber cover and an eye to which a handline can be attached to facilitate throwing it over wires or trees.

weighting, *n.* Use of a frequency selective network on the input of a noise meter to make the meter readings of noise proportional to the interfering effect the noise has on the human ear. See also "line weighting" and "receiver weighting."

weighting, C-message, *n.* A noise weighting used in a noise measuring set to evaluate noise on a line to be terminated in a WECo #500 or similar telephone set, which uses a T1 transmitter unit, a U1 receiver unit, and a 425E network.

weighting, flat, *n.* An amplitude-frequency characteristic which is flat over a specified frequency band. Used to measure noise on circuits which do not use telephone sets, such as broadcast and data circuits.

weighting, F1A line, *n.* A noise weighting used in a noise measuring set to evaluate noise on a line to be terminated by a WECo #302 or similar telephone set, which uses an F1A transmitter, HA1 receiver, and 101-A induction coil.

weighting, line, *n.* Type of noise weighting used, when the noise meter is bridged across the line at a subset. Further subdivided into:

Weighting	Subset
144 Line	— 337-144-46
F1A Line	— F1-HA1-101A
C-message	— U1-T1-425E

weighting, psophometric. See "psophometric weighting."

weighting, receiver, *n.* Type of noise weighting used when the noise meter is bridged across a telephone receiver of a specified type. Further subdivided into:

144 rec. wtg.	— 144 receiver
F1A rec. wtg.	— HA-1 receiver
C-message wtg.	— U-1 receiver

weighting, 3 kc flat, *n.* A weighting providing an amplitude-frequency characteristic which is substantially flat over the range from 30 Hz to 3000 Hz.

weighting network, *n.* A network whose loss varies with frequency in a prescribed standard manner.

Western Union joint. See "joint, Western Union."

West Ford, *n.* An ill-advised U.S. satellite project May 1963 which placed many millions of copper needles (RF dipoles) into orbit around the earth. They were intended to assist long-distance telecommunications, but have had no effect except to hamper radio astronomy observations. These dipoles are 1.8 centimeters in length, orbiting at a height of 3650 kilometers, and are intended to scatter radio waves at 8000 megahertz.

West terminal, *n.* An arbitrary designation for one terminal of a toll trunk or of a carrier circuit. Usually the western or southern terminal. See also "East terminal."

wet, *adj.* Carrying a flow of direct current.

wet circuit, *n.* A circuit through which direct current flows.

wetted circuit, *n.* An audio or carrier circuit on which a direct current is superimposed as an aid in decreasing contact resistance and inhibiting noise.

wetted contact, *n.* Relay contact whose closed resistance is eliminated by one of two techniques: (1) Coating the contacts with mercury. (2) Superimposing a small (one milliampere) direct current.

wetting, contact, *n.* Technique of obtaining resistance-free closure of base-metal relay contacts which carry only voice or carrier frequency currents. Accomplished by artificially introducing a one milliampere direct current through the relay contacts. Normally requires two high value, non-inductive resistances.

wetting, mercury contact, *n.* The coating of relay contacts with mercury to provide a resistance-free contact, even without any flow of direct current.

wetting agent, *n.* A chemical substance that reduces surface tension and therefore aids a liquid in spreading upon and wetting a solid surface.

Wheatstone bridge. See "bridge, Wheatstone."

wheel, measuring, *n.* Light-weight rubber-tired wheel fitted with a handle so it can be pushed along the ground by a walking person. Wheel circumference is usually exactly 3 feet, and it is fitted with a counter and index marks permitting an indication of feet and an estimation of inches of the distance traversed. Occasionally also fitted with a car bumper hitch. Used for rapid field measurements of pole lines, cable routes, etc.

whip antenna, *n.* The flexible metal pole used as an antenna on automobiles.

white noise, *n.* Random electrical noise which is flat with frequency, that is, has equal energy per cycle over a specified frequency band.

wicking, *n.* (1) The tendency for flux and solder to run in under the insulation of a wire when its end is being soldered to a terminal. (2) The longitudinal flow of water inside a cable due to capillary action.

Wide Area Data Service (WADS), *n.* A service to handle teletypewriter service over regular telephone lines. At the customers premises, the access lines will terminate in datasets which will permit voice coordination followed by transmission of teletypewriter or data signals.

Wide Area Telephone Service (WATS), *n.* A special direct distance dialing service whereby a subscriber gets a line arranged at his option for either inward or outward station service, but not for both, between his line and specified service areas. He may elect full-time unlimited service within that area, or he may elect measured-time service which permits up to ten hours' usage per month for a base rate, plus a fixed charge for each additional hour. See also "WATS. Inward" and "WATS, Outward."

wideband, *adj.* (1) Passing a wide range of frequencies without distortion. (2) Having a bandwidth of 20 kilohertz, or more. (3) Describing digital circuits or equipment capable of handling 50 kilobits-per-second signals.

wideband switch, *n.* A switch or matrix capable of passing a bandwidth greater than 4000 Hz. Typically, it is capable of switching 50 kbps signals.

Wien bridge, *n.* A four-arm alternating current bridge which can be used to measure capacitance or inductance in terms of resistance and frequency. Two adjacent arms have non-inductive resistors. The other two arms both have resistance and capacitance if used to measure capacitance, or resistance and inductance if used to measure inductance.

winch, *n.* A horizontal metal drum back of the cab of a telephone construction truck, driven by the engine, and filled with a ½-inch wire rope which can be used for hoisting poles, pulling cables, etc.

winding, *n.* The several turns of insulated wire that form a coil used in a relay, transformer, or other electromagnetic device. See also "primary winding" and "secondary winding."

winding, noninductive, *n.* A winding, such as that on a supervisory relay, so wound that it has a negligible inductance and thus serves as a low-loss shunt for the voice currents around the inductive winding. A noninductive winding is made by winding the "come" and "go" wires side by side, so that the magnetic field of one wire cancels that of the other.

winding, primary, *n.* A transformer winding which receives energy from a supply source, and uses it to create a magnetic flux in the transformer core.

winding, secondary, *n.* A transformer winding that receives its energy by electromagnetic induction from a primary winding.

window, radio, *n.* The band of radio frequencies between 30 MHz and 30,000 MHz which are capable of penetrating the earth's atmosphere. These frequencies are useful for deep-space communications, and radio astronomy. They also contribute "galactic noise" to radio receivers on earth.

wink-off, *n.* A feature of some last party release connectors which acts to release the calling switchtrain and free the calling line when the called party fails to hang up at the completion of the call.

wink operation, *n.* The method by which an incoming register-sender indicates readiness to receive pulses from the calling office. Indication is by a timed off-hook (wink) signal of NLT 140 milliseconds duration.

wink signal, *n.* A momentary interruption of current to a busy lamp. Used with key telephone sets to indicate a line being held. The wink is a 120 ipm signal: 0.03 second off + 0.47 second on.

wiped joint, *n.* A joint, as between two lead cable sheaths, made by wiping with molten solder.

wiper, *n.* On a step-by-step telephone switch a pair of springs, fixed to a hub secured to a shaft, which are formed at the end into a pair of contacts which wipe across matching pairs of bank contacts as the shaft is rotated. Upon reaching the correct set of contacts motion stops and the connection thus established carries the talking circuit or control circuits.

wiper, bridging. See "bridging wiper."

wiping contact, *n.* (1) A switch contact in which the moving contact rubs across the stationary contact, and in so doing removes any insulating film or dirt. (2) The action of relay springs which follow through after first touching, and in so doing rub, one against the other.

wire, *n.* A single metallic conductor, bare or insulated, solid or stranded, and of any cross-section but usually round.

wire, AC-type, *n.* Bell System designation for a switchboard wire consisting of quads of solid tinned 22 AWG copper conductors insulated with double cellulose acetate yarn and covered with a single lacquered cotton serving. Available in multiple quads in various colors. Used for quadded switchboard wiring.

wire, aluminum clad line, *n.* A lightweight, high strength line wire having a pure aluminum coating bonded to a high-strength steel core. It is corrosion resistant, and has a DC resistance 4.73 times that of copper wire. Available in sizes from #4 AWG to #12 AWG. Has a tensile strength of about 180,000 psi.

wire, annealed copper, *n.* Copper wire which was softened by heating after the wire drawing was complete. Used for jumper wires, inside wires, etc.

wire, armored underground, *n.* A paired 16 AWG copper wire having polyethelene insulation surrounded by helically applied flat steel armor wires, the whole covered with a polyvinyl chloride jacket. Used for direct burial underground telephone drops.

wire, bank, *n.* Wire used in wiring to terminals of switch banks. Usually a #24 AWG tinned solid copper conductor with one serving of cellulose acetate plus a braid of cotton.

wire, bare, *n.* A wire conductor which is not covered with any insulating material.

wire, bare strapping, *n.* A #20 or #22 AWG bare tinned solid copper wire used for strapping grounded or adjacent terminals.

wire, battery & ground, *n.* Paired, insulated, copper wire, usually 20 AWG and color coded Red (Battery) and Blue (Ground).

wire, "BB" iron. See "wire, galvanized iron."

wire, bell, *n.* Single conductor wire such as is used for wiring bell or buzzer circuits. Usually #18 AWG, and double cotton or plastic covered.

wire, bonding, *n.* Wire used for bonding, and grounding cable sheaths during testing and splicing operations. After the splice is completed, it is replaced with bonding ribbon if a bond is required. It is available in two types: (a) Annealed tinned copper wire, #16 AWG, in one pound spools. (b) Heavily lead coated bronze wire, .073 inch diameter, in 1½ pound spools containing 90 feet of wire. Also called "lashing wire."

wire, bridle, *n.* Paired copper wires of #18 AWG or #20 AWG, insulated with rubber and jacketed with neoprene, or insulated with black polyethelene. Polarity identification is provided by a longitudinal ridge moulded in the covering. Also available as a triple-conductor wire. Used to interconnect open wires on the same pole, or to connect from open wire to cable terminal. The 20 ga wire is also used as a fusible connection for lightning and high voltage protection.

wire, copper line, *n.* Hard drawn bare copper wire used for open wire toll lines, now being replaced by toll cable. The following sizes were common:

AWG	Diameter	Breaking Strength
8	.128 in.	826 lbs.
10	.104 in.	529 lbs.
12	.080 in.	337 lbs.

wire, copper-steel, *n.* Steel wire which is covered with a heavy coating of copper. It has better conductivity than steel, and higher tensile strength than copper. Available in conductivities which are 30% and 40% of pure copper wire of the same size.

wire, Copperweld-copper, *n.* Stranded wire designed for long-span construction, having some strands of Copperweld for tensile strength and some of copper for conductivity. Available in several types having varied ratios of Copperweld to copper, as follows:

Type	Makeup
A	1CW, 2Cu
D	2CW, 1Cu
F	1CW, 6Cu
G	2CW, 5Cu
J	3CW, 4Cu
K	4CW, 3Cu
N	5CW, 2Cu
P	6CW, 1Cu
E	7CW, 12Cu
EK	4CW, 15Cu

wire, cross-connecting. See "wire, bridle" and "wire, jumper."

wire, C rural, *n.* A self-supporting paired wire serving as a line wire in rural areas. Consists of 14 AWG copper-steel parallel conductors insulated with a common polyethelene jacket.

wire, C-type, *n.* Bell System designation for switchboard wire consisting of a solid tinned copper wire insulated with PVC and covered with a cotton serving and lacquer coating. Obtainable in 22 or 24 AWG pairs, triples, spiral-fours, and quads.

wire, distributing frame. See "wire, jumper."

wire, distribution, *n.* A multipair wire used where several drop wires would otherwise be required. Consists of several polyethelene insulated copper pairs cabled around a polyethelene covered extra-high strength galvanized steel messenger wire. Available in 2, 4, 6, 12, and 18 pairs of 22 AWG or 19 AWG wire. The lighter types use a .109 inch support wire, and the heavier types a .134 inch support wire.

wire, drop, *n.* A pair of parallel insulated wires under a common cover, used for subscriber's drops. Usually neoprene insulated, with 17 or 18 AWG bronze, copper, or copper-steel conductors.

wire, D station, *n.* A two-pair (spiral-4) 22 AWG insulated with polyethelene and covered with an extruded light olive gray PVC jacket, treated for low-friction pulling into ducts. Used for interior station wiring.

wire, D-type, *n.* Bell System designation for a switchboard wire consisting of a solid tinned copper wire insulated with enamel, double cellulose-acetate yarn, and covered with a cotton serving and lacquer coating. Available in 20 or 22 AWG in singles, pairs, triples, or spiral-fours. For circuits above 48 volts in moisture proof installations.

wire, duct, *n.* Paired or triple wires having 22 AWG solid, annealed, tinned copper conductors, insulated with color-coded thermoplastic. Used for short circuits in underground or building conduits.

wire, duplex, *n.* Wire having two insulated conductors, either parallel or spirally wrapped, and either with or without an outer braid or jacket.

wire, enameled, *n.* Wire which is insulated with a coat of baked enamel. Used in relay windings for its economy of space.

wire, extra high strength steel, *n.* A galvanized steel line wire having a tensile strength of 195,000 psi, which permits spans of 650 feet for #12 BWG wire in a medium loading area.

wire, field, *n.* A high-strength paired or spiral-4 quadded wire having tough insulation for field use by military forces. The conductors sometimes combine strands of steel and copper.

wire, flame-proof, *n.* Wire having textile insulation which is chemically treated so that it will not support combustion.

wire, flat station, *n.* A 4-conductor, ivory color, vinyl insulated flat wire having a pressure-sensitive adhesive back. Available with matching terminals, jacks, plugs, and connectors.

wire, fuse, *n.* Fine brass wire used to repair blown grasshopper fuses.

wire, fusible alarm, *n.* An insulated wire of a low melting point alloy used to run above the tops of distributing frames to form a fire alarm circuit.

wire, galvanized iron, *n.* An ordinary

steel line wire, heavily galvanized, of the grade designated "BB" (Best-Best). The tensile strength is approximately 53,000 pounds per square inch (psi).

wire, galvanized steel, *n.* Any of four galvanized steel line wires used for open wire telephone line construction. Available in four different tensile strengths, as follows:

Grade	Breaking Strength
BB	53,000 psi
85	85,000 psi
135	135,000 psi
195	195,000 psi

wire, ground, *n.* A single, soft-drawn copper wire, insulated with thermoplastic, used for connecting protectors and cable terminals to a ground. Available in #14, #12, and #6 AWG sizes.

wire, G-type, *n.* Bell System designation for a switchboard wire consisting of a solid tinned wire of 22 or 24 AWG, insulated with double cellulose acetate yarn and covered with a colored impregnated cotton braid. Used for surface wiring of step-by-step switches and relay units.

wire, hard, *n.* The practice of cabling directly between units of equipment, without passing through test jacks or cross-connect points.

wire, hard-drawn copper, *n.* Copper wire in which the last several gauge reductions in the drawing process were done without any annealing. The copper has therefore become work-hardened, and is very stiff and strong. Used for line wires which must have a high tensile strength.

wire, high strength steel, *n.* A galvanized steel line wire having a higher tensile strength than "BB" wire, and therefore allowing longer spans. Available #9, #10, #12, and #14 BWG sizes (#12 BWG only for type 135), and in two grades as follows:

Grade	Tensile Strength	Maximum Span*
85	85,000 psi	325 feet
135	135,000 psi	450 feet

*Assuming #12 BWG wire in a medium loading area.

wire, H-type, *n.* Bell System designation for a switchboard wire consisting of a single stranded tinned 22 AWG copper wire insulated with double cellulose acetate yarn and covered with a colored lacquered cotton braid. Used for wiring telephone sets.

wire, interior, *n.* Paired, triple, and quadded annealed copper wires with thermoplastic covering. Ridges on insulation indicate polarity. Available in 22 AWG and 19 AWG sizes, with beige or brown insulation. Used for stringing wires in basements or concealed spaces.

wire, J-type, *n.* Bell System designation for switchboard wire consisting of a solid tinned copper insulated with a black double cotton braid and impregnated. Available in 18, 20, 22, and 24 AWG. Used as a sleeved strap wire.

wire, jumper, *n.* Insulated copper conductors twisted together and used for cross-connections on distributing frames. Usually #22 AWG tinned solid copper conductors insulated with polyvinyl chloride and jacketed with clear nylon. Available with one, two, three, or four conductors, color coded as follows:

1: Single   White
2: Paired   Red & White
3: Triple   Red, White, & Blue
4: Spiral-4 Red & White + Blue & Black
4: Quad   Black & White + Red & Green

wire, K-type, *n.* Bell System designation for a switchboard wire consisting of a solid tinned 22 or 24 AWG single or paired wire insulated with a double cellulose acetate yarn and covered with a colored lacquered cotton braid. Used for cross-connections on crossbar system frames.

wire, lashing, *n.* (1) Cable lashing wire, used for spirally wrapping an aerial cable to its suspension strand. (2) Lead-coated bronze wire, .073

inch diameter, used for tying cable in position.

wire, line, *n.* A bare, high tensile strength copper or galvanized steel wire for stringing between poles on pin insulators.

wire, magnet, *n.* Soft, insulated copper wire in the range of sizes used for winding relay and transformer coils. Usually has enamel insulation.

wire, M-type, *n.* Bell System designation for a solid tinned 22 AWG copper wire insulated with double cellulose acetate yarn and covered with a lacquered cotton braid. Singles, pairs, and triples in various colors. Used in carrier panel equipment.

wire, multiple line, *n.* A generic term applied to any of the family of wires which consist of individually insulated conductors twisted into pairs which are then stranded about an insulated support wire.

wire, open, *n.* Bare line wires, spaced 12 inches, tied to insulators supported on crossarms bolted to the pole near its top.

wire, order, *n.* (1) A voice circuit, usually ringdown signaling, for passing information from an operator to a testdeskman, or between testdesks. (2) A telegraph order wire. (3) A teletype order wire.

wire, P-type, *n.* Bell System designation for a switchboard wire consisting of a solid tinned copper wire insulated with PVC and covered with a lacquered cotton serving. Laid with a bare tinned copper ground wire, and the combination covered with a braided shield and a PVC jacket. Available in 22 or 24 AWG in singles, pairs, and triples, with colors. For general use as shielded wire.

wire, pulling-in, *n.* A galvanized steel wire left in a vacant duct for later use in pulling in a cable or wires.

wire, pushback, *n.* A tinned copper wire covered with a braided cotton insulation which can be easily pushed back to expose the bare wire. Used for switch wiring and for strapping on selector distributing terminal assemblies.

wire, reinforcing, *n.* A hard-drawn, preformed wire about 12-15 inches long, which is spirally applied over an open wire conductor at the supporting insulator before application of the tie wire. It reinforces the conductor, prevents chafing, and distributes stresses caused by wire vibration.

wire, resistance, *n.* Wire which is made of an alloy, such as Nichrome or German Silver, which has a high resistance. Used in making wire-wound resistors.

wire, rubber-covered, *n.* Wire which is insulated with a covering of rubber. Preferred over plastic insulation for certain power applications.

wire, rural, *n.* A self-supporting, insulated paired wire consisting of two #14 AWG, 30% conductivity, EHS copper-steel conductors insulated with polyethelene. It has a breaking strength of 1100 pounds, and weighs 35 pounds per kilofoot.

wire, rural distribution, *n.* A distribution wire having 19 AWG conductors, but identical in other respects with suburban distribution wire. See also "wire, distribution."

wire, shield, *n.* (1) A grounded conductor strung above open wire communication conductors to shield them from low-frequency or noise induction. (2) A bare tinned copper wire inside the metallic braid of a shielded pair which facilitates connection to the shield. (3) A bare tinned copper wire which is laid with buried wire in rural districts as a shield against currents derived from lightning discharges to earth. (4) On electric power transmission lines, a grounded neutral conductor which is strung above the phase wires as a shield against lightning.

wire, shielded, *n.* Paired insulated

copper wire having a covering of metallic braid or metallic coated mylar tape which can be grounded to reduce interference from electrostatic induction. It very often includes a third conductor: a bare tinned copper wire just under the braid which facilitates grounding the braid.

wire, sleeve, *n.* (1) The wire which connects to the sleeve of a plug or jack .(2) The third wire associated with a talking pair which is used to carry supervisory signals.

wire, soft-drawn copper, *n.* Copper wire which was annealed just before the final wire drawing process. Used for bridle wire, ground wire, etc. Is easily bent, but retains its form.

wire, solid, *n.* Wire which consists of a single conductor, not of multiple strands.

wire, spinning. See "wire, lashing."

wire, station, *n.* A 22 AWG copper color-coded polyethelene insulated wire with a single overall polyvinyl jacket in ivory, beige, or brown. Available in 2, 3, or 4 conductor, or 2, 3, or 4 pair sizes. Used for station wiring where appearance is important.

wire, steel. See "wire, galvanized steel."

wire, stranded. See "conductor, stranded."

wire, strapping, *n.* A #20 or #22 AWG tinned solid copper conductor with one serving of cellulose acetate covered with a cotton braid. Braid may be skinned back without fraying. Used for strapping terminals where an insulated wire is required.

wire, suburban distribution, *n.* A distribution wire having 22 AWG conductors. See also "wire, distribution."

wire, support, *n.* The polyethelene covered galvanized steel messenger wire which furnishes support for a multi-pair distribution wire. See also "wire, distribution."

wire, switchboard, *n.* Color-coded insulated bulk wire of the type used in local cables.

wire, telegraph order, *n.* A multiparty Morse telegraph line having drops at all of the toll testboards in a particular district, used to pass information between testboards in a particular district without interrupting toll circuits.

wire, teletype order, *n.* A multi-party teletypewriter circuit having appearances at all toll testboards in a district. Used to pass coordinating information and telegraphic circuit orders between testboards.

wire, third, *n.* A wire associated with the "tip" and "ring" wires of a telephone circuit within a central office, used for the supervisory circuit. Usually called the "sleeve" or "control" wire.

wire, tie, *n.* A piece of wire, 20 to 30 inches long and of the same material as the line wire, used to tie open line wire to its supporting insulator.

wire, tinned, *n.* Wire which has been coated with a thin layer of tin to make it corrosion-resistant and to facilitate soldering.

wire, tinsel, *n.* A very flexible conductor made by serving one or more thin ribbon conductors over a nylon string core. Used to make telephone cords.

wire, tree, *n.* A paired wire having durable insulation which can resist abrasion from branches when run through trees.

wire, urban, *n.* A multiple line wire consisting of 16 twisted pairs of 24 AWG PVC insulated conductors, bunched into four groups and then stranded around a 109E steel polyethelene insulated support wire.

wire communication, *n.* Communication carried by wires, whether by direct currents, audio frequencies, or carrier frequencies, as distinguished from communication without interconnecting wires, such as by radio, laser, etc.

wire gauge. See "gauge, AWG" or "gauge, BWG."

wireholder, porcelain, *n.* An end-mounted porcelain knob insulator having a single lateral hole, and a heavy wood screw protruding from the mounting end. Can be screwed into a wooden wall and used to dead-end a drop wire.

wireholder, service mast, *n.* A porcelain wireholder fixed to a bracket which can be bolted to a service mast and used to deadend a drop wire.

wireless, *n.* Radio (British).

wire mile, *n.* A single conductor one mile in length.

wiremold, *n.* A two-piece rectangular metal surface conduit consisting of a base and snap-on cover. Available in widths of ½", ¾", and 1¼-inch.

wirephoto, *adj. n.* Facsimile, which see.

wire stripper, *n.* A pliers-type hand tool which cuts and pulls off the insulation from the end of an insulated wire without nicking the wire.

wires, unused, *n. pl.* Regular wires, not spare or unequipped, which are not required for future use and which are left dead in the cable form.

wires, unequipped, *n. pl.* Wires in a cable form which are formed out for future components, but which are not used initially.

wiretapping, *n.* The act of connecting to a telephone circuit for the purpose of surrepticiously obtaining information or evidence from the intelligence it carries.

wireway, *n.* A rectangular metal wiring trough with a hinged or screw cover, which can be fastened to a wall and used to contain a heavy wire run. Made of enameled sheet steel, and available in sizes 2½" x 2½", 4" x 4", 4" x 6", 6" x 6", and 8" x 8".

wire-wrapping, *n.* A type of electrical connection made by tightly coiling a wire around a square terminal having sharp corners.

wiring, C, *n.* Those switchboard or local cable wires which are required to be segregated for electrical reasons, such as carrying high-level tones.

wiring, D, *n.* Wiring not sewed into cable forms for electrical reasons.

wiring, printed. See "printed circuit."

wiring, surface, *n.* Wiring which is run loose and dressed against the mounting plate or panel.

wiring, U, *n.* Magnetically shielded wire or cable.

wiring diagram. See "diagram, wiring."

wobbulator, *n.* A test oscillator which continually and periodically varies its output frequency between two limits, so as to give an indication of response over a band of frequencies.

woofer, *n.* A large loudspeaker designed to reproduce the frequencies below 3500 hertz. Usually used with a "tweeter" and a "crossover network," which see.

woo-woo tone, *n.* No such number tone.

word, *n.* (1) A set of characters or symbols which is treated as a unit. (2) A telegraph word consisting of six character intervals. (3) A group of binary digits containing sufficient information to direct a logical operation.

word, memory, *n.* A group of bits read into or out of the memory, as a unit.

word, telegraph, *n.* By definition, a telegraph word consists of six character intervals.

working, closed-circuit, *n.* A method of operating a telegraph circuit in which current flows in the circuit when the transmitting device is at rest.

working, open-circuit, *n.* A method of single current telegraph transmission in which no current flows in the circuit when the transmitting device is at rest.

working reference system, *n.* An outmoded system for the rating of telephone circuits, consisting of two standard transmitting and receiving station loops connected by a variable, distortionless 3000 cycle bandwidth trunk. The overall loss of this reference system was 18 db, effective.

working voltage, *n.* The rated voltage, which can be applied to a device or conductor continuously without danger of breakdown.

wow, *n.* An undesired variation in pitch which occurs at a very slow rate, such as that experienced when one plays a phonograph record whose spindle hole is off-center.

wrap (wire), *v.* To make a connection between a wire and a special square terminal having sharp corners by tightly coiling the wire around the terminal. The sharp corners of the terminal bite into the wire and make a good connection without the use of solder.

wrap, longitudinal, *n.* A tape applied to a cable core in line with the axis of the core, as contrasted with a helical or spiral wrap.

wrap, spiral, *n.* The helical wrap of a tape or binder over a cable core.

wrench, lineman's, *n.* A heavy open-end wrench, 13 inches long, which will take the heads and nuts of ½", ⅝", ¾", and 1-inch bolts. Has a round hole near one end used for screwing pole steps into the pole.

wrench, terminal, *n.* Small hand socket wrench having sockets for 3/8" and 7/16" hex nuts.

write, *vt.* To introduce information into a memory device.

write pulse, *n.* A pulse which causes information to be stored in a memory cell.

wye connection. See "connection, wye."

X, *adj.* (1) Letter used as an abbreviation for the word "cross," as in "X-arm" for "cross-arm." (2) Abbreviation for reactance.

X-axis, *n.* (1) The horizontal axis on a graph, or on a cathode ray tube screen. See also "y-axis" and "z-axis." (2) One of the three optical axes of a quartz crystal.

X band, *n.* A radio-frequency band extending from 5,200 to 10,900 MHz.

x cut, *adj.* Said of a quartz plate cut for an oscillator when the X axis of the quartz crystal is perpendicular to the faces of the plate.

Xerox, *n.* A patented system of offset printing in which the paper is printed with electrostatic charges which attract and hold a powdered resin ink, which is then melted onto the paper with heat.

XY switch. See "switch, XY."

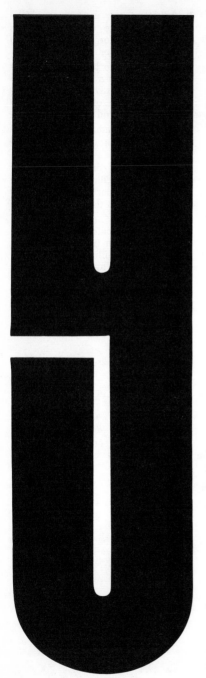

Y, *n.* The symbol for admittance.

Yagi antenna, *n.* A very directional microwave antenna consisting of a dipole connected to the lead-in wire, plus several parasitic dipoles in front (directors) and in back (reflectors) of the active dipole to increase the directivity. The Yagi is very widely used as a television receiving antenna.

y-axis, *n.* (1) The vertical axis on a graph or cathode ray tube screen. (2) One of the three mutually perpendicular axes of a crystal.

Y connection. See "connection, wye."

y cut, *adj.* Said of a quartz plate for an oscillator when the plate is cut so that the Y axis of the quartz crystal is perpendicular to the faces of the plate.

Yellow Pages, *n.* The classified advertising section of a telephone directory, sometimes bound and issued separately.

yield strength, *n.* The minimum mechanical stress at which a material will start to physically deform without a proportionate increase in load.

Y network, *n.* A star network having three branches, each of which has one terminal connected to a common node.

yoke, *n.* A bar of ferromagnetic material that interconnects two or more magnet cores.

Young's modulus. See "modulus of elasticity."

Z, *n*. The symbol for impedance.

z-axis, *n*. (1) Property of some cathode ray tube (CRT) circuits, by which a voltage applied to the "Z-axis" terminals can be used to brighten the CRT trace for a selected portion of the displayed waveform. (2) In a solid model, the axis mutually perpendicular to the "x" and "y" axes.

zener diode, *n*. A silicon diode which acts as a rectifier until the voltage increases to the point known as the zener voltage or avalanche voltage. At that point the diode becomes conducting, with a voltage drop which is independent of current.

zener voltage, *n*. Avalanche voltage. The voltage at which a zener diode becomes conducting with a voltage drop across the diode which is independent of current.

zero adjuster, *n*. A slotted-head screw on the front of electrical meters which can be used to bring the meter pointer to the zero position when the meter input is zero.

zero beat, *n*. The condition achieved when adjusting two circuits to the same frequency by listening to the two tones, when the "beat note" disappears.

zero bias, *n*. Of an electron tube, a condition where there is no potential difference between the cathode and the control grid.

zero level, *n*. (1) An audio power level of one milliwatt (Used for transmission measurements). (2) An audio power level of six milliwatts (Used for measurements with a volume indicator).

zero state, *n*. The condition of a binary memory cell when a "zero" is stored.

zero transmission level reference point, *n*. An arbitrary point in a transmission system, to which all relative levels at other points in the system are referred. The level at the OTLP is 0 dbr. The OTLP is usually the transmitting toll switchboard or testboard.

zippertube, *n.* Registered name of a variety of "temporary closure tubing."

zip tone. See "tone, splash."

zone, far, *n.* The region distant from a radio transmitting antenna in which the radiation field is stronger than the induction field, and in which the intensity of the radiation field varies inversely with the square of the distance from the antenna.

zone, instrument, *n.* A geographical area within which a particular type of telephone set is specified for transmission reasons. The less efficient telephones are used close to the central office, and the newer, more efficient telephones are used on the longer loops, thus providing adequate transmission with the least expensive loop cable plant.

zone, near, *n.* The region very close to a radio transmitting antenna in which the induction field predominates. The intensity of the induction field does not reduce in proportion to the square of the distance from the antenna.

zone, time, *n.* Any of the twenty-four zones, each 15 degrees wide, into which the earth's circumference is divided. The time within a time zone is everywhere the same, and adjacent zones have a one-hour time difference.

zone, transmitter (TZ). See "zone, instrument."

zone of mutual visibility, *n.* An area within which a communication satellite can be seen from both of a pair of satellite earth stations, usually stated in degrees of longitude.

zone of silence, *n.* A region within the "skip distance," in which the signals of a particular radio station cannot be heard.

zone registration, *n.* A method for automatically charging for sub-scriber-dialed short-haul toll. Each participating subscriber's line is equipped with a message register. During the toll call, meter pulses are transmitted to the calling subscriber's meter at a repetition rate that depends on the distance between the calling and called parties.

zoning, *n.* A system for selecting the type of subscriber's telephone instruments based on the electrical distance to the central office from which they are served. Places the older, less efficient instruments close to the central office. See also "zone, instrument."

zulu time, *n.* Time at the 0 degree meridian, or Greenwich standard time.

APPENDIX

abbreviations
acronyms
alphabetical designations

— A —

A—Ampere. Area.

AA—Automatic answer.

AAR—American Association of Railroads.

A&CP—Access and control point.

A&E—Architect and Engineer.

AB—Anyone who can talk business.

AC—alternating current.

AC&R—American Cable and Radio System.

ACC—Automatic carrier control.

acct.—Account.

ACD—Automatic call distribution. Automatic call distributor.

ACOC—Area Communication Operations Center.

ADA—After date of award of contract.

ADCSP—Advanced Defense Communication Satellite Project.

Add.—Addendum.

ad fin—ad finem, to the end.

ad hoc—For this specific purpose. For this case only.

adj—adjust, adjusted, adjustment.

ad lib—ad libitum, at pleasure, as you wish.

ADMS—Automatic digital message switch.

ADMSC—Automatic Digital Message Switching Center.

ADP—Automatic data processing.

ADPC—Automatic data processing center.

ADPE—Automatic data processing equipment.

ADPS—Automatic data processing system.

ADS—Automatic data set.

ADT—American District Telegraph.

ADU—Accumulation and distribution unit (AUTODIN).

ad val—ad valorem, according to value.

ADW—Aerial distribution wire. Air defense warning.

AESC—Automatic Electronic Switching Center.

a-f, a.f.—Audio frequency.

AF—Air Force.

afc—automatic frequency control.

AFCS—Air Force Communications Service.

AG—Again, try again.

A/G—Air-to-ground.

AGAMP—Automatic gain-adjusting amplifier.

agc—Automatic gain control.

AGE—Aerospace ground equipment.

AIC—Automatic intercept center.

AIOD—Automatic identification (on) out-dialed (calls).

AIS—Automatic intercept system.

ALC—Automatic load control.

ALGOL—ALGOrithmic Language.

ALM—Alarm.

alnico—Aluminum-nickel-cobalt.

alt—alternate.

a m—ante meridiem, before noon.

AM, a-m—Amplitude modulated.

A/M—Automatic-manual.

AMA—Automatic message accounting.

AMARS—Automatic Message Address Routing System.

AME—Amplitude modulation equivalent.

AML—Actual measured loss (transmission).

amp—Ampere(s).

ampl—amplifier.

ANC—All Number Calling.

ANI—Automatic Number Identification.

anl—Automatic noise limiter.

ANS—Answer.

ant—Antenna.

APC—Automatic phase control. Average power control.

APP—Auxiliary power plant.

approx—Aproximate, approximately.

aq—Aqua (water).

aq dest—aqua destilla, distilled water.

ARINC—Aeronautical Radio, Inc.

arm—Armature.

ARO—After receipt of order.

A route—Alternate route.

ARQ—Automatic repeat request.

arr—Arrestor.

ART—Artificial. Automatic reporting telephone. Alarm reporting telephone.

ARU—Audio response unit.

ASA—American Standards Association. Army Security Agency.

ASC—AUTODIN switching center.

ASCII—American Standard Code for Information Interchange.

ASPH—Asphalt.

ASR—Automatic Send/Receive.

assoc—Associates, associated.

asst—Assistant.

assy—Assembly.

AST—Anti-sidetone.

AT—Aerial tape armor.

AT&T—American Telephone and Telegraph Company.

ATB—All trunks busy.

ATMS—Automatic transmission measuring system.

ATS—Automatic trunk synchronizer.

ATT—Attended public telephone. Automatic toll ticketing. Attachment.

ATURS—Automatic traffic usage recording system.

aud—Audible.

auto—Automatic.

AUTODIN—AUTOmatic DIgital Network.

AUTOVON—AUTOmatic VOice Network.

AUTOSEVOCOM—Automatic secure voice network.

aux—Auxiliary.

av, aver—Average.

avc—Automatic volume control.

avoir—Avoirdupois.

AWG—American wire gauge.

AWPI—American Wood Preservers Institute.

AY—Anyone.

— B —

b—bel.

B—Magnetic induction.

bal—Balancing.

balun—balanced-to-unbalanced line transformer.

BASIC—Beginners All-Purpose Symbolic Instruction Code (for computers).

bat, batt—battery.

BB—Bunch block. Bus-bar layout (drawing). Broadband. Backboard.

BCD—Binary coded decimal.

BCD/B—Binary coded decimal/binary.

BCD/Q—Binary coded decimal/quaternary.

BCH — Bose-Chadhuri-Hocquenhem (error control code).

BCO—Battery cut-off.

BCU—Buffer control unit.

BDPSK—Binary differential phase-shift keying.

BDR—Bell doesn't ring.

BDW—Buried distribution wire.

BE—Band elimination.

BEF—Band elimination filter.

BER—Binary error rate.

BFO—Beat frequency oscillator.

bhp—Brake horsepower.

BIS—Business Information System.

BISCUS—Business information system/customer service.

BISTSS—Business information system/trunks and special services.

bit(s)—Binary digit(s).

BKI—Break-in.

bkr—breaker (circuit).

BL—Blue.

blk—block.

BLK—Black.

BMEWS—Ballistic Missile Early Warning System.

BNR—Messenger boy not returned.

BOD—Beneficial occupancy date.

BOM—Bill of Material.

BOT—Beginning of tape.

BP—Band pass, Binding post. Block parity (data).

BPC—Binding post chamber.

bpi—bits per inch (on tape).

bps—Bits per second.

BR, BWN—Brown.

BR, BRG—Bridge, bridging.

BRA—Base rate area.

BRB—Base rate boundary.

BRF—Bell rings faintly.

BRKT—Bracket.

BrT—Bridged tap.

BSP—Bell System Practice.

BT—Buried tape armor.

BTL—Bell Telephone Laboratories.

btry—battery.

Btu—British Thermal Unit.

Bur—Buried.

BUSH—Buy U.S. here.

BW—Bandwidth. Buried wire.

BWG—Birmingham wire gauge.

BWR—Bandwidth ratio.

BY—Busy, the line is busy.

— C —

C—Centigrade. Control. Capacitance. Confidential. Creosote (pole treatment).

ca—circa, about.

Ca—Cable.

CA—Cancelled. Cable.

CADW—Civil Air Defense Warning System.

cal—Calibrate, calorie.

calc—Calculate.

CAMA—Centralized Automatic Message Accounting.

canc—Cancel, cancellation.

CANTAT—Canada—Great Britain Transatlantic Telephone Cable.

CAO—Circuit allocation order. Communication authorization order.

cap—Capacitor.

Ca Pr—Cable pair.

CARR—Carrier.

CARS—Community antenna relay service.

CATV—Community antenna television.

CAU—Crypto ancillary unit.

C & W—Cable and Wireless, Ltd.

CAX—Community automatic exchange.

CB—Common battery. Coin box. Connecting block.

CBC—Can't be called.

CBDT—Can't break dial tone.

CBH—Can't be heard.

CBS—Common-battery signaling.

CC—Coin collect. Collect call.

CCIF—Comité Consultatif International Fernsprecht.

CCIR—Comité Consultatif International des Radio-communications.

CCIS—Common channel interoffice signaling.

CCIT—Comité Consultatif International Télégraphique.

CCITT—Comité Consultatif International Télégraphe et Téléphone.

CCN—Contract Change Notice.

CC-NDT—Can't call, no dial tone.

CCO—Can't call out. Circuit control office.

CC-OTH—Can't call, other.

CCSA—Common-control switching arrangement.

CCT—Circuit. Sometimes CKT.

CCTV—Closed-circuit television.

CCU—Common-control unit.

CD—Circuit description.

CDC—Construction design criteria.

CDF—Combined distributing frame.

CDO—Community Dial Office.

CDP—Communication data processor.

CDT—Control data terminal.

CDU—Central display unit.

C-E—Communications-Electronics.

CEM—Cement conduit.

cemf—Counter electromotive force.

CF—Can't find. Copy furnished. Central file. Count forward.

CFE — Contractor-furnished equipment.

cfh—cubic feet per hour.

cfm—Cubic feet per minute.

CFS—Call for service.

cgs—Centimeter-gram-second (Metric system of measurement).

CH—Can't hear, Coastal Harbor.

chez—At the home of (French) (telegram).

CHG—Charge.

CHN—Change.

Ch Opr—Chief Operator.

CI—Community of interest. Cast iron.

C-I—Concentrator-identifier.

CIB—centralized intercept bureau.

cir, circ—Circle, circular.

cir mil—Circular mil.

CKO—Checking operator (in an automatic toll ticketing system).

ckt—circuit (also "cct").

C/kt—Carrier to noise power density (independent of bandwidth).

CL—Center line.

cm—Centimeter.

Clk—Clerk.

CLOAX — Corrugated-laminated coaxial cable.

CLR—Combined line and recording. Clearance.

cm—centimeter.

CM—Class marks.

C-M—Control-monitor.

CMP—Camp-on.

CMR—Communication Moon Relay.

cm/sec—Centimeters per second.

C/N—Carrier-to-noise ratio.

CNL—Constant net loss.

Co.—Company.

CO, C.O.—Central office.

CO—Coinbox line. See also POstpay and PREpay.

c/o—Care of.

coax—coaxial.

CODAN — Carrier-operated device, anti-noise.

COM—Common.

comm, com—Communication.

coml—Commercial.

comp—comparator.

COMPAC—Commonwealth Pacific Cable.

COMSAT—Communication Satellite Corporation.

conc—concentrated, concentrator.

cond—conditioned. Conductor.

cont—control.

CONUS—Continental United States.

conv—converter.

coord—coordinate.

COPAN—Command Post Alerting Network.

copr—copyright, copyrighted.

COR—Contracting officer's representative.

cos—Cosine.

cosh—Hyperbolic cosine.

cot—Cotangent.

COTC—Canadian Overseas Telecommunications Corporation.

CP—Chemically pure. Corrosion protection.

CPCH—Calling party can't hear.

CPFF—Cost plus fixed fee.

CPIF—Cost plus incentive fee.

cpm—Cards per minute.

cps—Cycles per second.

CR—Customer's report.

CRB—Customer records and billing system.

CRC—Communications relay center.

crit—Critical.

CRO—Cathode ray oscilloscope.

CRT—Cathode ray tube (TV tube).

crypto—cryptographic.

CS—Cast steel.

CSA—Commercial Service Authorization.

csc—Cosecant.

CSM—Correed switching matrix.

CSP—Control switching point.

CST—Carrier (power) supply, transistorized.

CSU—Circuit switching unit.

CT—Center tap. Current transformer.

CTO—Cut-off.

ctrl—control.

CTS—Cable terminal section. Cable turning section.

CTT—Cable trouble ticket.

cu—Cubic.

CU—Control unit.

C-U, C/U—Common-user.

CUDAT—Common-user data.

cu ft—cubic feet.

cur—Current.

CURTS—Common-user Radio Transmission Sounding System.

cw—Continuous wave.

CWD—Creosoted wood duct.

CWO—Custom work order.

CWS—Copperweld steel.

cwt—Hundredweight.

CXR—Carrier.

CY—Calendar year.

—D—

D—Used to designate an intermediate dialing center on a toll ticket.

DA—Doesn't answer. Digit absorbing. Double armor (submarine cable).

db, dB—decibel.

dba, dBa—decibels (above reference noise) adjusted.

dbaO, dBaO—Circuit noise power referred to the zero transmission level point.

dbk—Decibels referred to one kilowatt.

DBL—Detailed billing number required (on a toll call chargeable to a PBX station.) Double connection.

dbm, dBm—decibels (above or below) one milliwatt.

dbmO, dBmO—Transmission level referred to the zero transmission level point.

DBO—Drop build out (capacitor).

dbr, dBr—Decibels relative to some specified level.

dbRAP—decibels above reference acoustical power.

dbrn, dBrn—Decibels above reference noise.

dbv, dBv—Decibels referred to one volt.

dbw, dBW—Decibels referred to one watt.

dc, DC—Direct current.

dcwv—direct current working volts.

DCA—Defense Communications Agency.

dcc—Double cotton covered.

DCS—Defense Communications System.

DCSS—Defense Communications Satellite System.

DD—Direct dialing. Direct dialed.

DDD—Direct distance dialing.

DECCO—Defense Commercial Communications Office.

DECEO—Defense Communication Engineering Office.

DED—Distant End Disconnect.

de-emph—de-emphasis.

def, defec—Defective.

DEFT—Dynamic Error-Free Transmission System.

deg, °—degree(s).

Del—Delayed.

△M—Delta modulation.

dem—Demodulator.

demod—demodulator.

demux—demultiplexer.

DF—Douglas fir (pole).

dia, D—Diameter.

diag—Diagram, diagonal.

diam, dia, D—Diameter.

DID—Direct Inward Dialing.

DIQd—Disc-insulated quad.

Dir—Directory.

dis—display.

disc—disconnect.

dist—distribution, distributor.

Dist—District.

DISTR—Distributor. Distribution.

DIV, DIVN—Division.

DIVA—Data-inquiry-voice answer.

DLE—Direct line equipment.

Dly—Delay.

DM—Delta modulation.

DMB—Disconnect and make busy.

DOC—Dynamic Overload Control.

DOD—Department of Defense. Direct Outward Dialing.

DON—Delayed order notice.

DP—Double-pole. Data processing.

DPC—Data processing center.

DPCM—Differential pulse code modulation.

DPDT—Double pole, double throw.

DPE—Data processing equipment.

DPS—Data processing system.

DPSK—Differential phase shift keying.

DPST—Double pole, single throw.

DRE—Directional reservation equipment.

DRO—Destructive readout.

DS—Telephone disconnected.

DSA—Dial service assistance.

DSB—Dial System B board. Double sideband.

DSBEC—Double sideband, emitted carrier.

DSBSC—Double sideband, suppressed carrier.

dsc—Double silk covered.

DSCS—Defense Satellite Communication System.

DSSCS—Defense Special Secure Communication System.

DSTE—Digital subscriber terminal equipment.

DTBP—Dedicated total buried plant.

DTE—Dial telephone exchange. (DCO — dial central office — is a preferred term).

DTF—Dial tone first.

DTI—Distortion Transmission Impairment.

DTL—Diode transistor logic.

DTMF—Dual tone multifrequency.

DTR—Down-time ratio.

DTWX—Dial Teletypewriter Exchange Service.

DUMP—Write out the contents of the register.

Dup—Duplicate.

DVBST—Direct-view bistable storage tube. (A storage type cathode ray tube.)

DVOM—Digital volt-ohmmeter.

DVM—Digital voltmeter.

DW—Don't want, doesn't want. Drop and block wire.

dwg—Drawing.

dx—distance. distance reception.

—E—

E—Voltage. East.

ea—each.

EAGE—Electrical aerospace ground equipment.

E & M—The recEive and transMit leads of a signaling system.

EAP—Emergency action program.

EAS—Extended area service.

EATMS—Electro-Acoustic Transmission Measuring System.

EAX—Electronic Automatic Exchange.

EC—Electrical conductor (grade of purity of a metal). Extra control (wire). Eastern cedar (pole).

ECN—Emergency (highway) Communication Network.

ECO—Electronic Central Office.

ECP—Engineering change proposal.

EDP—Electronic Data Processing.

EDPE—Electronic data processing equipment.

EF&I—Engineer, furnish & install.

eg—exempli gratia, for example.

EHF—Extremely high frequency (30-300 GHz).

EHS—Extra high strength (steel wire).

EIA—Electronic Industries Association.

elec—Electric, electrical.

Elec Eng—Electrical Engineer.

ELF—Extremely low frequency (3-300 Hz).

EM—Engineering manual.

EMC—Engineered military circuit.

Emer—Emergency.

emf—Electromotive force.

EMI—Electro-magnetic interference. See RFI.

EML—Expected measured loss (transmission).

EMP—Electromagnetic pulse (associated with an atomic bomb blast).

EMT—Electrical metallic tubing. (Thinwall conduit).

e.m.u.—Electromagnetic unit.

encl—enclose, enclosure.

ent—entrance.

EOM—End-of-message (indicator).

EOT—End of Transmission. End of tape.

EPC—Earth potential compensation.

EQ, equip—Equipment.

EQUAL—Equalizer.

equiv—Equivalent.

ERL—Echo return loss.

EROW—Executive right-of-way.

ERP—Effective radiated power.

ERS—Emergency Reporting System.

ERT—Estimated repair time.

ES—Echo suppressor. ESO—originating. EST—terminating.

ESC—Echo-suppressor control (lead).

ESS—Electronic Switching System.

est—Estimate, estimated.

e.s.u.—Electrostatic unit.

ETA—Estimated time of arrival.

et al—et aliae, and others.

ETB—End of (data) block.

etc—et cetera, and so forth.

ETD—Estimated time of departure.

ETR—Estimated time of restoral. Estimated time to restore.

et seq—et sequentia, and the following.

ETV—Educational Television.

ETX—End of text (of message).

EXCH—Exchange.

ext—extension, external.

EXTHEO—Extra-theoretical.

—**F**—

f, freq—Frequency.

f, F—Farad.

F—Final. Flat (rate). Flash (precedence).

F, Fahr—Fahrenheit.

f_0—frequency of the carrier.

FA—Fuse alarm.

fab, fabr—Fabricate.

fac—Facility, facilities.

FACD—Foreign area customer dialing.

FASE—Fundamentally Analyzable Simplified English. (A computer language).

FAT—Foreign area toll.

FAX—Facsimile.

FC—Find called (or calling) party. Fuse chamber.

FCC—Federal Communications Commission.

FD—Finished dialing. Fiber duct (conduit).

F/D—Focal length/Diameter (of a parabolic antenna).

FDM—Frequency division multiplex.

FDx—Full duplex.

FEC—Forward error correction.

FEMF—Foreign electromotive force.

FET—Field-effect transistor.

FEX—Foreign exchange.

fig(s)—Figure(s).

Fil—Filament.

fluor—Fluorescent.

fm, FM—Frequency modulation.

FMC—Fixed message cycle (announcer).

FNPA—Foreign numbering plan area.

FO—Flash override (precedence).

For Ex—Foreign exchange.

FORTRAN—FORmula TRANslation.

FOT—Optimum Traffic Frequency.

FPIS—Forward propagation ionospheric scatter.

fpm—feet per minute.

FPTS—Forward propagation tropospheric scatter.

freq—frequency.

freq-mult—frequency-multiplier.

FRT—Front.

FS—Message to follow sender (Forward if the addressee has already left). Frequency shift. Final (capacitance unbalance test) splice.

FSK—Frequency-shift keying.

FSN—Federal stock number.

FSP—Frequency-shift pulsing.

ft—foot, feet.

ft-lb—Foot-pound(s).

fwd—Forward.

FY—Fiscal year.

—G—

g, gm—Gram(s).

G—Electrical conductance. Giga-.

G, g—Force of gravity.

gal(s)—Gallon(s).

galv—Galvanized, galvanic.

GBH—Group busy-hour.

Gc—Gigacycles per second.

GC—Group connector.

GDF—Group distribution frame (carrier).

gen—Generator.

GFE—Government furnished equipment.

GHz—Gigahertz.

GI—Galvanized iron.

GL—Ground line.

GMT—Greenwich mean time.

GN—Green.

gnd, grd—ground.

GNT—Great Northern Telegraph Company (Denmark).

GOAM—Government-Owned and Maintained.

GOC—Greatest overall coefficient.

gph—gallons per hour.

gpm—Gallons per minute.

GPO—General Post Office.

grd, gnd—Ground.

grp—group.

GS—Galvanized steel.

GSS—Galvanized Steel strand.

GT—Gopher tape armor.

GTA—Grading terminal assembly.

GT&E—General Telephone and Electronics Corp.

—H—

h, H—Henry, henries.

HAT—Home area toll.

HC—House cable.

HDF—Horizontal distributing frame.

HDx—Half duplex.

hex—Hexagon, hexagonal.

hf—High frequency (3-30 MHz).

HFDF—High-frequency distribution frame.

HH—Hanging handset.

HIDF—Horizontal (side of the) intermediate distributing frame.

HL—Hot line.

HMDF—Horizontal (side of the) main distributing frame.

HNPA—Home numbering plan area.

Ho—Hotel.

HOP—House operating tape.

HP—Horse power, high pass.

Hq—Headquarters.

hr—hour.

HRT—High rate telemetry.

HSCP—High-speed card punch.

HSCT—High-speed compound terminal.

HSPTR—High-speed paper tape reader.

HT—Holding time. High tension.

ht—Height.

HTL—Hotel call, time and charges mandatory.

HU—High usage.

HV, hv—High voltage.

HVAC—Heating, ventilating, and air-conditioning.

HW—Handset, wall.

HWY—Highway.

Hz—Hertz.

—I—

i—Instantaneous value of current.

I—Current in amperes. Immediate (precedence).

IAW—In accordance with.

IB—Information bureau or operator.

ibid—ibidem, in the same place.

ICECAN—Iceland-Canada telephone cable.

ICL—Inserted connection loss.

ICSC—Interim Communication Satellite Committee (of INTELSAT).

ICT—Idle circuit termination. Intercept tape.

icw—Interrupted continuous wave.

id—idem, the same.

ID—Inside diameter.

IDF—Intermediate distributing frame.

IDSCP—Initial Defense Satellite Communications Project.

ie—id est, that is.

IEEE—Institute of Electrical and Electronics Engineers.

i-f, if—Intermediate frequency.

IFRB—International Frequency Registration Board.

IGFET—Insulated gate field-effect transistor.

IIP—Implementation and Installation Plan.

ILI—Idle line indicating.

impreg—Impregnated.

IMT—Intermediate tape.

in—Inches.

INC—Incoming, incoming trunk.

IND—Induction. Inductor, Indicated.

inf, info—information.

in-lb = Inch pound(s).

ins—Insulate, insulation.

int, inter—inter, intermediate, international, internal.

INTELSAT—International Telecommunications Satellite Consortium.

inv—Inverse, Invoice. Inverter.

INWATS—Inward wide-area telephone service.

I/O—Input/output.

IOC—Initial operating capability Inter-office communication.

IP—Interdigital pause.

IPA—Intermediate power amplifier.

iph—inches per hour.

ipm—impulses per minute. inches per minute.

IPR—In pulse to register.

ips, in/sec—Inches per second.

IPS—In pulse to sender.

IRAC—Interdepartmental Radio Advisory Committee.

ISB—Independent sideband.

iso—isolation.

ISO—International Standards Organization.

ITA—International telegraph alphabet.

ITA #2—International Telegraph Alphabet #2.

ITC—Intermediate toll center, also intercept, intercepted, intercepting.

IT&T—International Telephone and Telegraph Corporation.

ITPA—Independent Telephone Pioneers Association.

ITR—Integrated telephone recorder.

ITU—International Telecommunications Union.

ITV—Instructional television.

IW—Inside wire.

IWCA—Inside wiring cable.

IWCS—Integrated Wideband Communication System. (SEAsia).

—J—

JAN—Joint Army-Navy (specification).

JCENS—Joint Communications-Electronics Nomenclature System.

JCSAN—Joint Chief's of Staff Alerting Network.

jct—Junction.

JFET—Junction field-effect transistor.

J.O.—Job Order.

JOSS—Joint (military) overseas switchboard.

JP—Jute protection.

JT, Jt—Joint.

—K—

k—Kilo, one thousand.

KBD, KYBD—Keyboard.

kbps—Kilobits per second.

kc—Kilocycle(s).

KCO—Keep cost order.

kHz—Kilohertz, kilocycles per second.

kip—Kilopound, one thousand pounds.

km—kilometer.

kmc—kilomegacycles, gigacycles.

kohm—kilohm (one thousand ohms).

KP—Key pulsing.

KPF—Key pulse on front cord.

KSR—Keyboard send-receive.

KTS—Key telephone system.

KTU—Key telephone unit.

kv—Kilovolt(s).

kva—Kilovolt-ampere(s).

kvar—kilovar, kilovolt-ampere, reactive.

kw—Kilowatt.

kwh—Kilowatt-hour(s).

KYBD—Keyboard.

—L—

L—Inductance in henries. Lamp lead.

LA—Light wire armor.

LAMA—Local Automatic Message Accounting.

LAMC—Language and mode converter.

laser—Light Amplification by Stimulated Emission of Radiation.

lat—latitude.

lb—Pound.

LB—Local battery.

LBO—Line build-out (unit).

LBT CBS—Local-battery talking, common-battery signaling.

LC—Loading coil.

LCC—Loading coil case.

LD—Long distance. Loaded.

LDTP—Long-distance thrift pak.

LEF—Left-in telephone.

LEQ—Line equipment (Line of equipment).

LETS—Law Enforcement Teletypewriter Service.

LF—Low frequency (30-300 kHz).

LI—Left in place.

LIDF—Line intermediate distributing frame.

lin ft—Linear feet.

LIS—Line information store.

LIST—Listening.

LK—Looking for party.

LK ROUTE—Looking for route.

LL—Line (of telegraph) leg. Landline.

LLE—Long line equipment.

LLSU—Low level signaling unit.

LM—Leg multiple (telegraph).

LMF—Language media format.

ln, $\log_e$—natural logarithm, logarithm to the base e.

LO—Lock out.

loc—location, located, local.

loc cit—loco citato, in the place cited.

log, $\log_{10}$—logarithm to the base 10.

L_1—Line one.

LOS—Line of Sight.

LP—Liquified petroleum (gas). Low pass (filter). Log periodic (antenna). Loop. Looping. Lodgepole pine (pole). Load point.

LPI—Longitudinally (applied) paper insulation (on cable conductors).

LRU—Least replaceable unit.

LS—Line switch. Loading splice.

LSA—Limited space-charge accumulation (operation of solid-state diode oscillators).

LSB—Lower sideband.

LSCP—Low-speed card punch.

LSPTR—Low-speed paper tape reader.

LT—Letter telegram (22 word minimum). Link terminal.

LTB—Last trunk busy.

LTC—Line traffic coordinator.

L_2—Line two.

lub—Lubricate, lubricant.

LUF—Lowest usable (high) frequency.

LVR—Low voltage relay.

LW—Leave word.

LWA—Light wire armored.

—M—

m—Meter. Meridies (noon).

M—Thousand. Mutual inductance.

ma—Milliampere(s).

mach—machine.

mag—Magnet, magneto, magnetic.

MAGE—Mechanical aerospace ground equipment.

MAN—Manual.

maser—Microwave Amplification by Stimulated Emission of Radiation.

math—Mathematics, mathematical.

MATV—Master antenna television.

max—maximum.

Mbps—Megabits per second.

Mc—Megacycle(s).

MCC—Master control center (ESS).

MCM—Thousand circular mils.

MCW—Modulated continuous wave.

MDA—Multiple-digit-absorbing.

MDF—Main distributing frame.

MDW—Multiple drop wire.

meas—Measure, Measured.

mech—Mechanical.

med—Medium.

MEG—Megger, megohm(s).

MEP—Management - Engineering Plan.

mf, mfd—Microfarad(s).

MF—Multifrequency. Medium frequency (300-3000 kHz).

mfg—Manufactured.

mfr—manufacture, manufacturer.

MFSK—Multiple frequency shift keying.

MG—Messenger.

MGN—Multi-grounded neutral.

mh—Millihenry(s).

MH—Manhole.

MHz—Megahertz (megacycles per second).

mi—Mile.

mic—microphone.

mike—Microphone.

Mil—Mileage.

MILS—Missile Impact Locating System.

min—Minimum, minute.

misc—miscellaneous.

MLPP—Multilevel Precedence and Preemption.

mm—millimeter.

mmf—micromicrofarads, magnetomotive force.

MMF—Magnetomotive force.

MMU—Mass memory unit.

mod—Modulus, modulator, modified, modification.

modem—Acronym for modulator-demodulator.

MON—Monitor, monitoring.

MOS—Metal-oxide semiconductor.

MOSFET—Metal-oxide semiconductor field-effect transistor.

mot—motor.

MPC—Marker pulse conversion.

mph—Miles per hour.

MPWD—Machine-prepared wiring data.

MR—Message rate.

MS—Mobile service.

msc—miles of standard cable.

msec—millisecond.

msg—message.

MSK—Minimum phase-shift keying.

MSP—Maintenance Support Plan.

MSU—Message switching unit.

MT—Modified tape armor.

MTBF—Mean time between failures.

mtd—mounted.

MTD—Multiple tile duct.

mtg—mounting.

MTS—Mobile Telephone Service.

MTT—Magnetic tape terminal.

MTTE—Magnetic tape terminal equipment.

MTTF—Mean time to failure.

MTTR—Mean time to repair.

MTWX—Mechanized teletypewriter exchange.

MUF—Maximum useable frequency.

mult—Multiple.

MUR—Radio Relay Message Unit.

MUSA—Multiple-unit steerable antenna.

MUX—Multiplex.

MUXER—Multiplexer.

mv—Millivolt(s).

MV—Move.

mw—Milliwatt(s).

Mw—Megawatt.

M/W—Microwave.

MX—matrix.

—N—

N—Any number from 2 to 9. North.

NA—No access. Not applicable. Night alarm.

NAND—"Not and," a Boolean algebra expression which is the inverse of an "and" function.

NARC—Non-automatic relay center.

NASA—National Aeronautics and Space Administration.

naut—nautical.

NBFM—Narrow band frequency modulation.

NBO—Network building-out (capacitor). Usually "BOC."

NBS—New British Standard (wire gauge).

NC—No circuit (available). Normally closed.

NCR—No circuit available, circuit request left.

Ncs—No checking signal.

NCS—National Communication System.

NDRO—Non-destructive readout.

NE—Northeast.

NEC—National Electrical Code.

NECOS—Network coordinating station.

neg—Negative.

NESC—National Electrical Safety Code.

NF—Telephone listing not found. Noise Factor.

Nfy—Notify.

Nfyd—Notified.

NIB—Negative impedance booster.

NIC—Negative impedance converter.

NID—Network inward dialing.

NIOD—Network inward and outward dialing.

NL—Non-listed.

NLT—Not less than. Not lower than.

nm—nautical mile (6,076. feet).

NMS—Noise measuring set.

NMT—Not more than.

NO—Normally open.

No., Nr.—Number.

NOD—Network outward dialing.

NODAN—Noise-operated device for Anti-noise.

NOGAD—Noise-operated gain-adjusting device.

nom—Nominal.

nomen—Nomenclature.

non seq—non sequitur, it does not follow.

NOTAL—Not sent to all addresses.

NP—Northern pine (pole).

NPA—Numbering Plan Area.

NPR—Noise power ratio.

NQd—Non-quadded.

NRG—Not registered at hotel, club, etc.

NRZ—Non-return to zero.

nsec—nanosecond.

NTI—Noise Transmission Impairment.

NTSC—National Television Standards Committee.

NTTPC—Nippon Telegraph and Telephone Public Corporation (Japan).

nuit—Night delivery (French) telegram.

NW—Northwest.

NYPS—National Yellow Pages Service.

NZPO—New Zealand Post Office.

—O—

O—Operational immediate (precedence).

O&M—Operation and maintenance.

OBH—Office busy-hour.

OCR—Optical character reader.

OD—Outside diameter. Out of order.

ODD—Operator distance dialing.

OF—One of the firm. Overflow.

Ofc—Office.

Off—Official.

OFHC—Oxygen-free high-conductivity copper.

oflw—Overflow.

Off Prem—Off premises.

OGT—Outgoing Trunk.

OITT—Outpulse Identifier Trunk Test Frame.

OJT—On-the-job training.

OK—All correct, all right, approved.

OL—Other line.

OLR—Off-line recovery.

ONI—Operator Number Identification.

opm—operations per minute.

opp—Opposed, opposite.

opr—Operate, operated, operator.

OR—Orange.

osc—Oscillator.

osc-mult—oscillator-multiplier.

Orig—Originating, or Original.

OT—Overtime.

OTC—Originating toll center. Overseas Telecommunications Commission (Australia).

OTE—Hellenic Telecommunications Organization (Greece).

OTLP—Zero (dbm) transmission level point.

OW—Open wire, Order wire.

OWF—Optimum working frequency.

oz—Ounce.

—P—

P—Person-to-person. Priority (precedence). Pentachlorophenol (pole treatment). Pole.

PA—Power amplifier, public address.

PABX—Private automatic branch exchange.

PAM—Pulse amplitude modulation.

PAN—Panel (of a switchboard).

PAR—Peak-to-average ratio.

paramp—parametric amplifier.

PAX—Private automatic exchange.

PB—Push button.

PBR—Pole broken.

PBX—Private branch exchange.

pc(s)—Piece(s).

PC—Notification of delivery date and time. (telegram). Printed circuit.

PCB—printed circuit board.

pch, pchg—Punching (of a terminal block).

PCI—Panel call indicator.

PCM—Pulse code modulation.

pct—Percent.

PDM—Pulse duration modulation.

Pe—Polyethylene insulation.

PE—Pre-empt.

PEARL—Performance Evaluation of Amplifiers from a Remote Location.

PEP—Peak envelope power.

perm—Permanent.

PERT—Program Evaluation and Reporting Technique.

PEV—Peak envelope voltage.

pf—picofarad.

p.f.—Power factor.

PFM—Pulse frequency modulation.

pH—Hydrogen ion concentration (relative acidity).

PH—Phantom.

PHOTAC—Photo-typesetting and composing.

p.i.v.—Peak inverse voltage.

PL—Place.

PLM—Pulse length modulation.

PLS—Private line service (telegraph).

PLTTY—Private Line Teletypewriter Service.

p m—post meridiem, afternoon.

PM—Pulse modulation.

PN—Part number. Pseudo-noise.

P-NID—Precedence network in-dialing.

pnl—panel.

PO—Postpay coin telephone. See also CN.

P/O—Part of.

pol—Polar, polarized.

pos—Positive, position.

pot—Potential, potentiometer.

POTS—Plain old telephone service.

POTUS—President of the United States (Communications for).

p-p, p.p.—Push-pull.

P-P—Person-to-person. Peak-to-peak.

PPC—Peak power control.

PPCS—Person-to-person, collect and special instruction (toll call).

ppm—Parts per million.

PPM—Pulse position modulation.

pps—Pulses per second.

pr—Pair.

PRE—Prepay coin telephone. See also CN.

prep—preparation, prepare.

prf—pulse repetition frequency.

pri, prim—primary.

prob—Probable, probability.

prod—Product, production.

pro tem—pro tempore, temporarily.

PRRM—Pulse repetition rate modulation.

PRW—Paired wire.

PS—Program store. Permanent signal. Postscript.

p/s—Pulses per second.

Psd—Passed.

PSD—Permanent signal detection circuit.

PSF—Permanent signal finder.

psi—Pounds per square inch.

psig—pounds per square inch, gauge.

PSK—Phase shift keying.

PSL—power and signal list.

PT—Paper tape.

PTC—Primary technical control.

PTM—Pulse time modulation. Portable traffic monitor.

PTR—Paper tape reader. Printer. Poor transmission.

Pty—Party.

PVC—Polyvinyl chloride.

pW—picowatt.

PWAC—Present worth of annual charges.

PWB—Printed wiring board.

PWM—Pulse width modulation.

pWp—picowatt, psophometrically weighted.

pwr—power.

— Q —

Q—Quality of a resonant circuit, or of a capacitor. Quantity of electricity, in coulombs.

QA—Quick acting. Quality assurance.

qd—Quad.

QDPSK — Quaternary differential phase-shift keying.

QED—Quod erat demonstrandum. That which was demonstrated.

QEF—Quod erat faciendum. That which was constructed.

QFM—Quantized frequency modulation.

QPM—Quantized pulse modulation.

qt—Quart.

qty—quantity.

quad—quadruple.

qual—Quality, qualitative.

QUAM—Quantized amplitude modulation.

quan—quantity, quantitative.

qty—quantity, quantitative.

qv—quod vide, which see.

— R —

R, r—Resistance.

R—Ring. Routine (precedence).

RA—Ready-access.

rad—Radians, radius, radial, radio.

RADA—Random Access Discrete Address.

R&D—Research and Development.

RATT—Radio teletypewriter.

RC—Regional Center. Resistance-capacitance (coupling or network).

RCAC—Radio Corporation of America Communications.

RCD—Route control digit.

RCO—Receiver cuts out.

rcvr—receiver.

RD—Ringdown. Road.

RDI—Route digit indicator.

re—Regarding.

REA—Rural Electrification Administration. (U.S. Dept. of Agriculture)

reac—Reactive, reactor.

REC—Receiver.

rect—Rectifier, rectangle.

Ref—Referred, referenced.

REG—Register.

REINF—Reinforce.

REM, RM—Remove.

reperf—reperforator.

REPL, RPL—Replace.

res—Residence.

resis—Resistance.

resp—Respectively.

r-f, r f—Radio frequency.

RFB—Reason for backlog.

RFC—Radio frequency choke coil.

RFI—Radio frequency interference.

RFO—Reason for outage.

RFP—Request for proposal.

RG(X)/U—Designation for coaxial cable.

    R — Radio frequency.
    G — Government standard.
    (X) — Type number.
    /U — Universal specification.

RH—Receive hub (telegraph).

rheo—Rheostat.

RI—Routing indicator.

RIAA—Recording Industry Association of America.

RL—Receive leg (telegraph).

rls—Release.

RLT—Rack-level-terminal.

rms—Square root of mean square.

RO—Receive only.

R.O.—Routine Order.

ROH—Receiver off-hook.

RP—Reply paid (telegram). Restoration priority.

rpm—Revolutions per minute.

RPQ—Request for price quotation.

rps—Revolutions per second.

RR—Relay rack. Railroad.

RRX—Railroad crossing.

RS—Random splice.

RSEU—Remote scanner and encoder unit (for collection of traffic data).

RT—Rate.

RTE—Route.

RTLP—Reference Transmission Level Point.

RTTY—Radio teletypewriter.

R/W—Right(s)-of-way.

RX—Through toll operator.

RZ—Return to zero.

— S —

S—Used to classify a signal call. Salt (Greensalt pole preservative treatment). South.

S, Slv—Sleeve.

SA—Service assistant, Slow acting. Single armor (submarine cable).

SAC—Special area code.

SAFFI—Special Assembly for Fast Installations.

SAT—Stepped atomic time.

SATT—Strowger Automatic Toll Ticketing.

SB—Supply Bulletin.

SCA—Subsidiary carrier authorization.

SCAN—Switched Circuit Automatic Network.

scc—Single cotton-covered.

SCCF—Satellite Communication Control Facility.

SCF—Satellite Control Facility.

SCFD—Standard cubic feet per day (gas usage).

SCFM—Subcarrier frequency-modulation.

sched—Schedule.

schem—Schematic.

SCM—Single-channel modem.

SCN—Self-compensating network (in a telephone set).

SCOM—Site cutover manager.

SCOTICE—Scotland-Iceland telephone cable.

SCR—Silicon controlled rectifier.

SD—Schematic drawing.

SDF—Supergroup distribution frame.

SE—Southeast.

SEACOM—Southeast Asia Commonwealth cable.

SEC—Secondary.

sec—Second(s). Secant.

sech—Hyperbolic secant.

SEL—Selector.

SF—Straightforward. Single frequency.

SG—Supergroup.

SGC—Supergroup connector.

sgl—Single.

sgp—supergroup.

SH—Send hub (telegraph).

SHF—Super-high frequency (3-30 GHz).

Sht—Short.

SI—Special instruction (toll call).

SID—Sudden ionospheric disturbance.

sig—signal, signaling.

SIL—Speech interference level.

sin—Sine.

sinh—Hyperbolic sine.

SL—Slate (color). Send leg (telegraph).

slc—Straight line capacitance.

slf—Straight line frequency.

slw—Straight line wave length.

SN—Stock number.

S/N—Signal-to-noise ratio.

SNAPS—Standard notes and parts selection.

(S+N)/N—Signal-plus-noise to noise (ratio).

SO—Slow operate.

SOH—Start of header (card).

sol—Soluble, solenoid.

soly—Solubility.

SOM—Start of message indicator.

SONAD—Speech Operated Noise Adjusting Device.

SOP—Standard operating procedure.

SP—Single pole. Semi-public. Singing point. Signal processor (of an ESS). Southern pine (pole). Sewer pipe (conduit).

SPC—Stored program control.

SPDT—Single pole, double-throw (switch).

SPDTDB—Single-pole, double-throw, double-break.

SPDTNCDB—Single-pole, double-throw, normally-closed, double-break.

SPDTNO—Single-pole, double-throw, normally open.

SPDTNODB—Single-pole, double-throw, normally-open, double-break.

Spec(s)—Specification(s).

SPESS—Stored Program Electronic Switching System.

sp gr—Specific gravity.

spher—Spherical.

SPL—Splice.

SPR—Send priority and route digit.

SPRINT—Special police radio inquiry network.

SPSTNC—Single-pole, single-throw, normally-closed.

SPSTNO—Single-pole, single-throw, normally-open.

sq—Square.

SR—Slow release, Supervisor.

S/R—Send/receive.

SRE—Site resident engineer.

SS—Station-to-station. Stainless steel. Solid state. Semifinal (capacitance unbalance test) splice.

SSB—Single sideband.

SSBSC—Single sideband suppressed carrier.

ssc—Single silk-covered (insulation).

sse—Single silk covering over enamel insulation.

SSI—Start signal indicator.

SSM—Special safeguarding measures.

SSN—Switched Services Network.

SSP—Special service protection.

SSR—Switching selector-repeater.

St—Street, statute.

ST—Sidetone, Start.

sta—Station.

STC—Station technical control.

std—Standard.

STO—System test objectives.

STR—Sidetone reduction.

STX—Start of text (of message).

sub—Subscriber.

substa—Subscriber's station, substation.

sup—supply.

Supv, SUPV—Supervisor, supervisory.

svc—service.

s-w, s.w.—Short wave.

SW—Switch. Southwest.

swbd—Switchboard.

SWF—Short-wave fadeout.

swr—standing wave ratio.

sync—synchronous, synchronize.

sys—System.

SX—Simplex.

SxS, SXS—Step-by-step.

SYS—System.

— T —

T—Tip. Two ticket call. Tera-.

TA—Tape armored.

tab—Table, tabulate.

tan—Tangent.

tanh—Hyperbolic tangent.

tan⁻¹X—The angle whose tangent is "X."

TA-182—AN/TA-182 Signal convertor.

TAR—Technical action request.

TAS—Telephone answering service.

TASI—Time Assignment Speech Interpolation.

TAT—Transatlantic telephone (cable).

Tbl—Trouble.

T&C—Time and charges.

TC—Toll Center.

TCC—Telecommunications Coordinating Committee.

TCF—Technical control facility (PTC).

TCLR—Toll circuit layout record.

TCMF—Touch calling multi-frequency.

TCU—Teletypewriter control unit.

TD—Temporarily disconnected. Transmitter-distributor (teletypewriter). Test distributor.

TDM—Time division multiplex.

TDMA—Time-division multiple access.

TDMS—Transmission distortion measuring set.

TDR—Temporarily disconnected at customer's request.

TE—Transverse electric wave.

tech—Technical, technician.

tel—Telephone.

TELCO—Telephone Company.

telecon—teletypewriter conference.

TELEPAK—Telephone package.

TELEX—Automatic teletypewriter exchange service.

telg—Telegraph, telegram.

temp—Temperature, template.

term—Terminal.

TFE—Tetrafluorethylene.

tg—Telegraph.

TGC—Transmitter gain control.

TGF—Through-group filter.

THERM—Thermistor.

TIDF—Trunk intermediate distributing frame.

TL—Tie line.

TLK—Talk or talking.

TLP—Transmission level point.

TLR—Toll line release (key).

TM—Transverse magnetic wave. Time modulation. Technical manual.

TMS—Transmission measuring set.

T.O.—Technical Order.

TONLAR—Tone-Operated net loss adjuster.

TORC—Automatic Traffic Overflow Reroute Control.

tp—telephone.

TP—Terminal pole.

TPL—Terminal-per-line.

TPO—Telecommunications Program Objective.

TPS—Terminal-per-station.

TQC—Technical quality control.

tr, trsp—Transpose.

TR—Transmission report.

T/R—Transmit/receive.

trf—Tuned radio frequency.

TRFR—Transfer.

trig—Triginometry.

TRK—Trunk.

trnsf—Transfer.

TSB—Twin sideband.

TSF—Télégraphie sans fil (Telegraphy without wire).

TSO—Telecommunications Service Order.

TSP—Traffic service position.

TSR — Telecommunications Service Request.

TSS—Toll Switching System.

TSTA—Transmission, signaling, and test access.

TSU—Tape search unit.

TT—Temporarily transferred. Teletypewriter terminal.

TTB—Toll Testboard.

TTC—Teletypewriter center. Terminating toll center.

TT/N—Test tone to noise ratio.

TTS—Teletypesetter.

TTY—Teletypewriter.

TTYS—Teletypesetters.

TU—Traffic Unit. Transmission unit. Tape unit.

TWT—Traveling wave tube.

TWX—Teletypewriter exchange service.

TX—Terminating toll operator.

typ—typical.

TZ—Transmitter zone.

— U —

U—Expected, followed by a time or date. Unclassified.

UD—Not known whether party will be there today.

UG—Underground.

uhf, UHF—Ultra-high frequency (300-3000 MHz).

UKB—Universal keyboard.

UL—Underwriters' Laboratories, Inc.

UN—Unknown.

unbal—unbalanced.

UPS—Uninterruptible power supply.

USB—Upper sideband.

usec—microsecond.

USITA—United States Independent Telephone Association.

UTC—Coordinated universal time.

uuf—micromicrofarad.

UX—Not expected today, and do not know when party will be there.

— V —

v, V—Volts.

va, VA—volt-ampere(s).

vac—Vacant. Vacuum. Volts, alternating current.

var—Variable, variant, varley.

VAR—reactive volt-ampere(s).

vdc—volts, direct current.

VE—Value engineering.

VER—Verify, verified, or verifying operator.

vert—Vertical.

VF—Voice-frequency.

VFO—Variable frequency oscillator.

VFTG—Voice frequency telegraph.

vhf—Very high frequency (30-300 MHz).

VID—Video.

video—Video frequency.

VIDF—Vertical (side of the) intermediate distributing frame.

viz—videlicet, namely, that is.

vlf—Very low frequency (3-30 kHz).

vm—Voltmeter.

v/m—Volts per meter.

VMC—Variable message cycle (announcer).

VMDF—Vertical (side of the) main distributing frame.

VN—Verify number if it doesn't answer. Indicates that called number does not have intercepting service.

VNL—Via Net Loss.

VNLF—Via Net Loss Factor.

VODAS—Voice-operated device, anti-sing.

VOGAD—Voice-operated gain adjusting device.

VOLCAS—Voice Operated Loss Control and (echo and singing) Suppression circuit.

VOM—Volt-ohm meter.

vox—Voice operated transmission.

VPT—Voice plus telegraph.

VRI—Varistor.

vs—versus, against.

VSB—Vestigal sideband.

vswr—voltage standing wave ratio.

VT—Vacuum tube.

vtvm—Vacuum tube voltmeter.

vu—Volume unit(s).

— W —

w—Width.

w, W—Watts.

W—West.

WA—Wire armored.

WADS—Wide Area Data Service.

WATS—Wide Area Telephone Service.

WBS—Wideband system.

WC—Western cedar (pole).

W.C., W.Ch.—Wire Chief.

wdg—Winding.

WECo—Western Electric Company.

WH—We have, ready with called telephone or party. Western hemlock (pole).

whr, watt-hr—Watt hour(s).

WL—Western larch (pole).

WNO—Wrong number.

W.O.—Work Order.

w/o—without.

WP—Western pine (pole).

wpm—Words per minute.

Wrg—Wrong.

WRS—Working (transmission) reference system.

WS—Wire send.

WT—Will talk.

wt, wgt—Weight.

wtg—Weighting.

WU—Western Union Telegraph Co.

WW—Wire-wound (resistor).

W-W—Wall-to-wall (measurement).

— X —

X—Cross. Reactance. Any number from 0 to 9.

XA, X-arm—Crossarm.

X-bar—Crossbar.

XBL—Extension bell.

XBT—Crossbar tandem.

xcvr—transceiver.

XD—Crossed.

xfmr—transformer.

xmit—transmit.

xmsn—transmission.

xmtg—Transmitting.

xmtr—transmitter.

XOW—Express order wire.

XVR—Exchange voltage regulator.

— Y —

Y—Admittance in ohms.

YAG—Yttrium aluminum garnet, a solid-state laser material.

Yr—year.

— Z —

Z—Impedance in ohms. Transmission zone. Buzzer.

Z, Zulu—"Z" time zone, at Greenwich, Gr. Britain.

$°C$—Degrees centigrade.

$°F$—Degrees Fahrenheit.

Ω—Ohms.

Φ—Phase.

3P—Three pole.

3PDT—Three pole, double-throw.

3PST—Three-pole, single-throw.

4P—Four pole.

4PDT—Four-pole, double-throw.

4PST—Four-pole, single-throw.

4WTS—Four-wire terminating set.

7D—Seven-digit number.

ØTLP—zero (dbm) transmission level point.

APPENDIX b

laws
rules
and
theorems

index

LAWS

Ampere's Law. The line integral of the magnetic field strength or intensity taken around any closed path is proportional to the total current flowing across any area bounded by that path.

Conservation of Energy, Law of. In any change, there is no loss or gain of energy, but merely a transformation of energy from one form to another.

Coulomb's Law of Electric Charges. The attraction or repulsion between two electric charges is proportional to the product of their magnitudes and inversely proportional to the square of the distance between them.

Electrolytic Dissociation, Law of. When an acid, base, or salt is dissolved in water, a part or all of the molecules of the dissolved substance are broken up into parts called "ions," some of which are charged with positive electricity and are called "cations," and an equivalent number of ions which are charged with negative electricity and are called "anions."

Faraday's Law of Electric Fields. The line integral of the total electric field strength taken around any closed path is proportional to the negative rate of change, with respect to time, of the magnetic flux across any area bounded by that path.

Faraday's Law of Electrochemical Change. In the process of electrolytic change, equal quantities of electricity charge or discharge equivalent quantities of ions at each electrode. One gram equivalent weight of matter is chemically altered at each electrode for each 96,500 coulombs, or one faraday, of electricity passed through the electrolyte.

Faraday's Law of Magnetic Induction. The voltage induced in a circuit is proportional to the rate at which the magnetic flux which is linked with the circuit is changing.

Hartley's Law of Information Transfer. The total amount of information which may be transmitted over a band-limited transmission system is proportional to the product of the frequency range which it transmits by the time during which it is available for transmission.

Hooke's Law of Elasticity. Stress is proportional to strain for all materials which are not stressed beyond their elastic limit.

Inverse Square Law. When any radiation is emitted uniformly in all directions from a point, the amount received per unit area at any given distance from the source, assuming no absorption, is inversely proportional to the square of that distance.

Joule's Law for Electric Power. When a conductor contains ohmic resistance only and there are no counter-EMF's, then:

$E = IR = I/G$ so that

$P = I^2R = I^2/G = E^2/R = E^2G$, where: E = EMF in volts, I = current in amperes, G = conductance in ohms, R = resistance in ohms, and P = power in watts.

Kelvin's Law for Conductor Sizes. In sizing power conductors, the most economical area of conductor is that for which the annual cost of energy wasted (in heat loss) is equal to the interest on that portion of the capital outlay which may be considered as proportional to the weight of the conductor used.

Kepler's Laws of Motion. 1. Satellites move about the Earth in ellipses, at one focus of which the Earth is situated. 2. The radius vector joining each satellite with the Earth describes equal areas in equal times. 3. The cubes of the mean distances of the satellites from the Earth are proportional to the squares of their times of revolution about the Earth.

Kirchoff's Laws of Electric Networks. 1. The algebraic sum of the currents which meet at any point is zero. 2. The algebraic sum of the voltages around any closed path in a network is zero.

Lenz' Law. When an electromotive force is induced in a conductor by any change in the relation between the conductor and the magnetic field, the direction of the electromotive force is such as to produce a current whose magnetic field will oppose the change.

Magnetic Poles, Law of. The force of attraction or repulsion between two magnetic poles is proportional to the product of their magnitudes and inversely proportional to the square of the distance between them times the permeability of the intervening medium.

Maxwell's Law. A moveable portion of a circuit will always move in such a direction as to give the maximum number of flux linkages through the circuit.

Newton's Laws of Motion. 1. Every body continues in its state of rest or of uniform motion in a straight line except as it may be compelled to change that state by the action of some outside force. 2. Change of motion is proportional to force applied and takes place in the direction of the line of action of the force. 3. To every action there is always an equal and opposite reaction.

Ohm's Law. When the current within a circuit is steady, and there are no counter-EMF's within the circuit, the value of the voltage E between the terminals of the circuit is proportional to the current I, or:

$$E=IR$$

where the coefficient of proportionality R is called the resistance of the circuit. This equation may also be written:

$$I=E/R \text{ or } R=E/I$$

See also "Joule's Law."

Ohm's Law for Circuits with Counter-EMF. When the current within a circuit is steady but there is a counter-EMF within the circuit, the net voltage E equal to the circuit terminal voltage E_T minus the counter-EMF E_C is proportional to the current I, or:

$$E=E_T-E_C=IR$$

where the coefficient of proportionality R is called the resistance of the circuit.

Poynting's Law for AC Circuits. The average rate of flow of power in an alternating current circuit can be expressed as

$$P = BG \cos \theta$$

where B and G are the effective values of the sinusoidal alternating magnetic field and the component of the electric field which is perpendicular to the former, both fields having the same frequency and θ being the phase angle between them.

Stefan-Boltzmann Law. The total radiated energy emitted from a black body is proportional to the fourth power of its absolute temperature.

Thermodynamics, Laws of. 1. When mechanical work is transformed into heat or heat into work, the amount of work is always equivalent to the quantity of heat. 2. It is impossible by any continuous self-sustaining process for heat to be transferred from a colder to a hotter body.

Volta's Law of Potential Difference. The potential difference developed at the contact between two dissimilar conductors is the same whether the contact is direct or whether it is through one or more intermediate conductors.

Weber-Fechner Law of Stimulus. For human stimulus, the increase of a stimulus necessary to produce a just discernible increase in the resulting sensation bears a constant ratio to the total stimulus. The minimum perceptible differences in level are related approximately by the factor "the cube root of two," or 1.26.

Wiedemann-Franz-Lorenz Law. For any metallic conductor, the ratio of the electrical conductivity and thermal conductivity at a given temperature is independent of the type of metal.

Wien's Displacement Law. When the temperature of a radiating black body increases, the wavelength corresponding to maximum energy decreases in such a way that the product of the absolute temperature and wavelength is a constant, and varies as the fifth power of the absolute temperature.

RULES

Fermat's Principle of Wave Propagation. When propagating between two points, an electromagnetic wave will take the path that involves the least travel time.

Left-Hand Rule for Electron Flow. If the fingers of the left hand are placed around a wire in such a way that the thumb points in the direction of electron flow, the fingers will be pointing in the direction of the magnetic field produced by the wire.

Left-Hand Rule for Moving Conductors. For a moving current-carrying wire or an electron beam in a magnetic field: If the thumb, index, and second fingers of the left hand are placed to be mutually at right angles to each other, with the index finger pointing in the direction of the magnetic lines of force, the second finger in the direction of electron flow, the thumb will be pointing in the direction of motion of the wire or electron beam. Also called "Fleming's Rule."

Right-Hand Rule for Current Flow. If the fingers of the right hand are placed around a current-carrying wire in such a way that the thumb points in the direction of conventional current flow, the fingers will be pointing in the direction of the magnetic field produced by the wire.

Right-Hand Rule for Moving Conductors. For a moving current-carrying wire or an electron beam in a magnetic field: If the thumb, index finger, and second finger of the right hand are placed to be mutu-ally at right angles to each other, with the index finger pointing in the direction of the magnetic lines of force, the second finger in the direction of conventional current flow, the thumb will be pointing in the direction of motion of the wire or electron beam. Also called "Fleming's Rule."

THEOREMS

Compensation Theorem. Any impedance in an energized network may be replaced by a generator of zero internal impedance whose instantaneous generated voltage is equal to the instantaneous potential difference across the replaced impedance caused by the current flowing through the impedance.

Fourier Theorem. Any finite complex wave may be analyzed into components, each of which is a simple harmonic wave of definite and determinable amplitude and phase.

Maximum Power Transfer Theorems. 1. If a passive network is joined to an active network by two terminals the power that will be absorbed by the passive network will be maximum if the impedances measured in the two directions, prior to the connection, are conjugates. 2. If the magnitude, but not the angle, of a load impedance may be varied, then the maximum power will be absorbed when the magnitude of the load impedance equals the magnitude of the internal impedance of the source.

Norton's Theorem. If an impedance Z_L is connected between any two points of a circuit, the current I_L that will flow through this impedance is the same as if the impedance Z_L is connected to a generator whose constant generated current I_G is the same as the current I_{SC} that flows if the two points of the circuit are short-circuited, the constant-current generator being in parallel with an impedance Z_I measured prior to the connection back into the circuit, with each other source of driving voltage within the circuit replaced with an impedance equal to the internal impedance of that source.

Reciprocity Theorem. If any source of voltage E located at one point in a network produces a current I at any other point in the network, the same source of voltage E placed at the second point will produce the same current I at the first point.

Reciprocity Theorem, Rayleigh-Carson. If a radio-frequency voltage E, when inserted at a given point X in antenna #1, causes a current I to flow at a given point Y in distant antenna #2, then the same voltage E when inserted at point Y in antenna #2 will cause the same current I to flow at point X in antenna #1.

Superposition Theorem. If a network has more than one source of driving voltage, the current that flows at any point, or the voltage between any two points, is the sum of the currents or voltages at these points which would exist if each source of voltage were considered separately, each of the other sources being replaced at that time by an impedance equal to the internal impedance of that source.

Thevenin's Theorem. If an impedance Z_L is connected between any two points of a circuit, the current I_L that will flow through this impedance is the same as if the impedance Z_L is connected to a generator whose constant generated voltage E_G is the same as the voltage E_{OC} between the two points of the circuit, prior to the connection, and whose internal impedance Z_G is the same as the impedance Z_I measured, prior to the connection, back into the circuit, with each source of driving voltage within the circuit replaced with an impedance equal in value to the internal impedance of that source.

APPENDIX

useful data

index

SYMBOLS

The following symbols are used in this appendix, and are standard in most communication literature you will encounter.

SYMBOL   USE

a/b	Fraction, with numerator "a" and denominator "b"
arc tan	The angle whose tangent is - - -
C	Capacitance in farads
°C	Degrees, Centigrade
cm	Centimeter
cos	Cosine
cos Θ	Power factor. Cosine of the angle theta.
cot	Cotangent
cu	Cubic
dB	Decibel
dBa	Decibels above reference noise, adjusted
dBm	Decibels referred to one milliwatt
dBr	Decibels referred to an arbitrary point
dBrn	Decibels above reference noise of -90 dBm
dBv	Decibels referred to one volt
dBw	Decibels referred to one watt
E	Potential in (effective) volts
E_c	Potential across a capacitance
E_L	Potential across an inductance
f	Frequency in hertz
f_r	Frequency of resonance
°F	Degrees, Fahrenheit
GHz	Gigahertz
HP	Horsepower
Hz	Hertz
I	Current in (effective) amperes
j	Operator to rotate a vector 90°, $\sqrt{-1}$
K	Coupling coefficient. Inductances.
k	Kilo- (X 1000)
kHz	Kilohertz
km	Kilometer
L	Self inductance in henries
L_A	Inductance with fields aiding
L_o	Inductance with fields opposing
log	Logarithm
$\log^{-1}$	A number whose logarithm is - - -
M	Mutual inductance in henries
m	Meter. milli-
MHz	Megahertz
mm	Millimeter
ω	Omega, $2\pi f$
ϕ	Phi. Phase.
π	Pi. The ratio of circumference to radius. 3.1415926
P	Power in watts
Q	Quality. Quantity of electricity in coulombs.
R	Resistance in ohms
R_c	Resistance of a capacitor

SYMBOLS
(Continued)

R_L	Resistance of an inductance
rms	Root-mean-square
sin	Sine
T	Total time
t	Time constant. Elapsed time.
tan	Tangent
$\tan^{-1}$	The angle whose tangent is - - -
Θ	Theta. The angle between current and voltage in electrical degrees.
X	Reactance in ohms
X_C	Capacitive reactance in ohms
X_L	Inductive reactance in ohms
Z	Impedance in ohms. (Magnitude)
$Z\ /\Theta$	Impedance (Magnitude and phase angle).
0	Space signal
1	Mark signal
+	Plus
-	Minus
$\pm$	Plus or minus
$\mp$	Minus or plus
X	Multiplied by
$\div$	Divided by
=	Equals
$\equiv$	Equivalent to; congruent to; identical to
>	Greater than
<	Less than
$\sqrt{}$	Square root of
$\sqrt[3]{}$	Cube root of
°	Degrees of an angle
°C	Degrees of temperature, Centigrade
°F	Degrees of temperature, Fahrenheit

GREEK ALPHABET

LETTER	NAME	USE
A α	Alpha	Attenuation constant, absorption factor, angles, angle with x-axis, angular acceleration.
B β	Beta	Phase constant, angles, angle with y-axis.
Γ γ	Gamma	Propagation constant, electrical conductivity.
Δ δ	Delta	Permittivity (Cap), increment or decrement, unit elongation.
E ε	Epsilon	Dielectric constant, Base of the Naperian logarithms.
Z ζ	Zeta	A coordinate.
H η	Eta	Hysteresis, surface charge density, intrinsic impedance.
Θ θ	Theta	Angular phase displacement, angle of the radius vector.
I ι	Iota	Unit vector.
K κ	Kappa	Susceptibility, coupling coefficient.
Λ λ	Lamda	Wavelength, permeance (Cap).
M μ	Mu	Prefix micro-, permeability, amplification factor.
N ν	Nu	Reluctivity.
Ξ ξ	Xi	Coordinates.
O o	Omicron	- - - - - -
Π π	Pi	Circumference divided by diameter. (3.1415926)
P ρ	Rho	Resistivity, volume charge density.
Σ σ	Sigma	Summation of terms (Cap), standard deviation.
T τ	Tau	Time constant, volume resistivity.
Υ υ	Upsilon	Vernal equinox (Cap).
Φ φ	Phi	Magnetic flux, angles.
X χ	Chi	Electric susceptibility.
Ψ ψ	Psi	Dielectric flux, phase difference.
Ω ω	Omega	Resistance in ohms (Cap), Angular velocity, $2\pi f$

OHM'S LAW FOR DC CIRCUITS

Ohm's Law (by George Simon Ohm, 1827) states that the voltage (E) across a resistor is equal to the product of the direct current (I) flowing through it by its resistance (R).   This can be written symbolically as:

$$E = IR \quad volts \hspace{4cm} \text{(Equation 1)}$$

If we remember that direct current power is equal to voltage times current, written:

$$P = EI \quad watts \hspace{4cm} \text{(Eq 2)}$$

then Ohm's Law for direct currents can be written in the following equivalent forms:

$$E = IR = P/I = \sqrt{PR} \hspace{3cm} \text{(Eq 3)}$$

$$I = E/R = P/E = \sqrt{P/R} \hspace{3cm} \text{(Eq 4)}$$

$$R = E/I = E^2/P = P/I^2 \hspace{3cm} \text{(Eq 5)}$$

$$P = EI = I^2R = E^2/R \hspace{3cm} \text{(Eq 6)}$$

RESISTANCE FORMULAE

The total resistance of resistors in series is

$$R = R_1 + R_2 + R_3 + R_4 - - - - - etc. \hspace{2cm} \text{(Eq 7)}$$

The total resistance of resistors in parallel is

$$R = \cfrac{1}{\cfrac{1}{R_1} + \cfrac{1}{R_2} + \cfrac{1}{R_3} + \cfrac{1}{R_4} - - - - - etc.} \hspace{1.5cm} \text{(Eq 8)}$$

The total resistance of two resistors in parallel is

$$R = \frac{R_1 R_2}{R_1 + R_2} \hspace{4cm} \text{(Eq 9)}$$

OHM'S LAW FOR AC CIRCUITS

Ohm's Law applies to alternating current circuits as well, if one substitutes impedance (Z) for resistance (R), remembers to use effective values of currents and voltages, and takes into account the possible difference inphase between current and voltage. With those differences, the Ohm's Law equations become:

$$E = IZ = P/\cos\Theta = \sqrt{PZ/\cos\Theta} \hspace{2cm} \text{(Eq 10)}$$

$$I = E/Z = P/E\cos\Theta = \sqrt{P/Z\cos\Theta} \hspace{2cm} \text{(Eq 11)}$$

$$Z = E/I = E^2\cos\Theta/P = P/I^2\cos\Theta \qquad \text{(Eq 12)}$$

$$P = EI\cos\Theta = I^2Z\cos\Theta = E^2\cos\Theta/Z \qquad \begin{matrix}\text{(Eq 13)}\\\text{(Eq 14)}\end{matrix}$$

where Θ = arc tan X/R

The expression "$\cos\Theta$" is known as the "power factor" of the circuit. Circuit losses are at a minimum when the power factor equals 1.0; ie: when the current and voltage are in phase.

CAPACITANCE FORMULAE

The total capacitance of capacitors in parallel is:

$$C = C_1 + C_2 + C_3 + C_4 - - - - \text{etc.} \qquad \text{(Eq 15)}$$

The total capacitance of capacitors in series is:

$$C = \cfrac{1}{\dfrac{1}{C_1} + \dfrac{1}{C_2} + \dfrac{1}{C_3} + \dfrac{1}{C_4} - - - - \text{etc.}} \qquad \text{(Eq 16)}$$

The total capacitance of two capacitors in series is:

$$C = \frac{C_1 \, C_2}{C_1 + C_2} \qquad \text{(Eq 17)}$$

The quantity of electricity stored in a capacitor of C farads when the potential across the capacitor is E volts, in coulombs, is:

$$Q = CE \quad \text{(coulombs)} \qquad \text{(Eq 18)}$$

The energy stored, in watt-seconds (joules), in a capacitor of C farads at E volts is:

$$W = \frac{CE^2}{2} \text{ (watt-seconds)} \qquad \text{(Eq 19)}$$

INDUCTANCE FORMULAE

Self-Inductance

If several inductances are connected together, BUT NOT COUPLED together inductively, their total inductance will be:

When the inductances are connected in series:

$$L = L_1 + L_2 + L_3 + L_4 - - - \text{etc.} \qquad \text{(Eq 20)}$$

When the inductances are connected in parallel:

$$L = \frac{1}{\frac{1}{L_1} + \frac{1}{L_2} + \frac{1}{L_3} + \frac{1}{L_4} \text{ --- etc}} \qquad \text{(Eq 21)}$$

When two inductances are connected in parallel:

$$L = \frac{L_1 L_2}{L_1 + L_2} \qquad \text{(Eq 22)}$$

Coupled Inductance

If two inductances are connected together and COUPLED so that their inductive fields ADD, the total inductance will be

Inductances in series, with fields aiding:

$$L_A = L_1 + L_2 + 2M \qquad \text{(Eq 23)}$$

Inductances in parallel, with fields aiding:

$$L_A = \frac{1}{\frac{1}{L_1 + M} + \frac{1}{L_2 + M}} \qquad \text{(Eq 24)}$$

Where M is the mutual inductance between L_1 and L_2

If two inductances are connected together, and COUPLED so that their inductive fields SUBTRACT, the total inductance will be

Inductances in series, with fields opposing:

$$L_0 = L_1 + L_2 - 2M \qquad \text{(Eq 25)}$$

Inductances in parallel, with fields opposing:

$$L_0 = \frac{1}{\frac{1}{L_1 - M} + \frac{1}{L_2 - M}} \qquad \text{(Eq 26)}$$

Mutual Inductance

Where the magnetic fields of two inductances are interleaved, the mutual inductance between them will be

$$M = \frac{L_A - L_0}{4} \qquad \text{(Eq 27)}$$

where L_A is the total inductance with fields aiding, and L_0 is the total inductance with fields opposing.

Coupling Coefficient

The degree of coupling between two inductances may be expressed as a coupling coefficient, K, calculated as follows:

$$K = M / \sqrt{L_1 L_2} \qquad \text{(Eq 28)}$$

REACTANCE AND Q

The reactance of an inductance is:

$$X_L = 2\pi f L \qquad \text{(Eq 29)}$$

and the reactance of a capacitor is:

$$X_c = 1/2\pi f C \qquad \text{(Eq 30)}$$

The excellence of a reactor, in terms of its freedom from resistance losses, is a figure of merit called "Q", equal to its reactance divided by its resistance.

For an inductance in which L and R are in series:

$$Q = X_L/R_L = 2\pi f L/R_L \qquad \text{(Eq 31)}$$

For a capacitance in which C and R are in series:

$$Q = X_c/R_c = 1/2\pi f C R_c \qquad \text{(Eq 32)}$$

IMPEDANCE

Impedance is the vector sum of resistance and reactance, and acts to limit current flow in AC circuits just as resistance acts to limit current flow in DC circuits.
Impedance is designated by the symbols $Z\theta$, in which the symbol Z denotes the magnitude of the impedance in ohms and the symbol θ (theta) denotes the phase difference between current and voltage in electrical degrees.   Impedance can also be designated as $R \pm jX$, where R is the magnitude of the resistance vector and X is the magnitude of the reactance vector, which is at 90 electrical degrees from the resistance vector.

For a pure resistance R:

$$Z = R \quad , \quad \theta = 0° \qquad \text{(Eq 33)}$$

For a pure capacitance C:

$$Z = X_c \quad , \quad \theta = -90° \qquad \text{(Eq 34)}$$

For a pure inductance L"

$$Z = X_L \quad , \quad \theta = +90° \qquad \text{(Eq 35)}$$

For resistance and capacitance in series:

$$Z = \sqrt{R^2 + X_c^2} \qquad \Theta = \text{arc tan } X_c/R \qquad \text{(Eq 36)}$$

For resistance and inductance in series:

$$Z = \sqrt{R^2 + X_L^2} \qquad \Theta = \text{arc tan } X_L/R \qquad \text{(Eq 37)}$$

For capacitance and inductance in series:

$$Z = X_L - X_c \qquad \begin{array}{l} \Theta = 0° \text{ when } X_c = X_L \\ \Theta = -90° \text{ when } X_c > X_L \\ \Theta = +90° \text{ when } X_L > X_c \end{array} \qquad \text{(Eq 38)}$$

For resistance, capacitance, and inductance in series:

$$Z = \sqrt{R^2 + (X_L - X_c)^2} \qquad \Theta = \text{arc tan } \frac{X_L - X_c}{R} \qquad \text{(Eq 39)}$$

For resistance and capacitance in parallel:

$$Z = \frac{RX_c}{\sqrt{R^2 + X_c^2}} \qquad \Theta = -\text{arc tan } R/X_c \qquad \text{(Eq 40)}$$

For resistance and inductance in parallel:

$$Z = \frac{RX_L}{\sqrt{R^2 + X_L^2}} \qquad \Theta = \text{arc tan } R/X_L \qquad \text{(Eq 41)}$$

For resistance, capacitance, and inductance in parallel:

$$Z = \frac{R X_c X_L}{X_c^2 X_L^2 + (RX_L - RX_c)^2} \qquad \text{(Eq 42)}$$

$$\Theta = \text{arc tan } \frac{RX_c - RX_L}{X_L X_c}$$

Complex AC circuits may be solved by combining the foregoing equations for simple series or parallel circuits. For instance, the common case of an inductance having series resistance in parallel with a capacitor gives the equation:

$$Z = X_c\sqrt{\frac{R^2 + X_L^2}{R^2 + (X_L - X_c)^2}} \qquad \text{(Eq 43)}$$

$$\Theta = \text{arc tan } \frac{X_L X_c - X_L^2 - R^2}{R X_c}$$

RESONANCE

If a series AC circuit consisting of capacitance, inductance, and
resistance is tuned so that the capacitive reactance equals the
inductive reactance, $X_c = X_L$, then the impedance is at a minimum
and $Z = R$.   Under those conditions the circuit is said to be
resonant, and the frequency is:

$$f_r = \frac{1}{2\pi \sqrt{LC}}$$ (Eq 44)

The current at resonance is:

$$I = E/R$$ (Eq 45)

and the voltage across C or L at resonance is:

$$E_c = E_L = 2\pi fLI = \frac{2\pi fLE}{R}$$ (Eq 46)

If L and C are given in henries and farads, then f_r will be in
hertz.
If L and C are in microhenries and microfarads, then f_r will
be in megahertz.

TRANSIENT CURRENTS AND VOLTAGES

When a voltage is applied to a circuit containing C and R, or L and R,
the current will rise to its final value gradually, reaching 63.21%
{ $1-(1/\varepsilon)$ } of its maximum value in the first unit of time; 63.21%
of the remaining difference (86.46% of maximum) during the second
unit of time, etc. Similarly, when the voltage is removed from such
a circuit, the current falls gradually to 36.79% {$1/\varepsilon$} of its initial
value during the first unit of time, to 13.53% during the second unit
of time, etc.   This unit of time is called the "time constant" of
the circuit.

TIME CONSTANTS

The unit of time during which the current rises to 63.21% of its final
value or falls to 36.79% of its initial value is called the "time
constant" of the circuit.

For a circuit containing R and C, the time constant is:

$$t = RC \text{ seconds}$$ (Eq 47)

For a circuit containing R and L, the time constant is:

$$t = L/R \text{ seconds}$$ (Eq 48)

TIME CONSTANTS (Continued)

The current, as a percentage of the final (rising) or initial (falling) current, is as follows at the end of each of the first six time constants:

Time Constant	Rising Current % of Final	Falling Current % of Initial
1	63.21	36.79
2	86.46	13.53
3	95.02	4.98
4	98.17	1.83
5	99.33	0.67'
6	99.75	0.25

THE SOLUTION OF
RIGHT TRIANGLES

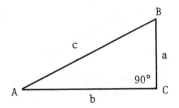

In any right triangle (in which one angle = 90°) of altitude a,
base b, and hypotenuse c, the following equations may be used
to solve for an unknown side or angle, given any two known sides
or angles.

$$\sin A = \cos B \qquad\qquad \cos A = \sin B \qquad \text{(Eq 49)}$$

$$\tan A = \cot B \qquad\qquad \cot A = \tan B \qquad \text{(Eq 50)}$$

$$a = \sqrt{c^2 - b^2} = c \sin A = c \cos B = b \tan A = b \cot B \qquad \text{(Eq 51)}$$

$$b = \sqrt{c^2 - a^2} = c \cos A = c \sin B = a \cot A = a \tan B \qquad \text{(Eq 52)}$$

$$c = \sqrt{a^2 + b^2} = a/\sin A = a/\cos B = b/\sin B = b/\cos A \qquad \text{(Eq 53)}$$

$$A = 90° - B$$

$$\sin A = \cos B = a/c \qquad \tan A = \cot B = a/b \qquad\qquad \text{(Eq 54)}$$

$$B = 90° - A$$

$$\sin B = \cos A = b/c \qquad \tan B = \cot A = b/a \qquad\qquad \text{(Eq 55)}$$

$$C = 90°$$

$$\text{Area} = 1/2\ ab \qquad\qquad\qquad\qquad\qquad\qquad \text{(Eq 56)}$$

THE SOLUTION OF
SCALENE TRIANGLES

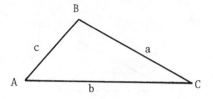

In any plane scalene triangle (no two sides equal) of sides a, b, and c and opposite angles A, B, and C, and given any three quantities including the length of one side, the following equations may be used to solve for any unknown side or angle.

$$a = b(\sin C/\sin B) = b \cos C + c \cos B \qquad \text{(Eq 57)}$$

$$b = a(\sin B/\sin A) = a \cos C + c \cos A \qquad \text{(Eq 58)}$$

$$c = a(\sin C/\sin A) = a \cos B + b \cos A \qquad \text{(Eq 59)}$$

$$= a\,[\sin(A+B)/\sin A\,]$$

$$\sin \tfrac{1}{2}A = \sqrt{\frac{(s-b)(s-c)}{bc}}, \text{ or} \qquad \text{(Eq 60)}$$

$$\sin A = (2/bc)\sqrt{s(s-a)(s-b)(s-c)} = \frac{a \sin B}{b} \qquad \text{(Eq 61)}$$

$$\sin B = \frac{b(\sin A)}{a} = \frac{b(\sin C)}{c} \qquad \text{(Eq 62)}$$

$$\sin C = (2/ab)\sqrt{s(s-a)(s-b)(s-c)} = \frac{c \sin A}{a} \qquad \text{(Eq 63)}$$

$$\text{where} \quad s = \tfrac{1}{2}(a+b+c)$$

$$\text{Area} = \tfrac{1}{2}ab \sin C \qquad \text{(Eq 64)}$$

NATURAL FUNCTIONS OF COMMON ANGLES

ANGLE	SIN	COS	TAN	COT
0°, 180°, -- 360°	0	1	0	INFINITY
5°, 175°, 185°, 355°	.087156	.996195	.087489	11.430052
10°, 170°, 190°, 350°	.173648	.984808	.176327	5.671282
15°, 165°, 195°, 345°	.258819	.965926	.267949	3.732051
20°, 160°, 200°, 340°	.342020	.939693	.363970	2.747477
25°, 155°, 205°, 335°	.422618	.906308	.466308	2.144507
30°, 150°, 210°, 330°	.500000	.866025	.577350	1.732051
35°, 145°, 215°, 325°	.573576	.819152	.700208	1.428148
40°, 140°, 220°, 320°	.642788	.766044	.839100	1.191754
45°, 135°, 225°, 315°	.707107	.707107	1	1
50°, 130°, 230°, 310°	.766044	.642788	1.191754	.839100
55°, 125°, 235°, 305°	.819152	.573576	1.428148	.700208
60°, 120°, 240°, 300°	.866025	.500000	1.732051	.577350
65°, 115°, 245°, 295°	.906308	.422618	2.144507	.466308
70°, 110°, 250°, 290°	.939693	.342020	2.747477	.363970
75°, 105°, 255°, 285°	.965926	.258819	3.732051	.267949
80°, 100°, 260°, 280°	.984808	.173648	5.671282	.176327
85°, 95° , 265°, 275°	.996195	.087156	11.430052	.087489
90° -- 270° --	1	0	INFINITY	0

The above functions have the following signs in the four quadrants:

	0°-90°	90°-180°	180°-270°	270°-360°
SIN	+	+	-	-
COS	+	-	-	+
TAN	+	-	+	-
COT	+	-	+	-

EQUIVALENT TEMPERATURES

To convert from Fahrenheit to Centigrade temperatures, use the following formula:

$$C^{\circ} = 5/9(F^{\circ} - 32^{\circ})$$ (Eq 65)

or to convert from Centigrade to Fahrenheit temperatures, use:

$$F^{\circ} = \frac{9}{5} C^{\circ} + 32^{\circ}$$ (Eq 66)

or, alternatively, use one of the following tables:

TABLE 2
FAHRENHEIT TO CENTIGRADE

F	C	F	C	F	C
1	-17.22	10	-12.22	100	37.78
2	-16.67	20	-6.67	200	93.33
3	-16.11	30	-1.11	300	148.89
4	-15.56	40	+4.44	400	204.44
5	-15.00	50	10.00	500	260.00
6	-14.44	60	15.56	600	315.56
7	-13.89	70	21.11	700	371.11
8	-13.33	80	26.67	800	426.67
9	-12.78	90	32.22	900	482.22

TABLE 3
CENTIGRADE TO FAHRENHEIT

C	F	C	F	C	F
1	33.8	10	50	100	212
2	35.6	20	68	200	392
3	37.4	30	86	300	572
4	39.2	40	104	400	752
5	41.0	50	122	500	932
6	42.8	60	140	600	1112
7	44.6	70	158	700	1292
8	46.4	80	176	800	1472
9	48.2	90	194	900	1652

Example:
Convert $186^{\circ}F$ to C°

Solution:
$$100^{\circ}F = 37.78^{\circ}C$$
$$80^{\circ}F = 26.67^{\circ}C$$
$$6^{\circ}F = -14.44^{\circ}C$$
$$\text{Answer} = \overline{50.01^{\circ}C}$$

TELEGRAPH CODES

INTERNAT'L		MORSE	INTERNAT'L		MORSE
•-	A	•-	-•	N	-•
-•••	B	-•••	---	O	•0•
-•-•	C	••0•	•--•	P	•••••
-••	D	-••	--•-	Q	•••-•
•	E	•	•-•	R	•0••
••-•	F	•-•	•••	S	•••
--•	G	--•	-	T	-
••••	H	••••	••-	U	••-
••	I	••	•••-	V	•••-
•---	J	-•-•	•--	W	•--
-•-	K	-•-	-••-	X	•-••
•-••	L	▬ *	-•--	Y	••0••
--	M	--	--••	Z	•••0•
•----	1	•--•	•-•-•-	.	••--••
••---	2	••-••	--••--	,	•-•-
•••--	3	•••-•	---•••	:	--•0•0•
••••-	4	••••-	-•-•-•	;	•-•-•
•••••	5	---	••--••	?	-••-•
-••••	6	••••••	-•--•-	()	•-••-
--•••	7	--••	•-----•	'	•••-•0•-•••
---••	8	-••••	-••-•	/	••-0-
----•	9	-••-			
-----	0	-			

• = Dot, - = Dash, * Doubly long dash, 0 = Space

The Morse code is used for wire telegraphy in the United States and Canada. The International Morse (Continental) code is used for wire telegraphy in other parts of the world, and for radio telegraphy world-wide.

TELETYPEWRITER CODES

ITA #2 12345	←BIT→	MOORE 1234567	ITA #2 12345	←BIT→	MOORE 1234567
11000	A	0011010	01101	0	1001010
10011	B	0011001	11101	1	0001101
01110	C	1001100	11001	2	0100101
10010	D	0011100	10000	3	0111000
10000	E	0111000	01010	4	1100100
10110	F	0010011	00001	5	1000101
01011	G	1100001	10101	6	0010101
00101	H	1010010	11100	7	0110010
01100	I	1110000	01100	8	1110000
11010	J	0100011	00011	9	1000110
11110	K	0001011	00111	.	1010001
01001	L	1100010	00110	,	1010010
00111	M	1010001	01110	:	1001100
00110	N	1010100	10011	?	0011001
00011	O	1000110	11010	'	0101010
01101	P	1001010	11110	(	0001011
11101	Q	0001101	01001	)	1100010
01010	R	1100100	11000	-	0011010
10100	S	0101010	10111	/	0010110
00001	T	1000101	01011	&	1100001
11100	U	0110010	00101	#	1010010
01111	V	1001001	10100	BELL	0100011
11001	W	0100011	11011	FIG	0100110
10111	X	0010110	11111	LET	0001110
10101	Y	0010101	01000	CR	1000011
10001	Z	0110001	00010	LF	1011000
			00100	SPC	1101000

Abbreviations:

FIG = Figures   CR = Carriage return   SPC = Space
LET = Letters   LF = Line feed

International Telegraph Alphabet #2 is the standard 5-bit,
7.42 unit Baudot code for start-stop teletypewriters.
The Moore code is a 7-bit, constant ratio (3 marks,
4 spaces) code much used on point-to-point radio circuits.

DATA & TELETYPEWRITER CODES

ASCII		BELL SYS	ASCII		BELL SYS
1234567	←BIT→	1234567P	1234567	←BIT→	1234567P
1000001	A	10000010	0000110	0	00001100
0100001	B	01000010	1000110	1	10001101
1100001	C	11000011	0100110	2	01001101
0010001	D	00100010	1100110	3	11001100
1010001	E	10100011	0010110	4	00101101
0110001	F	01100011	1010110	5	10101100
1110001	G	11100010	0110110	6	01101100
0001001	H	00010010	1110110	7	11101101
1001001	I	10010011	0001110	8	00011101
0101001	J	01010011	1001110	9	10011100
1101001	K	11010010	0111010	.	01110100
0011001	L	00110011	0011010	,	00110101
1011001	M	10110010	0101110	:	01011100
0111001	N	01110010	1101110	;	11011101
1111001	O	11110011	1111110	?	11111100
0000101	P	00001010	1110010	'	11100100
1000101	Q	10001011	0001010	(	00010100
0100101	R	01001011	1001010	)	10010101
1100101	S	11001010	1011010	–	10110100
0010101	T	00101011	1101010	+	11010100
1010101	U	10101010	1011110	=	10111101
0110101	V	01101010	0011101	/	00111010
1110101	W	11101011	1110000	BELL	11100001
0001101	X	00011011	1011000	CR	10110010
1001101	Y	10011010	0101000	LF	01010000
0101101	Z	01011010	0000010	SPC	00000101

Abbreviations: 1 = Mark signal   0 = Space
        CR = Carriage return   LF = Line feed   SPC = Space

The American Standard Code for Information Interchange (ASCII)
is an ASA standard, but changes have already been proposed as
shown on the following page.
The Bell System Code is the ASCII Code with an eighth bit
added to give even parity.

PROPOSED ASCII CODE

BIT→ 1234567		1234567		1234567		1234567
A	1000001	a	1000011	0	0000110	$ 0010010
B	0100001	b	0100011	1	1000110	% 1010010
C	1100001	c	1100011	2	0100110	{ 1101111
D	0010001	d	0010011	3	1100110	} 1011111
E	1010001	e	1010011	4	0010110	[1101101
F	0110001	f	0110011	5	1010110	] 1011101
G	1110001	g	1110011	6	0110110	BELL 1110000
H	0001001	h	0001011	7	1110110	CR 1011000
I	1001001	i	1001011	8	0001110	LF 0101000
J	0101001	j	0101011	9	1001110	BS 0001000
K	1101001	k	1101011			HT 1001000
L	0011001	l	0011011	.	0111010	VT 1101000
M	1011001	m	1011011	,	0011010	SOH 1000000
N	0111001	n	0111011	:	0101110	STX 0100000
O	1111001	o	1111011	;	1101110	ETX 1100000
P	0000101	p	0000111	?	1111110	EOT 0010000
Q	1000101	q	1000111	'	1110010	ACK 0110000
R	0100101	r	0100111	(	0001010	DC_1 1000100
S	1100101	s	1100111	)	1001010	DC_2 0100100
T	0010101	t	0010111	-	1011010	DC_3 1100100
U	1010101	u	1010111	+	1101010	DC_4 0010100
V	0110101	v	0110111	=	1011110	
W	1110101	w	1110111	/	1111010	
X	0001101	x	0001111	*	0101010	
Y	1001101	y	1001111	#	1100010	
Z	0101101	z	0101111	"	0100010	

Abbreviations:

CR = Carriage return, LF = Line feed, BS = Back space
HT = Horizontal tabulation,   VT = Vertical tabulation
SOH = Start of header,   STX = Start of text, ETX = End of text,
EOT = End of transmission, ACK = Acknowledge, DC = Device control.

DATA CODES
(Part 1)

HOLLERITH	IBM BCD		FIELDATA	PAPER TAPE
1234567890 11 12	8421BAP	←BIT→	0123456P	0123456P
100000000001	0001110	A	01100010	01100011
010000000001	0010110	B	11100011	11100010
001000000001	0011111	C	00010011	00010010
000100000001	0100110	D	10010010	10010011
000010000001	0101111	E	01010010	01010011
000001000001	0110111	F	11010011	11010010
000000100001	0111110	G	00110010	00110011
000000010001	1000110	H	10110011	10110010
000000001001	1001111	I	01110011	01110010
100000000010	0001101	J	11110010	11110011
010000000010	0010101	K	00001011	00001010
001000000010	0011100	L	10001010	10001011
000100000010	0100101	M	01001010	01001011
000010000010	0101100	N	11001011	11001010
000001000010	0110100	O	00101010	00101011
000000100010	0111101	P	10101011	10101010
000000010010	1000101	Q	01101011	01101010
000000001010	1001100	R	11101010	11101011
010000000100	0010011	S	00011010	00011011
001000000100	0011010	T	10011011	10011010
000100000100	0100011	U	01011011	01011010
000010000100	0101010	V	11011010	11011011
000001000100	0110010	W	00111011	00111010
000000100100	0111011	X	10111010	10111011
000000010100	1000011	Y	01111010	01111011
000000001100	1001010	Z	11111011	11111010

The Hollerith code is a 12-bit code without parity used to punch 80-column data cards.

The IBM Binary Coded Decimal (BCD) code uses seven bits: four for a binary coded decimal, two (AB) for control, and one to give odd parity.

The Fieldata code is an 8-bit code having both a regular (odd parity) and a paper tape (even parity) form.

DATA CODES
(Part 2)

HOLLERITH	IBM BCD		FIELDATA	PAPER TAPE
1234567890$\frac{1}{1}\frac{1}{2}$	8421BAP	←BIT→	0123456P	0123456P
000000000100	1010001	Ø	00001110	00001100
100000000000	0001000	1	10001111	10001101
010000000000	0010000	2	01001111	01001101
001000000000	0011001	3	11001110	11001100
000100000000	0100000	4	00101111	00101101
000010000000	0101001	5	10101110	10101100
000001000000	0110001	6	01101110	01101100
000000100000	0111000	7	11101111	11101101
000000010000	1000000	8	00011111	00011101
000000001000	1001001	9	10011110	10011100
000001001000	1110000	UC	10000011	10000010
000001001001	1110110	LC	01000011	01000010
000010011001	1101101	CR	00100011	00100010
000010001100	1101011	LF	11000010	11000011
000000000000	0000001	SPC	10100010	10100011
001000010001	1011110	.	10111111	10111101
001000010100	1011011	,	01110110	01110100
010000010000	0100000	:	11010110	11010100
000000110100	0001011	?	00110111	00110101
000010010000	0110001	'	01011110	01011100
000010010001	1001001	(	10010111	10010101
000010010010	1010001	)	00000111	00000101
000000000010	0000100	-	10000110	10000100
000001010001	0000111	+	01000110	01000100
000001010000	0001000	=	00100110	00100100
000000000100	0001011	/	00111110	00111100
001000010010	1011101	$	11100110	11100100
000100010100	0101001	%	- - -	- - -
001000010000	1011000	#	- - -	- - -
000100010000	0000010	@	- - -	- - -
- - - -	1101000	STOP	11110111	11110101

Abbreviations:

UC = Upper case, LC = Lower case, CR = Carriage return

LF = Line feed, SPC = Space

DECIBELS

The difference in level between two signals may be expressed as a
ratio of the two powers or, if the generator and load impedances
are equal, as a ratio of the two currents or two voltages.
The logarithm of these ratios is a dimensionless unit called the
decibel. The logarithmic relations between the decibel and the
ratios are as follows:

$$\text{Powers:}\quad dB = 10\ \log(P_1/P_2) \qquad\qquad\text{(Eq 67)}$$

$$\text{Currents:}\quad dB = 20\ \log(I_1/I_2) \qquad\qquad\text{(Eq 68)}$$

$$\text{Voltages:}\quad dB = 20\ \log(E_1/E_2) \qquad\qquad\text{(Eq 69)}$$

If the generator and load impedances are not equal, the above
equations for current and voltage ratios become:

$$\text{Currents:}\quad dB = 20\ \log\frac{I_1}{I_2} + 10\ \log\frac{Z_1}{Z_2} + 10\ \log\frac{\cos\Theta_1}{\cos\Theta_2} \qquad\text{(Eq 70)}$$

$$\text{Voltages:}\quad dB = 20\ \log\frac{E_1}{E_2} + 10\ \log\frac{Z_2}{Z_1} + 10\ \log\frac{\cos\Theta_1}{\cos\Theta_2} \qquad\text{(Eq 71)}$$

Table 4, which follows, gives values of dB corresponding to a number
of power, current, and voltage ratios, as determined by equations
67, 68, or 69, above.

OTHER LOGARITHMIC UNITS

dBm   A commonly used unit having dimension is the dBm, which
           specifies the amount of power in decibels above (or minus
dB below) a level of one milliwatt.   If the load impedance is
specified, usually 600 ohms resistive, the dBm can be used to
specify the number of volts across the load.   Table 5, which follows,
gives the power in watts corresponding to several levels of dBm.

dBm0   Used to specify a measurement of signal power in dBm
           referred to zero dBm at the reference transmission-
level point.   See also RTLP, below.

dBa   Decibels above reference noise, adjusted. Used to specify
           circuit noise levels in decibels above a 1000 hertz
reference noise power of -85 dBm.   Commonly used with an F1A
weighting network which simulates the frequency response of the
Bell System's F1A-HA1-101A telephone sets.

dBa0   Decibels of adjusted noise power referred to the zero
           dBm level at the reference transmission-level point.
See also RTLP, below.

dBrn   Decibels above reference noise, where the reference noise
           power is a 1000 hertz tone at -90 dBm.   Used with a 144
weighting network which simulates the frequency response of the
Bell System's 337-144-46A (desk stand) telephone sets. This unit
has been replaced by the "dBrnC".

dBrnC   Decibels above a reference noise of 1000 hertz at -90 dBm, but adjusted for C-message circuits with a C network which simulates the frequency response of the Bell System's T1-U3-425 (Type 500) telephone sets. The 3A Noise Meter reads in dBrnC.

dBr   Used to designate the signal level at any point in a transmission system, referred to an arbitrarily designated point known as a zero transmission-level point ($\emptyset$-TLP).

dBv   Decibels above or below a one volt reference voltage.

dBw   Decibels above or below a one watt reference power.

dBmOp   A level of interfering noise power as measured by a CCITT standard telephone psophometer which gives the same reading as an equal dBm of 800 hertz tone into 600 ohms, resistive.

pwp   Picowatts (10^{-12} watts) of power, psophometrically weighted.

dBx   Decibels above reference crosstalk coupling. Used to designate the crosstalk coupling between two telephone circuits in decibels above a minimum reference coupling of 90 dB, where the noise levels on disturbing and disturbed circuits are read with the same noise weighting.

dB RAP   Decibels above a specified reference acoustic power (RAP). Several values of RAP have been used in the past, but the value commonly accepted internationally today is:

$$RAP = 10^{-12} \text{ watt} \qquad \text{(Eq 72)}$$

The output of sound sources can seldom be measured directly, but can be calculated from a measurement of free field sound pressure level (SPL) in decibels above 0.002 microbar at a point of "r" feet from the sound source. The power level at the source is then:

$$P = SPL + 20\log r + 0.5 \text{ dB} \quad \text{(in dB RAP)} \qquad \text{(Eq 73)}$$

RTLP   Reference transmission-level point. That point in a transmission system which has a power level of zero dBm Also known as the $\emptyset$-TLP.

neper   European and Oriental literature generally specify the transmission losses in another dimensionless Naperian logarithmic unit called a "neper", which is defined as follows:

$$\text{Nepers} = 1/2 \log_{\varepsilon} (P_1/P_2) \qquad \text{(Eq 74)}$$

$$dB = 8.6858 \text{ nepers} \qquad \text{Neper} = 0.115130 \text{ dB} \qquad \text{(Eq 75)}$$

msc   Mile of standard cable.   This is an obsolete unit
             used before the advent of the decibel to specify
transmission losses.   It was the loss encountered by an 800
hertz tone in traversing 5280 feet of standard 22 AWG paper-
wrapped paired exchange cable.   It was sometimes called the
"800-cycle mile".   The msc cannot accurately be compared with
the decibel, but under certain conditions was roughly equivalent
as follows:

$$dB = 1.084 \ msc \qquad\qquad (Eq \ 76)$$

DECIBEL TABLE #4

LOSS (-)			GAIN (+)	
VOLTAGE OR CURRENT RATIO	POWER RATIO	dB	VOLTAGE OR CURRENT RATIO	POWER RATIO
1.0000	1.0000	0.0	1.0000	1.0000
0.9886	0.9772	0.1	1.012	1.023
0.9772	0.9550	0.2	1.023	1.047
0.9661	0.9333	0.3	1.035	1.072
0.9550	0.9120	0.4	1.047	1.096
0.9441	0.8913	0.5	1.059	1.120
0.9333	0.8710	0.6	1.072	1.148
0.9226	0.8511	0.7	1.084	1.175
0.9120	0.8318	0.8	1.096	1.202
0.9016	0.8128	0.9	1.109	1.230
0.8913	0.7943	1.0	1.122	1.259
0.8414	0.7079	1.5	1.189	1.413
0.7943	0.6310	2.0	1.259	1.585
0.7499	0.5623	2.5	1.334	1.778
0.7079	0.5012	3.0	1.413	1.995
0.6683	0.4467	3.5	1.496	2.239
0.6310	0.3981	4.0	1.585	2.512
0.5957	0.3548	4.5	1.679	2.818
0.5623	0.3162	5.0	1.778	3.162
0.5309	0.2818	5.5	1.884	3.548
0.5012	0.2512	6.0	1.995	3.981
0.4732	0.2239	6.5	2.113	4.467
0.4467	0.1995	7.0	2.239	5.012
0.4217	0.1778	7.5	2.371	5.623
0.3981	0.1585	8.0	2.512	6.310
0.3758	0.1413	8.5	2.661	7.079
0.3548	0.1259	9.0	2.818	7.943
0.3350	0.1122	9.5	2.985	8.913
0.3162	0.1000	10.0	3.162	10.000

DECIBEL TABLE #4
(Continued)

VOLTAGE OR CURRENT RATIO	POWER RATIO	dB	VOLTAGE OR CURRENT RATIO	POWER RATIO
0.2985	0.08913	10.5	3.350	11.22
0.2818	0.07943	11.0	3.548	12.59
0.2661	0.07079	11.5	3.758	14.13
0.2512	0.06310	12.0	3.981	15.85
0.2371	0.05623	12.5	4.217	17.78
0.2239	0.05012	13.0	4.467	19.95
0.2113	0.04467	13.5	4.732	22.39
0.1995	0.03981	14.0	5.012	25.12
0.1884	0.03548	14.5	5.309	28.18
0.1778	0.03162	15.0	5.623	31.62
0.1679	0.02818	15.5	5.957	35.48
0.1585	0.02512	16.0	6.310	39.81
0.1496	0.02239	16.5	6.683	44.67
0.1413	0.01995	17.0	7.079	50.12
0.1334	0.01778	17.5	7.499	56.23
0.1259	0.01585	18.0	7.943	63.10
0.1189	0.01413	18.5	8.414	70.79
0.1122	0.01259	19.0	8.913	79.43
0.1059	0.01122	19.5	9.441	89.13
0.1000	0.01000	20.0	10.000	100.00
0.0562	0.00316	25.0	17.78	316.23
0.03162	0.00100	30.0	31.62	1000.00
0.01778	3.162×10^{-4}	35.0	56.23	3162.
0.01000	10^{-4}	40.0	100.00	10000.
5.623×10^{-3}	3.162×10^{-5}	45.0	177.8	31620.
3.162×10^{-3}	10^{-5}	50.0	316.2	10^{5}
10^{3}	10^{-6}	60.0	1000.	10^{6}
3.162×10^{-4}	10^{-7}	70.0	3.162×10^{3}	10^{7}
10^{4}	10^{-8}	80.0	10^{4}	10^{8}
3.162×10^{-5}	10^{-9}	90.0	3.162×10^{4}	10^{9}
10^{5}	10^{-10}	100.0	10^{5}	10^{10}

TABLE 5 — POWER LEVEL IN WATTS

ABOVE ZERO dBm

dBm	WATTS	dBm	WATTS
0	.001000	12	0.01585
1	.001259	15	0.03162
2	.001585	20	0.1
3	.001996	30	1.0
4	.002512	40	10.0
5	.003163	50	10^2
6	.003982	60	10^3
7	.005012	70	10^4
8	.006310	80	10^5
9	.007944	90	10^6
10	.010000	100	10^7

BELOW ZERO dBm

dBm	WATTS	dBm	WATTS
0	1.000×10^{-3}	-12	6.310×10^{-5}
-1	7.943×10^{-4}	-15	3.163×10^{-5}
-2	6.310×10^{-4}	-20	10^{-5}
-3	5.012×10^{-4}	-30	10^{-6}
-4	3.981×10^{-4}	-40	10^{-7}
-5	3.163×10^{-4}	-50	10^{-8}
-6	2.512×10^{-4}	-60	10^{-9}
-7	1.996×10^{-4}	-70	10^{-10}
-8	1.585×10^{-4}	-80	10^{-11}
-9	1.259×10^{-4}	-90	10^{-12}
-10	1.000×10^{-4}	-100	10^{-13}

TABLE 8
MATHEMATICAL CONSTANTS AND THEIR LOGARITHMS

CONSTANT		LOG_{10}
π	3.141 592 654	0.497 149 9
2π	6.283 185 3	0.798 179 9
3π	9.424 778 0	0.974 271 1
4π	12.566 370 6	1.099 209 9
$\pi/2$	1.570 796 3	0.196 119 9
$\pi/3$	1.047 197 6	0.020 028 6
$\pi/4$	0.785 398 2	9.895 089 9 - 10
$1/\pi$	0.318 309 9	9.502 850 1 - 10
$1/2\pi$	0.159 154 9	9.201 820 1 - 10
$1/4\pi$	0.079 577 5	8.900 790 1 - 10
π^2	9.869 604 4	0.994 299 7
$4\pi^2$	39.478 417 6	1.596 359 7
$1/\pi^2$	0.101 321 2	9.005 700 3 - 10
$1/4\pi^2$	0.025 330 3	8.403 640 3 - 10
$\sqrt{\pi}$	1.772 453 9	0.248 574 9
$\sqrt{\pi/2}$	1.253 314 1	0.098 059 9
π^3	31.006 276 7	1.491 449 6
$\sqrt[3]{\pi}$	1.464 591 9	0.165 716 6
$1/\sqrt{\pi}$	0.564 189 6	9.751 425 1 - 10
ε	2.718281828	0.434 294 5
$1/\varepsilon$	0.367 879 441	9.565 704 5 - 10

TABLE 9
VALUES OF $2\pi f$

f equals	$2\pi f$	$Log_{10}2\pi f$
16	100.530 965	2.002 299 9
16-2/3	104.719 755	2.020 030 2
20	125.663 706	2.099 210 8
25	157.079 633	2.196 120 8
30	188.495 559	2.275 294 9
33-1/3	209.439 510	2.321 059 8
40	251.327 412	2.400 227 6
42	263.893 783	2.421 430 1
50	314.159 265	2.497 149 9
54	339.292 006	2.530 573 7
60	376.991 118	2.576 330 6
66	414.690 230	2.617 723 5
66-2/3	418.879 020	2.622 089 2
135	848.230 016	2.928 513 3
180	1130.973 354	3.053 451 4
300	1884.955 590	3.275 301 8
400	2513.274 120	3.400 238 7
420	2638.937 826	3.421 429 2
1000	6283.185 3	3.798 179 9

where:

2π = 6.2831853 , and

Log 2π = 0.798 179 9

TABLE 10—EQUIVALENT ANGLES AND TIMES

RADIANS OF ARC	DEGREES OF ARC	MINUTES OF ARC	SECONDS OF ARC	TIME *
1	57.2958	3437.75	206265.	3hr 49min 11sec
.01745	1	60	3600	0hr 4min 0sec
2.90888×10^{-4}	.016666	1	60	0hr 0min 4sec
4.84814×10^{-6}	.000278	.016666	1	0hr 0min.07sec
.261799	15	900	54000	1hr
2.90888×10^{-4}	.016667	15	900	1min

* If the arc expresses longitude difference, then there is an
equivalent time difference shown in the "Time" column.

TABLE 11—EQUIVALENT LENGTHS

mm	cm	meter	kilometer	inch	foot	yard	chain	mile	nautical mile
1	0.1	0.001	10^{-6}	.03937	.003281	.001094	4.971×10^{-5}	6.2137×10^{-7}	5.3961×10^{-7}
10	1	0.01	10^{-5}	.39370	.032808	.010936	4.971×10^{-4}	6.2137×10^{-6}	5.3961×10^{-6}
1000	100	1	10^{-3}	39.3700	3.28083	1.093611	.04971	6.2137×10^{-4}	5.3961×10^{-4}
10^6	10^5	1000	1	39370.	3280.83	1093.61	49.7096	.62137	.53961
25.4001	2.54001	.02540		1	1/12	1/36	1.26263×10^{-3}	1.52783×10^{-5}	1.32671×10^{-5}
304.801	30.4801	.304801		12	1	1/3	.015151	1.89394×10^{-4}	1.6447×10^{-4}
914.402	91.4402	.914402		36	3	1	.045454	5.68182×10^{-4}	4.93387×10^{-4}
20117.	2011.7	20.117	.020117	792	66	22	1	.01250	.010855
1.60935×10^{-6}	160935.	1609.35	1.60935	63360.	5280	1760	80	1	.86836
- -	185200.	1852.	1.852	72913.	6076.1	2025.4	- -	1.151	1

TABLE 12—EQUIVALENT AREAS

Sq cm.	Sq m.	CIRC MIL	SQ. INCH	SQ. FOOT	SQ. YARD	SQ. MILE	ACRE
1	.0001	1.9735×10^5	.15500	1.07639×10^{-3}	1.1960×10^{-4}	--	--
10,000	1	--	1550	10.76387	1.195985	3.8610	2.47104
5.0671×10^{-6}	--	1	7.854×10^{-7}	--	--	--	--
6.451626	6.451626×10^{-4}	1.27324×10^6	1	6.9444×10^{-3}	7.71605×10^{-4}	--	--
929.034	.092903	--	144	1	.111111	--	2.29568×10^{-5}
8361.31	.836131	--	1296	9	1	3.22831×10^{-7}	2.06612×10^{-4}
--	2.589998×10^6	--	--	2.78784×10^7	3.0976×10^6	1	640
--	4046.87	--	--	43560.	4840.	1.5625×10^{-3}	1

TABLE 13 — EQUIVALENT VOLUMES

Cu cm.	Cu m.	CU INCH	CU FOOT	CU YARD	ACRE-FOOT	LITRE	FL. OUNCE	GALLON	IMP. GALLON
1	10^{-6}	.061023	3.53144×10^{-5}	1.30794×10^{-6}	- -	9.9997×10^{-4}	.033814	2.6417×10^{-4}	2.1997×10^{-4}
10^{6}	1	61023.	35.3144	1.307943	8.10708×10^{-4}	999.973	33814.1	264.173	219.972
16.38716	1.6387×10^{-5}	1	5.78704×10^{-4}	2.14334×10^{-5}	- -	1.63868×10^{-2}	.5541	4.3290×10^{-3}	3.60467×10^{-3}
28317.	.028317	1728.	1	.037037	- -	28.316	957.568	7.481	6.2293
764559.	.764559	46656.	27	1	6.19835×10^{-4}	764.54	23836.	202.0	168.17
- -	1233.49	- -	43560.	1613.33	1	- -	- -	325872.	271347.
1000.03	10^{-3}	61.025	.035316	1.3080×10^{-3}	- -	1	33.8147	.264177	.219925
29.5737	2.95737×10^{-5}	1.80469	1.04438×10^{-3}	- -	- -	.029573	1	.007812	.006505
3785.4	3.7854×10^{-3}	231.0	.13368	4.95111×10^{-3}	3.06869×10^{-6}	3.7853	128	1	.83268
4546.1	4.5460×10^{-3}	277.3	.16054	5.94599×10^{-3}	3.68531×10^{-6}	4.54596	153.72	1.20094	1

TABLE 14—EQUIVALENT WEIGHTS

CARAT	m gram	gram	k gram	GRAIN	OUNCE	POUND	TON
1	200	0.2	.0002	3.08647	7.05478×10^{-3}	4.4092×10^{-4}	- -
.005	1	.001	10^{-6}	.015432	3.52739×10^{-5}	2.20462×10^{-6}	- -
5	1000	1	.001	15.4324	.035274	2.20462×10^{-3}	1.10231×10^{-6}
5000.	10^6	1000	1	15432.	35.2739	2.20462	1.10231×10^{-3}
.3240	64.7989	.064799	6.4799×10^{-5}	1	2.2857×10^{-3}	1/7000	- -
141.748	28349.5	28.3495	.02835	437.5	1	1/16	3.125×10^{-5}
2267.97	4535992.	453.592	.45359	7000	16	1	5×10^{-4}
- -	- -	907185.	907.185	- -	32000.	2000	1

TABLE 15—EQUIVALENT PRESSURES

INCH OF MERCURY	FOOT OF WATER	GRAM PER SQ CM	POUND PER SQ INCH	POUND PER SQ FOOT	ATMOSPHERE
1	1.13299	3.4531	.49116	70.727	.033421
.88265	1	3.0479	.43352	62.426	.029499
.289595	.328095	1	1.4223×10^{-2}	2.0482	9.6784×10^{-4}
2.0360	2.3066	70.307	1	144	.068046
.01413	.016018	.48824	6.9445×10^{-3}	1	4.7254×10^{-4}
29.921	33.899	1033.2	14.696	2116.2	1

TABLE 16—EQUIVALENT VELOCITIES

FEET PER SECOND	FEET PER MINUTE	MILES PER HOUR	KILOMETER PER HOUR	KNOTS	NAUTICAL MILES/HOUR
1	60	.6818	1.0973	.5921	.5921
.016667	1	.011364	.01829	9.868×10^{-4}	9.868×10^{-4}
1.4667	88	1	1.6093	.8684	.8684
.9113	54.68	.6214	1	.5396	.5396
1.69889	101.33	1.1516	1.853	1	1

TABLE 17—EQUIVALENT RATES OF FLOW

CU CM PER SEC	CU FT PER MIN	CU FT PER SEC	CU YARD PER MIN	GALLON PER MIN	GALLON PER SEC	LITER PER SEC	LBS WATER PER MIN
1	2.11886×10^{-3}	3.53144×10^{-5}	- - -	.01585	2.6417×10^{-4}	9.9997×10^{-4}	.132217
472.0	1	.016667	.037035	7.482	.1247	.4720	62.4
2.8317×10^{4}	60	1	2.2222	448.83	7.4805	28.3217	3744.
1.27427×10^{4}	27	0.45	1	201.976	3.367	12.74	1684.8
630901	.13368	2.228×10^{-3}	4.95106×10^{-3}	1	.016667	.06308	8.34163
3785.4	8.0192	0.13365	0.297	60	1	3.78495	500.398
1000.03	2.12	.035322	.078493	15.85	.264166	1	132.288
- - -	.016026	7.213×10^{-3}	5.93542×10^{-4}	.11988	1.99841×10^{-3}	7.55926×10^{-3}	1

TABLE 18—EQUIVALENT POWER

BTU PER MINUTE	FT LB PER SEC	FT LB PER MIN	dBm	WATTS	KILOWATTS	HORSE-POWER
1	12.96613	777.968	+ 42.45	17.580	.01758	.023575
.077124	1	60	+ 31.32	1.35582	1.3558×10^{-3}	1.8182×10^{-3}
1.2854×10^{-3}	1.6667×10^{-2}	1	+ 13.54	2.2597×10^{-2}	2.2597×10^{-5}	3.0303×10^{-5}
7.16155×10^{-5}	9.28589×10^{-4}	5.57154×10^{-2}	+ 1.0	.001259	1.259×10^{-6}	1.68857×10^{-6}
.056896	.73756	44.254	+ 30.	1	.001	1.3410×10^{-3}
56.896	737.56	44254.	+ 60.	1000	1	1.3410
42.418	550	33000.	+ 58.73	745.7	.7457	1

Note: In the United States and Great Britain the value of the horsepower is usually taken as 746 watts (absolute) when rating electrical machinery.

TABLE 19—EQUIVALENT ENERGY

	B T U	GRAM-CALORIE	JOULE	WATT-HOUR	KILOWATT-HOUR	FOOT-POUND	HP-HOUR
B T U	1	251.98	1054.8	.2930	2.930×10^{-4}	777.97	3.9292×10^{-4}
GRAM-CALORIE	3.9685×10^{-3}	1	4.186	1.1628×10^{-3}	1.1628×10^{-6}	3.0874	1.5593×10^{-6}
JOULE	9.480×10^{-4}	.23889	1	2.778×10^{-4}	2.778×10^{-7}	.73756	3.725×10^{-7}
WATT-HOUR	3.4130	860.01	3600	1	.001	2655.3	1.3410×10^{-3}
KILOWATT-HOUR	3413.0	860010.	3.600×10^{6}	1000	1	2.6552×10^{6}	1.3410
FOOT-POUND	1.2854×10^{-3}	3238.9	1.35582	3.7662×10^{-4}	3.7662×10^{-7}	1	5.0505×10^{-7}
HP-HOUR	2545.0	641300.	2.6845×10^{6}	745.7	.7457	1.9800×10^{6}	1

TABLE 20
CABLE AND WIRE DATA

FACILITY	GAUGE AWG	CAPAC. µf/mile	CHARACTER IMPEDANCE	LOADING	RESISTANCE ohms/kft	dB @ 1 kHz per kft
- C A B L E -						
Polyethelene insul.	26	.083	942 $\sqrt{44.5°}$	NL	83.3	.549
" "	26	.083	1100 $\sqrt{16.6°}$	D88	84.7	.339
" "	26	.083	1192 $\sqrt{20.8°}$	H88	84.7	.345
" "	24	.083	721 $\sqrt{44.2°}$	NL	51.9	.436
" "	24	.083	1100 $\sqrt{11.3°}$	D88	53.2	.210
" "	24	.083	1160 $\sqrt{14.6°}$	H88	53.2	.232
" "	22	.083	576 $\sqrt{43.8°}$	NL	32.6	.341
" "	22	.083	1135 $\sqrt{7.5°}$	D88	33.9	.133
" "	22	.083	1051 $\sqrt{9.7°}$	H88	33.9	.151
" "	19	.083	402 $\sqrt{42.8°}$	NL	16.3	.239
" "	19	.083	723 $\sqrt{9.7°}$	H44	17.6	.106
" "	19	.083	1395 $\sqrt{2.8°}$	B88	17.6	.064
" "	19	.083	1135 $\sqrt{4.0°}$	D88	17.6	.070
" "	19	.083	1017 $\sqrt{5.2°}$	H88	17.6	.080
" "	19	.066	464 $\sqrt{42.6°}$	NL	16.3	.212
" "	19	.066	811 $\sqrt{9.8°}$	H44	17.6	.096
" "	19	.066	1565 $\sqrt{2.8°}$	B88	17.6	.058
" "	19	.066	1290 $\sqrt{4.0°}$	D88	17.6	.065
" "	19	.066	1137 $\sqrt{5.2°}$	H88	17.6	.072
Paper insulated	16	.066	320 $\sqrt{40.6°}$	NL	8.71	.142
" "	13	.062	242 $\sqrt{36.9°}$	NL	4.36	.114
Urban Distribution	24	.264	- - -	NL	60.0	.492
Suburban Distr.	22	.116	- - -	NL	34.8	.303
Rural Distribution	19	.137	- - -	NL	17.4	.227
UG Service, Rubber	19	.280	- - -	NL	17.4	- -
- W I R E -						
C Rural Wire,Steel	.083"	.072	- - -	NL	23.3	.227
C Rural Wire, CWS	14	.065	- - -	NL	15.5	.208
C Rural Wire, CWS	12	.069	- - -	NL	10.8	.167
Drop Wire, CWS	18	- -	- - -	NL	24.2	- -
Drop Wire, CWS	17	- -	- - -	NL	16.0	- -
Drop Wire, Bronze	17	- -	- - -	NL	16.0	- -

TABLE 21
BARE COPPER WIRE

Conductor Size	Wire Diameter	Cross-Sectional Area		Weight		Hard-Drawn	
						Minimum Ultimate Strength	D-C Resistanc at 20C (68F)
Awg	inch	circular mils	square inch	lb per M ft	lb per mile	pounds	ohms per M ft
44	0.0020	4.00	0.00000314	0.0121	0.0639		
43	.0022	4.84	.00000380	.0147	.0774		
42	.0025	6.25	.00000491	.0189	.0999		
41	.0028	7.84	.00000616	.0237	.125		
40	.0031	9.61	.00000755	.0291	.154		
39	.0035	12.2	.00000962	.0371	.196		
38	.0040	16.0	.0000126	.0484	.256		
37	.0045	20.2	.0000159	.0613	.324		
36	.0050	25.0	.0000196	.0757	.400		
35	.0056	31.4	.0000246	.0949	.501		
34	.0063	39.7	.0000312	.120	.634		
33	.0071	50.4	.0000396	.153	.806		
32	.0080	64.0	.0000503	.194	1.02		
31	.0089	79.2	.0000622	.240	1.27		
30	.0100	100	.0000785	.303	1.60		
29	.0113	128	.000100	.387	2.04		
28	.0126	159	.000125	.481	2.54		
27	.0142	202	.000158	.610	3.22		
26	.0159	253	.000199	.765	4.04		
25	.0179	320	.000252	.970	5.12		
24	.0201	404	.000317	1.22	6.46		
23	.0226	511	.000401	1.55	8.16		
22	.0253	640	.000503	1.94	10.2		
21	.0285	812	.000638	2.46	13.0		
20	.0320	1020	.000804	3.10	16.4		
19	.0359	1290	.00101	3.90	20.6		
18	.0403	1620	.00128	4.92	26.0	85.5	6.64
17	.0453	2050	.00161	6.21	32.8	108	5.26
16	.0508	2580	.00203	7.81	41.2	135	4.18
15	.0571	3260	.00256	9.87	52.1	170	3.31
14	.0641	4110	.00323	12.4	65.7	214	2.63
13	.0720	5180	.00407	15.7	82.9	268	2.08
12	.0808	6530	.00513	19.8	104	337	1.65
11	.0907	8230	.00646	24.9	131	423	1.31
10	.1019	10380	.008155	31.43	166.0	529.3	1.039
9	.1144	13090	.01028	39.61	209.2	660.9	0.8241
8	.1285	16510	.01297	49.98	263.9	826.1	.6532
7	.1443	20820	.01635	63.03	332.8	1030	.5180
6	.1620	26240	.02061	79.44	419.4	1280	.4110
5	.1819	33090	.02599	100.2	528.8	1590	.3260
4	.2043	41740	.03278	126.3	667.1	1970	.2584
3	.2294	52620	.04133	159.3	841.1	2439	.2050
2	.2576	66360	.05212	200.9	1061	3002	.1625
1	.2893	83690	.06573	253.3	1338	3688	.1289
1/0	.3249	105600	.08291	319.5	1687	4518	.1022
2/0	.3648	133100	.1045	402.8	2127	5519	.08021
3/0	.4096	167800	.1318	507.8	2681	6720	.06362
4/0	.4600	211600	.1662	640.5	3382	8143	.05045

Based on ASTM Specifications B1-56, B2-52, B3-56, and B258-57.
Reprinted Courtesy of Anaconda Wire and Cable Company

Ultimate Strength is based on ASTM specification requirements, using minimum values for hard- and medium-hard drawn and maximum values for soft annealed.

TABLE 22
GALVANIZED STEEL TELEPHONE AND TELEGRAPH WIRE

WIRE SIZE		MINIMUM BREAKING STRENGTH (LBS.)					
BWG	Wire Diameter	EBB	BB	Grade 85	Grade 135	Grades 190 and 195	Weight Pounds Per Mile
4	.238″	2028	2271				811
6	.203	1475	1652				590
8	.165	975	1092				390
9	.148	785	879	1462			314
10	.134	645	722	1199		2680	258
11	.120	515	577				206
12	.109	425	476	793	1213	1800	170
14	.083	247	277	460			99
	Stranding			Grade 80	Grade 130		
4	3 x .138			3624	5610		823
6	3 x .117			2604	4295		590
8	3 x .096			1753	2915		396

TABLE 23

SOLID WIRE COPPERWELD TELEPHONE CONDUCTORS

CONDUCTOR Size and Type	DIAMETER Inch	BREAKING STRENGTH Lbs.	WEIGHT Lbs. per 1,000 Ft.	WEIGHT Lbs. per Mile	DC RESISTANCE Ohms per 1,000 Ft. at 68° F.	CROSS SECTION Sq. In.	TRANSMISSION EQUIVALENT Decibels (db) per Loop Mile — Dry	TRANSMISSION EQUIVALENT Decibels (db) per Loop Mile — Wet	CHARACTERISTIC IMPEDANCE (Z) Ohms per Loop Mile
Popular Sizes for Long Span Construction									
.128" H.S. 40% Cond.	.128	1,647	45.47	240.1	1.614	.01287	.107	.111	710
.104" H.S. 40% Cond.	.104	1,177	30.01	158.5	2.445	.008495	.144	.152	800
.080" E.H.S. 30% Cond.	.080	900	17.76	93.77	5.509	.005027	.256	.262	1,100
Long Span Conductors to Meet Special Requirements									
.165" H.S. 40% Cond.	.165	2,523	75.55	398.9	.9715	.02138	.071	.075	635
.104" E.H.S. 40% Cond.	.104	1,325	30.01	158.5	2.445	.008495	.144	.152	800
.104" H.S. 30% Cond.	.104	1,283	30.01	158.5	3.260	.008495	.182	.188	880
.102" E.H.S. 30% Cond.	.102	1,460	28.81	152.1	3.396	.008155	.186	.194	890
.080" H.S. 40% Cond.	.080	770	17.76	93.77	4.133	.005027	.213	.219	980

The above values are based on open wire construction using 35 pairs of CS Insulators per mile with 12-inch spacing between conductors.

COPPERWELD 3-WIRE STRANDED CONDUCTORS FOR SPECIAL LONG SPANS

CONDUCTOR	DIAMETER Inch	BREAKING STRENGTH Lbs.	WEIGHT Lbs. per 1,000 Ft.	WEIGHT Lbs. per Mile	DC RESISTANCE Ohms per 1,000 Ft. at 68° F.	CROSS SECTION Sq. In.
3 No. 6 Awg E.H.S. 30% Cond.	.349	9,754	220.3	1163	.4513	.06185
3 No. 8 Awg E.H.S. 30% Cond.	.277	6,282	138.5	731.5	.7176	.03890
3 No. 10 Awg E.H.S. 30% Cond.	.220	4,160	87.13	460.0	1.141	.02446
3 No. 12 Awg E.H.S. 30% Cond.	.174	2,565	54.80	289.3	1.814	.01539

Reprinted Courtesy of Copperweld Steel Company

TABLE 24

GALVANIZED STEEL STRAND
Utilities Grade

SIZE		STRANDING Wires Diam.	BREAKING STRENGTH	WEIGHT Lbs/Kilofoot
2M	3/16"	7 X .065	2400#	80#
3M	1/4"	3 X .120	3150#	117#
4M	9/32"	7 X .093	4600#	164#
6M	5/16"	3 X .145	6500#	171#
6M	5/16"	7 X .109	6000#	225#
8M	3/8"	3 X .165	8500#	220#
10M	3/8"	7 X .120	11,500#	273#
16M	7/16"	7 X .145	18,000#	399#
25M	1/2"	7 X .165	25,000#	517#

COPPERWELD STRAND
EHS, 30% Cond.

SIZE		STRANDING Wires Diam.	BREAKING STRENGTH	WEIGHT Lbs/Kilofoot
6M		3 X .128	6282#	139#
7M		3 X .144	7922#	175#
9M		3 X .162	9754#	220#
8M	5/16"	7 X .102	9196#	204#
12M	3/8"	7 X .128	13,890#	324#
16M	7/16"	7 X .144	16,890#	408#
20M	1/2"	7 X .162	20,460#	515#

Printed by The Strathmore Co., Aurora, Ill.

TECHNICAL BOOKS FROM TELEPHONY

● **Transmission**, by M. A. Clement, 52 pgs., size 8½" x 11"—Price: $4.00 each; 25 or more: $3.00 each.

A reprint of one of *Telephony* Magazine's most popular series of articles, "Transmission" is a basic treatment of the elementary principles of telephone transmission, particularly as they relate to central office, plant layout, and maintenance. The aim is toward application and practice rather than the academic and theoretical aspects of the subject. Beginning with an introduction to transmission.

● **Glossary of Communications**, by Emerson C. Smith, 547 pages, size 5¼" x 8" — Introductory price: $5 each.

Still the only telephone glossary available, this new edition is more than ten times greater in scope and content than its 1954 predecessor. The Glossary of Communications has been totally revised, expanded and updated to provide a useful and indispensable reference manual that will be of daily value for anyone in the industry.

● **Engineering Economics**, by Ollie Smidt, 20 chapters, size 8½" x 11"—Price: $3.00 each; 25 or more: $2.00 each.

An easy approach to the subject of long range fundamental planning which can, and should, be understood at all levels of management. The book includes a complete set of time value of money conversion tables.

● **Common Control of Telephone Systems**, by J. G. Pearce, 40 pages, illustrated, size 8½" x 11"—Price: $2.00 each; 25 or more: $1.50 each.

Six comprehensive articles on the technique and principles of common control systems, as published in *Telephony*. Includes a description of a typical system, greatly simplified for better understanding of general principles of design and operation. Other sections include Component Parts, Relays; Switching Devices; Circuits; and Translators and Registers.

● **Data Communications**, 64 pages, Illustrated, size 8½" x 11"—Price: $2.00 each; 25 or more: $1.50 each.

A compilation of 12 articles by seven leading authorities in the field of telephone data communications, reprinted from a series published during 1966 in *Telephony*. Each article provides an in-depth look at data communications in the telephone industry. It includes articles on theoretical and practical aspects of data communications, engineering for data transmission, technical concepts, data transmission for industrial customers, transmitting data for railroads, coordination of data services, and others.

● **Electronic Switching**, by J. G. Pearce, 122 pages, illustrated, size 8½" x 11"—Price $4.00 each; 25 or more: $3.50 each.

Considered the first real textbook on electronic switching, this book has been compiled from a 20-part series published in *Telephony*. Each chapter probes the function and application of this latest advancement in the industry. Beginning with Chapter one—"The Introduction and Evolution of Electronic Switching"—the author competently covers a subject of deep interest throughout the industry.

(Continued on other side)

BOOK ORDER FORM

Please send me the following books published by Telephony.

Enclosed is my check for $_____

_____

_____

_____

NAME _____

COMPANY _____

ADDRESS _____

clip and send this form to:

Book Department
Telephony Publishing Corp.
53 W. Jackson Blvd.
Chicago, Ill. 60604

ALLOW 3-4 WEEKS FOR DELIVERY

TECHNICAL BOOKS FROM TELEPHONY

continued

- **Telephony's PBX Service Adviser's Handbook**, by Gilbert R. Brackett, 132 pages, size 4½" x 7"—Price: $3.50 each; 25 or more: $3.00 each.

Long needed in the industry, this series of 22 articles reprinted from *Telephony* provides the first complete handbook for PBX Service Advisers. Some of the many detailed sections are: The Service Adviser's Responsibilities, Meeting the PBX Customer, When visiting PBX's, Instructional Observation, Peg Counts, PBX Attendants, and more.

- **Telephony's Telephone Traffic Engineering Handbook**, by Gilbert R. Brackett, 226 pages, illustrated, size 5" x 7¼"—Price: $5.00 each; 25 or more: $4.00 each.

A completely revised second edition in a totally new looseleaf format. This reprint of a popular series of articles published in *Telephony* provides brief explanations of traffic engineering principles and their application to the smaller step-by-step automatic exchanges. The handbook was designed to help those charged with the responsibility of traffic engineering, in the administration of their jobs, and to answer general, everyday questions on traffic functions and performances. Many sections of the handbook have been revised, and three new ones added.

- **ABC of the Telephone**, 4 volumes, published by Telephony Publishing Corp.
Vol. 1. 84 pages, 8½" x 11"—Price: 1-5 copies $1.50 each; 6-25 copies, $1.35 each; 26-50 copies, $1.20 each; 51-500 copies, $1.05 each; 501-1,000 copies, $.95 each.

Reprint of first 21 installments of article by Frank E. Lee which appeared in *Telephony*.

Covers fundamental information concerning electrical circuits, telephone transmitters and receivers, induction coils, generators, ringers, relays, line protection, dials, automatic switching, drop wire installation. Particularly beneficial to beginners.

Vol. II. 78 pages. Prices same as Vol I.
Covers sub-station protector installation, station wire installation, subscriber station installation, fault locating, relay circuits, planned maintenance program, electronic testing of cable and drop wire, crosstalk and transmission developments, attenuation and loading coil theory.

Vol. III. 125 pages, Price: 1-5 copies, $2.50 each; 6-25 copies, $2.25 each; 26-50 copies, $2.00 each; 51-500 copies, $1.75 each; 501-1,000 copies, $1.60 each.

Reprint of 31 informative articles by Frank E. Lee which have appeared in *Telephony* since the publication of Volumes I and II. The easy-to-read and easy-to-understand chapters cover a broad range of vital topics, including storage batteries, metallic rectifiers, electronic tubes, multiple line key equipment, carrier circuits, community dial offices, how to read circuit drawings, and many other helpful and important subjects. Illustrated.

Vol. IV. 109 pages. Prices same as Vol. III.

Reprint of 26 *Telephony* articles by Frank E. Lee featuring outside plant construction. Included are practical articles on planning additions to the outside plant; selecting, placing, guying, anchoring of poles; installation of cable plant; open wire construction; transpositions; multi-pair distribution wire; line concentrators; plus three articles on stimulating sales in a changing market and keeping up with new ideas.

BOOK ORDER FORM ON OTHER SIDE